Physical Chemistry

PHYSICAL CHEMISTRY

Gordon M. Barrow

PROFESSOR, DEPARTMENT OF CHEMISTRY
AND CHEMICAL ENGINEERING
CASE INSTITUTE OF TECHNOLOGY

INTERNATIONAL STUDENT EDITION

McGRAW-HILL BOOK COMPANY, INC.

New York   Toronto   London

KŌGAKUSHA COMPANY, LTD.

Tokyo

PHYSICAL CHEMISTRY

INTERNATIONAL STUDENT EDITION

TOSHO PRINTING CO., LTD. TOKYO, JAPAN

Preface

An introductory physical-chemistry text might well be prefaced with a description or definition of the subject of physical chemistry. There is, however, no well-defined set of subject matter that constitutes physical chemistry, and any attempt to give a description of the subject in terms comparable with those used to define organic or inorganic chemistry would only be misleading.

It will become apparent that physical chemistry is not a branch of chemistry that stands beside organic and inorganic chemistry. It is rather to be thought of as an approach, or method, which is applicable to all branches of chemistry.

In practice, the principal activities that are classified as physical chemical are usually easily recognized. These activities are generally concerned with the phenomena that arise from, and are, hopefully, interpretable in terms of, molecular behavior. The physical chemist tends to apply a quantitative treatment to the systems with which he deals. The attitude with which the subject is approached is that physical chemistry is primarily the study of the molecular world and the explanation of chemical phenomena on the basis of molecular behavior. It is this attitude that is found in the laboratories of the world where research and development in physical chemistry are being actively pursued. It is hoped that some of the flavor and excitement that surround much of this activity will be evident even as the basic techniques of the subject are learned. Furthermore, added interest in all branches of chemistry, in biochemistry, and in engineering should arise from an appreciation of the detailed molecular features that are revealed by a physical-chemical approach.

It is, of course, still frequently necessary to measure and tabulate the physical properties of chemical compounds. While such data are invaluable, the collection of these data does not in itself embody the spirit of modern physical chemistry. It is useful, but not in itself very interesting, to report that the boiling point of water is 100°C and that of hydrogen sulfide −62°C. More in the spirit of physical chemistry and of considerably more interest is the question why, of these two related compounds, that with the lower molecular weight should have the higher boiling point, contrary to the usual rule. The explanation requires a very detailed and complete understanding of the nature and behavior of the molecules of the two compounds.

The principal goal of the studies that will be undertaken can be considered to be the explanation of large-scale, or macroscopic, phenomena on the basis of detailed molecular information. Alternatively, the study can set as its goal the advancement of our knowledge of the molecular world with no necessary regard for macroscopic behavior. With either attitude it is necessary to learn the techniques that reveal molecular features and to work with these techniques so as to feel an intimacy with the world of molecular dimensions. It is interesting to note, for example, that people outside of chemistry and similar fields are most impressed with the small size of molecules. The chemist, on the other hand, seldom thinks of molecules in this way. He can be quite at ease calling a chemical bond "long" if it is several per cent longer than normal—but still has a length of only 10^{-8} cm! It is such a familiarity with many aspects of molecules and molecular phenomena that it is hoped will be achieved.

The approach of physical chemistry is characteristically quantitative and therefore necessarily mathematical. Physical chemistry is, however, not just mathematics. In this regard it should be mentioned that difficulty sometimes arises with the subject because of its blend of physical quantities and theories with mathematical operations. These difficulties are certainly diminished by a good grounding in the necessary mathematics, including some differential and integral calculus, before encountering physical chemistry. It is true, however, that there are advantages to studying physical chemistry at an early stage and therefore at a time before much mathematical background has been acquired. This introduction to physical chemistry has been presented, in so far as possible, so that the material can be handled with various degrees of mathematical training. It will be noticed that some derivations, even those involving a somewhat advanced integration, have been followed through completely. In such cases the purely mathematical step has been isolated and pointed out, and it can, if necessary, be passed over without the derivation losing its significance.

The text treats the topics that are of interest and importance in modern physical chemistry. These topics present some difficulties that are not encountered in some of the more traditional subjects. It is possible, however, to restrict the developments to very simple examples—diatomic molecules, for example, are used to illustrate techniques that in practice are applied to much larger molecules. In this way the subjects of current interest can be treated, or at least illustrated, without undue difficulty.

Several somewhat extended treatments have, however, been included and are indicated by asterisks at the section headings. These sections are not necessary for the continuity of the text and can be omitted. They allow, however, further advances to be made into a number of areas of modern physical chemistry and, if time allows, they will enhance an introductory physical-chemistry course. Problems based on these sections are likewise indicated by an asterisk.

The over-all organization of the subject is based on the recognition that two rather different situations are approached in physical chemistry.   One of these, which is dealt with in the first half of the text, allows one to keep one's eye on a single or a few molecules at a time.   The second situation is that in which the interplay of many molecules (i.e., communal effects) must be handled, and such subjects are treated in the latter half of the text.

It may be worth mentioning that many of the problems at the ends of the chapters have been selected to emphasize or reveal some aspect of the molecular world as well as to provide the necessary practice in manipulating the new quantities that are introduced.   It is of value, therefore, to "consider" the magnitude of the quantity that is calculated in each of the problems.

Many people have been of great assistance to me over the past few years in the preparation of the manuscript for this book.   I would like to thank my wife, Harriet, not only for her encouragement but also for her considerable help in correcting and typing the manuscript at various stages in its development.   I have also been greatly aided by the advice and suggestions of many reviewers and colleagues, and I would particularly like to mention Professors I. M. Klotz and A. L. Allred at Northwestern University.   I would also like to express my appreciation to the Guggenheim Foundation for a fellowship which provided me with an opportunity to bring together the material which constitutes this book.

Gordon M. Barrow

Contents

ix

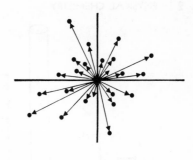

Properties of Gases

The study of the nature of gases provides an ideal introduction to physical chemistry. The principal goal of this study is here considered to be the information that can be obtained about the molecular nature of gases and, furthermore, about the nature of the molecules themselves. A considerable appreciation of the world of molecules results. This appreciation is obtained, moreover, without recourse to the more elaborate theories and experiments which will later be encountered. The deduction of some of the innermost details of the molecular world from the simple experimental results of this chapter and the equally simple theory of the following chapter should be appreciated as a beautiful accomplishment of science.

A prerequisite to the study of the molecular properties of gases is the tabulation of some of the experimental results for gas behavior and the consolidation of these results into compact statements. These statements are the empirical gas laws, and it is these gas laws which constitute the principal part of this chapter. The understanding of these results in terms of the molecular nature of gases forms the subject of the following chapter. It is then that our first look into the molecular world will be obtained.

Seldom are the experimental and theoretical aspects of a study so neatly separated as they are here. A clear illustration is provided of how these two aspects of scientific study go hand in hand to lead to a more profound understanding of an apparently remote world. The division of the subject into its empirical and theoretical aspects ignores the historical sequence of the events. It is true, however, that most of the results reported in this chapter predate the theoretical deductions of the following chapter. For reference one can recall that the molecular view of matter was born with the nineteenth century and became quite mature and respectable by the end of that century. The early dates attached to some of the empirical studies should emphasize the fact that these studies were indeed purely empirical and were not appreciably guided by any existing theory.

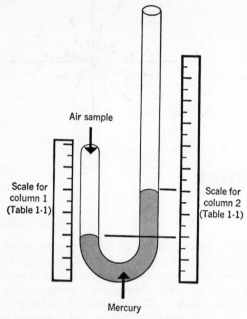

Air sample

Scale for
column 1
(Table 1-1)

Scale for
column 2
(Table 1-1)

Mercury

Fig. 1-1. Apparatus for the measurement of the relation between the pressure and the volume of a sample of air.

1-1. Boyle's Law. As early as the year 1660 Robert Boyle performed a series of experiments in which he determined the effect of pressure on the volume . of a given amount of air. Boyle's insistence on recourse to experimental observation as a scientific method did much to advance science, and it seems fitting that the compact statement which resulted from his pressure-volume studies should bear his name.

The apparatus which Boyle used was particularly simple, but not at all easy to construct in those days, consisting of a simple bent glass tube sealed at one end, as indicated in Fig. 1-1. After adding a little mercury through the open end of the tube to seal off a quantity of air in the closed end, he measured the volume of the enclosed air for various amounts of mercury added through the open end. His experimental results consisted of the measured length of the air column, which was proportional to the volume of air, and the difference in the heights of the two mercury columns. The difference in the mercury levels was then added to the height of mercury, $29\frac{1}{8}$ in., corresponding to the pressure of the atmosphere on the open end. Table 1-1 shows some of the results that he obtained.

Table 1-1. Data of Boyle on the Pressure-Volume Relation of Air

Length of air column (arbitrary units)	Difference in Hg levels (in.)	Difference plus atmospheric pressure ($29\frac{1}{8}$ in.)	Product of columns 1 and 3
(1)	(2)	(3)	(4)
12	0	$29\frac{2}{16}$	349
10	$6\frac{3}{16}$	$35\frac{5}{16}$	353
8	$15\frac{1}{16}$	$44\frac{3}{16}$	353
6	$29\frac{11}{16}$	$58\frac{13}{16}$	353
4	$58\frac{2}{16}$	$87\frac{14}{16}$	351
3	$88\frac{7}{16}$	$117\frac{9}{16}$	353

Qualitatively it is immediately obvious that, as the pressure on the air increases, the volume of the air decreases. Such data prompt one to go further and to see whether or not there exists a simple quantitative relation between the pressure P and the volume V. One tries the relation

$$P \propto \frac{1}{V} \tag{1}$$

or, more conveniently,

$$P = \frac{\text{const}}{V} \tag{2}$$

or

$$PV = \text{const} \tag{3}$$

The data are easily confronted with the final form of this relation, and the last column of Table 1-1 shows the calculated product of the pressure and the volume. The units used are not pertinent since it is only the constancy of the result which is of interest. Within experimental error a constant value is obtained, and so Boyle was able to conclude that the volume of air varies inversely as the pressure. Later experiments showed that this relation required the temperature to be maintained constant and furthermore showed that many gases, as well as air, conformed quite closely to this behavior. Boyle's law can now be written as follows: *the volume of a gas varies inversely as the pressure, the temperature remaining constant.*

Processes which are performed at constant temperature are said to be *isothermal*. The pressure-volume data which are obtained at constant temperature in demonstrating Boyle's law are frequently exhibited on a plot of P versus V. The hyperbolic curve which is obtained, as in Fig. 1-2, at any given temperature, is called an *isotherm*.

According to Boyle's law the pressure and volume of a given amount of gas, at a fixed temperature, vary such that the product PV always has the same value. Sometimes one deals with an isothermal process which takes the gas from the initial values P_1 and V_1 to some new values P_2 and V_2. Since the product of P and V is constant, one can write a frequently convenient form of Boyle's law as

$$P_1 V_1 = P_2 V_2 \tag{4}$$

Later it will be shown that more accurate measurements reveal that gases do not, in fact, behave exactly in accordance with Boyle's law. It is convenient, to begin with, to ignore these additional complications of gas behavior and to restrict our attention to what is known as *ideal* behavior.

The simplicity of Boyle's law and the student's previous familiarity with it should not lead to the view that this would be the "expected" behavior. For liquids and solids, by contrast, no simple relation exists between V and P. The fact, for example, that doubling the pressure on a gas reduces its volume to half its original value is a rather remarkable result that the theory of the next chapter must explain.

1-2. Charles', or Gay-Lussac's, Law. More than a century elapsed before the counterpart of Boyle's law, a relation between the temperature and gas volume, was discovered. The reason for this long interval stems from the

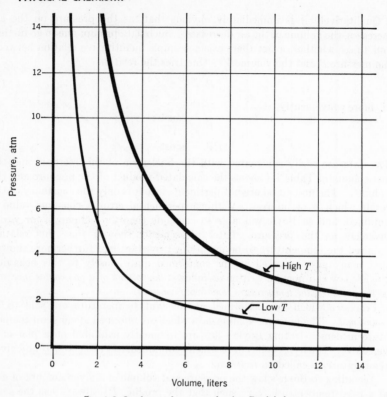

Fig. 1-2. Isotherms for a gas obeying Boyle's law.

difficulty of the concept of temperature as compared with that of pressure. Although qualitative differences between hot and cold can be readily recognized, the means for making quantitative measurements of the "degree of heat," or, in the words of Gay-Lussac, "tensions of caloric," are not so easily devised. Toward the end of the eighteenth century, however, the use of the expansion of a liquid in a glass tube, i.e., a modern thermometer, was generally accepted as a satisfactory method for measuring temperature. Furthermore, some agreement had been reached to choose the freezing point of water as a zero of the temperature scale and the boiling point as 100°. The existence of thermometers, with the centigrade scale, allowed investigations to be made of the variation of the volume of a gas with the temperature.

The early work of Charles in 1787 and of Gay-Lussac in 1808 showed that, if the pressure is kept constant, the volume of a gas varies linearly with the temperature in a manner indicated by the solid lines of Fig. 1-3. An algebraic expression for such linear relations is

$$V = V_0 + \frac{V_0}{273} t \tag{5}$$

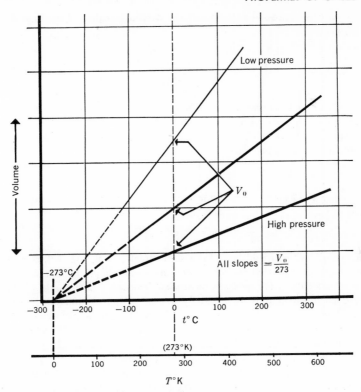

Fig. 1-3. Variation of the volume of a sample of gas at different constant pressures as a function of the temperature according to Charles' law.

where V_0 is the volume at 0°C, V is the volume at a temperature t°C, and the term $V_0/273$ is deduced from the slopes of the experimental curves.

The extrapolation to low temperatures of data such as those of Fig. 1-3 is revealing. Either graphically or analytically from Eq. (5) one finds that all the curves tend to $V = 0$ at a temperature of about −273°C. In view of this common behavior, it is often more convenient to measure temperatures from this point, i.e., from $t = -273$°C, rather than from the zero of the centigrade scale. If the size of the degree is kept the same as in the centigrade scale, but the zero is shifted, the *absolute Kelvin temperature scale* is obtained. Using the best modern value for absolute zero, temperatures T on this scale are related to centigrade-scale temperatures t by

$$T = t + 273.16 \qquad (6)$$

A temperature on this absolute scale is denoted by the abbreviation A or, preferably, by the abbreviation K, after Lord Kelvin.

The previous algebraic expression for the temperature dependence of the

volume can be expressed in terms of the absolute scale.   Rearrangement of
Eq. (5) gives

$$V = V_0 \frac{273 + t}{273} \tag{7}$$

or
$$V = \frac{V_0}{273} (273 + t)$$

On the absolute temperature scale 273 is the temperature corresponding to
V_0 and can be denoted at T_0.   Likewise, $273 + t$ is the absolute temperature
at which the volume is V, and this temperature can be labeled as T.   With
this notation Eq. (7) becomes

$$\frac{V}{T} = \frac{V_0}{T_0} \tag{8}$$

which, since V_0/T_0 is a constant for a given amount of gas at a fixed pressure,
implies

$$\frac{V}{T} = \text{const} \quad \text{or} \quad V \propto T \tag{9}$$

This result, which could have been seen directly from Fig. 1-3, is Charles',
or Gay-Lussac's, law that *the volume of a given mass of gas varies directly as the
absolute temperature, the pressure remaining constant*.   Like Boyle's law, this
relation is approximately followed by almost all gases, and obedience of a
gas to Charles' law constitutes another feature of ideal-gas behavior.

The temperature at which all volume-temperature curves extrapolate to zero
volume is $-273.16°C$, or $0°K$.   In a later chapter it will be shown that this
temperature is literally an *absolute* zero of temperature.   For the present this
temperature need be considered only as a point for the zero of a convenient
temperature scale.   One need not worry about the peculiarity of gases having
zero volume as the extrapolation might indicate.   Gases will have condensed
to liquids and frozen to solids before such a temperature is reached, and
behavior in accordance with Charles' law will not exist near absolute zero.

Experiments such as those of Charles and Gay-Lussac show that the thermal
expansion of gases, at constant pressure, is proportional to the expansion of
mercury, or some other liquid, in a glass tube.   This way of stating the results
of this section emphasizes the arbitrary nature of a temperature scale, such
as the centigrade scale, and indicates that it is really a fortunate coincidence
that liquid in glass thermometers behaves so conveniently.   A more sophisticated approach to temperature uses the expansion of a gas as a means of defining a temperature scale.   A *gas thermometer* has the advantage of making
use of the expansion of gases, a property which is approximately the same for
many gases.   The coefficient of expansion of a liquid, on the other hand, is a
property characteristic of the individual liquid.   Furthermore, the expansion
of a gas with temperature is more easily subject to theoretical reasoning and
can be correlated with yet another and even more basic temperature scale.
In practice, of course, one uses a mercury in glass thermometer, or some
more elaborate device, to measure temperatures since, as Charles' law shows,

such devices give a temperature scale which is proportional to that based on the expansion of an ideal gas.

1-3. The Combined Gas Laws. The gas laws of Boyle and of Charles can be combined into one convenient expression which gives the dependence of the gas volume on both the temperature and the pressure.

Consider a given mass of gas which has a volume V_1 at a pressure P_1 and a temperature T_1. A relation is required that allows the calculation of the volume V_2, which the gas will have when the pressure is changed to P_2 and the temperature to T_2. This relation can be found from the previous two gas laws by dividing the total change into two parts: first, the pressure is thought of as being changed from P_1 to P_2, the temperature remaining at T_1; and, second, the temperature is then considered to change from T_1 to T_2, the pressure remaining constant at P_2. These changes can be indicated as

$$P_1 T_1 V_1 \rightarrow P_2 T_1 V_x \rightarrow P_2 T_2 V_2$$

where V_x denotes the intermediate volume.

In the first step the temperature is constant, and Boyle's law can be used to obtain

$$V_x = V_1 \frac{P_1}{P_2} \tag{10}$$

The second step proceeds at constant pressure, and Charles' law can be used to obtain

$$V_2 = V_x \frac{T_2}{T_1} \tag{11}$$

Elimination of V_x from these two equations gives, for the over-all process,

$$V_2 = V_1 \frac{P_1}{P_2} \frac{T_2}{T_1} \tag{12}$$

or

$$\frac{P_1 V_1}{T_1} = \frac{P_2 V_2}{T_2} \tag{13}$$

Since any values can be assigned to the pressures and temperatures, this result implies that for a given mass of gas

$$\frac{PV}{T} = \text{const} \tag{14}$$

The last two of these equations are useful in handling problems involving gases when both pressure and temperature are changed.

1-4. Avogadro's Hypothesis and the General Gas Law. The relations of the preceding sections show how the pressure and temperature affect the volume of a given amount of a given gas. A very useful generalization can be made by straying from a purely empirical development. Recognition of the molecular nature of matter allows the hypothesis of Avogadro, first proposed in 1811 but only generally appreciated in 1860, to be introduced. Avogadro suggested that *equal volumes of different gases at the same temperature and pressure contain the same number of molecules*. Furthermore, it will be recalled that 1 mole of any compound contains the same number of molecules and that this number, known as *Avogadro's number* and represented by N, has the value 6.024×10^{23}.

In terms of moles, Avogadro's hypothesis can be expressed as follows: The same volume is occupied by 1 mole of any gas at a given temperature and pressure. Experimentally one finds that at 1 atm pressure and 0°C this volume is 22.414 liters.

The results which stem from Avogadro's hypothesis can now be used to generalize the combined gas law of Sec. 1-3. For a particular experiment the amount of a given gas, to which Eq. (14) might be applied, can be measured in moles. Since the volume of gas at a given pressure and temperature is proportional to the amount, i.e., the weight or number of moles, of the gas, Eq. (14) can be written as

$$\frac{PV}{T} = n(\text{const})' \tag{15}$$

where n is the number of moles and the new constant term is the value for 1 mole of this particular gas.

If 1 mole of each of a number of different gases is considered, each gas will, according to Avogadro's hypothesis, occupy the same volume at the same temperature and pressure. At 0°C and 1 atm, for example, 1 mole of any of the gases will occupy 22.414 liters. If such data are inserted in Eq. (15), it is apparent that they require the constant term to be the same, to the extent that Avogadro's hypothesis is obeyed, for all the gases. The constant, which will be important in many connections, is called the *gas constant* and is denoted by R. The behavior of all gases that obey Boyle's law, Charles' law, and Avogadro's hypothesis can now be expressed by the relation

$$PV = nRT \tag{16}$$

where R is a constant and is the same for all gases.

This result is useful in making gas-volume calculations and is, moreover, a summary of the empirical laws of Boyle and Charles and the hypothesis of Avogadro. The principal goal of the theory of the nature of gases, to be developed in the next chapter, will be the theoretical derivation of this important result.

The gas constant R which has here been introduced is of sufficient importance in many physical-chemistry phenomena so that it is worthwhile devoting a section to considering its numerical values.

1-5. The Gas Constant. A numerical value for the gas constant can be obtained most readily from the previously mentioned result that at 1 atm and 0°C one mole of a gas occupies 22.414 liters. Substitution of these data in the gas-law expression [Eq. (16)] gives

$$R = \frac{PV}{nT} = \frac{(1)(22.414)}{(1)(273.16)} = 0.08205 \text{ liter atm/deg mole}$$

If the volume is expressed in cubic centimeters instead of liters, the result is

$$R = 82.05 \text{ cc atm/deg mole}$$

These values are sufficiently useful in gas-volume problems so that it is worthwhile committing one of them to memory. In using such constants and Eq. (16), it is, of course, necessary to be sure that the pressure is in atmospheres, the temperature is in degrees absolute, and the volume is in the same units as those of R.

The gas constant not only enters into PVT calculations but also, as will frequently be seen in succeeding chapters, plays a very important role in all phenomena which involve the energies of molecular systems. This aspect of the gas constant is less surprising when one notices that R involves the dimensions of work, or energy. If pressure is written as force per unit area and the volume as area times length, one sees dimensionally that

$$\text{Pressure} \times \text{volume} = \frac{\text{force}}{\text{area}} \times \text{area} \times \text{length} = \text{force} \times \text{length}$$

The dimensions of force times length are those of energy. It follows that R has the dimensions of energy per degree per mole. Some numerical values involving energy units can now be obtained.

We first obtain R in cgs units. The cgs pressure unit is dynes per square centimeter, and to make use of Eq. (16) it is necessary to know the value of 1 atm pressure in these units. A pressure of 1 atm supports a column of mercury 76 cm high, and since the density of mercury is 13.596 g/cc, the mass of a column of mercury of 1 sq cm cross section and 76 cm high is (76)(13.596) g. The force, or weight, of this column on the 1-sq cm base is, therefore, (980.7)(76)(13.596) = 1.013 $\times$ 10^6 dynes. The desired relation is

$$1 \text{ atm} = 1.013 \times 10^6 \text{ dynes/sq cm}$$

With this value for the pressure and with the volume of the mole of gas measured in cubic centimeters, one obtains

$$R = 8.314 \times 10^7 \text{ ergs/deg mole}$$

where the erg is the cgs unit of energy equal to 1 dyne-cm.

A more convenient unit is the joule, which is related to the erg by the expression

$$1 \text{ joule} = 10^7 \text{ ergs}$$

For this unit

$$R = 8.314 \text{ joules/deg mole}$$

In chemistry the most generally used energy unit is that of the calorie. This unit is based on the amount of heat required to raise the temperature of 1 g of water by 1°C. The calorie is now defined so that

$$1 \text{ cal} = 4.184 \text{ joules}$$

In terms of calories, one obtains

$$R = 1.9872 \text{ cal/deg mole}$$

In future work it will be well worthwhile to remember the value of R in calories per degree mole, but, for present purposes of PVT calculations, the units which involve the pressure and volume explicitly will be more useful.

1-6. Dalton's Law of Partial Pressures. Another empirical result which will have to be explained by the theory of the next chapter is that obtained by Cavendish in 1781 and Dalton in 1810. An empirical generalization, known as *Dalton's law of partial pressures*, follows from experiments in which the pressures exerted by given amounts of gases put separately into a container are measured and compared with the pressure obtained when the same amounts of the gases are placed in the container together.   The results of such experiments show that *the total pressure exerted by a mixture of gases is equal to the sum of the pressures which each component would exert if placed separately into the container.*

This law makes it profitable to introduce the term *partial pressure* to denote the pressure exerted by one component of a gaseous mixture.   The total pressure P is then the sum of the partial pressures P_i of the components, i.e.,

$$P = P_1 + P_2 + P_3 + \cdots \tag{17}$$

Dalton's law, furthermore, allows each of the partial pressures to be treated as if each of the components were occupying the container separately.   The ideal-gas law can then be applied to each component to give

$$P = n_1 \frac{RT}{V} + n_2 \frac{RT}{V} + n_3 \frac{RT}{V} + \cdots$$

$$= (n_1 + n_2 + n_3 + \cdots) \frac{RT}{V}$$

$$= n \frac{RT}{V} \tag{18}$$

where n is the total number of moles of the gas mixture in the volume V.

The final result [Eq. (18)] shows that the expression $PV = nRT$ can be used for mixtures of gases as well as for pure gases.   The fact that both Boyle's and Charles' laws are independent of the type of molecules that make up the gas leads to this result.

In dealing with gas mixtures, it is frequently necessary to be able to express the fraction which one component contributes to the total mixture.   Two of the most convenient ways of doing this are the use of the *pressure fraction* and the *mole fraction*.   The pressure fraction of the ith component is defined as P_i/P and can be seen to be identical with the mole fraction, defined as n_i/n, by writing

$$\frac{P_i}{P} = \frac{n_i(RT/V)}{n(RT/V)} = \frac{n_i}{n} \tag{19}$$

A noteworthy property of units such as the pressure and mole fractions is that the sum of the pressure fraction or of the mole fraction of all the components of the system is unity, thus:

$$\frac{n_1}{n} + \frac{n_2}{n} + \frac{n_3}{n} + \cdots = 1$$

and
$$\frac{P_1}{P} + \frac{P_2}{P} + \frac{P_3}{P} + \cdots = 1 \tag{20}$$

If one can refrain from anticipating the explanation of gas properties in terms of molecular theory, the properties of gas mixtures embodied in Dalton's law seem quite remarkable.   If gases are thought of as nothing more than homogeneous fluids, it is not at all obvious that they should obey such a simple law as that of Dalton.   The independent behavior of the components of a gas mixture was, in fact, one of the results that stimulated the ideas of the molecular nature of matter.

1-7. Graham's Law of Effusion.   The process by which a gas moves from a high pressure to a lower pressure through a porous wall or a very small-diameter tube is known as *diffusion*.   If the process consists of molecular rather than bulk flow, through an orifice, the word *effusion* is used.   The rate with which a gas effuses, under given conditions, is a property characteristic of the gas. Since it is rather difficult, both experimentally and theoretically, to deal with the absolute rates of effusion of gases through an orifice of well-defined dimensions, attention is usually confined to the relative rates of effusion of gases.

Measurements of the effusion ratios of a number of gases were made by Graham in 1829.   He found that, at a constant temperature and at a constant-pressure drop, the rates of effusion of various gases were inversely proportional to the square roots of the densities of the gases.   If the effusion rate is denoted by v and the density by d, this result, for gases 1 and 2, is written as

$$\frac{v_1}{v_2} = \sqrt{\frac{d_2}{d_1}} \tag{21}$$

An alternative and frequently convenient form of this law can be obtained by application of the result $PV = nRT$.   The number of moles n can be written as w/M, where w is the mass of gas in the volume V and M is the gram-molecular weight.   The density can then be written as

$$d = \frac{w}{V} = M\frac{P}{RT} \tag{22}$$

The density ratio of two gases, at the same pressure and temperature, is, therefore, equal to the ratio of the molecular weights of the two gases.   With this result Graham's law becomes

$$\frac{v_1}{v_2} = \sqrt{\frac{M_2}{M_1}} \tag{23}$$

This effusion law makes itself evident, for example, in the fact that a system which is satisfactorily leakproof to air, molecular weight about 28, may fail to hold gases like hydrogen, molecular weight 2, or helium, molecular weight 4.

Graham's law provides yet another property of gases for which the theory of the nature of gases must account.

1-8. The Viscosity of Gases.   When a fluid flows through a pipe, tube, or trough, flow occurs only as a result of the application of a driving force to the fluid.   The resistance to flow which this force overcomes is dependent on the viscosity of the fluid.

A quantitative definition of the viscosity can be made by considering the flow of a fluid near the bottom of a rectangular container as shown in Fig. 1-4. A gas or liquid flowing in a tube or trough forms a very thin stationary layer in

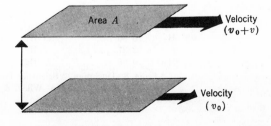

Fig. 1-4. The relative motion of two layers of a fluid. The viscosity of the fluid requires a force to be applied to the upper layer to keep it moving relative to the lower layer.

Area A

Velocity (v_0+v)

Velocity (v_0)

contact with the walls of the container. The force required to make the fluid flow results from having to push the fluid relative to this stationary layer. The flow can be understood in terms of a force required to move a layer of fluid relative to another layer. This force is proportional to the areas A of the layers and to the difference in velocity v that is maintained between the layers and is inversely proportional to the distance l between the layers. The *coefficient of viscosity*, or simply the viscosity, is introduced as a proportionality factor, and the equation

$$\text{Force} = \eta \frac{Av}{l} \tag{24}$$

can be written. The viscosity can be thought of as the force required to make a layer of unit area move with a velocity 1 cm/sec greater than the velocity of another layer 1 cm away. Thick liquids, like molasses, have high viscosities; thin liquids, like gasoline, have low viscosities. Gases have relatively much lower, but not zero, viscosities.

In practice one invariably measures viscosity from the rate of flow through a cylindrical tube. Again the fluid forms a stationary layer along the wall, and a force is required to make the fluid flow through the tube. By integrating the force required to move the annular layers of the fluid relative to this layer, as will be done when the viscosity of liquids is studied in Chap. 12, Eq. (24) can be extended to give the rate of flow through a cylindrical tube as a function of the viscosity η, the radius of the tube r, and the pressure difference $P_2 - P_1$ applied over the tube of length L. The result that will be obtained is

$$\text{Rate of flow} = \frac{\pi(P_1 - P_2)r^4}{8L\eta} \tag{25}$$

where the rate of flow is measured as the volume of gas, measured at 1 atm, passing through the tube per second. Measurement of all the quantities other than η in Eq. (25) allows this quantity to be determined.

Table 1-2 shows viscosity data for some gases. When all the quantities in Eq. (25) are given in cgs units, the viscosity η is obtained in cgs units which are given the name *poise*. This unit, however, is inconveniently large, and for gases the unit *micropoise*, equal to 10^{-6} poise, or *centipoise*, equal to 10^{-2} poise, is often used.

1-9. The Nonideal Behavior of Gases. The PVT behavior of gases has, so far,

Table 1-2. Gas Viscosities at 25°C*
(Poise)

Gas	Viscosity	Gas	Viscosity
N_2	1.78×10^{-4}	CO	1.76×10^{-4}
O_2	2.08	CO_2	1.50
H_2	0.90	HI	1.72
A	2.27	He	1.97
H_2O	0.98	Hg	2.50

* From S. Dushman, "Scientific Foundations of Vacuum Technique," John Wiley & Sons, Inc., New York, 1949.

been presumed to follow Boyle's and Charles' laws and Avogadro's hypothesis and to lead to the result $PV = nRT$. When measurements are extended to higher pressures or even when very accurate measurements are made at ordinary pressures, it is found that deviations from these laws do exist. Behavior in accordance with the expression $PV = nRT$ is elegantly simple and is at least approximately obeyed by almost all gases. Such behavior is said to be *ideal*, or *perfect*. The gas laws summed up by $PV = nRT$ are known as the *ideal-gas laws*, and a gas which would behave in accordance with these laws is known as an *ideal gas*. Real gases may behave essentially ideally over certain pressure and temperature ranges. More generally, real gases will exhibit deviations from these laws and are said to behave as *nonideal*, or *imperfect*, *gases*.

The very accurate data illustrated in Fig. 1-5 show the deviations from ideal behavior at relatively low pressures. The PVT behavior is no longer expressed by $PV = nRT$. It is frequently necessary to have an expression which gives the volume as a function of the pressure and temperature. Such expressions are called *equations of state*. The results of Fig. 1-5 might lead to the use of an expression, for 1 mole of gas, like

$$PV = RT + b'P$$

or

$$PV = RT(1 + bP)$$

(26)

where b' and b are characteristic of the given gas and, moreover, are functions of temperature.

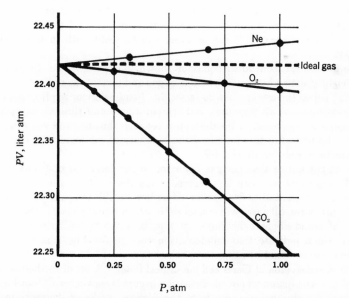

Fig. 1-5. Accurate data for the product PV for 1 mole of the gas as a function of pressure, at 0°C. (*Adapted from Louis P. Hammett, "Introduction to Study of Physical Chemistry,"* McGraw-Hill Book Company, Inc., New York, 1952.)

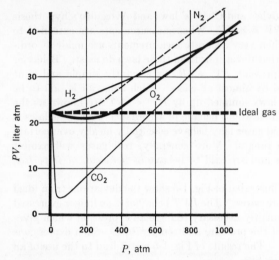

Fig. 1-6. The product PV versus P for 1 mole of gas at 0°C.

Further data at higher pressures, as shown in Fig. 1-6, indicate that a more flexible expression is required, and a frequently used empirical equation of state, known as a *virial equation*, is written. Thus for one mole

$$PV = RT + BP + CP^2 + \cdots \qquad (27)$$

where $B, C, \ldots$ are called the *virial coefficients* and again are functions of the nature of the gas and the temperature. Other equations of state which attempt to reproduce the results, such as those of Figs. 1-5 to 1-7, have been proposed and are used. Some of these will be dealt with in the following chapter.

The deviations from ideal behavior shown in Figs. 1-5 and 1-6 are more conveniently shown by treating 1 mole of gas and plotting as ordinate the ratio PV/RT, called the *compressibility factor* Z. Ideal behavior requires Z to have the value unity at all pressures and temperatures, and the gas imperfection is immediately apparent as the difference between the observed value of Z and unity. To illustrate this function, the behavior of methane at a number of temperatures is shown in Fig. 1-7.

One might notice that the gas behavior so far described does not account for all the results that can be observed when the PVT relations of gases are studied. If such studies are conducted at low enough temperatures and high enough pressures, all gases will condense to form a liquid phase. This extreme aspect of nonideal-gas behavior must now be investigated since results will appear which indicate that condensation can, in fact, be looked on as an extreme case of nonideal-gas behavior.

1-10. Condensation of Gases and the Critical Point. A set of isotherms which extend into the region where condensation occurs is shown for CO_2 in Fig. 1-8. The data for this figure came from the pioneer works of Andrews in 1869 on the behavior of gases. The higher temperature isotherms show only slight

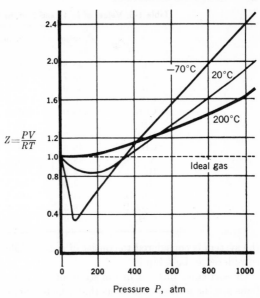

$$Z = \frac{PV}{RT}$$

deviations from the hyperbolic curves expected for an ideal gas. A lower-temperature isotherm, such as that labeled A, also conforms somewhat to ideal behavior at the low-pressure large-volume end. As the pressure is decreased at such a temperature, the volume increases approximately according to Boyle's law until the point on the dotted line of Fig. 1-8 is reached. At this point the gas begins to condense to a liquid. Now the volume decreases as the gas is entirely converted to a liquid, the pressure staying constant at the equilibrium vapor pressure for that temperature. When the left limit marked off by the dotted line is reached, the entire gas has been condensed and further application of pressure results in only a minor decrease in volume, as shown by the steep section at the left end of the isotherm.

The region beneath the dotted curve is seen to represent situations in which liquid and vapor coexist. To the right and above this region

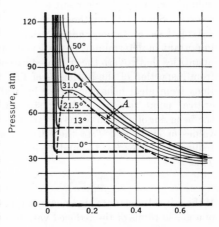

Fig. 1-8. Isotherms of CO_2 near the critical point. (*From E. D. Eastman and G. K. Rollefson, "Physical Chemistry," McGraw-Hill Book Company, Inc., New York, 1947.*)

Table 1-3. Values of P, V, and T at the Critical Point

	P_c (atm)	V_c (cc/mole)	T_c (°K)
N_2	33.5	90.0	126.1
O_2	49.7	74.4	153.4
CO	35.0	90.0	134.0
CO_2	73.0	95.7	304.3
CCl_4	45.0	275.8	556.2
NH_3	111.5	72.4	405.6
H_2O	217.7	45.0	647.2
CH_4	45.6	98.8	190.2
A	48.0	77.1	150.7
H_2	12.8	65.0	33.3
He	2.26	57.6	5.3
$n\text{-}C_5H_{12}$	33.0	310.2	470.3
CH_3OH	78.5	117.7	513.1
C_6H_6	47.9	256.4	561.6

the system is considered to consist of a gas, while to the left of the region it is considered to be a liquid.

Of particular interest in the study of the nonideal behavior of gaseous systems are the isotherms such as that which touches the top of the dotted curve of Fig. 1-8. This isotherm is called the *critical isotherm*, and its temperature, the *critical temperature*, is seen to be the highest temperature at which the gas can be condensed to a liquid. The point at which this isotherm shows its horizontal point of inflection is called the *critical point*, and the pressure and volume per mole at this point are known as the *critical pressure* and *critical volume*. Some data for the critical point are shown in Table 1-3.

1-11. Law of Corresponding States. The intermolecular factors that are important in determining how a gas deviates from ideal behavior are also the quantities that govern the critical-state constants. In view of this and, indeed, from inspection of the isotherms of Fig. 1-8, we might expect that the deviations from ideal behavior shown by real gases depend on how far from the critical point the gas is being studied. We might further try to explain the behavior of a gas in terms of variables which easily reveal the relation of the values of P, V, and T to the critical conditions. To do this, we define the reduced variables P_R, V_R, and T_R in terms of the critical constants P_c, V_c, and T_c as

$$P_R = \frac{P}{P_c} \qquad V_R = \frac{V}{V_c} \qquad T_R = \frac{T}{T_c} \tag{28}$$

If the critical constants are known, it is possible, of course, to treat the behavior of a gas in terms of the reduced variables just as easily as in terms of the ordinary variables.

One can investigate the merits of these reduced variables by plotting the compressibility factor $Z = PV/RT$ for a gas as a function of the reduced pressure. Such plots can be made for various reduced temperatures. When this is done for a number of different gases, as in Fig. 1-9, the gratifying result

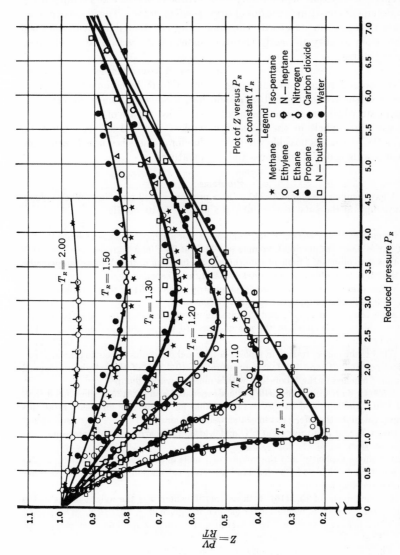

Fig. 1-9. The compressibility as a function of the reduced pressure at various reduced temperatures. [From *Gouq-Jen Su, Ind. Eng. Chem.,* **38**: 803 (1946).]

is obtained that all gases behave nearly alike in terms of these variables. This result is equivalent to the statement that all gases deviate from ideal behavior in a way that depends only on the reduced pressure and temperature. This statement constitutes the *law of corresponding states.* The name expresses the fact that gases in states with the same values of the reduced variables will deviate from ideality to nearly the same extent and are said to be in corresponding states.

The law of corresponding states introduces a considerable simplification into the treatment of nonideal gases. The uniform behavior of such gases in terms of the reduced variables should not, however, obscure the fact that critical data which are characteristic of the detailed nature of the molecules of each gas are implicit in the reduced variables. No "ideal" generalization such as $PV = nRT$ is possible when the behavior of gases is studied accurately or over a wide range of pressures and temperatures.

Problems

1. A gas occupies a volume of 250 cc at a pressure of 742 mm Hg. What volume will it occupy, at the same temperature, at a pressure of 10 mm Hg?

Ans. 18,600 cc.

2. Prepare plots of P versus V at 25 and 300°C for a sample of a gas obeying Boyle's and Charles' laws and having a volume of 100 cc at 25°C and 1 atm.

3. Plot the volume of 1 mole of an ideal gas as a function of the absolute temperature over the range 0 to 400°K at pressures of 0.2, 1, and 5 atm.

4. What volume will an ideal gas occupy at a temperature of 0°C if its volume at 100°C is 3.64 liters, the pressure remaining constant?

5. A gas is collected at 24°C and 735 mm Hg pressure in a bulb of volume 0.763 liter. What would be the volume of the gas at standard temperature and pressure (STP) (0°C and 1 atm)? *Ans.* 0.678 liter.

6. What is the concentration in moles per liter and molecules per cubic centimeter of an ideal gas at 25°C and (a) 1 atm pressure, (b) 10^{-6} mm of Hg, which is a typical "vacuum" reached in the laboratory with a mercury-vapor pump?

7. A 500-cc bulb weighs 38.7340 g when evacuated and 39.3135 g when filled with air at 1 atm pressure and 24°C. Assuming that air behaves as an ideal gas at this pressure, calculate the effective molecular weight of air. *Ans.* 28.2 g.

8. Insert T_0 and P_0 to represent 0°C and 1 atm, and rearrange the expression

$$PV = nRT$$

so that it shows explicitly that the volume of 1 mole of gas at 0°C and 1 atm is 22.414 liters and that Boyle's and Charles' laws allow the calculation of the volume at other pressures and temperatures.

9. Rearrangement of Eq. (16), with $n = w/M$, where w is the weight of gas in the volume V, and $d = w/V$, where d is the gas density, gives $M = (d/P)RT$. The density of gas which behaves ideally is 2.76 g/liter at a pressure of 2 atm and a temperature of 25°C. What is the molecular weight?

10. The following data have been obtained for the density of CO_2 as a function of pressure at 10°C:

P (atm)	d (g/liter)
0.68	1.29
2.72	5.25
8.14	16.32

By a suitable graphical extrapolation based on the expression $M = d/P(RT)$ obtain the molecular weight of CO_2.

11. Into a gas bulb of volume 2.83 liters are introduced 0.174 g of H_2 and 1.365 g of N_2, which can be assumed to behave ideally. The temperature is 0°C. What are the partial pressures of H_2 and N_2, and what is the total gas pressure? What are the mole fractions of each gas? What are the pressure fractions?

Ans. $P_{H_2}/P = n_{H_2}/n = 0.639$.

12. A synthetic sample of air can be made, except for the minor components, by mixing 79 cc of N_2 with 21 cc of O_2, both measured at 1 atm and 25°C. What volume of air would be obtained if this synthetic sample were compressed to 5.37 atm, the temperature being 25°C? What are the weight fractions, pressure fractions, and mole fractions of the two components? Calculate the effective molecular weight to which this composition corresponds, and compare with the value obtained in Prob. 7.

13. A tube with a porous wall allows 0.53 liter of N_2 to escape per minute from a pressure of 1 atm to an evacuated chamber. What will be the ratio of the amount escaping under the same conditions for He, CCl_4 vapor, and UF_6?

14. In 1846 Graham reported the following results for the time taken, relative to air, for given volumes of various gases to diffuse:

Gas............	Air	O_2	CO	CH_4	CO_2
Time...........	1.000	1.053	0.987	0.765	1.218

How well do these data substantiate Graham's law of diffusion?

15. The virial equation that has been given for 1 mole of methane at 20°C is

$$\frac{PV}{RT} = 1 - 2.0236 \times 10^{-3}P + 3.723 \times 10^{-6}P^2 + 43.59 \times 10^{-12}P^4$$

(a) Show that, up to pressures of a few atmospheres, the slope of the curve for methane, like those of Fig. 1-5, is essentially constant.

(b) Calculate the pressure for the minimum in this curve of PV/RT versus P, and verify that it is a minimum. What is the value of PV/RT at this point compared with that of an ideal gas?

(c) At what two pressures is $PV/RT = 1$?

(d) Plot the compressibility factor PV/RT versus pressure up to 1,000 atm.

16. The variation in the volume with temperature and with pressure is often stated, for gases, liquids, and solids, in terms of the coefficient of expansion $\alpha = 1/V_0(\partial V/\partial T)_P$ and the compressibility $\beta = -1/V_0(\partial V/\partial P)_T$, where V_0 is the volume at 0°C.

(a) Calculate α and β for an ideal gas at 0°C and 1 atm pressure.

(b) Calculate α and β for an ideal gas at 0°C and 100 atm pressure.

(c) At what pressure would an ideal gas have a compressibility equal to that of a typical liquid, for which $\beta = 10^{-5}$ atm^{-1}?

17. The following values for the coefficient of expansion $\alpha = 1/V_0(\partial V/\partial T)_P$ for N_2 have been reported for the ice point 0°C:

P (cm Hg)	99.828	74.966	59.959	33.311
α (°C^{-1})	0.0036740	0.0036707	0.0036686	0.0036652

Calculate a value for the absolute zero of temperature from these data.

18. At 100°C and 1 atm pressure the density of water vapor is 0.0005970 g/cc.

(a) What is the molar volume, and how does this compare with the ideal-gas value?

(b) What is the compressibility factor Z?

Ans. (a) V(obs) = 30.18; V(ideal) = 30.62; (b) $Z = 0.986$.

19. For the isotherm of argon at $-50°C$ the following data have been obtained:

P (atm)......	8.99	17.65	26.01	34.10	41.92	49.50	56.86	64.02
V (liters).....	2.000	1.000	0.667	0.500	0.400	0.333	0.286	0.250

The critical temperature and pressure are $151°K$ and 48 atm. Plot a compressibility versus reduced pressure for this temperature, and compare with the curves of Fig. 1-9.

20. Suppose that the freezing point and boiling point of ethyl alcohol, -116 and $78.5°C$, had been used for the basis of a temperature scale and that it had been decided that there should be $1000°$ between these two reference points. What would be the coefficient of expansion of an ideal gas on the basis of this temperature scale? What would be the value of absolute zero on this temperature scale?

Ans. $\alpha = 0.00123$ deg^{-1}; freezing point of ethyl alcohol is $812°$ absolute.

21. Part of a gas stream of composition 80 per cent methane and 20 per cent hydrogen by volume leaks by effusing through a partially porous section of a pipe through which the gas is being pumped. What is the composition of the gas that is lost?

Ans. CH_4, 59 per cent; H_2, 41 per cent.

22. Show by reference to Fig. 1-8 that one can carry a gas from the left of the dashed liquid-vapor equilibrium region to the right of that region without encountering an observable phase change. Conclude, therefore, that the terms gas and liquid are really meaningful only when two different phases occur together.

23. Attempt to sketch the P versus V isotherms for 1 mole of water in the temperature range 25 to 400°C. Use the following data, which are found in the handbooks, as guides, and indicate what parts of the sketch are determined by these data.

(a) The critical point has $t_c = 374°C$, $P_c = 218$ atm, and the critical density $d_c = 0.4$ g/cc.

(b) The normal boiling point of water is 100°C.

(c) The equilibrium vapor at the normal boiling point behaves nearly ideally.

(d) The vapor pressure of water at 25°C is 23 mm Hg, and the vapor then behaves ideally.

(e) The density of liquid water is 1 g/cc and is not very sensitive to temperature and pressure.

2

The Kinetic-molecular Theory
of Gases

2-1. The Kinetic-molecular Gas Model. In the preceding chapter, in which the physical behavior of gases was studied from an empirical point of view, no attention was given to the natural questions: Why is it that a gas obeys Boyle's law? Charles' law? Why does it have the viscosity it has? And so forth. In this chapter an attempt will be made to understand gases so that such questions can be answered. The kinetic-molecular theory is not, however, primarily introduced to provide an explanation of the gas laws. It is the quantitative look into the molecular world that is provided by this theory that is our principal interest.

It is not possible to deduce the nature of gases directly from the measured properties. These data must be used in a roundabout manner. The procedure is to guess at the essential characteristics of gases and on this basis to deduce their physical properties. A comparison of the deduced properties with those observed allows the usefulness of the guesses to be estimated. A body of assumptions, such as that concerning gases, is called a *model*. The model that is mentally constructed is supposed to embody all the features necessary to determine the behavior to be explained. Although models are generally recognized as being gross oversimplifications, they are expected to contain all the *essential* features for the purpose for which they are constructed. The use of models is not uncommon in chemistry.

The gas laws and the properties of gases described in Chap. 1 can be understood through a model according to which gases are composed of a large number of small particles, called *molecules*, that move about and collide with one another and with the walls of the container. The complex mass of chemical knowledge that led to thinking in terms of molecules need not be investigated here. It is enough to recognize that the conception of chemical compounds, i.e., all of matter, as being composed of fundamental particles evolved gradually and that during the 1800s the concept of atoms and molecules became generally accepted. This idea was applied primarily to chemical studies and proved valuable in explaining the compositions and reactions of chemical substances. Such applications of atomic theory do not, however, lead to information on the size, shape, or properties of the individual molecules.

This molecular concept provided the basis, however, on which the behavior of gases could be studied. In this application, known as the *kinetic-molecular theory of gases*, much information on the properties of individual molecules appeared. The work of Boltzmann, Maxwell, and Clausius during the late 1800s was primarily responsible for the development of the theory.

The kinetic-molecular model for a gas is described by the following statements:

1. A gas is made up of a large number of particles, or molecules, that are small in comparison with both the distances between them and the size of the container.

2. The molecules are in continuous motion.

3. Collisions among the molecules and between the molecules and the walls of the container are perfectly elastic; i.e., none of the translational energy is lost at a collision.

The first step with this model is to show that it does lead to the observed properties of gases.

2-2. The Pressure of a Gas. The pressure exerted by n' molecules, each of mass m, that are contained in a cubic container of side l can be calculated. The pressure exerted by these molecules is the result of their collisions with the walls of the container. The stipulation of a cubic container is not necessary but does simplify the derivation.

To begin with, only one of the n' molecules will be considered. Let its velocity, which may be in any direction in space, be u. This velocity can be resolved into the components u_x, u_y, and u_z, which are perpendicular to the walls of the container as drawn in Fig. 2-1. The effect of the x component of velocity of the one molecule will now be considered. As a result of this velocity component in the x direction the molecule will collide with one end of the container, which is perpendicular to the x axis, bounce back, and subsequently collide with the opposite end. It is the total effect of such impacts with the container walls that, according to the kinetic-molecular theory, produces the gas pressure.

The force exerted by collisions of this one molecule on a side, that labeled A, for instance, is obtained first. The force exerted by the impacts are calculated from the rate of change of momentum. [We recall that $f = ma$ and $a = dv/dt$. Thus $f = m(dv/dt) = (d/dt)(mv)$, or the force equals the rate of change of momentum.] When the molecule moves toward wall A, it has a momentum of mu_x; after collision it moves away from the wall with a momentum $-mu_x$. The number of such momentum changes per second at wall A is the number of collisions which the molecule makes with wall A per second. Since the molecule travels a distance u_x in 1 sec and since the distance traveled

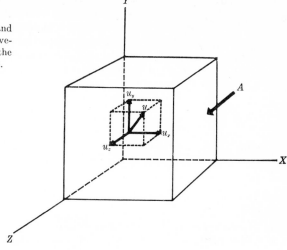

Fig. 2-1. Coordinates and molecular velocity and velocity components for the derivation of gas pressure.

between collisions with side A is $2l$, the number of collisions per second with A is $u_x/2l$. The rate of change of momentum, i.e., the change of momentum per second, is therefore

$$2mu_x \frac{u_x}{2l} = \frac{mu_x^2}{l} \tag{1}$$

This is the force one molecule exerts on side A. Since the pressure is the force per unit area, the pressure exerted by one molecule on side A is

$$\frac{mu_x^2/l}{l^2} = \frac{mu_x^2}{l^3} = \frac{mu_x^2}{V} \tag{2}$$

where $V = l^3$ is the volume of the container. Since the pressure of a gas is the same on all walls of the container, the qualification "on side A" can now be discarded and the result mu_x^2/V is the pressure due to one molecule of the gas.

It is more convenient to have a relation involving the velocity in space u rather than the x component of this velocity. The relation between the component velocities is, as will be recalled for the more familiar resolution along two perpendicular directions,

$$u^2 = u_x^2 + u_y^2 + u_z^2 \tag{3}$$

The motion of the molecule will be such that the component velocities will have time averages that are equal and the square of the average velocity in the x direction will be related to the square of the average velocity in space by the relation

$$u_x^2 = \tfrac{1}{3}u^2 \tag{4}$$

With this expression the pressure due to the one molecule in the container is

$$P = \frac{\tfrac{1}{3}mu^2}{V} \tag{5}$$

For n' molecules in a volume V the pressure can, in a simple calculation, be taken as n' times that of the one molecule. A more detailed calculation than can be given here shows that even if a molecule experiences many collisions with other molecules in a passage across the container, the net effect is that n' molecules give n' times the pressure of one molecule. Since it cannot be postulated that all the molecules move with the same velocities, i.e., the same speeds and same direction, it is necessary to multiply an *average* pressure which one molecule would exert by the total number of molecules. An average value is denoted by writing a bar over the symbol for the quantity. The average molecular velocity, being a measure of both the direction and the magnitude of the rate of molecular movement, is zero. The square of the velocity, on the other hand, measures only the magnitude of this quantity, and each of the n' molecules contributes to the gas pressure according to the average value of u^2. The gas pressure for n' molecules in a container of volume V is, therefore, given as

$$P = \frac{\frac{1}{3}n'm\overline{u^2}}{V}$$

or

$$PV = \tfrac{1}{3}n'm\overline{u^2} \tag{6}$$

This equation is, in a way, the end result of the present derivation. Before this result can be compared with the empirical gas laws, however, some further aspects of the molecular velocities must be considered.

2-3. Molecular Velocities, Kinetic Energies, and Temperature. Frequently, as in this case, it is more convenient to arrange the result to show explicitly kinetic energy rather than molecular speed. The average kinetic energy of one molecule of a gas is written as $\overline{ke}$. This quantity is related to the square of the average molecular velocity by

$$\overline{ke} = \tfrac{1}{2}m\overline{u^2} \tag{7}$$

Equation (6) can now be written as

$$PV = \tfrac{2}{3}n'(\tfrac{1}{2}m\overline{u^2})$$

and replacement of the velocity term according to Eq. (7) gives

$$PV = \tfrac{2}{3}n'\overline{ke} \tag{8}$$

The empirical results of the previous chapter dealt with molar quantities of gases. The present theoretical results are in terms of molecular quantities. Avogadro's number N relates the number of molecules n' to the number of moles n by the relation

$$n' = nN \tag{9}$$

Equation (8) can now be written as

$$PV = \tfrac{2}{3}n(N\overline{ke}) \tag{10}$$

Furthermore, we introduce the term KE to denote the kinetic energy of an Avogadro's number of molecules and rewrite Eq. (10) as

$$PV = \tfrac{2}{3}n\text{KE} \tag{11}$$

At this stage it is necessary to recall the empirical result

$$PV = nRT$$

and to compare the kinetic-molecular-theory result [Eq. (11)] with this expression. Historically the apparent discrepancy between the two relations presented no problem. Heat and temperature had often been associated, in a qualitative way, with the idea of agitation and motion of the particles of the hot material. It was a straightforward matter, therefore, to make the theoretical deduction agree with the experimental law by putting $\frac{2}{3}$KE equal to RT, or

$$KE = \tfrac{3}{2}RT \qquad (12)$$

Thus if the average translational kinetic energy of an Avogadro's number of molecules, i.e., 1 mole, has the value $\frac{3}{2}RT$, then the ideal-gas laws, as embodied in $PV = nRT$, are derivable from the postulates of the kinetic-molecular theory.

Some of the empirical results given in Chap. 1 have now been derived. The expression $PV = \frac{2}{3}n$KE, together with the postulate KE $= \frac{3}{2}RT$, in effect reproduces Boyle's and Charles' laws. Furthermore, the derived result $PV = nRT$ holds for any gas; i.e., it is independent of the molecular weight or any other property characteristic of a given compound. This expression can hold for two different gases at the same temperature and pressure only if equal volumes of the different gases contain the same number of moles or molecules. Thus Avogadro's hypothesis is derived. Dalton's law follows directly from the original postulates since, on the assumption that molecules are noninteracting and occupy no appreciable volume, one set of gas molecules will have no effect on another set. Each gas in a mixture will therefore have the pressure that it would exert if it were in the container by itself.

2-4. Numerical Values for Molecular Energies and Velocities. As previously pointed out, the intention in this chapter is to reveal some of the properties of the molecules of which a gas is composed. It has been shown so far that the qualitative postulates of the kinetic-molecular theory are a sufficiently accurate description of the molecular world to lead to the ideal-gas laws. More quantitative information is obtained from the result that the kinetic energy of an Avogadro's number of molecules is $\frac{3}{2}RT$.

The value of 1.987 cal/deg obtained in Sec. 1-5 for R yields for this energy at 25°C the result

$$\tfrac{3}{2}RT = (\tfrac{3}{2})(1.987)(298) = 900 \text{ cal/mole}$$

This calculation shows that at 25°C the translational-motion contribution to the energy of any ideal gas will be about 900 cal/mole.

The average kinetic energy of one molecule of the gas can be calculated as

$$\overline{ke} = \frac{KE}{N} = \frac{3}{2}\frac{R}{N}T \qquad (13)$$

Since much of our subsequent work will be concerned with the energies of individual molecules and atoms, it is useful to introduce a new constant k, called *Boltzmann's constant,* defined as

$$k = \frac{R}{N} \qquad (14)$$

Boltzmann's constant is therefore the gas constant per molecule, and the average kinetic energy of one molecule is

$$\overline{ke} = \tfrac{3}{2}kT \tag{15}$$

The most generally used units for k are ergs per degree, and in these units it has the value

$$k = \frac{8.314 \times 10^7}{6.024 \times 10^{23}} = 1.380 \times 10^{-16} \text{ erg/deg molecule}$$

The average kinetic energy of a gas molecule at 25°C is

$$\overline{ke} = (\tfrac{3}{2})(1.380 \times 10^{-16})(298) = 6.17 \times 10^{-14} \text{ erg}$$

Although the values of these kinetic energies are very important and will become progressively more meaningful, they are at first difficult to appreciate. It is therefore worthwhile to consider a related and more readily visualized molecular property, velocity.

The kinetic energy of an Avogadro's number of molecules can be written

$$KE = N(\tfrac{1}{2}m\overline{u^2})$$

or

$$KE = \tfrac{1}{2}(Nm)\overline{u^2}$$

$$= \tfrac{1}{2}M\overline{u^2} \tag{16}$$

where M is the gram-molecular weight. A molecular-velocity term is obtained by combining this result with the kinetic-molecular-theory postulate $KE = \tfrac{3}{2}RT$ to get

$$\overline{u^2} = \frac{3RT}{M}$$

or

$$\sqrt{\overline{u^2}} = \sqrt{\frac{3RT}{M}} \tag{17}$$

The cumbersome term $\sqrt{\overline{u^2}}$ is known as the *root-mean-square* (rms) *velocity*. It is necessary to note that this term implies that each of the molecular velocities is squared, then the average value of the squared velocities is taken, and, finally, the square root of this average is determined. This procedure leads to a quantity which is different from a simple average speed but different only, as will be seen in Sec. 2-9, by about 10 per cent. For the present, the values of $\sqrt{\overline{u^2}}$ which are deduced will be taken as representative of average molecular speeds.

If cgs units are used, R has the value 8.314×10^7 erg/deg and the rms velocity is calculated in centimeters per second. For N_2 at 25°C, for example, we obtain

$$\sqrt{\overline{u^2}} = \sqrt{\frac{(3)(8.314 \times 10^7)(298.16)}{(28.02)}} = 5.15 \times 10^4 \text{ cm/sec}$$

$$= 1,150 \text{ miles/hr}$$

Table 2-1 shows further results for a few simple molecules. It should be kept in mind that at a given temperature the average kinetic energy of the molecules of different compounds is the same. It follows that, at a given temperature, light molecules have greater speeds than heavy molecules.

The units of miles per hour are not convenient, of course, for calculations

Table 2-1. Average Speeds of Gas Molecules (Equal to 0.921 $\sqrt{\overline{u^2}}$) at 25°C

	In cm/sec	In miles/hr
H_2	1.77×10^5	3,960
He	1.26	2,820
H_2O	0.59	1,320
N_2	0.47	1.060
O_2	0.44	990
CO_2	0.38	845
Cl_2	0.30	671
Hg	0.18	400
HI	0.22	490

involving molecules. It is well, however, to make a mental note, in units that can be comprehended, of such properties of molecules as the velocities. It should be appreciated that these interesting quantitative results are due to the rather simple deductions of the kinetic-molecular theory in conjunction with the empirical ideal-gas laws.

An important question remains as to the distribution of the molecular speeds that go into the average, or the rms, velocity. In Sec. 2-9 we shall see that there are, in fact, many molecules moving much faster and many much slower than the average values tabulated here.

2-5. The Mean Free Path, Collision Diameter, and Collision Number. The kinetic-molecular derivation in the preceding sections did not take into account how frequently the molecules of a gas collide with one another. The derivation of the pressure exerted by a gas in Sec. 2-2 was based on the idea that the molecules bounce back and forth between the walls of the container. We shall see that, for many gas pressures, a molecule of the gas would actually collide many times with other molecules in traversing the container. It can be shown, however, that these collisions in no way affect the derivation of the pressure of a gas. This implies that no information about molecular collisions can be obtained from calculations such as that of the pressure of a gas.

The following section will show that the viscosity of a gas is dependent on the collisions of the gas molecules with each other. A kinetic-molecular derivation of the viscosity of a gas will therefore lead to added information on the experiences of the rapidly moving gas molecules. Three questions come to mind about the collision properties of the molecules of a gas: How far, on the average, does a molecule travel between collisions? How many collisions per second does a molecule experience on the average? And how many collisions per second take place in 1 cc of a gas? Our lack of feeling for the molecular world is impressed on us when we try to guess the answers to these questions.

Before proceeding to the calculation of gas viscosities, we shall show that the answers to all three questions can be related to one molecular property. This property is the diameter of the molecules of the gas. The use of only one quantity, the diameter, to define the size of the molecules means that the simplifying assumption of spherical molecules is being made. Furthermore, the use of a single quantity to describe the volume of the molecule implies that they are being treated as hard, incompressible spheres. The diameter is denoted by σ, and, since here it will be related to the collision properties of molecules, values obtained for it will be known as *collision diameters*.

Let us consider a particular molecule A in Fig. 2-2, moving in the direction indicated. If the speed of the molecule A is $\bar{c}$ cm/sec, it will travel a distance of $\bar{c}$ cm in 1 sec. Furthermore, if only A is assumed to move and all the other molecules remain stationary, molecule A will collide in 1 sec with all the molecules that have their centers within the cylinder of Fig. 2-2. In fact, the path of A will be bent by the collisions, but this does not affect the derivation. The volume of the cylinder, whose radius is equal to the molecular diameter, is $\pi\sigma^2\bar{c}$. The number of molecules in the cylinder is $\pi\sigma^2\bar{c}n^*$, where n^* is the number of molecules per cubic centimeter. The mean free path, i.e., the distance traveled between collisions, is the length of the cylinder $\bar{c}$ divided by the number of collisions occurring as the molecule traverses this length. Thus, if L is introduced to denote the mean free path length,

$$L = \frac{\bar{c}}{\pi\sigma^2\bar{c}n^*} = \frac{1}{\pi\sigma^2 n^*} \tag{18}$$

A more detailed calculation shows that this result is not exactly correct. The assumption that only molecule A moves implies a relative speed of the colliding molecules of $\bar{c}$ cm/sec. In fact, as Fig. 2-3 suggests, if the molecules are all moving with the speed $\bar{c}$, all types of collisions will occur, ranging from glancing collisions, where the relative speed may be very small, to head-on

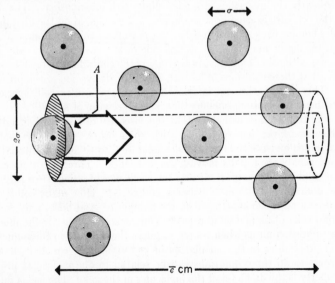

Fig. 2-2. Path swept out by molecule A in 1 sec. Molecules are shown greatly enlarged compared with the distances between them.

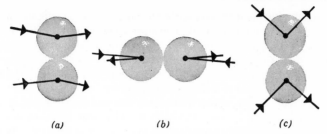

Fig. 2-3. Types of molecular collisions. The relative velocity in an average collision is $\sqrt{2}\,\bar{c}$. (a) Relative velocity = 0. (b) Relative velocity = $2\,\bar{c}$. (c) Relative velocity = $\sqrt{2}\,\bar{c}$.

collisions, where the relative speed is $2\bar{c}$. In an average collision, it turns out, the molecules move at right angles to each other, and the relative speed is $\sqrt{2}\,\bar{c}$. A correct result can be obtained in place of Eq. (18) by recognizing that, although molecule A moves a distance $\bar{c}$ cm in 1 sec, it collides with other molecules with a relative speed of $\sqrt{2}\,\bar{c}$. The mean free path is then

$$L = \frac{1}{\sqrt{2}\,\pi\sigma^2 n^*} \tag{19}$$

The answer to the first question, i.e., How far does a molecule travel between collisions?, has now been shown to be dependent on the as yet unknown quantity σ.

The second problem to be investigated is the number of collisions per second that a molecule makes. This is called the *collision number* and is denoted by Z_1. In relation to the other molecules, the molecule A travels with an effective speed equal to $\sqrt{2}\,\bar{c}$ cm/sec. The number of collisions per second of this molecule is therefore equal to the number of molecules in a cylinder of radius σ and of length $\sqrt{2}\,\bar{c}$. We thus have

$$Z_1 = (\sqrt{2}\,\bar{c})(\pi\sigma^2)n^*$$
$$= \sqrt{2}\,\pi\sigma^2\bar{c}n^* \tag{20}$$

The last of the three problems to be investigated is the number of collisions occurring in a unit volume per unit time. As can be imagined, this quantity is of considerable importance in understanding the rates of chemical reactions. The number of collisions per second per cubic centimeter is also called the collision number but is denoted by Z_{11}.

The collision number Z_{11} is closely related to the number Z_1. Since there are n^* molecules per cubic centimeter and each of these molecules has Z_1 collisions per second, the total number of collisions per second per cubic centimeter will be $\frac{1}{2}n^*Z_1$. The factor $\frac{1}{2}$ ensures that each collision will not be counted twice. We therefore obtain

$$Z_{11} = \frac{1}{2}\sqrt{2}\,\pi\sigma^2\bar{c}(n^*)^2$$
$$= \frac{1}{\sqrt{2}}\,\pi\sigma^2\bar{c}(n^*)^2 \tag{21}$$

Both of the collision numbers and the mean free path have now been expressed in equations that involve the molecular diameter σ. Since the molecular speeds and the number of molecules per cubic centimeter of a particular gas can be determined, only molecular diameters need be known to evaluate L, Z_1, and Z_{11}. Many methods, as we shall see, are available for determining the size of molecules. For the present, the kinetic-molecular derivation of gas viscosities will be relied upon to yield these values.

2-6. The Kinetic Theory of Gas Viscosity. The molecular theory, in accordance with which molecules move freely about, with large spaces between them, might seem at first to imply a complete absence of viscous forces. The source of viscous drag in gases can be understood, however, by focusing attention on two layers of a gas moving parallel to each other but with different flow rates. Over and above their random thermal motion, the molecules in the faster-moving layer will have a greater velocity component in the direction of flow than will the molecules in the slower layer. But because of their random movement some of the molecules of the faster layer will move into the slower layer, imparting to it their additional momentum in the direction of flow and thus tending to speed it up. Likewise, some of the molecules of the slower layer will reach the faster layer and tend to slow it down. The net effect of this exchange of molecules is a tendency toward equalizing the flow rates of the different parts of the gas. The viscous effect is just the difficulty of moving one part of a fluid with respect to another part.

A simplified kinetic-molecular theory of viscosity can be given on the basis of this. Consider two layers of unit area, separated by a distance equal to the mean free path, of a gas flowing as in Fig. 2-4. The gas flows in the x direction with a velocity v and a velocity gradient dv/dy; i.e., the flow rate increases by an amount dv for each increment of distance dy in the y direction. Since the layers under consideration are a mean free path apart, on the average a molecule leaving one layer will arrive in the other layer, collide, and contribute its greater or lesser momentum in the flow direction to that layer. According to a simple approach, which gives almost the correct result, one-third of the molecules have an x component of velocity, one-third a y component, and one-third a z component. Only the third with a y component are effective in the momentum exchange between the gas layers.

The momentum increment which each transferred molecule adds to or subtracts from the new layer is $m[L(dv/dy)]$, that is, m times the difference in flow velocity of the two layers. The force between the two layers can again be calculated from the rate of change of momentum. It is now necessary therefore to calculate the number of these molecular transfers per second.

The molecules which pass a cross section such as that shown shaded in Fig. 2-4 will have carried their excess or deficit of momentum in the flow direction a distance L, their mean free path. They can be treated therefore as if they all started in the lower layer of flowing gas and ended in the upper layer of Fig. 2-4. The number of molecules which cross a section, such as that shaded, in 1 sec are those which are in the lower volume shown and have a y component of velocity upward and those which are in the upper volume shown and have a y component of velocity downward. These two volumes are both drawn with

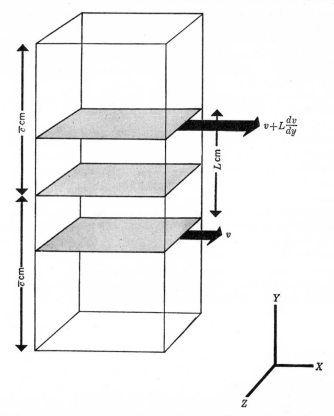

Fig. 2-4. Two layers of a gas moving in the x direction with a velocity gradient of dv/dy.

a length $\bar{c}$ cm so that in 1 sec all the molecules with the appropriate direction of flight will have passed the shaded cross section. If there are n^* molecules per cubic centimeter, there will be $\frac{1}{6}n^*\bar{c}$ molecules in the lower volume, all of which will move into the upper volume in 1 sec. A similar number will move down into the lower volume in 1 sec. The total interchanges between layers therefore are $\frac{1}{3}n^*\bar{c}$ per second.

The rate of change of momentum is then $(\frac{1}{3}n^*\bar{c})[mL(dy/dy)]$, and according to Newton's law this is the force exerted by the layers on each other. Thus

$$f = \tfrac{1}{3}n^*\bar{c}mL \frac{dv}{dy} \tag{22}$$

The coefficient of viscosity η has previously been defined by Eq. (24) of Chap. 1, which, in differential form and for the unit-layer areas of this derivation, is

$$f = \eta \frac{dv}{dy} \tag{23}$$

Comparison of these equations gives for the kinetic-molecular derivation of viscosity the result

$$\eta = \tfrac{1}{3} n^* \bar{c} m L \tag{24}$$

A more detailed derivation takes into account the detailed distribution of molecular velocities and leads to the slightly different, correct expression

$$\eta = \tfrac{1}{2} n^* \bar{c} m L \tag{25}$$

It is this expression that will be used in the deduction of the molecular properties σ, L, Z_1, and Z_{11}.

It is now convenient to replace L by means of Eq. (19) so that an expression involving the collision diameter

$$\eta = \frac{\bar{u} m}{2 \sqrt{2}\, \pi \sigma^2} \tag{26}$$

is obtained.

This important result allows the calculation of the collision diameter of a gas molecule from measurements of the viscosity of the gas. It is necessary also to have values for the mass of a molecule of the gas and the average velocity of the gas molecules. So far we have obtained results only for the rms velocity, which, according to Eq. (17), has the value $\sqrt{3RT/M}$. A later section will point out that the average of the magnitudes of molecular velocities, i.e., the average speed, is only slightly different and is given by

$$\bar{c} = \sqrt{\frac{8RT}{\pi M}} \tag{27}$$

Before proceeding to a discussion of the values for the molecular properties which have been introduced in the preceding section, it is interesting to point out an implication of Eq. (26) on the nature of the viscosity of gases. For a given gas, m and σ are constants, and $\bar{c}$ varies as the square root of T, according to Eq. (27). The theoretical derivation makes the prediction therefore that the viscosity of a gas should be independent of the pressure and proportional to the square root of the absolute temperature. This rather remarkable result (it seems "reasonable" that the viscosity of a gas should increase as the gas is compressed and becomes more dense) was one of the few theoretical deductions to be made before the experimental measurements had been performed. Maxwell's prediction of this behavior and its subsequent experimental verification provided one of the most dramatic triumphs of the kinetic-molecular theory. It should be pointed out, however, that at higher pressures the nonideal behavior of gases seriously interferes with these deduced relations.

2-7. Numerical Values of Collision Properties. As an example we consider the calculation of the collision properties σ, L, Z_1, and Z_{11} for N_2 at 1 atm and 25°C.

Table 1-2 gives the viscosity as

$$\eta = 178 \times 10^{-6} \text{ poise}$$

The number of molecules in 1 cc at 25°C and 1 atm is

$$n^* = \frac{6.024 \times 10^{23}}{(22,414)(298.16/273.16)}$$
$$= 2.462 \times 10^{19}$$

The average molecular speed is

$$\bar{c} = \sqrt{\frac{(8)(8.314 \times 10^7)(298.16)}{\pi(28.02)}} = 0.475 \times 10^5 \text{ cm/sec}$$

and the mass of one molecule is

$$m = \frac{28.02}{6.024 \times 10^{23}} = 4.65 \times 10^{-23} \text{ g}$$

With these data the collision diameter of the N_2 molecule can be calculated from a rearrangement of Eq. (24) as

$$\sigma = \sqrt{\frac{\bar{c}m}{2\sqrt{2}\,\pi\eta}}$$
$$= 3.74 \times 10^{-8} \text{ cm} = 3.74 \text{ A}$$

With this value of the molecular diameter, Eqs. (19) to (21) can be used to obtain the remaining collision properties of N_2 at the specified conditions. Thus

$$L = \frac{1}{\sqrt{2}\,\pi\sigma^2 n^*}$$
$$= 6.50 \times 10^{-6} \text{ cm} = 650 \text{ A}$$
$$Z_1 = \sqrt{2}\,\pi\sigma^2 2\bar{c}n^*$$
$$= 7.31 \times 10^9 \text{ collisions/sec}$$
$$Z_{11} = \frac{1}{\sqrt{2}}\,\pi\sigma^2\bar{c}(n^*)^2$$
$$= 8.99 \times 10^{28} \text{ collisions/(cc)(sec)}$$

Table 2-2 shows similar results for a few other simple molecules.

The data of Table 2-2 indicate the details which can be obtained about the molecular world from the kinetic-molecular theory. A valuable insight into molecular phenomena is provided by these data, and an effort should be made to become familiar with the order of magnitude of these quantities.

The molecular diameters can first be considered. The results serve immediately to substantiate the kinetic-molecular postulate that the molecules are small in comparison with the container size. Molecular dimensions, as Table 2-2 shows, are typically of the order of 10^{-8} cm. In spite of the small scale of the molecular world, it is not difficult to become accustomed to thinking in terms of molecular dimensions. One aid is an appropriate unit of length.

Table 2-2. Some Kinetic-molecular-theory Gas Properties (at 25°C and 1 Atm)

	σ (A)	L (cm)	Z_1 (collisions/sec)	Z_{11} [collisions/(cc)(sec)]
N_2	3.74	6.50×10^{-6}	7.3×10^9	9.0×10^{28}
O_2	3.57	7.14	6.1	7.5
CO_2	4.56	4.41	8.6	10.6
HI	3.50	7.46	3.0	3.7
H_2	2.73	12.3	14.4	17.7
He	2.18	19.0	6.6	8.1

The *angstrom* (abbreviated A) is the unit in which molecular dimensions are almost always expressed. It is defined as

$$1 \text{ A} = 10^{-8} \text{ cm} \tag{28}$$

The molecules listed in Table 2-2 are all quite simple, and the diameters show no large variations. It is to be noted, however, that molecules such as He and H_2 have diameters of about 2 A, while molecules with more atoms, such as CO_2, or more electrons, such as Cl_2, have diameters of 3 or 4 A. With a little experience we forget the small scale of the molecular world and quite casually say that a molecular distance is long because it is a fraction of an angstrom longer than expected.

We shall encounter several other methods for obtaining molecular dimensions. It is important, therefore, to realize that the diameters of Table 2-2 reflect the particular method by which the size of the molecules was measured. The determination of a collision diameter requires, to begin with, the assumption of a spherical molecule so that its size can be specified by the single variable, the diameter. Many molecules, as we shall see when more precise methods of molecular structure are dealt with, are very poorly represented by spheres. A second characteristic of the molecular dimensions, such as those reported in Table 2-2, is that they depend on the collision properties of the molecules. If molecules are soft, like sponge-rubber balls, instead of hard, like billiard balls, the collision diameter is not necessarily of the same length as the molecular diameter measured by some other means. In spite of these difficulties, collision diameters do provide a fairly satisfactory measure of molecular sizes.

The mean free path of gases at 1 atm pressure, though hundreds of times larger than the molecular diameter, is short compared with the size of ordinary containers. The molecules of a gas in such a container will therefore collide many times with one another between the collisions that they make with the walls of the container. It is instructive, in this regard, to calculate the mean free path for a gas at a relatively low pressure. A typical, easily obtained vacuum used by chemists has a pressure of about 10^{-5} mm Hg. At this pressure, i.e., $10^{-5}/760 = 1.32 = 10^{-8}$ atm, and 0°C

$$n^* = \frac{6.02 \times 10^{23}}{22,414} \frac{1.32 \times 10^{-8}}{1}$$

$$= 3.55 \times 10^{11} \text{ molecules/cc}$$

For N_2, with $\sigma = 3.74 \times 10^{-8}$ cm, we calculate from Eq. (19)

$$L = 450 \text{ cm}$$

At a pressure of 10^{-5} mm Hg the situation is very different from that at atmospheric pressure. The molecules will, on the average, bounce back and forth off the walls of the container many times before they happen to collide with other molecules. This feature of molecular behavior must be recognized in the design of high-vacuum equipment. Because of the bouncing of the molecules between the walls of the container, the molecules cannot be "sucked out" by a vacuum pump. To achieve fast pumping, large-diameter tubing must be used so that the molecules will have a good chance of bouncing down to the pump and being expelled.

Finally the collision numbers Z_1 and Z_{11} can be considered. The very many collisions per second that a molecule experiences, together with the short distance traveled between collisions and the very high molecular velocities, should indicate the tremendous rapidity of events in the molecular world. At low pressures, as Eq. (20) indicates, the collision number Z_1 decreases according to n^*. The number of collisions Z_{11} occurring in each cubic centimeter of the gas is even more sensitive to pressure since the factor n^* occurs in Eq. (21) to the second power.

Data such as those given in Table 2-2 represent the average behavior of the molecules of a gas and constitute some of the most important results of the kinetic-molecular theory. After introduction of one new concept, it will be shown that some of the phenomena of the molecular world can be investigated in even more detail.

2-8. Degrees of Freedom. The average kinetic energy of a molecule resulting from its translational motion has been shown to be

$$\overline{ke} = \tfrac{1}{2}m\overline{u^2} = \tfrac{3}{2}kT \tag{29}$$

It is of value to investigate this energy in terms of the energies contributed by the x, y, and z components of the molecular velocity. The velocity in space is related to the component velocities by

$$u^2 = u_x^2 + u_y^2 + u_z^2 \tag{30}$$

Multiplication by $\tfrac{1}{2}m$ and averaging the squared velocities gives

$$\tfrac{1}{2}m\overline{u^2} = \tfrac{1}{2}m\overline{u_x^2} + \tfrac{1}{2}m\overline{u_y^2} + \tfrac{1}{2}m\overline{u_z^2}$$

or

$$\overline{ke} = (\overline{ke})_x + (\overline{ke})_y + (\overline{ke})_z \tag{31}$$

The total translational energy can therefore be regarded as being made up of the kinetic energies resulting from the x, y, and z velocity components. It is to be noted that the kinetic energy breaks up into separate components only because the velocities can be resolved along three perpendicular axes. Such a resolution gives the square of the total velocity in terms of the squares of the components, and no cross terms such as $u_x u_y$ appear.

These components of the kinetic energy represent the average energy of the molecules as a result of their motion in each of the three perpendicular directions. Since

$$(\overline{ke})_x = (\overline{ke})_y = (\overline{ke})_z \tag{32}$$

we obtain the result

$$\begin{aligned} (\overline{ke})_x &= \tfrac{1}{2}kT \\ (\overline{ke})_y &= \tfrac{1}{2}kT \\ (\overline{ke})_z &= \tfrac{1}{2}kT \end{aligned} \tag{33}$$

The average kinetic energy for each of the perpendicular directions in which the molecules are free to move is therefore $\tfrac{1}{2}kT$ per molecule or $\tfrac{1}{2}RT$ per mole.

These three perpendicular directions are examples of what are called *degrees of freedom*. The deduction, summarized in Eqs. (33), could therefore be expressed as follows: *The average kinetic energy of a molecule per degree of freedom is* $\frac{1}{2}kT$. This statement is more far-reaching and important than can be immediately shown. Although, so far, only kinetic energy of translation has been attributed to molecules, it will be seen later that they also can, in general, have kinetic energy as a result of their rotation and of the vibration of one part of the molecule against the other. These motions also represent degrees of freedom, and the expectation of a kinetic energy of $\frac{1}{2}kT$ for each rotational and each vibrational degree of freedom—although at times not realized on account of quantum rules that are then important—is very useful.

2-9. Distribution of Molecular Velocities. Having considered the rms velocity in Sec. 2-4 and having obtained values for this quantity from Eq. (17), we now investigate in more detail the magnitudes of the molecular speeds that contribute to this average value.

The basic relation for handling this problem is known as *Boltzmann's distribution.* This distribution law will be of great importance in later chapters, and its origin will be dealt with in more detail in the following chapter.

Here it will only be mentioned that the fraction of molecules dn/n that lie in the velocity range between u_x and $u_x + du_x$ depends in an exponential manner on the kinetic energy of the molecules with this velocity. Furthermore, the lower the kinetic energy and the higher the temperature, the greater is this fraction. The quantitative distribution law for this one dimensional distribution is, according to Boltzmann,

$$\frac{dn/n}{du_x} = A e^{-(\text{ke})_x/kT}$$
$$= A e^{-\frac{1}{2}mu_x^2/kT} \tag{34}$$

where A is a slightly temperature-dependent proportionality constant. The expression dn/n gives the fraction of the total number of molecules that have the x component of their velocity in the range du_x. The exponential term contains the ratio of the kinetic energy, corresponding to u_x, to the energy kT. The exponential term will depend on the relative values of these energies: for the x component of the kinetic energy less than kT the term will be relatively large, and for the kinetic energy greater than kT the term will be relatively small.

A graph of this one-dimensional velocity distribution is shown in Fig. 2-5. This plot shows the fractions of molecules that have velocity components in the various velocity ranges. Because of the exponential form of the distribution law, the probability that molecules will have very high velocities falls off fairly rapidly. The most probable velocity component is seen to be in the range around zero. It must be remembered that we are dealing here with the distribution of velocities in only one dimension and that the high probability of a zero velocity in one direction does not imply that the most probable speed is zero.

In addition to the velocity scale, a kinetic-energy scale can be attached to Fig. 2-5. This scale is shown along the top of the figure, and since the square of the velocity occurs in the kinetic energy, the kinetic-energy scale is positive on both sides of the origin. Qualitatively from the figure, or more accurately

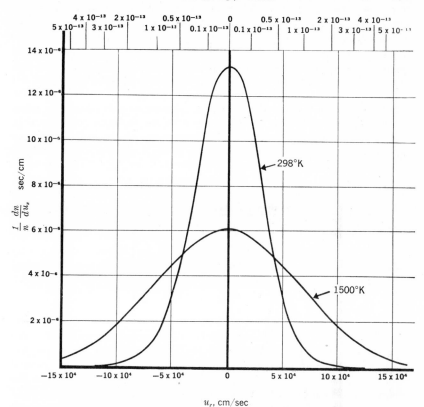

Fig. 2-5. The one-dimensional velocity distribution for N_2 molecules at 298 and 1500°K.

by replotting on a linear energy scale, it can easily be verified that the total kinetic energy for this one-dimensional motion is indeed $\frac{1}{2}RT$ per mole.

The distribution law in three dimensions was derived by Maxwell in 1860. What is of interest, when three dimensions are considered, is the distribution of the speeds of the molecules, i.e., the magnitude but not the direction of the molecular velocities. The fraction of molecules dn/n that have speeds between c and $c + dc$ is given, according to the Maxwell-Boltzmann relation, as

$$\frac{dn/n}{dc} = Be^{-\frac{1}{2}mc^2/kT}c^2 \tag{35}$$

where B is a proportionality constant. This expression is plotted for the molecules of nitrogen in Fig. 2-6. We notice first that the most probable speed is not zero but has a value more like the rms velocity with which we have previously dealt. Furthermore, speeds can be only positive, and the plot of Fig. 2-6 differs therefore from the one-dimensional velocity plot of Fig. 2-5. The existence of a maximum population at a speed other than zero can be explained without a detailed derivation of Eq. (35). The exponential factor operates in both the one- and three-dimensional expressions to give a continuously decreasing number of molecules with high speeds. It is the presence of the c^2 term in the three-dimensional distribution that leads to a most probable speed which is not zero.

Figure 2-7 shows points whose density represents the probability, according to the Maxwell-Boltzmann distribution, of molecules having velocities of various magnitudes and directions. One can check, for example, that in any one direction the distribution corresponds to that shown in Fig. 2-5. The

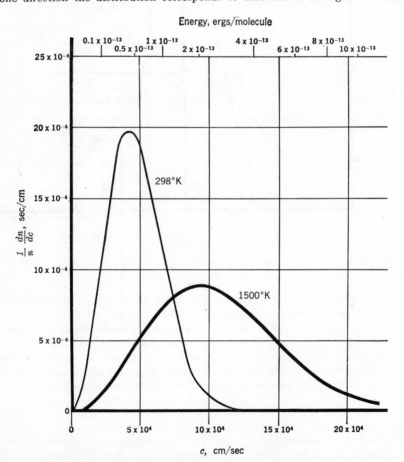

Fig. 2-6. The distributions of the speeds of N_2 molecules at 298 and 1500°K.

Fig. 2-7. Graphical representation of the factors of the Maxwell-Boltzmann distribution.

(a)

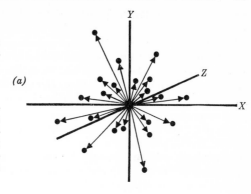

(a) Representation of the magnitude and direction of the velocities of molecules in space. All molecules with velocities between c and $c + dc$ will give points in a spherical shell of radius c and thickness dc.

(b)

(b) Density of points along an axis of (a). Curve is that of Fig. 2-5.

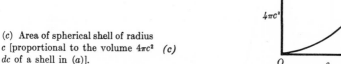

u_z

(c) Area of spherical shell of radius c [proportional to the volume $4\pi c^2\, dc$ of a shell in (a)]. *(c)*

$4\pi c^2$

O c

$\dfrac{1}{n}\dfrac{dn}{dc}$

(d) Product of (b) and (c). Proportional to the number of points *(d)* in spherical shells with radius u.

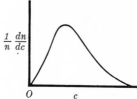

O c

probability of molecules having a speed between c and $c + dc$, in any direction in space, depends both on the point density in Fig. 2-7 and also on the volume of the spherical shell shown in that figure. Since this volume is $4\pi c^2\, dc$, the three-dimension distribution involves both the exponential term and a c^2 term. These act in opposite manners and give the net effect of a maximum probability at some nonzero speed.

The Maxwell-Boltzmann distribution shows that, as indicated in Fig. 2-6, at low temperatures the molecules tend to have speeds bunched in a relatively narrow range.   At higher temperatures the distribution is broader, and—what is for some purposes very important—the high-speed end of the curve tends to spread out to much higher speeds.

Knowledge of the distribution equation allows the calculation of any desired kind of average.   The distribution law of Eq. (35) can be shown to be consistent with the previous result [Eq. (17)] that the square root of the average of the squares of the molecular velocities, or molecular speeds, is given by

$$\sqrt{\overline{u^2}} = \sqrt{\frac{3RT}{M}} \tag{36}$$

The average speed is obtained by adding together, by an integration, the product of the fraction of molecules in a given range by the speed corresponding to that range and dividing by the total number of molecules.   In this way it is found that the average speed $\bar{c}$ is, as previously mentioned in Sec. 2-6,

$$\bar{c} = \sqrt{\frac{8RT}{\pi M}} \tag{37}$$

Another speed that is sometimes used is the most probable speed α, which corresponds to the maximum in the distribution curve.   By differentiating the distribution expression [Eq. (35)] and setting the derivative equal to zero to find the value of c for the curve maximum, we obtain

$$\alpha = \sqrt{\frac{2RT}{M}} \tag{38}$$

These three speeds—the rms, the average, and the most probable—are not very different, being in the ratio

$$\sqrt{\overline{u^2}}:\bar{c}:\alpha = 1:0.92:0.815 \tag{39}$$

One or the other of these usually provides sufficient information on the molecular speeds in any given problem.   Where a more detailed knowledge of the molecular speed distribution is required, reference must be made to the distribution expression or to graphs such as Fig. 2-6.

2-10. Theory of Nonideal Behavior—van der Waals' Equation.   The simple model of the kinetic-molecular theory is satisfactory in that it leads to the derivation of the ideal-gas laws.   We have seen, however, that real gases show PVT relations that deviate more or less widely from the ideal laws.   A question naturally arises as to the possibility of understanding these deviations by the use of a more elaborate model for a gas than that used previously.   This can be done, and in our quest for molecular information it is of interest to investigate what refinements of the previous treatment are necessary.

In 1873, the Dutch chemist van der Waals showed that the addition of two items to the molecular model of Sec. 2-1 could account for much of the deviations of real gases from ideal behavior.   He attributed the failure of the derived $PV = nRT$ relation to duplicate the behavior of real gases to the neglect of:

1. The volume occupied by the gas molecules
2. The attractive forces among the molecules

The corrections introduced by the recognition of these two factors will be treated one at a time.

When n moles of a gas are placed in a container of volume V, the volume in which the molecules are free to move is equal to V only if the volume occupied by the molecules themselves is negligible. The presence of molecules of nonvanishing size means that a certain volume, called the *excluded volume*, is not available for the molecules to move in. If the volume excluded by 1 mole of a gas is represented by b, then instead of writing $PV = nRT$ a more appropriate equation would be

$$P(V - nb) = nRT \qquad (40)$$

The excluded volume b is usually treated as a constant which is characteristic of each gas and must be determined empirically so that a good correction to the simple gas-law expression is obtained.

The relation of b to the size of the molecules can be seen by considering Fig. 2-8. The molecules are again assumed to be spherical and to have a diameter σ. The volume in which the centers of two molecules cannot move because of each other's presence is indicated by the lightly shaded circle in Fig. 2-8. The radius of this sphere is equal to the molecular diameter. The volume excluded per pair of molecules is $\frac{4}{3}\pi\sigma^3$. We then obtain

$$\text{Excluded vol per molecule} = \frac{1}{2}\left(\tfrac{4}{3}\pi\sigma^3\right)$$

$$\text{Actual vol of a molecule} = \tfrac{4}{3}\pi\left(\frac{\sigma}{2}\right)^3$$

$$= \frac{1}{8}\left(\tfrac{4}{3}\pi\sigma^3\right)$$

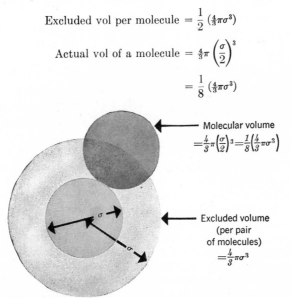

Molecular volume
$$= \tfrac{4}{3}\pi\left(\tfrac{\sigma}{2}\right)^3 = \tfrac{1}{8}\left(\tfrac{4}{3}\pi\sigma^3\right)$$

Excluded volume
(per pair
of molecules)
$$= \tfrac{4}{3}\pi\sigma^3$$

Fig. 2-8. The excluded volume (dashed line) for a pair of molecules according to van der Waals' treatment.

It is seen, therefore, that the excluded volume is four times the actual volume of the molecules, i.e.,

$$b = 4N \left[\tfrac{4}{3}\pi \left(\frac{\sigma}{2} \right)^3 \right] \tag{41}$$

We might be tempted to make use of our previously determined values of σ to calculate b. It is more satisfactory, however, to adjust b so that the derived equation corresponds as well as possible to the observed PVT data. This procedure, required principally by the difficulties caused by the second correction term, results in van der Waals' equation being *semiempirical*. The form of the derived equation follows from a theoretical treatment, but the numerical values of the constants appearing in the equation are obtained from the experimental PVT data. Semiempirical equations are not uncommon in chemistry and frequently are considerably more satisfactory than more empirical relations, such as the virial expression [Chap. 1, Eq. (27)].

The second van der Waals' correction term concerns the attractive forces among molecules. That such forces exist is clearly demonstrated by the tendency of all gases to condense at temperatures low enough so that these forces can overcome the kinetic energy of the molecules. That these attractions exist is clear; exact knowledge of their source and quantitative values for them are much harder to come by. The semiempirical approach, however, requires only that a suitable term representing these attractions be inserted. Its value can be obtained by adjusting it, as is done with b, to give an equation that best fits the PVT data.

The attraction a molecule exerts on its neighbors tends to draw them in toward itself; i.e., the attraction acts with the confining pressure to hold the molecules together. The effect of one molecule in helping to hold the gas together through these forces of attraction is proportional to the number of nearby molecules on which it can act. If there are n moles of gas in a volume V, this number is proportional to n/V, the number of moles per unit volume. Since each of the neighboring molecules is likewise attracting its neighbors, the total pulling together of the gas due to these interactions is proportional to $(n/V)^2$. The gas is confined therefore not only by the external pressure P but also by these intermolecular attractions, which contribute a term proportional to $(n/V)^2$. If the proportionality factor is denoted by a, van der Waals' complete equation becomes

$$\left(P + \frac{an^2}{V^2} \right) (V - nb) = nRT \tag{42}$$

The success of this equation in fitting the PVT behavior of real gases is judged by choosing values of a and b, different for each gas, to give as good a fit to the observed data as possible. Although perfect agreement for all ranges of pressure and temperature is not obtained, the improvement over the ideal-gas-law expression $PV = nRT$ is very considerable. Figure 2-9 and Table 2-3 indicate the amount of improvement in regions of very nonideal behavior. The success of van der Waals' equation in representing PVT

behavior is very much better than could be expected for any purely empirical expression with only two adjustable constants.   The behavior in the two-phase region, such as shown in Fig. 2-9, cannot be followed by van der Waals' equation, and the maxima and minima must be disregarded.

2-11. Van der Waals' Equation and the Critical Point. As Fig. 2-9 shows, van der Waals' equation follows reasonably well the behavior of a gas near the region of liquid-vapor equilibrium.   There will, moreover, be one temperature for which van der Waals' equation, with given values of a and b, will show a horizontal point of inflection.   The P versus V curve calculated from van der Waals' equation at this temperature can be identified with the critical isotherm.   When this is done, a convenient, but not always the most satisfactory, way of obtaining values for a and b is available.

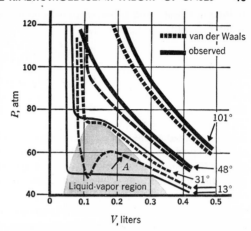

Fig. 2-9. Comparison of van der Waals' PV curves for CO_2 with the observed behavior near the critical point.

Equation (42) can be rearranged and written for 1 mole to give

$$P = \frac{RT}{V - b} - \frac{a}{V^2} \tag{43}$$

To investigate the horizontal point of inflection on a plot of P versus V, we obtain

$$\frac{dP}{dV} = \frac{-RT}{(V - b)^2} + \frac{2a}{V^3} \tag{44}$$

and

$$\frac{d^2P}{dV^2} = \frac{2RT}{(V - b)^3} - \frac{6a}{V^4} \tag{45}$$

At the critical point the first and second derivatives are zero and the pressure,

Table 2-3. Molar Volumes of CO_2 at 320°K.   Comparison of van der Waals' Equation and the Ideal-gas Law near the Critical Temperature

P (atm)	V (liters)		
	Observed	van der Waals	Ideal
1	26.2	26.2	26.3
10	2.52	2.53	2.63
40	0.54	0.55	0.66
100	0.098	0.10	0.26

volume per mole, and temperature can be written as P_c, V_c, and T_c.   At this point Eqs. (43) to (45) become

$$P_c = \frac{RT_c}{V_c - b} - \frac{a}{V_c^2} \tag{46}$$

$$0 = \frac{-RT_c}{(V_c - b)^2} + \frac{2a}{V_c^3} \tag{47}$$

and

$$0 = \frac{2RT_c}{(V_c - b)^3} - \frac{6a}{V_c^4} \tag{48}$$

These three equations can be solved for a, b, and R in terms of P_c, V_c, and T_c. The gas constant R, of course, is better known by other means, but it appears in van der Waals' equation as if it were another adjustable constant.   After some manipulation, the following relations are obtained:

$$b = \tfrac{1}{3}V_c \tag{49}$$
$$a = 3P_c V_c^2 \tag{50}$$
$$R = \frac{8P_c V_c}{3T_c} \tag{51}$$

With these results, the critical data of Table 1-3 can be used to obtain values for the van der Waals' constants a and b.   Constants evaluated in this way should result in a good fit of curves calculated from the van der Waals' equation to the experimental results in the neighborhood of the critical point.   If the PVT behavior in some other region is of particular interest, it might be advantageous to adjust the values of a and b to something other than those calculated from Eqs. (49) and (50).

Values of a and b for some simple compounds are given in Table 2-4.   Also shown are the values of the molecular diameter σ calculated from the excluded volume b.

The molecular diameters calculated from van der Waals' equation are seen to be in fair agreement with those obtained from viscosity measurements. This encourages considerable confidence in these numbers as giving the effective diameters of molecules.

Table 2-4. Values for the Constants in van der Waals' Equation

	a (atm liters^2/mole^2)	b (liters/mole)	Molecular diam (A)
N_2	1.39	0.0391	3.14
O_2	1.36	0.0318	2.93
CO	1.49	0.0399	3.16
CO_2	3.59	0.0427	3.23
CCl_4	20.39	0.1383	4.78
HCl	3.67	0.0408	3.18
A	1.35	0.0322	2.94
H_2	0.244	0.0266	2.76
He	0.034	0.0237	2.66
H_2O	5.464	0.0305	2.90
CH_4	2.253	0.0428	3.23

Some discussion of the values of the van der Waals' constant a might seem called for. It seems advisable, however, to leave the subject of intermolecular forces until it is treated fully in a later chapter.

In spite of the success of the van der Waals' equation in handling the PVT behavior of real gases, in much of our subsequent work we shall revert to the simple ideal-gas expression $PV = nRT$. At low pressures and not too low temperatures, deviations from this relation are for many purposes not serious. For theoretical derivations the simplicity of the ideal-gas expression and the fact that it applies to all gases without adjustment of any constants make its use very advantageous.

2-12. Van der Waals' Equation and the Law of Corresponding States. The empirical data plotted in Fig. 1-9 show that, as the law of corresponding states claims, all gases behave in a similar manner when they are treated in terms of the reduced variables P_R, V_R, and T_R. It is interesting to show that van der Waals' equation is consistent with the law of corresponding states in that, when it is written in terms of the reduced variables, no quantities remain to be empirically adjusted for the particular gas to which it is applied.

The constants a, b, and R are related to the critical-point constants by Eqs. (49) and (50). These relations can be substituted for a, b, and R and used to write van der Waals' equation in a form that shows the critical constants explicitly. Rearrangement of this equation leads to only the terms P/P_c, V/V_c, and T/T_c. Introducing the reduced variables P_R, V_R, and T_R to represent these ratios, we have

$$\left(P_R + \frac{3}{V_R^2}\right)\left(V_R - \frac{1}{3}\right) = \frac{8}{3}T_R \tag{52}$$

In this form it can be seen that van der Waals' equation is consistent with the empirical law of corresponding states. This form of van der Waals' equation applies to all gases and illustrates the fact that in terms of the reduced variables all gases behave in a like manner.

Problems

1. Calculate the pressure exerted by 10^{23} gas particles, each of mass 10^{-22} g, in a container of volume 1 liter. The rms velocity of the particles is 10^5 cm/sec.
What is the total kinetic energy of these particles?
What must be the temperature?
Ans. $P = 33$ atm; energy $= 1,200$ cal; $T = 2420°$K.

2. A 1-liter gas bulb contains 1.03×10^{23} H_2 molecules. If the pressure exerted by these molecules is 6.34 mm Hg, what must the average squared molecular velocity be? What must the temperature be?

3. Estimate the number of molecules left in a volume the size of a pinhead, about 1 cu mm, when air is pumped out to give a vacuum of 10^{-6} mm Hg at 25°C.
Ans. 3.24×10^7.

4. For 25°C calculate and compare the average kinetic energies, speeds, and momenta of the molecules of He and Hg.

5. Calculate the average molecular rms velocities of He atoms at 10, 100, and 1000°K in units of centimeters per second and miles per hour. What values would be obtained if the pressure was specified to be 10^{-5} mm Hg?

6. The kinetic-molecular theory attributes an average kinetic energy of $\frac{3}{2}kT$ to each particle. What velocity would a mist particle of mass 10^{-12} g have at room temperature according to the kinetic-molecular theory? Compare this value with the molecular velocities of Table 2-1.   *Ans. v*(rms) = 0.35 cm/sec.

7. How much heat must be added to 3.45 g of neon in a 10-liter bulb to raise the temperature from 0 to 100°C? By what ratio is the average squared velocity changed by this temperature change?

8. How many degrees would the temperature of 1 mole of liquid water be raised by the addition of an amount of energy equal to the translational kinetic energy at 25°C of 1 mole of water vapor?   *Ans.* 49°C.

9. The following values are given for the speed of sound in air:

Temp (°C).............	20	100	500	1000
Speed (m/sec).........	344	386	553	700

Compare these with the rms velocities of N_2 molecules at these temperatures.

10. Using the value of σ from Table 2-4 for argon, calculate the mean free path, the average number of collisions a molecule experiences per second, and the average number of collisions per cubic centimeter per second for the molecules of argon at 0°C and 1 atm pressure. What values would be obtained at 1000°C and 1 atm? What values at 0°C and 100 atm?

11. Derive an expression for the mean free path for any gas in terms of the collision diameter, the temperature, and the pressure. Prepare a convenient graph showing the variation of the mean free path with pressure for 0°C and the pressure range 10^{-6} mm Hg to 1 atm if the gas is nitrogen.

12. Using Eq. (27) for the average speed of a gas, obtain expressions for the collision numbers Z_1 and Z_{11} as functions of σ, M, P, and T. For the pressure range 10^{-6} mm Hg to 1 atm show graphically the variation of Z_1 and Z_{11} with pressure for N_2 at 0°C.

13. Consider a volume V enclosed by a rectangular box of cross section 1 sq cm and length V and containing n' molecules. Give an expression for the number of molecules striking one end of the container per second. If this end were removed and replaced by a perfect evacuating pump, what would be the expression for the rate of evacuation in molecules per second?

14. The ratio of the number of molecules that have a speed three times the average speed $\bar{c}$ to the number that have the average speed is a guide to the number of fast molecules that are present.

(*a*) Calculate this ratio for a gas at 25°C.

(*b*) Calculate the ratio of the number of molecules with speeds $3\bar{c}_{25°C}$ to the number with $\bar{c}_{25°C}$ for a gas at 40°C.

Note from this calculation how a small temperature increase has a large effect on the number of fast molecules.   *Ans.* (*a*) 3.46 $\times$ 10^{-4}; (*b*) 5.46 $\times$ 10^{-4}.

15. Plot the one-dimensional and three-dimensional population versus velocity and speed curves for H_2 molecules at 0°C. Replot these curves to show population as a function of energy.

16. By graphical means show that the population-energy curves of Prob. 15 are consistent with an average translational energy of $\frac{1}{2}kT$ per degree of freedom. Graphically obtain the average and the most probable speeds, and compare with the values calculated from the given formulas.

17. In view of the kinetic-molecular-theory expression for the relation of molecular velocities to molecular weights, would you expect Graham's law of diffusion to be based

on diffusion rates that are expressed as relative volumes diffusing per unit time or relative masses of gases diffusing per unit time?

18. Compare the volume of 20 g of HCl at 100°C and 50 atm pressure given by the ideal-gas law with that given by van der Waals' equation.

Ans. V(ideal) = 0.335 liter; V(van der Waals) = 0.281 liter.

19. Show that at fairly low pressures, where $PV = nRT$ can be inserted in the van der Waals' correction term, the van der Waals' equation for 1 mole can be reduced to

$$PV = RT(1 + BP)$$

where

$$B = \frac{b}{RT} - \frac{a}{(RT)^2}$$

Use this approximation to calculate a virial coefficient at 20°C from the van der Waals' constants for CH_4. Compare with the value given in Prob. 1-15.

Ans. $B = -0.00211$ atm^{-1}.

20. Plot the isotherms for CO_2 at 320°K, using the data of Table 2-3, on the basis of the observed, van der Waals', and ideal behavior. Calculate additional values where needed to draw in the full curves.

21. The compressibility factor $Z = PV/RT$ for CO is 0.9920 at 25°C and 75 atm and 1.7412 at 25°C and 800 atm. Calculate the percentage errors introduced at these two conditions if (*a*) the ideal-gas law and (*b*) van der Waals' equation is used to calculate the volume of 1 mole of CO.

22. The pressure exerted by 5 moles of nitrogen in a 1-liter gas bulb is found to be 98.4 atm at 250°K. What pressure would have been expected:

(*a*) From ideal-gas behavior?

(*b*) From van der Waals' equation?

23. Calculate, according to van der Waals' equation, the pressure that would have to be applied to N_2 to reduce the total volume to a value equal to four times the excluded volume (*a*) at a temperature of 25°C, (*b*) at a temperature of 1000°C.

Ans. (*a*) 151 atm, (*b*) 835 atm.

24. Plot P versus V for 1 mole of H_2O at 100°C on the basis of van der Waals' equation. Compare, on the same graph, the actual PV curve estimated from the facts that (*a*) at 100°C the density of liquid water is 0.958 g/cc and that of the equilibrium water vapor is 0.000597 g/cc, (*b*) at lower pressures the vapor behaves almost ideally, and (*c*) liquid water is compressed by about 0.04 per cent of its volume by a pressure increase of 100 atm.

25. Deduce, making use of van der Waals' approach and the critical data of Table 1-3, the diameter of a normal pentane C_5H_{12} molecule. Compare with the value obtained from gas viscosities. *Ans.* $d = 4.34$ A.

26. Obtain Eqs. (49) to (51) from the critical-point relations [Eqs. (46) to (48)].

3

Introduction to Atomic and

Molecular Structure

The kinetic-molecular theory of the properties of gases provides a great deal of information on the nature and behavior of molecules. This information results, so to speak, from an external view of the molecules. Much of the physical chemistry with which we shall deal in later chapters will be more understandable if we here continue our investigation of the molecular world and now consider the internal structure of molecules.

Any attempt to learn about the events which occur inside molecules may seem like a rather bold undertaking. The electrons and the atoms which make up molecules do indeed exhibit behavior that is quite outside our ordinary experience. In spite of this, in a period of less than forty years—from about 1890 to 1930—investigators of the role of electrons and atoms in molecular bonding went from a state of almost complete ignorance to our complete understanding "in principle" of this aspect of molecular structure. In the course of this development a new approach to scientific theory and a new type of mechanics had to be learned. The exciting and still-continuing story of our gropings into the world within molecules is now introduced.

The subject can be divided into three parts. First, the components of the atom are sorted out so that the atom can be recognized as being made up of a central, heavy nucleus with some external arrangement of electrons. Second, some aspects of the nature of light and electromagnetic radiation are studied so that the very important experiments on atomic spectra can be presented. These experiments provide the principal data that a detailed theory of an atom must account for. Finally, the partially successful atomic-structure theory of Bohr is presented, and then the present quantum-mechanical approach to atomic and molecular structure as provided by the Schrödinger equation is introduced.

THE COMPONENTS OF ATOMS

By the end of the nineteenth century a very large number of organic and inorganic compounds had been studied and their elemental constituents had been determined. Avogadro's hypothesis had finally provided the means for determining the number of each kind of atom in the molecule so that, for example, water could be written as H_2O rather than, as previously, HO. It had even been possible to deduce such detailed information as the fact that the single-bonded carbon atom binds its four groups essentially tetrahedrally. Avogadro's number and the kinetic-molecular theory had given quantitative data for the size of molecules and for other molecular properties. In spite of these advances in chemistry, the details of the atom, and, therefore, of many aspects of the molecule, remained a complete mystery. It was not until the electron, the component of the atom that is of principal chemical interest, had been discovered and its charge and mass measured that any further progress into the nature of atoms and molecules could be made.

3-1. The Electron. The electrical nature of chemical compounds was rapidly appreciated after the chance discovery by Galvani in 1791 of the effect of an electric charge on the nerve and muscle of a frog's legs. Soon afterward Volta constructed the early equivalent of a dry cell, and it became apparent that chemical reactions could produce electricity and, furthermore, that electricity could produce chemical reactions. The quantitative electrolysis experiments of Faraday around 1830 greatly extended the appreciation of the electrical nature of chemical compounds. In all these experiments, however, the electrons which were responsible for the observed phenomena were in a bound state; i.e., they were in a metallic conductor or were associated with a chemical species. It was not until near the end of the nineteenth century that it became possible to study electrons free from any complicating medium.

The development of a good mercury vacuum pump by Geissler in 1855 soon led to experiments in which a voltage was placed across two electrodes sealed in an evacuated glass tube. Qualitative experiments led Crookes, whose name tubes of this type now bear, to deduce that the applied voltage draws electrons from the negatively charged electrode, the cathode, and directs them through space to the positively charged electrode, the anode. It was experiments with such a beam of free electrons by J. J. Thomson, working at Cambridge around 1900, that provided the initial important data on the nature of electrons. The apparatus used by Thomson is sketched in Fig. 3-1. Some of the electron beam, accelerated from the cathode toward the anode, passed through the slits in the anode and formed a well-defined narrow beam which passed on down the tube. Thomson then applied an electric or magnetic field perpendicularly to the beam and observed the deflection of the beam, as indicated by the fluorescent spot, at which the beam struck the scale at the end of the tube. Applied fields tend to bend the beam from its normally straight course. This bending, for a given arrangement, can be shown by a detailed analysis to be proportional to the charge e of the electron and inversely proportional to its mass m_e. This second factor enters because the momentum $m_e v$ of the electron opposes the

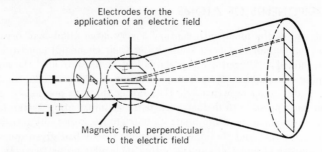

Fig. 3-1. Thomson's apparatus for determining e/m for the electron.

tendency of the beam to bend. From deflection measurements Thomson deduced the ratio e/m_e for the electron. The best value for this ratio is now

$$\frac{e}{m_e} = 5.273 \times 10^{17} \text{ esu/g} \tag{1}$$

The charge is given in electrostatic units (esu), which are appropriate to the cgs system of units. This unit of charge is defined such that two unit charges separated in vacuum from each other by 1 cm exert a force of 1 dyne on each other.

These e/m_e experiments of Thomson provided essential information on the properties of the electron. It became immediately evident that a determination of e or m_e separately was needed. It was Thomson again who set up the first successful experiment to do this.

His experiment depended on the freeing of electrons from the molecules of a gas by means of the passage of X rays through the gas. This process was allowed to occur in the presence of supersaturated water vapor. The electrons condensed droplets of water and attached themselves to these droplets. The number of droplets formed in a given experiment was estimated from their size, as determined by their rate of fall, and the total amount of condensed water. Measurement of the total charge of the condensed water, together with the assumption that each droplet carried only one electron, allowed the charge of the electron to be estimated. Thomson obtained a value of 6.5×10^{-11} esu for e. A more elegant experiment by R. A. Millikan in 1909, using droplets of oil, provided a more accurate value. The best present value for the charge of the electron is

$$e = 4.802 \times 10^{-10} \text{ esu} \tag{2}$$

This value gives, with the result for e/m_e, the mass of the electron as

$$m_e = 0.9107 \times 10^{-27} \text{ g} \tag{3}$$

It is, perhaps, more informative to calculate the ratio of the mass of an electron to that of a hydrogen atom. Since

$$m_{\text{H}} = \frac{1.008}{6.024 \times 10^{23}} = 1.673 \times 10^{-24} \text{ gram} \tag{4}$$

we obtain

$$\frac{m_e}{m_H} = \frac{1}{1,837} \tag{5}$$

This result, that the mass of the electron is very small compared with the mass of the hydrogen atom as a whole, became available to Thomson and stimulated the first modern theory of the atom.

3-2. The Atomic Theories of Thomson and Rutherford. For want of more information Thomson assumed that an atom consisted of a spread-out, heavy, positively charged sphere of matter in which were embedded the small, light electrons. This model was satisfactory to the extent that the electrostatic forces of repulsion among the electrons could be balanced by the attractive forces between the positively charged mass and the electrons to give an electrostatically stable system.

New experimental studies by Ernest Rutherford, also at the Cavendish Laboratory at Cambridge, were soon to show that this model was entirely untenable. In 1910 Rutherford, with the help of Geiger and Marsden, studied the scattering produced in a beam of α particles as the beam passed through a thin metal film. The beam of α particles, which are the nuclei of helium atoms, was obtained from radioactive materials that had recently been studied by the Curies. These particles were known to be fast, penetrating units. Most of the α-particle beam passed, as expected, through the metal film with little or no deviation. Much to Rutherford's amazement, however, some of the α particles were scattered through large angles and even bounced back from the metal film. Rutherford then showed that this result was not consistent with Thomson's theory that the mass of an atom was spread out rather diffusely over the volume occupied by the atom.

Rutherford recognized that what was required to explain his scattering results was the concentration of the mass of the atom into a small, dense core, or *nucleus*, so that the few collisions that occurred between the α particles and this small core would result in large-angle scattering. To fit the data, Rutherford deduced that the positive, massive part of the atom, now known to be made up of protons and neutrons, had a diameter of about 10^{-13} cm. This number was to be contrasted with the values of about 10^{-8} cm for the dimensions of atoms and molecules. Rutherford recognized from this that an atom had a *nucleus*, a dense, positively charged central core with a diameter about one hundred-thousandth of the atom itself. Rutherford further theorized that the electrons of an atom revolve about the nucleus in the manner of the planets about the sun, but it was his recognition that the atom had a nucleus that was to be his most important contribution.

The *nuclear atom* of Rutherford was a great step in the discovery of the nature of the atom. At this stage two distinct problems remained. One was the detailed nature of the newly discovered nucleus, and this problem remains one of great interest but now generally attracts the attention of physicists rather than chemists. The second problem concerned the behavior of the electrons of the atom.

Rutherford's planetlike picture for the electrons was unsatisfactory in that electrons moving in circular or elliptical orbits would be accelerated toward the center of the atom.   Although the forces of attraction to the nucleus might be balanced by the centrifugal force of the orbiting electron, the laws of electrodynamics made it perfectly clear that an accelerated charge would radiate energy and that an atom, such as Rutherford proposed, would "run down."   This atomic theory also had the defect of not leading to any explanation for the great number of empirical data which had been accumulated from studies of atomic spectra.   Since the explanation of these spectral results was recognized as constituting the principal test of any atomic theory, we now digress at some length to consider these results.   In so doing we shall encounter some new attitudes regarding the nature of light and electromagnetic radiation that were to influence the ideas of atomic structure.

ELECTROMAGNETIC RADIATION AND ATOMIC SPECTRA

3-3. The Wave Nature of Light.   Much of our present knowledge of the detailed nature of atoms and molecules comes from experiments in which light or, more generally, radiation and matter interact.   Atomic spectroscopy was the first of such experiments to provide the data necessary for advancing the theory of the atom.   Before treating these experiments, however, it is necessary to discuss briefly some features of the behavior of light.   Some of the phenomena displayed by light can be understood by treating light as a wave motion, and it is this theory which is first considered.

Visible light is one example of radiation which is called *electromagnetic radiation*.   Other examples are X rays, ultraviolet light, infrared light, radar and television waves, and radio waves.   All these types of radiations are similar in that many of their effects can be understood in terms of electric and magnetic disturbances traveling with the speed of light.   The radiation is said to consist of electric and magnetic fields oscillating perpendicular to the direction of propagation of the radiation.   The different kinds of electromagnetic radiation listed above are distinguished by the different frequencies of this oscillation.   It is only the wave nature of the oscillation which need be discussed here.   A more detailed understanding of the electric and magnetic fields will not be required until a later chapter.

The oscillations associated with electromagnetic radiation, which has a velocity of propagation c, are characterized by the wavelength λ and the frequency ν.   These three quantities can be related by reference to Fig. 3-2.   Each sine curve gives the value of the electric or the magnetic field of the radiation as a function of the distance from the source at a given time.   The movement of the wave to the right with a velocity c cm/sec is indicated by the displacement of the wave picture after several short time intervals.

A hypothetical observer, a Maxwell-demon type, is considered to be stationed at a distance c cm from the origin.   He watches the radiation pass by his position for 1 sec.   Since the velocity of the radiation is c cm/sec, in this 1 sec he sees all the wave pass by which was initially between his position and the origin.   Since the length of one cycle or wave is λ cm, there are c/λ waves

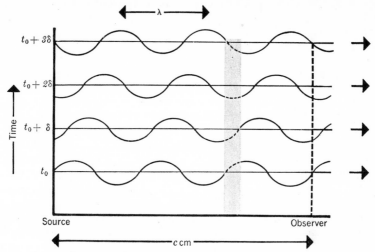

Fig. 3-2. The electric or magnetic field of electromagnetic radiation moving outward from the source in a sinusoidal manner.

in this distance.   The observer would count c/λ cycles/sec and would obtain for the frequency of oscillation of the wave motion the result

$$\nu = \frac{c}{\lambda} \tag{6}$$

This relation can be illustrated by some numerical values.   The velocity of electromagnetic radiation in vacuum is independent of wavelength or frequency and has the value

$$c = 2.9979 \times 10^{10} \text{ cm/sec} \tag{7}$$

The categories into which electromagnetic radiation is divided correspond to different ranges of wavelengths or frequencies.   Light, or visible radiation, has wavelengths between about 4,000 and 7,500 A.   Yellow light, for example, has a wavelength of about 5,800 A, or 5.8×10^{-5} cm, and its frequency is, therefore,

$$\nu = \frac{c}{\lambda} = \frac{3 \times 10^{10}}{5.8 \times 10^{-5}} = 5.2 \times 10^{14} \text{ cycles/sec} \tag{8}$$

The observer of Fig. 3-2 would see, for this radiation, 5.2×10^{14} oscillations of the electric or magnetic field for each second he observed the radiation.

It is customary to describe a particular electromagnetic radiation in terms of either its wavelength or its frequency.   The cgs units of centimeters for wavelength and cycles per second for frequency are not always convenient.   For visible and ultraviolet radiation, for example, the wavelength is usually expressed in angstroms.

The inconveniently large numbers that occur when cycles per second are used for the frequency are apparent from the example of yellow light. More convenient numbers are obtained by using a unit which differs from cycles per second by a factor equal to the velocity of light. Frequencies so expressed are denoted by $\bar{\nu}$ and are calculated as

$$\bar{\nu} = \frac{1}{\lambda} \tag{9}$$

For λ in centimeters, $\bar{\nu}$ has the units reciprocal centimeters, or cm^{-1}. In the example of yellow light, the frequency could be expressed as

$$\bar{\nu} = \frac{1}{\lambda} = \frac{1}{5.8 \times 10^{-5}} = 17,000 \text{ cm}^{-1} \tag{10}$$

It should be recognized that $\bar{\nu}$, like ν, is a measure of frequency. It is particularly convenient and dimensionally easy to use since its reciprocal is the wavelength of the radiation. Table 3-1 shows the wavelengths and frequencies corresponding to the various classifications of electromagnetic radiation.

3-4. The Corpuscular Nature of Light. The description of light as a wave motion successfully explained many of the phenomena which were observed. Diffraction and interference effects, such as the colors produced by an oil film on water, were readily accounted for. This theory of the nature of light, however, never succeeded in completely displacing the "corpuscular theory," originally due to Newton. This second theory views light, or radiation, as consisting of a flow of particles or corpuscles.

Each of the theories for the nature of light had its advocates in the years of controversy which extended into the beginning of the twentieth century. It gradually became clear that some phenomena, such as diffraction and interference effects, could be most easily explained on the basis of the wave theory, while other phenomena, such as the photoelectric emission of electrons from metals, seemed to require the corpuscular theory.

The dilemma of these two somewhat satisfactory, but very different, theories of the nature of light persisted for more than two centuries. The dilemma was finally resolved, but not by a simple proof that one theory was correct and the other incorrect. A deeper understanding of the nature of physical theories was required. The behavior of light could sometimes be described by one

Table 3-1. Electromagnetic Radiations

Description	Typical wavelength		Typical frequency	
	In cm	In A	In cycles/sec	In cm^{-1}
X rays....................	1×10^{-8}	1	3×10^{18}	
Ultraviolet light............	2×10^{-5}	2,000	1.5×10^{15}	50,000
Visible light................	5×10^{-5}	5,000	0.6×10^{15}	20,000
Infrared radiation..........	1×10^{-3}	.....	3×10^{13}	1,000
Radar or microwaves.......	1	.....	3×10^{10}	1
Radio waves...............	3×10^{5}	.....	1×10^{5}	

theory and sometimes by the other theory. No conflict arises unless one tries to say that light *is* a wave motion or *is* a flow of particles. The two descriptions of the nature of light were finally united by the work of Max Planck in 1900.

3-5. Planck's Quantum Theory of Radiation. A bold step which was to have great consequences in the development of physics and chemistry was taken by Max Planck in 1900. At that time he was attempting to explain the experimental results for the energy emitted by a hot body as a function of the frequency or wavelength of the radiation. All previous attempts to explain the energy distribution that would be emitted by the vibrating atoms of the hot body had been unsuccessful. Planck was led to the unprecedented view that the energy of the oscillating particles was "quantized," i.e., that only certain discrete energies were allowed. He further assumed that transitions between these allowed energies could occur and that the energy unit, or "quantum," emitted when the oscillator moved to a lower allowed energy state was related to the frequency of the emitted radiation by the relation

$$\Delta\epsilon = h\nu \tag{11}$$

Here $\Delta\epsilon$ is the energy of the quantum of radiation, ν is the frequency of the radiation, and h is a constant which is known as Planck's constant and has the value 6.624×10^{-27} erg-sec. On the basis of this relation Planck obtained an expression which correctly gave the energy distribution of the radiation of a hot body.

One sees in Planck's equation a tying together of the two theories of light. The energy of a quantum of radiation, a corpuscular-theory concept, can be calculated from the frequency of the radiation, a wave-motion concept. Yellow light, for example, can be described as having a frequency of oscillation of 5.2×10^{14} cycles/sec or as consisting of a flow of quanta, or photons, each with an energy of

$$\Delta\epsilon = (6.624 \times 10^{-27})(5.2 \times 10^{14})$$
$$= 3.4 \times 10^{-12} \text{ erg} \tag{12}$$

The importance of this equation will be made clear in the study of atomic spectra.

Planck's original suggestion, coupled with Einstein's later development, constituted more than a convenient expression which relates frequency and quantum energy. The assumption that an oscillator can have only certain discrete energies was a break with the accepted ideas and was to start a completely new phase in the development of chemistry and physics. Since Newton's time it had been held that energy changes in nature occur in a continuous manner. It will become apparent that the development of our present knowledge of atoms and molecules awaited Planck's bold suggestion that at atomic dimensions energies are quantized.

3-6. The Spectroscopic Method. The experimental results which are pertinent to our study of atomic structure are those obtained in investigations of the interaction of radiation and atoms. There are two arrangements for such experiments. The radiation *emitted* by a heated sample in which there are atoms of the material under investigation can be studied. Alternatively, the *absorption* of radiation by the sample when radiation is passed through it can be measured. Valuable information is obtained from such experiments when the effects for various frequencies are determined.

An instrument for spreading out the different frequencies of radiation is known as a *spectrograph*, if a photographic plate is used to detect the radiation, or a *spectrometer*, if some electronic device is used. In the ultraviolet, visible, and infrared regions such instruments ordinarily make use of a prism, often of glass or quartz, to separate the different frequencies. A schematic diagram of a prism instrument is shown in Fig. 3-3. Since the refractive index of the prism material is different for different frequencies (in general it is greater for lower frequencies), the different frequencies of the radiation will experience different amounts of bending. As a result, the radiation will be spread out along the photographic plate, or other detector, according to its frequency.

In regions of the electromagnetic spectrum other than the ultraviolet, visible, and infrared, quite different instruments are used to accomplish the sorting out of different frequencies. The experimental results for the spectra of atoms were, however, generally obtained with prism instruments.

3-7. Atomic Spectra. Throughout the latter half of the nineteenth century many measurements of the emission spectra of atoms were made. These spectra all showed that only certain well-defined frequencies of radiation were emitted. For most atoms with many electrons an extremely complicated pattern appeared on the photographic plate, as illustrated in Fig. 3-4. Some

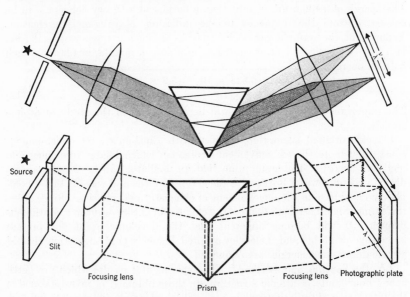

Fig. 3-3. Optical arrangement of a prism spectrograph.

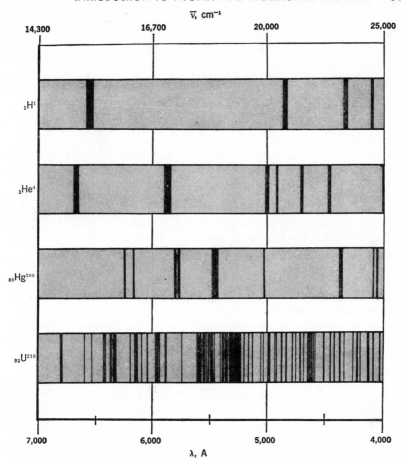

Fig. 3-4. The spectral lines in the visible region for some atoms of different atomic number.

atoms, such as sodium and especially hydrogen, fortunately gave much simpler patterns.   Since theoretical studies of atomic structure were centered on the simpler atoms, particularly on the hydrogen atom, it is sufficient to consider here the experimental studies of the hydrogen-atom spectrum.   The spectrum obtained from the radiation emitted by hydrogen atoms at high temperature is shown in Fig. 3-4.

Considerably before the nature of atoms was understood, it was recognized that the radiation emitted by a hot, or *excited*, atom presented a body of valuable data on the internal nature of the atom.   The actual spectra were of little use, however, until some pattern or relation could be found for the frequencies of the emitted radiation.   The initial step in bringing these data to bear on the problem of atomic structure was the completely empirical one of discovering some basic design in the emitted frequencies.

Many unsuccessful attempts were made to explain the observed spectral lines as harmonics or overtones of some set of fundamental frequencies. Gradually, however, a completely empirical approach yielded some understanding of the spectra of the simpler atoms.   Finally, in 1885 Balmer showed that the frequencies of some of the observed spectral lines of the hydrogen atom, now known as the *Balmer series,* could be expressed by the empirical equation

$$\bar{\nu} = 109{,}677 \left(\frac{1}{2^2} - \frac{1}{n_1^2} \right) \quad \text{cm}^{-1} \tag{13}$$

where $n_1 = 3, 4, 5, \ldots$.

This entirely empirical correlation proved a valuable clue, and very shortly it was shown by Rydberg that a more general expression of this type could be written to correlate the frequencies of all the observed spectral lines of the hydrogen atom.   The expression, known as a *Rydberg formula,* is

$$\bar{\nu} = 109{,}677.581 \left(\frac{1}{n_2^2} - \frac{1}{n_1^2} \right) \quad \text{cm}^{-1} \tag{14}$$

By assigning suitable integers to n_1 and n_2, as indicated in Table 3-2, one calculates frequencies which correspond to the frequencies of the spectral lines. The lines are grouped in series which are calculated from a given value of n_2 and are named after the discoverer of the series.   The Rydberg formula, since it can be used to generate all the spectral lines of the hydrogen atom, provides a concise analytical summary of the spectral data.

It is important to recognize, as was apparent after the publication of Planck's $\Delta\epsilon = h\nu$ relation, that the emission of only specific frequencies of radiation by an atom corresponds to the emission of quanta of discrete energies.   This can be emphasized by making use of Planck's relation to write the Rydberg formula more explicitly in terms of energy.   The result is

$$\Delta\epsilon = 2.18 \times 10^{-11} \left(\frac{1}{n_2^2} - \frac{1}{n_1^2} \right) \quad \text{ergs} \tag{15}$$

The spectroscopic results show, therefore, that the electron of the hydrogen atom can change its energy only by the definite amounts that are calculated from the Rydberg formula.

Table 3-2. Hydrogen-atom Spectral Series and Rydberg Integers for the

Equation $\bar{\nu} = 109{,}677 \left(\dfrac{1}{n_2^2} - \dfrac{1}{n_1^2} \right)$ cm^{-1}

Series	n_2	n_1	Spectral region
Lyman	1	2, 3, 4, . . .	Ultraviolet
Balmer	2	3, 4, 5, . . .	Visible
Paschen	3	4, 5, 6, . . .	Infrared
Brackett	4	5, 6, 7, . . .	Infrared
Pfund	5	6, 7, 8, . . .	Infrared

The next step is clearly that of finding some description or model for the hydrogen atom that will lead to only certain allowed energies for the electron. The possible changes in the energy of the electron, furthermore, must correspond to the energies of the observed emitted quanta. The methods suggested by Bohr and by Schrödinger to solve this problem and other problems of the behavior of electrons in atoms and molecules occupy the remainder of the chapter.

QUANTUM DESCRIPTIONS OF THE ATOM

3-8. The Bohr Atom. In 1913 Niels Bohr proposed a model for the hydrogen atom which retained the earlier nuclear model of Rutherford but made further stipulations as to the behavior of the electron. A dramatic explanation of the Rydberg spectral expression resulted. Many modern ideas about atomic and molecular structure stem from Bohr's theory. This theory has the advantage over a later, more generally applicable theory in that it makes use of a more concrete and more easily visualized approach.

Many attempts had been made following Rutherford's scattering experiments to explain the behavior of the electron of the hydrogen atom. It was necessary to deduce a structure that was stable and that accounted for the observed spectrum. All theories based on the accepted rules of mechanics and electricity suffered, as did Rutherford's suggestion, from an inherent instability. Bohr approached the problem aware of Planck's successful but unprecedented introduction of quantum restrictions and the further success of Einstein with Planck's $\Delta\epsilon = h\nu$ relation. The arbitrary nature of Bohr's theory of the atom was apparent. Its success in explaining the observed phenomena was to be its only justification.

The model chosen by Bohr to represent the hydrogen atom is made up of the following postulates:

1. The electron revolves about the nucleus in a circular orbit.

2. Only orbits in which the electron has an angular momentum that is an integral multiple of $h/2\pi$ are allowed.

3. The electron does not radiate energy when it is in an allowed orbit. It can gain or lose energy only by jumping from one allowed orbit to another.

On the basis of this model, Bohr calculated the radii and energies of the allowed orbits and showed that the observed spectrum could be predicted theoretically.

The linear momentum of a particle of mass m moving with a velocity v is mv. The corresponding expression for a rotating particle is the angular momentum defined as $I\omega$, where I is the moment of inertia and ω is the angular velocity in radians per second. The moment of inertia is equal to mr^2, where r is the radius of the orbit. A linear velocity of v leads to $v/2\pi r$ revolutions/sec and an angular velocity of $2\pi(v/2\pi r) = v/r$ radians/sec. Thus the angular momentum is

$$I\omega = mr^2 \frac{v}{r} = mvr \tag{16}$$

Bohr's second postulate requires, therefore, that

$$mvr = n\frac{h}{2\pi} \qquad \text{where } n = 1, 2, 3, \ldots \qquad (17)$$

The integer n, known as a *quantum number*, is arbitrarily introduced, as is the factor $h/2\pi$. Only certain values of the angular momentum are allowed, and this quantity is said to be *quantized* in units of $h/2\pi$.

The size of the allowed orbits can be calculated by requiring that the centrifugal force of the rotation be balanced by the electrical attraction to the nucleus. The centrifugal force is given by $f = ma$, where a, the acceleration toward the nucleus, is shown in Fig. 3-5 to be v^2/r. The coulombic attraction between the nucleus of charge $+e$ and the electron of charge $-e$ is e^2/r^2. For a state of balance

$$\frac{mv^2}{r} = \frac{e^2}{r^2} \qquad (18)$$

Rearranging this expression and introducing the quantum condition, one gets

$$r = n^2\frac{h^2}{4\pi^2me^2} \qquad \text{where } n = 1, 2, 3, \ldots \qquad (19)$$

The radii of the allowed orbits are found to depend, therefore, on the quantum number n and on known constants. Substitution of numerical values for these constants gives

$$r = n^2(0.529) \qquad \text{angstroms} \qquad (20)$$

Although no experimental values are available for direct comparison with this result, it is apparent that, at least for small values of n, the size of the allowed orbits is quite reasonable compared with the molecular dimensions deduced from the kinetic-molecular theory.

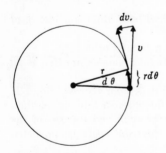

Fig. 3-5. Relation of the radial acceleration to the orbital velocity and the radius. (v_r and a_r are the radial velocity and acceleration.)

$$\frac{dv_r}{v} = \frac{r\,d\theta}{r} = d\theta$$

Therefore $dv_r = v\,d\theta$

and $a_r = \frac{dv_r}{dt} = \frac{v\,d\theta}{dt} = vw = \frac{v^2}{r}$

A much more critical test of Bohr's theory is provided by the calculation of the energies of these allowed orbits. It is the energy differences of these orbits which must explain the frequencies of the emitted radiation.

The kinetic energy of the electron in an orbit is given by $\frac{1}{2}mv^2$. The potential energy of the electron as a function of its distance from the nucleus is given by Coulomb's law as

$$\text{Potential energy} = -\frac{e^2}{r} \qquad (21)$$

This function is shown in Fig. 3-6. The choice of a zero potential energy at infinite separation of the electron and the nucleus makes the potential energy negative for all finite distances. The total energy of the electron is

ϵ = kinetic energy + potential energy

$$= \tfrac{1}{2}mv^2 - \frac{e^2}{r} \qquad (22)$$

The previous expression for balanced forces

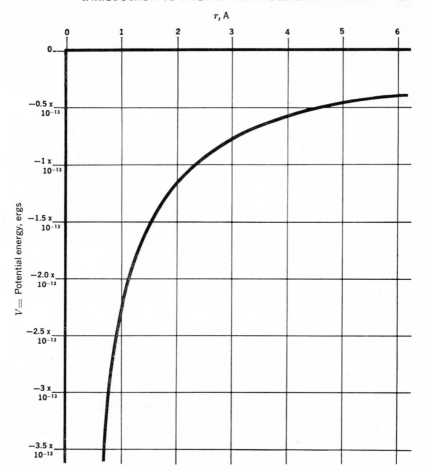

Fig. 3-6. The potential energy of a pair of charges $+e$ and $-e$ as a function of the distance between them, according to Coulomb's law.

gives the relation $\frac{1}{2}mv^2 = e^2/2r$. This relation allows Eq. (20) to be reduced so that the total energy can be written as

$$\epsilon = \frac{e^2}{2r} - \frac{e^2}{r} = -\frac{e^2}{2r} \tag{23}$$

Substitution for r from Eq. (19) now gives

$$\epsilon = -\frac{2\pi^2 me^4}{n^2 h^2} \tag{24}$$

If cgs units are used for all the constants, the energies of the various allowed orbits are obtained in ergs. For comparison with spectral results, it is more convenient to convert to the units of reciprocal centimeters, which are frequency units. Planck's relation $\Delta\epsilon = h\nu$ shows that frequency units are proportional to energy units.   Division of energy in ergs by h gives the units of cycles per second, and further division by c gives reciprocal centimeters.   In this way Eq. (24) can be written as

$$\epsilon = - \frac{2\pi^2 me^4}{n^2 h^3 c} \qquad cm^{-1} \tag{25}$$

Substitution of numerical values for all the constants gives, finally,

$$\epsilon = - \frac{109{,}735}{n^2} \qquad cm^{-1} \qquad \text{where } n = 1, 2, 3, \ldots \tag{26}$$

Each allowed orbit, according to the Bohr model of the hydrogen atom, is characterized by a value of the quantum number n and has a definite energy and radius.   The orbit with the lowest energy is that with $n = 1$, and it is this orbit which the electron normally occupies at room temperature.   Other orbits have large quantum numbers and according to Eq. (26) higher, i.e., less nega-

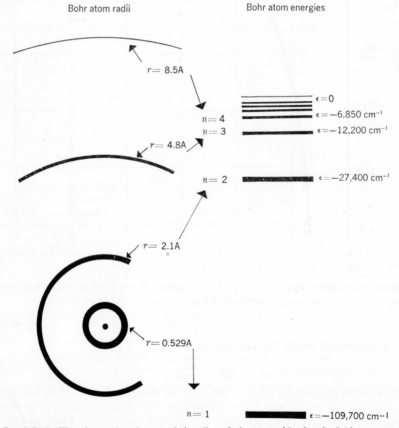

Fig. 3-7. Radii and energies of some of the allowed electron orbits for the hydrogen atom according to Bohr.

tive, energies.   The energies and radii of the allowed orbits are illustrated in Fig. 3-7.

An excited atom, i.e., an atom with the electron in an orbit other than that of lowest energy, can give up some of its extra energy by emitting a quantum of radiation.   The energy which the quantum contains is equal to the difference in energy of the two orbits involved in the electron jump.

If the initial higher-energy orbit has the quantum number n_1 and the lower-energy orbit to which the electron jumps has the quantum number n_2, the energy of the quantum that is emitted is given by

$$\Delta\epsilon = \left(-\frac{109,735}{n_1^2}\right) - \left(-\frac{109,735}{n_2^2}\right) \tag{27}$$

This quantity is equal to the wave number of the radiation that has quanta of the energy of this transition.   Thus,

$$\bar{\nu} = 109,735\left(\frac{1}{n_2^2} - \frac{1}{n_1^2}\right) \quad \text{cm}^{-1} \tag{28}$$

In this principal result of the Bohr theory the quantum numbers n_1 and n_2 can take on various integral values which are restricted only in that n_1 is greater than n_2.   This derived expression is seen to be almost identical to the empirical formula of Rydberg [Eq. (14)], and with some minor elaborations of the Bohr postulates the agreement can be even further improved.   The explanation of the spectral series of Table 3-2 is further clarified by the transitions indicated between Bohr atom energy levels in Fig. 3-8.

The Bohr theory can claim, therefore, the considerable achievement of having provided a model for the hydrogen atom which is consistent with the experiments of Rutherford and which, moreover, leads to an explanation of the hydrogen-atom spectral data.   The triumph of the Bohr theory was, however, short-lived.   Attempts to extend the approach to atoms with more than one electron were unsuccessful.   Furthermore, no explanation was provided for the fact that atoms combine to form molecules.   A more general criticism was that the Bohr treatment involved the uncomfortable combination of arbitrary quantum assumptions and the ordinary rules of mechanics and electrostatics.

In 1923 an important new concept in the continuing search into the nature of the atom was introduced by Louis de Broglie.   He suggested that electrons, like light, had a dual particle-wave nature.   The complete lack of recognition of the wave nature of the electron in the Bohr theory was then recognized as a further weakness of that atomic theory.   The next major development was, indeed, strongly influenced by the recently revealed wave nature of the electron.

3-9. Wave Mechanics and the Schrödinger Equation.   Although Bohr was the first to recognize and apply the fact that the nature of the atom was not to be understood by strictly classical methods, even he did not immediately realize that a completely new approach was needed.   Bohr's theory tried to apply classical methods with quantum restrictions somewhat arbitrarily added.   In 1926 a new approach, called *wave*, or *quantum, mechanics*, was developed independently by W. Heisenberg and Erwin Schrödinger.   In this method new

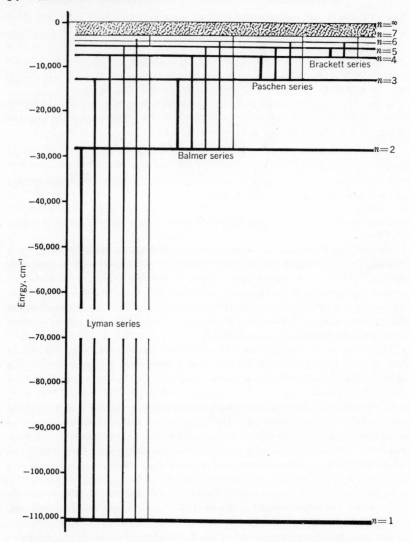

Fig. 3-8. The hydrogen-atom spectral series on a Bohr-atom energy-level diagram.

interpretations were given to the classical laws, such as those of Newton, which had seemed so certain and so generally applicable in the two and a half centuries of their development.

The most generally used formulation of wave mechanics is that of Schrödinger. His method gives an equation and set of rules that allow the calculation of the behavior of matter, particularly matter with the dimensions of atoms and molecules. His *wave equation* is, in a sense, the exact counterpart of Newton's laws of motion. Newton's laws, which are always presented without any derivation or proof, let one calculate the mechanical behavior of objects of ordinary and even planetary size. Schrödinger's equation is likewise presented without derivation or proof and is of particular interest in chemistry since it deals with the behavior of objects down to molecular and atomic, but probably not subnuclear, dimensions. Just as one uses and becomes trusting in $f = ma$, so must one use and, to the extent that seems justifiable, become trusting in the Schrödinger equation.

In a study of an atom, the quantities that might be of prime interest would be the energies of the electrons of the atom and the positions of the electrons relative to the nucleus and, possibly, relative to one another. The Schrödinger method yields directly the energies of the particles, in this case the electrons, of the system. It leads, however, to less specific information on the positions of the particles of the system. Only the probability that the particle, or electron, is at a given position is obtained from wave mechanics. The lack of information on the exact position of a particle at some specific time seems to be a characteristic of atomic dimensions and not to be a defect in the Schrödinger method.

In studying the hydrogen atom by application of the Schrödinger method we shall see in a later chapter that the allowed energies of the electron are obtained and are the same as those deduced by Bohr. The probability of the electron being at a given distance from the nucleus is also given, and the probability function obtained is related to the orbits of the Bohr theory. To obtain these results, the Schrödinger equation makes use only of the data for the mass of the electron and the potential energy which it experiences as a result of the coulombic attraction to the nucleus.

Just as one practices applying the ordinary laws of motion to simple problems, such as inclined planes and pulley systems, so also is it helpful to practice using the Schrödinger equation on some simple systems of atomic dimensions. Study of the Schrödinger equation is conveniently begun with problems in which the particle under consideration is required to move along one dimension only. For such a particle, the potential energy will be some function of this one dimension, which can be taken along the x axis and can be represented by $U(x)$. The information which will go into the Schrödinger equation in a particular problem will be the nature of $U(x)$ and the mass m of the particle. The information which we attempt to obtain is the allowed values of the energy of the particle and the probability of the particle being at various positions along the x axis. Solution of the Schrödinger equation will yield a function of x, denoted by $\psi(x)$, or simply ψ, which is called the *wave function* for the particle. It is the square of this function which gives the probability of the particle being at various distances along the x axis.

The Schrödinger equation in one dimension is

$$-\frac{h^2}{8\pi^2 m}\frac{d^2\psi}{dx^2} + U(x)\psi = \epsilon\psi \qquad (29)$$

The behavior of a particle is deduced, according to Schrödinger, by finding some algebraic or trigonometric function which will solve this differential equation when the appropriate values of $U(x)$ and m have been substituted. Thus satisfactory solution functions ψ will exist only for certain values of ϵ, and these are the allowed energies of the particle. Finally, the probability function ψ^2 is readily obtained from the solution functions ψ.

The equation and method are more understandable when applied to an example. The one-dimensional potential function of Fig. 3-9 leads to simple Schrödinger-equation solutions and yet can be looked upon as a model for a number of molecular problems. Between $x = 0$ and $x = a$ the potential has a constant value which can be taken as zero, and elsewhere the potential is infinitely high. An electron in a piece of wire, for example, is subject to a potential which for some purposes can be so represented. Of more chemical interest is the fact that the double bonding, or π, electrons of a conjugated system of double bonds in a molecule behave approximately as though the potential which they experience is such a simple square-well function. The present purpose, however, is only to show how the Schrödinger equation is applied to a specific problem and to illustrate the nature of the solutions that are obtained.

In the region $0 < x < a$ the potential-energy function is $U(x) = 0$, and the Schrödinger equation in this region is

$$-\frac{h^2}{8\pi^2 m}\frac{d^2\psi}{dx^2} = \epsilon\psi \tag{30}$$

It is now necessary to find well-behaved solutions for this equation. The function ψ must be zero outside the potential well since there the potential is infinitely high, and there is no probability of the particle being in such a region. To be well behaved, and prevent a discontinuity in ψ, the function ψ in the region between 0 and a must be such that it equals zero at $x = 0$ and $x = a$.

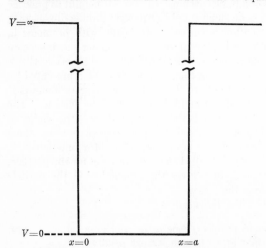

Fig. 3-9. The "square-well" potential for the Schrödinger-equation example.

Functions which solve the differential equation and also satisfy these boundary conditions can be seen by inspection to be

$$\psi = A \sin \frac{n\pi x}{a} \qquad \text{where } n = 1, 2, 3, \ldots \qquad (31)$$

and A is some constant factor. The expression $n\pi x/a$ has, as can be checked, been arranged so that the function goes to zero at $x = 0$ and at $x = a$ for any integral value of n. That the function satisfies the Schrödinger equation can be tested by substitution to give

$$\text{Left side} = -\frac{h^2}{8\pi^2 m}\left(-\frac{n^2\pi^2}{a^2}\right) A \sin \frac{n\pi x}{a}$$

$$= \frac{n^2 h^2}{8ma^2}\left(A \sin \frac{n\pi x}{a}\right) \qquad (32)$$

$$\text{Right side} = \epsilon\left(A \sin \frac{n\pi x}{a}\right) \qquad (33)$$

The left and right sides of Eq. (30) are equal, and the expression

$$\psi = A \sin\left(\frac{n\pi x}{a}\right)$$

is therefore a solution if

$$\epsilon = \frac{n^2 h^2}{8ma^2} \qquad n = 1, 2, 3, \ldots \qquad (34)$$

No really different solution can be found, and no energies other than these will result. The value $n = 0$ in Eq. (31) provides, it should be mentioned, a solution to Eq. (30) but gives a wave function that is everywhere zero. This leads to a zero probability of a particle being anywhere in the box and is therefore unacceptable. The allowed energies ϵ, which are represented in Fig. 3-10, are seen to be quantized as a result of the quite natural introduction of the integers in the solutions of the Schrödinger equation. A similar situation occurs generally in atomic and molecular problems. The quantum phenomena, which were so arbitrarily introduced in the Bohr theory, are seen to result much more naturally in Schrödinger's approach.

The functions ψ and ψ^2 are shown in Fig. 3-10, alongside the corresponding energy level, for the first few states. The ψ^2 functions show the relative probability of the particle being at various positions when the quantum number has some particular value. If one assigns a value to A such that the total probability of the particle being between $x = 0$ and $x = a$ is unity, the wave functions are said to be *normalized*.

The probability curves of Fig. 3-10, which are typical of those obtained in other such problems, are by no means understandable in terms of the behavior of ordinary-sized objects. The presence of positions at which the probability of finding the particle is zero is most striking. Similarly, a particle in a "box" of atomic or molecular dimensions can have only certain allowed energies and is not even permitted to have zero energy. Only the success of the Schrödinger method in treating a number of problems where the solutions can be tested against experiment makes us put up with such strange results.

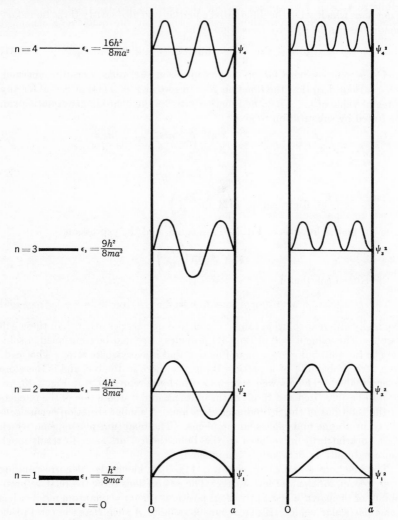

Fig. 3-10. The energy levels, the wave functions ψ, and the probability-distribution functions ψ^2 for the first few Schrödinger-equation solutions for the potential of Fig. 3-9.

This "particle-in-a-box" problem should be appreciated as being typical of those encountered in applying the Schrödinger equation to problems of chemical interest. In general, three dimensions will be involved and the potential-energy function will be somewhat more complicated. The procedure, however, will consist in writing the Schrödinger equation with the suitable potential function and particle mass and then looking for suitable solution functions. This process will generally lead to only certain allowed energies. Rather than proceeding immediately to more complicated systems, it will be more worthwhile to take up two applications of the particle-in-a-box problem. These should be of help in obtaining some feeling for the quantum-mechanical approach to the atomic and molecular world.

3-10. Examples of the "Particle-in-a-box" Calculation

Example 1.   The quantum behavior of an electron in an atom or a molecule can be compared, very approximately, with that of an electron in a potential well such as that of Fig. 3-10, which has the dimension of a few angstroms. If, to be definite, the atom or molecule is represented by a potential well of 3 A width, the necessary numerical values for the calculation of the electron energy are

$$h = 6.624 \times 10^{-27} \text{ erg-sec}$$

$$m = \frac{1}{1,836} \frac{1}{6.024 \times 10^{23}} = 9.107 \times 10^{-28} \text{ gram}$$

and $$a = 3 \times 10^{-8} \text{ cm}$$

These give the result

$$\epsilon = \frac{n^2 h^2}{8ma^2} = n^2(1.5 \times 10^{-11}) \qquad \text{ergs/molecule} \qquad (35)$$

The energy-level pattern will be of the same form as that of Fig. 3-10, and, as the next section will show, the electron will normally occupy the lowest allowed energy level.

The emission of a quantum of radiation as the electron of an excited atom or molecule goes from the $n = 2$ to the $n = 1$ level or the absorption of a quantum for the $n = 1$ to $n = 2$ transition might be observed spectroscopically.   The energy involved in such a transition is calculated as

$$\Delta \epsilon = 1.5 \times 10^{-11}(2^2 - 1^2) = 4.5 \times 10^{-11} \text{ erg/molecule} \qquad (36)$$

The wavelength of radiation emitted or absorbed in such a transition is obtained with the help of Planck's equation $\Delta \epsilon = h\nu$ and the relation $\lambda = c/\nu$. The energy change would lead, therefore, to radiation with a wavelength of about 1,000 A.   This corresponds to ultraviolet radiation, and it is a fact that atoms and simple molecules do generally absorb radiation in this region.   In this regard, the simple square-well model is satisfactory.   The finer details of the energy-level pattern for an atom or molecule and even the qualitative behavior at higher energies require, of course, a three-dimensional treatment and a better approximation to the potential energy.

Finally, it is informative to obtain the energies of the allowed levels in the energy units used in the kinetic-molecular theory.   The energy in calories per Avogadro's number of atoms or molecules, if the simple square-well model of this section is assumed and only one electron of each particle can be in an excited state, is given by

$$E = \frac{n^2(1.5 \times 10^{-11})(6.024 \times 10^{23})}{4.184 \times 10^7}$$

$$= n^2(21,600) \qquad \text{cal/mole} \qquad (37)$$

where n is the quantum number of the excitable electron.   From this result it is apparent that the $n = 2$ level is of very high energy compared with the $n = 1$ level in terms of the available room-temperature thermal energy of $\frac{1}{2}RT$ per degree of freedom.   A general and very useful conclusion that is indicated by the present calculation is that *the allowed energy levels for electrons in atoms and molecules are usually very widely spaced compared with ordinary thermal energies.*

Example 2.   As a second example, we can see what the Schrödinger equation says about a problem which we have previously studied by classical methods. This is the problem of the energies of the molecules of a gas that is in a container of given volume at some fixed temperature.   To be more specific, the molecules can be taken as N_2 molecules, with $m = 28/6.024 \times 10^{23}$ g, and the container can be considered to be cubic and to have a length of 10 cm.   The allowed energy levels for motion of the molecules in one dimension are calculated, as in the previous example, to give the result

$$\epsilon = n^2(1.2 \times 10^{-33}) \qquad \text{ergs/molecule}$$

or $$E = n^2(1.73 \times 10^{-7}) \qquad \text{cal/mole} \qquad (38)$$

In contrast to the previous example, the energy spacing between the allowed levels is now found to be very small.   These allowed energies are nothing more than the allowed translational energies with which the molecules move about as a result of their thermal kinetic energy of translation.

In Chap. 2 it was shown that the average kinetic energy of translation per degree of freedom is $\frac{1}{2}RT$, or about 300 cal/mole at room temperature.   This result was derived from the classical supposition that any kinetic energy was allowed.   The quantum-mechanical treatment shows that the translational energies are, in fact, quantized but that the spacings between the allowed energies are so small that it is a very good approximation to make the classical assumption.   Such systems, therefore, can be treated as if all energies are allowed, and the classical results so deduced will be valid.

These two examples, one involving a particle confined to an atom or molecule, and the other a particle confined to an ordinary-sized container, illustrate an important general result.   The quantum restrictions on all objects confined to regions of ordinary size can be neglected since the allowed energies are then very closely spaced.   Quantum jumps are not observed, for example, for a tennis ball confined to a tennis court.   A molecule in an ordinary container is not different in this regard, nor are the planets in the solar system.   When particles are confined to regions in space which are of angstrom dimensions, however, the quantum restrictions become important.   It is this effect which prevented the classical theories of mechanics from being extrapolated to atomic and molecular systems.   Electrons confined to atoms or molecules are allowed only certain energies.   In a like manner, the atoms of a molecule are held in a fairly fixed position relative to one another, and, as we shall see, the energy which such atoms can have is also quantized.

The important qualitative conclusion which should be drawn from the two particle-in-a-box calculations is that *the more closely confined a particle is, the greater will be the spacing between the allowed energy levels.*

3-11. The Energy Levels for a Particle in a Three-dimensional Box.   The Schrödinger equation can be applied, with little added complexity, to the three-dimensional problem of a particle in a cubic container.   For a three-dimensional problem the potential energy will in general be a function of three coordinates, and for a cubic potential box the cartesian coordinates of Fig. 3-11 are convenient. The differential equation that must be solved is now the Schrödinger equation in three dimensions, which is

$$-\frac{h^2}{8\pi^2 m}\left(\frac{\partial^2\psi}{dx^2} + \frac{\partial^2\psi}{dy^2} + \frac{\partial^2\psi}{dz^2}\right) + U(x,y,z)\psi$$
$$= \epsilon\psi \quad (39)$$

where it must be expected that the solution function ψ will depend on the three coordinates x, y, and z. For such differential equations it is often profitable to see whether or not they can be

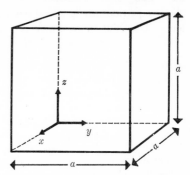

Fig. 3-11. The three-dimensional square-well potential function (the potential V is infinitely high except inside the box, where it can be assigned the value zero).

separated into parts, each part involving only one of the three coordinates. For the cubic container of Fig. 3-11 the potential energy can, for example, be written as $U(x) + U(y) + U(z)$, where each function is like the one-dimensional potential-energy well of Fig. 3-9. Now one can try the substitution

$$\psi(x,y,z) = \varphi(x)\varphi(y)\varphi(z) \quad (40)$$

and see whether or not such a separated function solves Eq. (39). Substitution of Eq. (40) into Eq. (39) gives

$$-\frac{h^2}{8\pi^2 m}\left[\varphi(y)\varphi(z)\frac{d^2\varphi(x)}{dx^2} + \varphi(x)\varphi(z)\frac{d^2\varphi(y)}{dy^2} + \varphi(x)\varphi(y)\frac{d^2\varphi(z)}{dz^2}\right]$$
$$+ [U(x) + U(y) + U(z)]\varphi(x)\varphi(y)\varphi(z) = \epsilon[\varphi(x)\varphi(y)\varphi(z)] \quad (41)$$

Division by $\varphi(x)\varphi(y)\varphi(z)$ gives

$$-\frac{h^2}{8\pi^2 m}\left[\frac{1}{\varphi(x)}\frac{d^2\varphi(x)}{dx^2} + \frac{1}{\varphi(y)}\frac{d^2\varphi(y)}{dy^2} + \frac{1}{\varphi(z)}\frac{d^2\varphi(z)}{dz^2}\right]$$
$$+ U(x) + U(y) + U(z) = \epsilon \quad (42)$$

If the total energy is interpreted as arising from contributions that can be associated with the three cartesian coordinates, the allowed energy of the particle can be written as

$$\epsilon = \epsilon_x + \epsilon_y + \epsilon_z \quad (43)$$

and the Schrödinger equation of Eq. (42) can be broken down to three identical equations of the type

$$-\frac{h^2}{8\pi^2 m}\frac{1}{\varphi(x)}\frac{d^2\varphi(x)}{dx^2} + U(x) = \epsilon_x$$

or
$$-\frac{h^2}{8\pi^2 m}\frac{d^2\varphi(x)}{dx^2} + U(x)\varphi(x) = \epsilon_x\varphi(x) \quad (44)$$

These equations are identical with that written for the one-dimensional problem. The solution to the three-dimensional square-box problem is therefore

$$\psi = \varphi(x)\varphi(y)\varphi(z)$$

with
$$\varphi(x) = A_x \sin \frac{n_x \pi x}{a} \qquad n_x = 1, 2, 3, \ldots$$

$$\varphi(y) = A_y \sin \frac{n_y \pi y}{a} \qquad n_y = 1, 2, 3, \ldots \qquad (45)$$

$$\varphi(z) = A_z \sin \frac{n_z \pi z}{a} \qquad n_z = 1, 2, 3, \ldots$$

One might try to visualize the probability distribution ψ^2 which is obtained from this wave function, but a graphical representation will be seen to be rather difficult. The allowed energy levels for a particle in this three-dimensional cubic potential-energy box are

$$\epsilon = \epsilon_x + \epsilon_y + \epsilon_z$$
$$= \frac{n_x^2 h^2}{8ma^2} + \frac{n_y^2 h^2}{8ma^2} + \frac{n_z^2 h^2}{8ma^2}$$
$$= (n_x^2 + n_y^2 + n_z^2) \frac{h^2}{8ma^2} \qquad (46)$$

These solutions show that the Schrödinger equation for this three-dimensional example can be separated into one-dimensional contributions. The quantum-mechanical treatment is, therefore, parallel to the classical discussion of Sec. 2-8 in that the 3 degrees of freedom in which the particle behavior can be described again appear.

It is characteristic of a three-dimensional quantum mechanical problem, as we shall see, that three quantum numbers appear. The energy and the wave function in a three-dimensional box can be specified, for example, by assigning integral values to n_x, n_y, and n_z. These numbers need not, of course, be the same.

3-12. The Boltzmann Distribution. The Schrödinger equation gives a method for calculating the allowed energies of atomic and molecular systems. It thereby allows us to take one of the two necessary steps toward an understanding of energy of molecular systems. The second, and in this connection equally important, step was taken by Boltzmann. His distribution law shows how a large number of particles distribute themselves throughout a set of allowed energy levels. For a hydrogen atom, for example, the Schrödinger equation leads to the allowed energy levels characterized by the quantum numbers $n = 1$, $n = 2$, and so forth. The Boltzmann-distribution law then states that for an Avogadro's number of hydrogen atoms a certain number will have their electron in the $n = 1$ state, another number in the $n = 2$ state, and so forth.

According to Boltzmann, the ratio of the number of particles n_i that have energy ϵ_i, as represented in Fig. 3-12, compared with the number of particles n_0 that have energy ϵ_0 can be written in the form

$$\frac{n_i}{n_0} = e^{-(\epsilon_i - \epsilon_0)/kT}$$
$$= e^{-\Delta\epsilon_i/kT} \qquad (47)$$

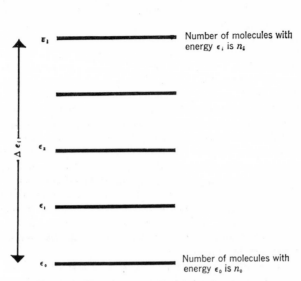

ϵ_1 — Number of molecules with energy ϵ_i is n_i

ϵ_0 — Number of molecules with energy ϵ_0 is n_0

Fig. 3-12. Notation for the Boltzmann distribution.

It is well here to treat this distribution expression as one of the basic postulates, as is the Schrödinger equation. With these two postulates it is possible, in principle, to obtain the probability functions and the energies of the allowed quantum states and to deduce how many of the atoms or molecules of a given system will be in these various quantum states. A complete description of all chemical systems can, in principle, be built from these postulates. The importance of the interjection *in principle* will become very apparent as the complexities of molecular systems are encountered. It is true, nevertheless, that the Schrödinger equation and the Boltzmann-distribution expression are bases on which much molecular behavior can be understood.

Equation (47) can, moreover, be used as one of the nicest approaches to the definition of temperature. In this approach, the temperature of a system that has a given ratio of n_i/n_0 is defined to be the value of T, which, when substituted in Eq. (47), leads to the calculation of this ratio. It can, furthermore, be shown that temperature so defined is equivalent to that which occurs in the relation $PV = nRT$ and to that which occurs in the expression for the average energy per degree of freedom of 1 mole of gas $E = \frac{1}{2}RT$. The proportionality constant k in Eq. (47) can be identified with R/N. These identifications, which are not necessary for subsequent treatments, are developed in the following section.

The form of the Boltzmann equation shows that, if $\Delta\epsilon_i$ is large compared with kT, the ratio n_i/n_0 will be very small. At the other extreme, $\Delta\epsilon_i$ is small compared with kT, and n_i is then nearly equal to n_0. It is the appearance of the term kT in the Boltzmann-distribution equation that makes it important in quantized systems. The importance of kT in classical, or nonquantized, systems has already been emphasized with regard to the average kinetic energy per degree of freedom value of $\frac{1}{2}kT$.

The initial question concerning the normal quantum state of the electron of the hydrogen atom can now be answered. The energy of the $n = 2$ orbit compared with that of the $n = 1$ orbit is so much greater than kT at room temperature that only an infinitesimal fraction of the atoms will have their electron in the higher energy state. At much higher temperatures, however, the population of the higher-energy orbits will become appreciable. At such temperatures, the atoms will gain energy as the electrons go to these higher energy states. A possibility arising from such a distribution is the emission of radiation which will result when such excited atoms return to their ground state.

The populations of the different allowed molecular translational energies, as calculated in Example 2, Sec. 3-10, correspond to the other extreme, where the spacing of the energy levels is very small. Successive levels will have very nearly the same population. The distribution of molecules throughout the whole range of translational energy levels leads, as will be shown in Sec. 3-14, to the same energy-distribution curve as obtained classically by the corresponding Maxwell-Boltzmann–distribution law.

Other types of molecular energies besides electronic and translational energies occur, and for these energies the energy-level spacing may be more comparable with the room temperature value of kT. The population of the higher energy levels, and therefore the average energy content of the molecules, will then be a sensitive function of the temperature. It should be apparent that the Boltzmann-distribution equation will be of fundamental importance, not only for determining which of the allowed energy levels are occupied, but also in determining the average energy of a collection of molecules.

It is sometimes more convenient to deal with the energy that an Avogadro's number of molecules, i.e., of 1 mole, would have in one state as compared with the energy they would have in another state. If this molar-energy quantity is used in Boltzmann's equation, it is necessary to compare the energy of these N molecules in a given quantum state with the energy $NkT = RT$ instead of with kT. The distribution equation is then written as

$$n_1 = n_0 e^{-\Delta E_i / RT} \tag{48}$$

where ΔE_i is the energy of an Avogadro's number of molecules in the ith level compared with an Avogadro's number in the lowest level.

*3-13. Identification of the Boltzmann-distribution Temperature Scale with That of the Ideal Gas. If the Boltzmann distribution is taken as defining temperature in terms of the relative population of energy levels spaced by an amount $\Delta \epsilon_i$, it is necessary to show that temperature so defined is equivalent to that introduced in the treatment of ideal gases. The temperature in the Boltzmann distribution can, for the moment, be designated by τ, and it will now be shown that τ is equivalent to the absolute temperature T. This will be done by a comparison of the average energy of a one-dimensional gas calculated from the Schrödinger equation and the Boltzmann distribution with the value of $\frac{1}{2}RT$ deduced to give the ideal-gas law $PV = nRT$.

If the index i is used in place of the quantum number n to avoid confusion with the symbol n_i for the number of molecules in the ith quantum level, the energies of the allowed states are given, according to Eq. (34), as

$$\epsilon_i = i^2 \frac{h^2}{8ma^2} \qquad i = 1, 2, 3, \ldots \tag{49}$$

First, a relation is obtained for the number of molecules n_1 in the lowest, $n = 1$, level when a total of an Avogadro's number N of molecules are considered. The expression

$$N = n_1 + n_2 + n_3 + \cdots \tag{50}$$

can be converted by the use of the Boltzmann expression to give

$$\begin{aligned} N &= n_1 + n_1 e^{-(\epsilon_2 - \epsilon_1)/kT} + n_1 e^{-(\epsilon_3 - \epsilon_1)/kT} + \cdots \\ &= n_1 + n_1 e^{-(2^2 - 1^2)h^2/8ma^2 kT} + n_1 e^{-(3^2 - 1^2)h^2/8ma^2 kT} + \cdots \end{aligned} \tag{51}$$

Very many terms in this summation will occur, and with little error, except in the first few terms, the 1^2 terms in the exponentials can be dropped to simplify Eq. (51) to

$$\begin{aligned} N &= n_1(1 + e^{-2^2 h^2/8ma^2 kT} + e^{-3^2 h^2/8ma^2 kT} + \cdots) \\ &= n_1 \sum_{i=0}^{\infty} e^{-i^2 h^2/8ma^2 kT} \end{aligned} \tag{52}$$

The allowed energy levels are closely spaced, and the summation of Eq. (52) can be replaced by an integral to give

$$N = n_1 \int_0^{\infty} e^{-i^2 h^2/8ma^2 kT} \, di \tag{53}$$

The integral can be converted to a standard definite integral by the substitution

$$x = i \sqrt{\frac{h^2}{8ma^2 kT}} \qquad \text{and} \qquad di = \sqrt{\frac{8ma^2 kT}{h^2}} \, dx$$

to give

$$N = n_1 \sqrt{\frac{8ma^2 kT}{h^2}} \int_0^{\infty} e^{-x^2} \, dx \tag{54}$$

The integral has the value $\frac{1}{2}\sqrt{\pi}$, and the desired relation is obtained as

$$n_1 = \frac{2Nh}{\sqrt{8ma^2 \pi kT}} \tag{55}$$

Now the total energy above the energy zero of the potential well can be calculated. This total energy is given by the summation of the energy of each level times the number of molecules in that level, i.e., the number of molecules that have that much energy. Thus

$$\begin{aligned} E &= n_1\epsilon_1 + n_2\epsilon_2 + n_3\epsilon_3 + \cdots \\ &= n_1(\epsilon_1 + \epsilon_2 e^{-\epsilon_2/kT} + \epsilon_3 e^{-\epsilon_3/kT} + \cdots) \\ &= n_1\left(\frac{1^2 h^2}{8ma^2} + \frac{2^2 h^2}{8ma^2} e^{-2^2 h^2/8ma^2 kT} + \frac{3^2 h^2}{8ma^2} e^{-3^2 h^2/8ma^2 kT} + \cdots\right) \end{aligned} \tag{56}$$

Again there will be many terms in this series, and, except for the first term, it is expressed satisfactorily as

$$E = \frac{n_1 h^2}{8ma^2} \sum_{i=0}^{\infty} i^2 e^{-i^2 h^2/8ma^2 k\tau} \tag{57}$$

or as the integral equation

$$E = \frac{n_1 h^2}{8ma^2} \int_{i=0}^{\infty} i^2 e^{-i^2 h^2/8ma^2 k\tau} \, di \tag{58}$$

Again the integral is simplified by the substitution $x = i\sqrt{h^2/8ma^2 k\tau}$, and here the result is

$$E = \frac{n_1 h^2}{8ma^2} \left(\frac{8ma^2 k\tau}{h^2}\right)^{\frac{3}{2}} \int_0^{\infty} x^2 e^{-x^2} \, dx \tag{59}$$

The integral has the value $\frac{1}{4}\sqrt{\pi}$, and the value of E is therefore

$$E = \frac{n_1 \sqrt{\pi} \, h^2}{32ma^2} \left(\frac{8ma^2 k\tau}{h^2}\right)^{\frac{3}{2}} \tag{60}$$

Substitution of the expression for n_1 obtained in Eq. (55) gives, finally, the result

$$E = \frac{2Nh \sqrt{\pi} \, h^2}{32ma^2(8ma^2 k\tau)^{\frac{1}{2}}} \left(\frac{8ma^2 k\tau}{h^2}\right)^{\frac{3}{2}}$$
$$= \frac{1}{2}(Nk)\tau \tag{61}$$

This is the result obtained from the Schrödinger equation and the Boltzmann distribution for the kinetic energy of an Avogadro's number of molecules of a monatomic gas moving in one dimension.

The ideal-gas-law result $PV = nRT$ has already been shown in Sec. 2-3 to require this kinetic energy to have the value

$$E = \frac{1}{2}RT \tag{62}$$

Comparison of Eqs. (61) and (62) shows the identity of the two temperature scales and furthermore confirms, as we have already been assuming, that the constant k in the Boltzmann distribution is indeed R/N.

3-14. Types of Molecular Energies. The principal object of this introductory chapter on atomic and molecular structure is to show that the energy of a molecular system can be understood in terms of a detailed knowledge of the molecule. In practice, it is frequently very difficult to deduce the energy and description of a system from Schrödinger's equation and Boltzmann's distribution. It is almost always possible, however, to understand a molecule sufficiently to classify its energy in a way which greatly aids the understanding of many aspects of its chemical behavior. In Chaps. 8 to 10 we shall return to a direct investigation of the finer details of atomic and molecular structure.

The energy content of a molecule can be discussed in terms of the energy that it would have if it were in the lowest allowed quantum state, the so-called *zero-point energy*, and in terms of any excess energy resulting from its occupancy of a higher-energy quantum state. This excess energy can be called *thermal energy* since, as Boltzmann's distribution shows, the occupancy of high-energy quantum states is dependent on the temperature of the system. The zero-point energy, on the other hand, is the energy when the molecule is in the lowest allowed state and this energy is temperature-independent.

The total molecular energy of an Avogadro's number of molecules is represented by the symbol E. This total energy is made up of the zero-point energy E_0 and the thermal energy E_{thermal}, or, as is frequently convenient to write, $E - E_0$.

The thermal energy is that energy possessed by a molecule as a result of available energy levels other than those of lowest energy being occupied. The kinetic energy of translation of $\frac{3}{2}RT$, for example, is such thermal energy since this is the average energy over and above that which the molecules would have in the lowest translational energy level. For gas-phase molecules the thermal energy can be easily understood and, for very many molecules, can be satisfactorily calculated. For liquids and solids the cooperative behavior of the molecules usually makes any discussion of the thermal energy much more difficult. It will be sufficient, for the present, to treat only gas-phase systems.

There are four different classifications under which the thermal energy of a molecule can be treated. These types of energies are:

Electronic
Vibrational
Rotational
Translational

It has already been pointed out that molecules usually have very widely spaced electronic energy levels and that, therefore, only the lowest electronic state is occupied at room temperature. The electronic contribution to the thermal energy of most molecules is therefore zero. The average translational energy per mole has been shown to be $\frac{3}{2}RT$. In addition, a molecule consisting of more than one atom can have energy as a result of rotation of the molecule and as a result of vibration of the atoms of the molecule against one another. These motions lead to allowed energy levels, and, in general, the molecules can occupy the higher energy levels as well as the zero energy level. Some quantum aspects of translational-, rotational-, and vibrational-energy patterns must now be treated so that the total thermal energy of a molecule can be estimated.

3-15. Quantum Interpretation of Translational-energy Distribution. It is of interest to see, at least qualitatively, that the allowed energy levels for a particle in a box and the Boltzmann-distribution law lead to a distribution of molecular velocities that corresponds to the classical Maxwell-Boltzmann distribution of Sec. 2-9.

For a one-dimensional system the distribution throughout the energy-level pattern is dependent on the Boltzmann-type exponential factor $e^{-\Delta \epsilon_i / kT}$ or, substituting $\Delta \epsilon_i = \frac{1}{2}mu_x^2$, on the factor $e^{-mu_x^2/kT}$, as in Sec. 2-9. The fall-off of velocity probability, as shown in Fig. 2-5, corresponds therefore to the fall-off in population of the higher energy states shown in Fig. 3-13.

The three-dimensional distribution law, shown on a classical basis in Figs. 2-6 and 2-7, suggests that the lowest allowed energy level is not that of highest

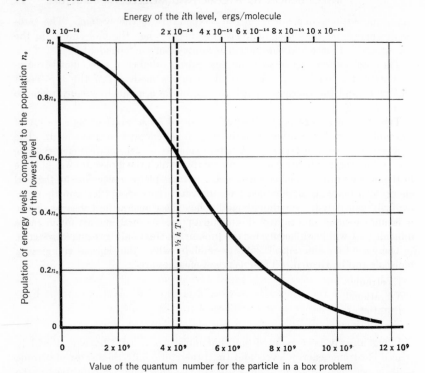

Fig. 3-13. The quantum-mechanical interpretation of the one-dimensional translational-energy distribution for N_2 at 25°C in a 10-cm container.   [Calculated from Eqs. (34) and (47).]

population.   The explanation of this feature can be given in terms of the three-dimensional allowed-energy expression for a cubic container,

$$\epsilon = (n_x^2 + n_y^2 + n_z^2) \frac{h^2}{8ma^2} \qquad (63)$$

The Boltzmann exponential factor again operates to give a decreasing population with increasing energy.   A new feature enters to produce the maximum in the population-energy curve.

A number of different states, characterized by different values of n_x, n_y, and n_z, may correspond to the same allowed particle energy.   Thus the energy $6h^2/8ma^2$ can result from

$$
\begin{array}{lll}
n_x = 2 & n_y = 1 & n_z = 1 \\
\text{or} \quad n_x = 1 & n_y = 2 & n_z = 1 \\
\text{or} \quad n_x = 1 & n_y = 1 & n_z = 2 \\
\end{array}
$$

In a similar way the states that correspond, for example, to an energy $66h^2/8ma^2$ can be described by the quantum numbers:

n_x	n_y	n_z
8	1	1
1	8	1
1	1	8
7	4	1
1	7	4
4	1	7
7	1	4
4	7	1
1	4	7

The Boltzmann-distribution expression written in Eq. (47) corresponds to the population of *each* state of a given energy. It is clear therefore that the total population of the states with energy $66h^2/8ma^2$ will be nine times as great as would be expected if a single state corresponded to that energy. It is this *multiplicity* factor that corresponds to the increased volume element illustrated for the Maxwell-Boltzmann distribution in Fig. 2-7. The exponential energy factor again tends to reduce the population of higher energy levels, while the multiplicity of the energy levels generally increases at higher energies. One should recognize that the same features occur in this quantum approach to translational energies as do in the classical treatment of Sec. 2-9.

The Boltzmann-distribution law can be written to show explicitly the population of an *energy level* rather than that of an individual *quantum state*. To do this, one introduces the *multiplicity*, or *degeneracy*, denoted by g_{ϵ_i}, and writes

$$\frac{n_{\epsilon_i}}{n_0} = g_{\epsilon_i} e^{-(\epsilon_i - \epsilon_0/kT)} \tag{64}$$

where n_{ϵ_i}/n_0 is the number of particles with energy ϵ_i compared with the number with ϵ_0. Thus, for the particle in a cubic box, g for the state with energy $6h^2/8ma^2$ is 3 and for the state with energy $66h^2/8ma^2$ is 9. For a particle in a one-dimensional square well all allowed energy states have a multiplicity of unity, while for a three-dimensional box the multiplicity generally increases with increasing energy.

An interpretation of the translational-energy distributions can, therefore, be given either in terms of a classical treatment, as was done in Sec. 2-9, or on the basis of quantized energies, as had been discussed here.

For almost all our future work, however, these distribution details will not be important. The feature that will be of prime value is that, *from both classical and quantum treatments, the average translational energy of an Avogadro's number of molecules is $\frac{1}{2}RT$ per degree of freedom.*

3-16. Rotational Energy. As with objects of ordinary dimensions, the rotation of a nonlinear molecule can be treated in terms of rotation about three perpendicular axes. Each of these rotations can be treated separately, as were translations in the x, y, and z directions. The three rotations constitute

3 degrees of freedom, and classically it would be expected that, on the basis of $\frac{1}{2}RT$ kinetic energy per degree of freedom, the rotational energy would total $\frac{3}{2}RT$. For a linear molecule, rotation about only the two axes which are perpendicular to the molecular axis constitutes molecular rotation. A change in angular momentum about the axis of the molecule would depend on a change in the motions of the electrons of the molecule. Such a change could occur only by exciting the molecule to a higher electronic state, and this, as has been mentioned, would require a very large amount of energy for most molecules. Linear molecules have, therefore, only 2 molecular rotational degrees of freedom and classically would be expected to have RT kinetic energy.

The quantum-mechanical calculation of the rotational energies of a molecule shows, as is expected from our previous discussion of the particle-in-a-box problem, that only certain discrete energies of rotation are allowed. For each rotational degree of freedom a diagram of the allowed energies can be drawn.

For most molecules the spacing of these allowed energy levels, which will be studied in greater detail in Chap. 10, is quite small compared with a room temperature value of kT. We shall see that the spacing of these levels can be studied spectroscopically, and it is then found that a typical wavelength of radiation to cause a transition from one rotational energy level to the next higher one is 1 cm. At this wavelength the energy of a quantum is about 2×10^{-16} erg, which is small compared with kT.

The closeness of the allowed levels means that, as for translational-energy levels, the quantum restrictions are unimportant in their effect on the average energy per degree of freedom. *The classical result that there will be $\frac{3}{2}RT$ cal/ mole rotational energy, or RT for linear molecules, is valid.*

It is necessary only to mention that very light molecules (H_2 is the most prominent example) do not have sufficiently small energy-level spacings to allow the classical result to be used for the average rotational energy. For such molecules the population of each of the rotational-energy levels must be calculated and the average rotational energy determined. Furthermore, at temperatures much below room temperature kT becomes comparable with the rotational spacing of many molecules.

3-17. Vibrational Energy. The vibration of a diatomic molecule consists of the motion of the atoms toward and away from each other. The chemical bond in this regard behaves very like a spring. Since the bond confines the atoms to fairly small displacements, the amplitude of vibration being about 10 per cent of the bond length, the vibrational energy is quantized. Spectroscopic studies show that radiation with a wavelength of about 0.001 cm will raise a molecule to its next higher energy level. The energy of quanta of this wavelength is 2×10^{-13} erg, and the vibrational-energy-level spacing is seen to be comparable with the energy kT.

The average vibrational energy of a diatomic molecule can be obtained by direct calculation if the energy-level pattern is known. Solution of the Schrödinger equation for this problem, as is obtained in Chap. 10, will show that the vibrational-energy levels form an equally spaced set. The separation between these allowed energies depends on the nature of the chemical bond and on the masses of the atoms.   The fraction of molecules that occupy the higher energy levels at a given temperature can be calculated from Boltzmann's distribution.   These molecules contribute to the vibrational thermal energy in a way that will be treated in detail in the following chapter.

Polyatomic molecules also are capable of vibrations.   Here again it is a good approximation to think of the chemical bonds as behaving like springs. Such systems of "weights" and springs can be set vibrating in a number of different ways.   Each of these vibrations, called *modes of vibration*, corresponds to a vibrational degree of freedom.   Each such degree of freedom has a set of allowed energy levels that is just like that for a diatomic molecule.   The vibrational energy of a polyatomic molecule is obtained by summing the average energy in each of these degrees of freedom.

We must now see how many vibrational degrees of freedom a molecule with n atoms will have.   If the n atoms were very loosely bound together to form the molecule, the total number of degrees of freedom would be calculated as $3n$; that is, 3 translational degrees of freedom would be assigned to each atom. For actual molecules the bonds are sufficiently strong so that it is usually not convenient to think of the atoms moving independently.   The coupling of the atoms does not, however, change the total number of degrees of freedom of the system.   Only the way of counting these degrees of freedom is changed.

The translation of the molecule as a whole accounts for 3 degrees of freedom. For a nonlinear molecule another 3 are attributed to the rotational degrees of freedom.   The remaining $3n - 6$, or $3n - 5$ for linear molecules, must be made up by vibrational degrees of freedom.   It is concluded, therefore, that a molecule with n atoms will have $3n - 6$ (or $3n - 5$ if the molecule is linear) vibrational degrees of freedom.   There will be this number of vibrational-energy-level diagrams throughout which the molecules will be distributed according to Boltzmann's relation.

In the following chapter, the average vibrational energies of molecules will be calculated by using the ideas introduced here.

3-18. Thermal Energies.   The contributions of translational, rotational, vibrational, and electronic energies to the total molecular energy can now be summarized.   The thermal energy for 1 mole of a gaseous compound can be written as

$$E - E_0 = E_{\text{trans}} + E_{\text{rot}} + E_{\text{vib}} + E_{\text{elec}}$$
$$= \tfrac{3}{2}RT + \tfrac{3}{2}RT \text{ (or } RT\text{)} + E_{\text{vib}} + 0 \qquad (65)$$

The information of the previous sections which shows that the quantization of translation and rotation is usually of no importance in this regard and that the electronic excitation is almost always negligible at ordinary temperatures has here been used.

The energy content of an Avogadro's number of molecules can, therefore, be written as

$$E = E_0 + (3RT + E_{\text{vib}}) \qquad \text{nonlinear molecules}$$

or $\qquad E = E_0 + (\tfrac{5}{2}RT + E_{\text{vib}}) \qquad \text{linear molecules} \qquad (66)$

Table 3-3. Molecular Energy Levels and Thermal Energies

| | Typical energy-level spacing | | Thermal energy $E\text{-}E_0$ |
	In ergs/molecule*	In cal/mole†	In cal/mole
Electronic.....	10^{-11}	100,000	0
Vibrational....	10^{-13}	1,000	Calculated from Boltzmann distribution
Rotational....	10^{-16}	1	$\frac{3}{2}RT$ (or RT for linear molecule)
Translational..	10^{-34}	10^{-18}	$\frac{3}{2}RT$

* Cf. the room-temperature value of $\frac{1}{2}kT$ of 2×10^{-14} erg/molecule.
† Cf. the room-temperature value of $\frac{1}{2}RT$ of 300 cal/mole.

It is for such statements as these that the preliminary investigation of molecular structure of this chapter has been introduced. Molecular quantum restrictions are summarized in Table 3-3 and indicated schematically in Fig. 3-14. In Chaps. 8 to 10 we shall return to more detailed studies of the theory and the experimental investigations which deal with the nature of molecules.

The understanding of the allowed molecular energy levels and such derived quantities as the average energy of molecules distributed throughout such energy schemes will soon be seen to be a necessary preliminary to the full understanding and use of the powerful methods of thermodynamics which are now to be studied. Although the methods of thermodynamics are very different from the approaches used so far and will, in fact, seem at first to be quite unrelated to our search for details of the molecular world, they will finally appear as invaluable windows into this world.

Problems

1. Review the argument that water has the formula H_2O and not HO based on the experimental result that 2 volumes of water vapor would on decomposition yield 2 volumes of H_2 and 1 volume of O_2.

2. What is the wavelength and the frequency (in cycles per sec and reciprocal centimeters) of radiation whose quanta have energies of 3×10^{-13} erg?
Ans. $\lambda = 66,200$ A; $\nu = 4.53 \times 10^{13}$ sec^{-1}; $\bar{\nu} = 1,510$ cm^{-1}.

3. What is the energy in ergs per quantum and calories per Avogadro's number of quanta for the quanta of radiation in the ranges of electromagnetic radiation shown in Table 3-1? Compare the values with the room-temperature value of the average translational kinetic energy of a molecule.

4. The Lyman series of spectral lines from atomic hydrogen have frequencies (in reciprocal centimeters) given by the expression

$$\bar{\nu} = 109,677 \left(\frac{1}{1^2} - \frac{1}{n_1^2} \right) \quad \text{cm}^{-1} \quad \text{where } n_1 = 2, 3, 4, \ldots$$

For the line with $n_1 = 2$:

(a) Calculate the frequency in cycles per second and the wavelength in angstroms of the radiation. *Ans.* $\nu = 2.47 \times 10^{15}$ sec^{-1}; $\lambda = 1,210$ A.

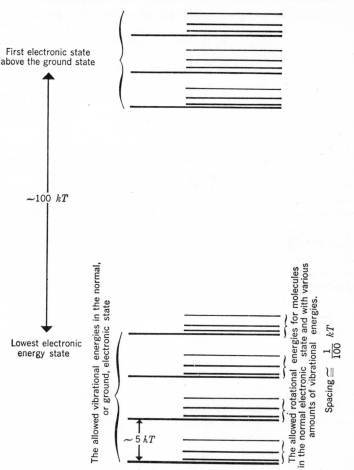

First electronic state
above the ground state

~100 kT

Lowest electronic
energy state

The allowed vibrational energies in the normal,
or ground, electronic state

~5 kT

The allowed rotational energies for molecules
in the normal electronic state and with various
amounts of vibrational energies.

Spacing $\cong \frac{1}{100} kT$

Fig. 3-14. Schematic representation of typical molecular energy levels.   Translational-energy levels are too closely spaced to be represented.   They are spaced by approximately $10^{-10}RT$. A value of kT at room temperature is assumed in the diagram.

(b) Calculate the energy of the quanta of this radiation in ergs per quantum and in calories per Avogadro's number of quanta.

$Ans.$ 1.634×10^{-11} erg/quantum; 235,000 cal/mole.

(c) In what region of electromagnetic radiation does this spectral line fall?

5. Compare the energy necessary to excite the electron of the hydrogen atom from the $n = 1$ to the $n = 2$ orbit with the average translational energy of a molecule at 25°C.   At what temperature is the average molecular translational energy equal to this hydrogen-atom excitation energy?

6. Calculate the energy in ergs and the wavelength and wave number of the radiation

emitted when the electron of a hydrogen atom drops from the $n = 6$ orbit to the $n = 5$ orbit. *Ans.* $\epsilon = 2.66 \times 10^{-12}$ erg; $\lambda = 7,460$ A.

7. What are the radii given by the Bohr theory for the $n = 1, 5, 10,$ and 20 orbits?

8. Plot on a scale that is linear in frequency, such as the spectrograms of Fig. 3-4, the first four transitions of the Brackett series. Add an energy and a wavelength scale to the plot.

9. The spectrum of the ion He^+ has been obtained and exhibits, in addition to many other lines, spectral lines at $329{,}170$; $390{,}120$; $411{,}460$; and $421{,}330$ cm^{-1}. Show that a Rydberg-type expression will represent the frequencies of these lines. What is the ratio of the constant for He to that for the H atom?

10. Derive an expression, according to the Bohr theory, for the energy levels of the He^+ ion. What Rydberg-type formula does this lead to for the spectral transitions?

11. What are the kinetic and the potential energies, according to the Bohr theory, of an electron in (a) the $n = 1$ orbit of the hydrogen atom, (b) the $n = 4$ orbit of the hydrogen atom?

Ans. (a) Potential $= -4.35 \times 10^{-11}$ erg; kinetic $= +2.17 \times 10^{-11}$ erg;
total $= -2.17 \times 10^{-11}$ erg.

12. What are the velocities in centimeters per second and angstroms per second of an electron in the $n = 1$ and $n = 4$ orbits of the hydrogen atom? How many times per second does the electron complete a cycle around the nucleus for the $n = 1$ and for the $n = 4$ orbits? How many seconds does it take for each cycle in each of these orbits? Compare the velocity of an electron in an atom with a typical molecular velocity.

13. Calculate the energies of the three lowest quantum states for an electron confined to an infinitely walled square potential well of width 10 A. Show graphically the shape of ψ and ψ^2 for these three states.

Ans. $0.602 \times 10^{-12}, 2.41 \times 10^{-12}, 5.42 \times 10^{-12}$ erg.

14. Calculate an expression for the allowed energy levels of a baseball, of mass 5 oz, confined to a baseball park of length 350 ft. To what velocity jumps do these correspond?

15. The probability of finding a particle at a given position is given by ψ^2. If the wave function for a particle in a square well is $\psi = A \sin (n\pi x/a)$, find, by a suitable integration, what the total probability is that the particle be found between $x = 0$ and $x = a$. Replace A by a suitable term so that $\int_{x=0}^{x=a} \psi^2 \, dx$ is always unity, i.e., so that one particle will be found somewhere in the well.

16. The average one-dimensional translational energy of an N_2 molecule was shown by the kinetic-molecular theory to have the value $\frac{1}{2}kT$. What would be the quantum number of an average N_2 molecule at 25°C in a container of 10 cm length? What would be the energy separation between successive allowed quantum states at this energy? *Ans.* $n = 4.17 \times 10^9$, $\Delta\epsilon = 9.83 \times 10^{-24}$ erg.

17. Attempt to represent graphically and qualitatively the probability of a particle being at various positions in a cubic potential box for the quantum states $n_x = n_y = n_z = 1$ and $n_x = 2, n_y = n_z = 1$. What are the energies of these states if the box is cubic with dimension 5 A and the particle is an electron?

18. Calculate the number of hydrogen atoms that have $n = 2$ compared with the number that have $n = 1$ at 25°C. At what temperature would 1 per cent of the atoms have $n = 2$? *Ans.* $T = 25{,}700°$K.

19. Indicate by vertical lines erected on an energy abscissa the relative populations of the first five quantum states for an electron confined to a one-dimensional square

potential well of width 100 A.   Make such a chart for $T = 298°K$ and $T = 1000°K$.

20. Check several points on the graph of Fig. 3-13.   Make a similar graph for $1500°K$, using an ordinate in terms of $(n_0)_{1500°K}$.   [The relative values of $(n_0)_{298°K}$ and $(n_0)_{1500°K}$ can be obtained if Sec. 3-13 has been studied.]   Add a velocity abscissa scale to these plots, and compare the shapes of these curves with those given in Fig. 2-5.

21. What is the thermal energy of an Avogadro's number of rigid, i.e., nonvibrating, diatomic molecules at $298°K$?   At $1000°K$?

Ans. $E_{298} - E_0 = 1,480$; $E_{1000} - E_0 = 4970$ cal/mole.

22. Consider a reaction in which two monatomic molecules combine to give a rigid, i.e., nonvibrating, diatomic molecule.   Express the energy content of each species in terms of the zero-state energy and the translational- and rotational-energy contributions.   Write an expression for the difference in energy between the product and the sum of the reactants.   Will more or less energy be given out by the reaction as the temperature is raised?

23. The vibrational-energy levels of HCl consist of an evenly spaced set with a separation of $2,990$ cm^{-1}.   Calculate the ratio of the number of molecules in one energy level to the number of molecules in the next lower level at $25°C$.   Do the same for I_2, for which the vibrational energies are spaced by 215 cm^{-1}.

Ans. $(n_1/n_0)_{HCl} = 5.4 \times 10^{-7}$; $(n_1/n_0)_{I_2} = 0.35$.

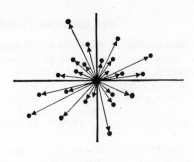

4

The First Law of Thermodynamics

4-1. Thermodynamics. A powerful method for studying chemical phenomena, which can be developed quite independently of the atomic and molecular theory of the preceding chapters, is that of *thermodynamics*. The name implies a study of the flow of heat, but it will be seen that the subject treats the more general quantity, energy. The energy changes associated with chemical reactions are themselves of considerable importance and will be dealt with in this and the following chapter. Even greater chemical interest, however, stems from the fact that the equilibrium position of a reacting system can be related to these energy changes. Much of the succeeding thermodynamic development will be directed toward associating thermal properties with the equilibrium state of a chemical system.

Thermodynamics is a logical subject of great elegance. Three concise statements, the three laws of thermodynamics, are made that sum up our experiences with energy. From these statements logical deductions are then drawn that bear on almost every aspect of chemistry.

The validity of thermodynamics depends only on the three generalizations and on the logic of the succeeding deductions. Thermodynamics is, therefore, independent of any model or theory, such as the molecular theory, for the nature of matter. Any alteration in our present ideas and theories about the nature of molecules would, therefore, in no way affect the validity of any thermodynamic result. Thermodynamics has a permanence which might, for example, be compared with that of Euclid's geometric theorems in plane geometry, which is not shared by our ever-changing views on the nature of atoms and molecules.

Modern physical chemistry, however, attempts to understand the nature of the chemical world and does so primarily in terms of the atomic and molecular theory. While thermodynamics can be kept aloof from these molecular ideas, it need not be so kept. In practice, one deals with thermodynamics most frequently when detailed molecular ideas are used to try to explain or calculate some thermodynamic result. It will be found that the ability to understand thermodynamic quantities on a molecular basis, while not at all necessary for the study of thermodynamics, is a very valuable aid to the study of chemistry and of the molecular world.

The introduction from time to time of molecular explanations will provide a concrete model on which thermodynamic quantities can be understood.   Most students will find this quite helpful.   It cannot be emphasized too strongly, however, that the molecular model need not be introduced in our study of thermodynamics.

4-2. The Equivalence of Heat and Work. The development of modern thermodynamics requires some prior comments on the nature of energy.   It is the object of this section to recount that heat and work can be considered to be forms of energy.   Today, when it seems obvious that work used up in over-coming friction, for example, appears as heat, it is difficult to realize that a time existed when heat and work were not recognized as even being related quantities.

The unlikely beginning of the recognition of the relation between heat and work is usually attributed to the ideas of Count Rumford, originally Benjamin Thompson of Massachusetts, who was in charge of boring cannon in Munich in 1798 for the king of Bavaria.   The boring operation required a large amount of work and produced much heat.   Although the accepted theory at the time held that heat was a substance, called *caloric*, and that the boring operation released caloric as a result of the grinding up of the iron, Rumford convinced him-self that the heat was a manifestation of the work that was performed.   It remained, however, for a less applied scientist to make the equivalence of heat and work generally accepted.

The very thorough and careful experiments of James Joule in the 18′0s not only showed that mechanical work could be converted into heat but also provided a numerical relation for the amount of heat obtained when a given amount of work is converted to heat.

In a typical experiment work was performed by a falling weight, and this work was transferred by a system of pulleys to a paddle that turned in a con-tainer filled with water.   In a given experiment the work could be calculated from the size of the weight and the distance through which it fell.   Such work would now be measured in joules, 1 joule being defined as 10^7 ergs and 1 erg being the cgs unit of work equal to 1 dyne-cm.   The heat produced by the stirring of the water was measured by the temperature rise and the weight of the water.   The unit for measuring this heat is the calorie, 1 cal being the heat required to raise the temperature of 1 g of water by 1°C.   Using different amounts of work and various weights of water, Joule found that there was a quantitative relation between the amount of work done and the amount of heat produced.   Modern results give this relation as

$$1 \text{ cal} = 4.180 \text{ joules} \tag{1}$$

[In modern practice one frequently takes Eq. (1) as a definition of the value of the calorie in terms of joules and in this way avoids the complications in defin-ing the size of the calorie that arise from the variation in the heat capacity of water with temperature.]

One should appreciate that the deduction of this relation represents more than, for instance, the working out of the conversion equation between inches and centimeters. In spite of the earlier work of Rumford, the quantities given a numerical relation by Joule were not even generally accepted as being related before his compelling experiments.

Since we shall frequently have occasion to add or subtract energies that are heat and work, considerable use will be made of Joule's relation for the mechanical equivalent of heat.

One should notice that the mechanical equivalent of heat is deduced from experiments in which work is converted to heat rather than heat to work. The important process of the conversion of heat to work is less easily performed, and the complications of conversion in this direction are, in part, the concern of the second law of thermodynamics. The Joule relation, nevertheless, applies to conversion in either direction, giving the heat produced when a given amount of work is converted to heat or the work produced when a given amount of heat is converted to work.

4-3. Energy and the Conservation of Energy. The Joule experiments suggest that heat and work be described as different forms of the more general quantity, energy, and that the form of energy can be changed but its total amount is constant, i.e., that energy is conserved. It was indeed at about the time of Joule's studies that the important *conservation-of-energy* law was suggested. This generalization, that *energy can be neither created nor destroyed*, is essentially a statement of the first law of thermodynamics. It is customary, as will be done in the next section, to state this law in a form that is more directly applicable to chemical problems. Before doing this, however, it is necessary to make the conservation-of-energy law more meaningful by considering what is meant by the term energy.

The Joule experiment in which the temperature of water is raised by the expenditure of mechanical work is an illustration of the conservation-of-energy law if heat and work, as previously defined, are accepted as forms of energy. Consider, however, what would happen if Joule's experiment were performed with a mixture of ice and water in the calorimeter. The expenditure of work would then result in no temperature rise, the water-ice mixture staying at 0°C. Energy might seem to have been used up rather than conserved. The difficulty is surmounted by the introduction of "latent heat" as another form of energy. The work has, therefore, gone into melting some ice and converting it to water which, even at the same temperature, has a higher energy content.

One might also consider the process performed when an automobile engine charges a storage battery. Work is expended, but no appreciable temperature rise or melting occurs. Again, the conservation-of-energy law would have to be relinquished except for our inclusion of "chemical energy," resulting from some chemical change in the battery, as yet another form to be included in our concept of energy.

One should appreciate from these examples that the conservation-of-energy law includes the rather flexible word energy. Rather than defining energy by listing the ways in which it can occur, it seems desirable to leave the definition open so that the conservation law cannot possibly be violated. Nuclear reactions that create energy with no change other than a decrease in mass of the system provide a good illustration of the merits of this approach. In such reactions the conservation-of-energy law would have been violated if types of energy had been listed but mass had not been included.

This discussion of the forms which energy can take is pertinent to a study of chemical thermodynamics since chemical systems store energy in ways other than as simple thermal or mechanical energy. It is frequently possible to determine changes in the amount of stored energy when chemicals react only by adding up the measurable amounts of heat and work that occur and then relying on the constancy of the total energy to give a value for the change in the less easily observed chemical energy. It is for such applications that the chemical statement of the first law of thermodynamics is designed.

4-4. The First Law of Thermodynamics. In chemical systems the conservation-of-energy law is most easily handled in terms of three quantities: the work that is performed, the heat that flows, and the energy that is stored in the system. To be more specific, we consider some process that takes a system from an initial state represented by a to a final state represented by b. The system may be anything from a mechanical device to a container holding one or several chemical compounds. The process may be a change in temperature or pressure, the doing of mechanical work, the occurrence of a chemical reaction, and so forth. It is convenient to introduce the symbols

q = heat absorbed by system
w = work done by system
ΔE = change in *internal energy* of system

It is important to memorize the exact meaning of these symbols. If heat is absorbed by the system, for example, q has a positive value. If heat is given out, q has a negative value. Likewise, if the system does work on the surroundings, w has a positive value, whereas, if the surroundings do work on the system, w has a negative value.

The first law of thermodynamics can now be stated by the two equations

$$\Delta E = q - w$$
$$\text{and} \qquad \Delta E = E_b - E_a \qquad (2)$$

The first equation expresses the conservation result that any net energy in the form of heat and work, $q - w$, is not created or destroyed but must correspond to the change ΔE in the stored energy.

The second equation states that, for a process taking the system from state a to state b, the internal-energy change depends only on state a and state b and not on the way in which the system was transformed from one state to the other. This is also a generalization of our experiences with energy.

Consider the cyclic, schematic process of Fig. 4-1 that carries the system from a to b and then back to a. If two paths were available that had different values of ΔE, it would be possible to carry the system around the cycle and end

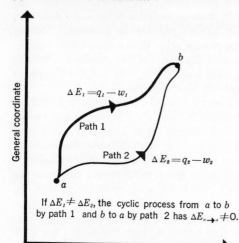

Fig. 4-1. Illustration that for E to be a state function, $\oint dE = 0$ and ΔE is independent of path.

up with more stored energy than initially. It is found, for example, that, no matter what is done with 1 g of water at 25°C and 1 atm pressure, 1 g of water at 25°C and 1 atm pressure always has the same internal energy. It is not possible, for example, to use such a sample of water and to gain a net change in $q - w$ for a process that returns the water to its original state. Since a net change in ΔE for a cyclic process is never observed, it follows that, no matter how the system is taken from a to b, the internal-energy change will be the same and will depend only on states a and b.

This independence on reaction path is neatly expressed by the fact that the function remains unchanged when a cyclic process is performed and the system is returned to its initial state. Mathematically this is stated as

$$\oint dE = 0 \qquad (3)$$

Functions, such as the internal energy, for which the cyclic integral is zero, are known as *state functions* and will be denoted by capital letters. With this understanding the first law can be simply expressed as

$$\Delta E = q - w \qquad (4)$$

For an infinitesimal change in the system the first law is written as

$$dE = \bar{d}q - \bar{d}w$$

where the barred d's indicate that the derivative, like any changes in the functions q and w, are dependent on the way in which the process occurs. The symbol $\bar{d}$ indicates what is called an *inexact*, or *imperfect*, differential, while the symbol d indicates an exact differential and appears only before state functions.

This law is used in chemistry in a number of ways. The measurement of q and w for a chemical reaction, for example, allows the calculation of the difference in internal energy of the reactants and the products. Such internal-energy terms are of considerable direct importance. The explanation of such internal energies, moreover, represents a challenge to our molecular theories that leads us into a fuller understanding of the molecular basis of the energies of chemical systems.

Before applying the first law to chemical systems, some properties of heat, work, and internal energy will be illustrated by some simple examples.

4-5. Dependence of q and w on the Reaction Path.   In taking a system from some state a to some new state b there are, in general, a number of different paths available.   It is important to recognize that, although the internal-energy change will be the same for all paths, the amounts of heat and work will generally be different for different paths.   This is implied by the use of the small letters q and w to represent heat and work.   That q and w depend on the reaction path can be illustrated by some examples.

The weight of Fig. 4-2a might be taken from its initial position a to its final

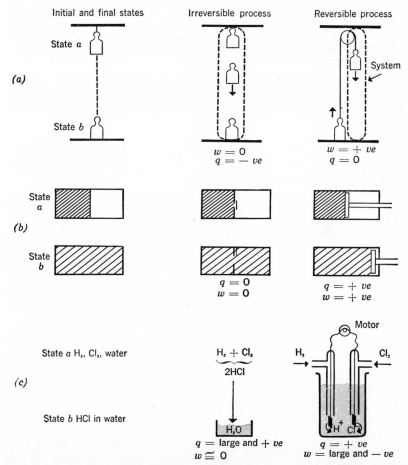

Fig. 4-2. Illustrations of the dependence of q and w on the way in which a process is performed.

position b in two different ways.   If the weight is attached over a pulley to another slightly smaller weight, the process can be carried out so that no heat is evolved but the system performs work on the second weight.   Alternatively, the weight is simply allowed to drop, which means that no work is done by the falling weight, but heat is generated as a result of its impact with the floor. As the weight cools to room temperature, it would be found that an amount of heat would be evolved that would be equal to the work done in the first process. Both processes have the same initial and final states, and the first law requires, therefore, that ΔE be the same for each process.   In the first process q is zero, and w has a positive value.   In the second process q has a negative value, and w is zero.

A second illustration is shown in Fig. 4-2b.   State a consists of a chamber with gas in one half and the other half evacuated.   State b consists of this same amount of gas filling the entire chamber.   Again a number of different ways, or paths, are available for taking the system from a to b.   The simplest is to open a stopcock in the partition and allow the gas to rush into the evacuated compartment.   By this process the gas does no work on the surroundings, and it is found that, if the gas behaves ideally, no heat will be given out or absorbed.   It follows from Eq. (4) that there is no difference in the internal energy of the gas in the states a and b.   An alternative path for the process consists in letting the gas expand against a piston until it again fills the entire container.   If this arrangement is used, the gas does work on the piston.   It is found that, if the temperature is to be kept constant, an amount of heat equal to this amount of work must be added.   Again it is seen that q and w depend on how the process is performed but that ΔE depends only on the states a and b.

A similar variety of available paths occur in chemical processes.   Consider two different ways in which H_2, Cl_2, and water can be converted into a hydrochloric acid solution.   One process, illustrated in Fig. 4-2c, involves the direct reaction of H_2 and Cl_2 to form HCl gas which can then be dissolved in water. For this process a considerable amount of heat is given off both in the H_2,Cl_2 reaction and in the solution of HCl in water.   Only a small amount of work would be involved.   A second process would consist in making H_2 give up electrons and Cl_2 accept electrons as in the reactions

$$\begin{array}{r} H_2 \rightarrow 2H^+ + 2e^- \\ 2e^- + Cl_2 \rightarrow 2Cl^- \\ \hline H_2 + Cl_2 \rightarrow 2H^+ + 2Cl^- \end{array}$$

The net reaction, since the process would be performed in water, is the formation of hydrochloric acid.   Such reactions can be performed in an electrochemical cell, as illustrated in Fig. 4-2c, in which the flow of electrons can be made to do electrical work.   When the reaction is performed in this way, a large amount of work is done by the system and at the same time some heat is liberated.   Again the amounts of heat and work are dependent on the path, but it would be found that ΔE is again dependent only on the initial and final states.

It is necessary to emphasize this essential difference between ΔE and the quantities q and w because we shall frequently calculate ΔE from determinations of q and w. If we had sufficient detailed molecular information on the states a and b, we could calculate E_a and E_b directly. It would then be immediately obvious that ΔE equals $E_b - E_a$ and is dependent only on the states a and b.

4-6. Work in Chemical Processes. In almost all the chemical examples considered in the first half of this book the work term will be a consequence of the expansion or contraction of the system against an external pressure. Later chapters will deal with electrochemical systems where the work results from the production of electrical energy. For present purposes, it is convenient to have an explicit expression for the work performed by a change in the volume of the system against a confining pressure.

A gas or liquid in a cylinder, as in Fig. 4-3, at a pressure P exerts a force on the piston which can be balanced by a force f acting on the piston shaft. If the piston has a cross section area A, the pressure P, being the force per unit area, produces a force

$$f = PA \tag{5}$$

For an infinitesimal expansion resulting from a movement dl of the piston, the work is calculated from the force times the distance through which the force moves as

$$dw = f\,dl \tag{6}$$

which, with the insertion of A in the numerator and denominator, can be written as

$$dw = \frac{f}{A}\,(A\;dl) \tag{7}$$

In this latter form, f/A can be identified with the pressure in the cylinder and $A\,dl$ with the change in volume of the cylinder. Thus the work of expansion can be written in the often convenient form

$$dw = P\,dV$$

or
$$w = \int_a^b P\,dV \tag{8}$$

The integration can, of course, be performed only if a relation is known between the pressure of the gas or liquid in the cylinder and the volume of the cylinder.

It should be noted that, when the system expands and does work, dV is

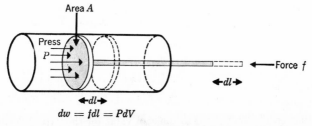

$$dw = fdl = PdV$$

Fig. 4-3. The work of expansion.

positive; and, in agreement with our previous sign convention, dw is positive.

The derivation of Eq. (8) has assumed a state of balance in the system. The pressure of the gas has been taken as exerting a force PA which is equal to the force f which the piston shaft utilizes to do work. Expansion under these conditions would in reality not occur. The force exerted by the gas would have to be somewhat greater than the opposing force of the piston.

Equation (8) applies to the important idealized case in which the forces are balanced or infinitesimally away from balance. Such processes are said to be *reversible*, and the name arises, in this example, because the work performed by the expansion could be stored and by an infinitesimal change in the force on the piston shaft could be used to reverse the process and compress the gas to its original volume.

If the gas is expanded in a process in which the force exerted by the gas is greater during the expansion than is the force on the piston shaft, the process is said to be *irreversible*. Less work will be done by such processes than is done in reversible processes. All processes in real systems occur only because of a lack of balance, and, to this extent, all real processes will be somewhat irreversible.

4-7. The Internal Energy of an Ideal Gas. It is often convenient, both in introductory illustrations and actual practice, to treat gases as if they behave ideally. Such behavior introduces considerable simplicity into many thermodynamic results.

An important experiment by James Joule in 1843 was directed at the study of the internal energy of a gas. The deductions from these very early experiments are now known to apply exactly to ideal gases and only approximately to real gases. The experiment, performed in an apparatus such as that depicted in Fig. 4-4, consisted in filling one of the two bulbs with air at a pressure of about 20 atm, the other bulb being evacuated. The surrounding water bath was stirred, and its temperature was recorded. The stopcock connecting the two bulbs was then opened, and the thermometer was read. In these experiments Joule observed no temperature change. More sensitive experiments would show that real gases do generally show a small temperature effect, as will be discussed in a later section. Joule's result corresponds, however, to ideal behavior.

From Joule's experiments it is deduced that, since no net work is done by the gas on the surroundings and no heat is given up or absorbed, the internal energy, according to Eq. (4), must remain unchanged. We can write, therefore, for ideal gases

$$\left(\frac{\partial E}{\partial V}\right)_T = 0 \tag{9}$$

A more complete characterization of an ideal gas than that given in Sec. 1-9 is that, not only is the equation of state, $PV = nRT$, applicable, but also $(\partial E/\partial V)_T = 0$.

The Joule experiment has led to the zero value for the partial derivative of internal energy with respect to volume, but the result could equally well have

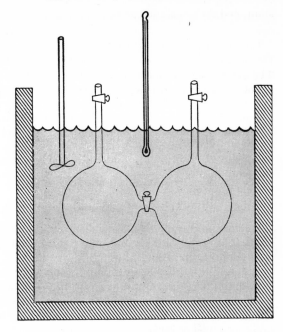

Fig. 4-4. Apparatus for the Joule experiment on the heat effect of expansion of a gas.

been expressed as $(\partial E/\partial P)_T = 0$. The independence of the internal energy from pressure and volume gives the frequently useful result that *the internal energy of an ideal gas depends only on the temperature.*

This result is immediately understandable on the basis of our kinetic-molecular model. The absence of attractions and repulsions between the molecules of a gas was seen to be the basis for obedience to the $PV = nRT$ law. The absence of such interactions, furthermore, means that the energy of the gas will be unaffected by the average distance between molecules. For non-ideal gases, on the other hand, these interactions do occur, and the gas molecules have a different average potential energy when the average intermolecular distance is changed.

4-8. Illustrations of the Equation $\Delta E = q - w$. Two examples, of a rather nonchemical nature, can now be given to illustrate how the first law of thermodynamics is applied.

Example 1. Calculate q, w, and ΔE for the conversion, at 100°C and 1 atm, of 1 mole of water into steam.

The heat required for this process is the latent heat of vaporization, which is given in tables as 9720 cal/mole. Thus, we have immediately

$$q = 9720 \text{ cal}$$

Since the work done in the process results from the expansion of the system, it is calculated from $\not{d}w = P\,dV$. Furthermore, the pressure remains constant, and the integration gives

$$w = \int_{V_1}^{V_2} P \, dV = P \int_{V_1}^{V_2} dV$$
$$= P(V_2 - V_1)$$

The volume of 1 mole of liquid water V_1 is about 18 cc, and the volume of 1 mole of steam V_2 can be estimated from the ideal-gas value of

$$V_2 = (\tfrac{373}{273})(22,400) = 30,600 \text{ cc}$$

The work of expansion is then obtained as

$$w = (1)(30,600 - 18) = 30,600 \text{ cc atm}$$
$$= 740 \text{ cal}$$

The first-law equation now allows the calculation of the internal-energy change as

$$\Delta E = q - w = 9,720 - 740 = 8980 \text{ cal}$$

For this process most of the added heat is seen to go into increasing the internal energy of the water, and only a small fraction is expended in pushing back the atmosphere.

It should be noted that the direct calculation, on the basis of our knowledge of molecular behavior, of the energy of 1 mole of liquid water compared with 1 mole of steam would be a task that is still so difficult that it could not be accomplished. The thermodynamic method lets us obtain this quantity from easily measured or calculated energy effects.

Example 2. Calculate q, w, and ΔE for the reversible expansion of 10 moles of an ideal gas from an initial pressure of 1 atm to a final pressure of 0.1 atm at a constant temperature of 0°C. A reversible expansion is one in which the confining pressure is just infinitesimally less than the gas pressure throughout the expansion.

Since q cannot now be directly calculated, we proceed to the other two quantities, ΔE and w.

The internal energy of an ideal gas, as was seen in the previous section, depends only on the temperature. In this expansion the temperature remains constant, and we can write

$$\Delta E = 0$$

Again the work term is work of expansion and is calculated from $\int P \, dV$. Both P and V change as the expansion occurs, but the relation $PV = nRT$, with constant T, allows the integration to be performed. Thus

$$w = \int P \, dV$$
$$= \int_{V_1}^{V_2} \frac{nRT}{V} \, dV = nRT \ln V \Big]_{V_1}^{V_2}$$
$$= nRT \ln \frac{V_2}{V_1} = nRT \ln \frac{P_1}{P_2} \tag{10}$$

The final expression in terms of pressures follows from the fact that the temperature is constant, and

$$P_1 V_1 = P_2 V_2 \quad \text{or} \quad \frac{V_2}{V_1} = \frac{P_1}{P_2}$$

Substitution of numerical values gives

$$w = (10)(1.987)(273)(2.303) \log \frac{1.0}{0.1}$$
$$= 1250 \text{ cal}$$

Finally the first-law expression is used to obtain

$$q = \Delta E + w$$
$$= 0 + 1250$$
$$= 1250 \text{ cal}$$

In this example all the absorbed heat is expended in the work of expansion, and the internal energy of the gas remains unchanged.

4-9. Constant-volume Processes. A special type of process that is often encountered is one which proceeds at constant volume. Here some of the special features of such processes are treated.

For a constant-volume process the work of expansion is zero, and if no other work, such as electrical work, is performed, the first-law equation takes on the special form

$$\Delta E = q \tag{11}$$

The heat evolved or absorbed gives directly the change in internal energy.

Heat capacities of gases are frequently studied in constant-volume systems. The heat capacity at constant volume, denoted by C_v, is defined as the heat absorbed per degree rise in temperature by 1 mole of gas held at constant volume. Symbolically we write

$$C_v = \left(\frac{dq}{\partial T}\right)_V \tag{12}$$

In view of Eq. (11) the definition of the constant-volume heat capacity can be written as

$$C_v = \left(\frac{\partial E}{\partial T}\right)_v \tag{13}$$

The special case of the constant-volume heat capacity of an ideal gas is sometimes encountered. The internal energy of an ideal gas was seen, in Sec. 4-7, to be independent of P and V, and, therefore, the restricting subscript on Eq. (13) can be dropped. Thus, for an ideal gas,

$$C_v = \frac{dE}{dT} \quad \text{and} \quad dE = C_v dT \tag{14}$$

regardless of changes in pressure or volume.

4-10. Constant-pressure Processes and Enthalpy. Even more frequently encountered in chemistry than constant-volume processes are those performed at constant pressure. All reactions occurring in the open and subject to atmospheric pressure are examples. A new thermodynamic function that is particularly convenient for dealing with constant-pressure processes is now introduced. This function, denoted by H, is defined by the equation

$$H = E + PV \tag{15}$$

and is called the *enthalpy*, or the *heat content*.   The former word is preferable since it avoids the implications of the latter.   Since E and PV depend only on the state of the system, i.e., are state functions, so also is the enthalpy and it is therefore designated by a capital letter.   It is well to recognize that Eq. (15) is the defining equation for the enthalpy, and it is therefore a generally applicable equation that can be used in any calculation involving enthalpy.

That the enthalpy is particularly convenient for constant-pressure processes can now be shown.   For any infinitesimal change in the system the enthalpy change is, according to Eq. (15), related to changes in the other variables by

$$dH = dE + P\,dV + V\,dP \tag{16}$$

If no work other than expansion is involved, as here is usually the case, $P\,dV$ can be put equal to $đw$; and the first law can be used to replace the first two terms on the right of Eq. (16) by

$$dE + Pd\,V = dE + đw = đq \tag{17}$$

Moreover, for a constant-pressure process $dP = 0$, and Eq. (16) reduces to

$$dH = đq \tag{18}$$

For processes at constant pressure we have the frequently useful result that the change in enthalpy is equal to the heat absorbed.

The enthalpy should be recognized as a property rather like the internal energy.   For solids and liquids, as we shall see, changes in enthalpy are usually almost equal to the changes in internal energy.   This follows from the fact that for these states the volumes are relatively small and changes in the PV term are generally negligible.

It is perhaps easiest to see that enthalpy is a measure of the energy content of a system, as is internal energy, by asking how much additional energy is absorbed by 1 mole of an ideal gas at, say, 1 atm when the temperature is raised.   Focusing our attention on the individual molecules of the gas, we can see that they will increase their translational, their rotational, and their vibrational energy as a result of this temperature rise.   All these changes are included in the increase in internal energy E of the system.   An additional amount of energy will be taken up by the system, however, as a result of the work of expansion.   This work, which is an additional energy-storage mode of the gas, is calculated as

$$\int_T^{T+1} P\,dV = \int_T^{T+1} d(PV)$$

Since the enthalpy is defined as $H = E + PV$, it measures not only the energy stored in the individual molecules of the gas but also that which depends on the total volume occupied by the gas.   Thus both H and E measure the energy content of a system, but they do so in somewhat different ways.

Measurements of heat capacities are made at constant pressure as well as at constant volume.   The constant-pressure heat capacity C_p is defined as

$$C_p = \left(\frac{đq}{\partial T}\right)_p \tag{19}$$

Furthermore, in view of the constant-pressure result [Eq. (18)], we can write

$$C_p = \left(\frac{\partial H}{\partial T}\right)_p \tag{20}$$

For ideal gases some simplification is again possible. Since E and PV are then functions only of temperature, it follows from the definition of H that it also is a function only of temperature. For the special case of ideal gases one can eliminate the restriction of constant pressure and write

$$C_p = \frac{dH}{dT} \quad \text{or} \quad dH = C_p\, dT \tag{21}$$

For ideal gases the two simple relations (14) and (21) can be combined with the definition of H to give a relation between the two heat capacities. Differentiation of Eq. (15) with respect to temperature gives

$$\frac{dH}{dT} = \frac{dE}{dT} + \frac{d}{dT}\,(PV)$$

For 1 mole of an ideal gas the final term becomes

$$\frac{d}{dT}\,(RT) = R$$

and we obtain

$$C_p = C_v + R \tag{22}$$

This relation is understandable when it is recognized that to raise the temperature of a gas at constant volume it is necessary only to increase the internal energy of the gas. When the temperature rise occurs at constant pressure, one must add heat, not only to increase the internal energy but also to take care of the work of expansion. The work of expansion, when 1 mole of an ideal gas is heated 1° at constant pressure, is calculated as

$$w = \int P\,dV = \int d(PV) = \int_T^{T+1} R\,dT = R$$

For nonideal gases the difference between C_p and C_v will, of course, not be exactly equal to R.

For liquids and solids the expansion with increasing temperature is relatively small, and the work of expansion is also small. The difference between C_p and C_v is then frequently negligible.

Some experimental heat-capacity results for nitrogen are shown in Table 4-1,

Table 4-1. $C_p - C_v$ for N_2 as a Function of Temperature and Pressure*

	$C_p - C_v$ (cal/deg mole)			
	0 atm	50 atm	100 atm	200 atm
−50	(1.987)	3.1	4.4	5.3
0	(1.987)	2.6	3.2	4.0
100	(1.987)	2 3	2.5	2.9
200	(1.987)	2.1	2.2	2.4
400	(1.987)	2.0	2.1	2.2

* From data of W. E. Deming and L. E. Shupe, *Phys. Rev.*, **37**: 638 (1931).

and there it can be seen that the difference between C_p and C_v for a gas at relatively low pressures, where ideal behavior is approached, is very nearly the value of R.

4-11. The Joule-Thomson Coefficent for Real Gases. Following the experiments of Joule that failed to detect a heat effect when a gas was allowed to expand freely, more refined and sensitive experiments directed toward the same end were performed by Joule and Thomson. Since these results on the temperature change experienced by real gases, as these gases expand freely, are of great practical importance in the liquefaction of gases, as we shall see later, it is now necessary to report the type of experiment and the results of Joule and Thomson.

In their experiments a flow system was used which allowed the gas to pass from a high pressure to a low pressure through a throttling valve. The system was thermally insulated so that, as the gas passed through the valve, no heat could be absorbed or given off; that is, $q = 0$.

The measurements consisted of the pressure and temperature readings on either side of the throttling valve. In this way a sensitive measure of the temperature change of the gas on expansion was obtained. Typical results are those shown in Table 4-2. It is clear that the effect sought for unsuccessfully by Joule had been observed. The nonideal behavior is revealed by the temperature changes that accompany the expansion. It is results such as these to which we shall return when the liquefaction of gases is studied.

It is of interest to investigate what happens to 1 mole of gas as it passes through the throttling valve from the high pressure P_1 to the low pressure P_2. The heat-absorbed q has already been said to be zero.

The net work can be easily calculated by reference to Fig. 4-5, where we think of one piston operating to push 1 mole of gas through the valve and another piston operating to retain the gas at the low-pressure side of the valve. The work done on the gas by the first piston is

$$\int P \, dV = P_1 \int_{V=0}^{V=V_1} dV = P_1 V_1 \tag{23}$$

while the work done by the gas on the second piston is similarly $P_2 V_2$. The net work w is, therefore,

$$w = P_2 V_2 - P_1 V_1 \tag{24}$$

Substitution of known quantities in the first-law expression

$$\Delta E = q - w$$

Table 4-2. Joule-Thomson Coefficents, $\mu_{JT} = (\partial T/\partial P)_H$ for He and N$_2$
(Deg/atm)

$t°C$	$(\partial T/\partial P)_H$ for He	$(\partial T/\partial P)_H$ for N$_2$
-100	-0.058	$+0.649$
0	-0.062	$+0.266$
100	-0.064	$+0.129$
200	-0.064	$+0.056$

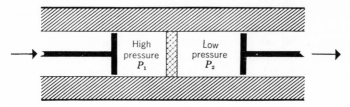

Fig. 4-5. Schematic representation of the Joule-Thomson throttling process.

gives

$$E_2 - E_1 = 0 - (P_2V_2 - P_1V_1)$$
$$= P_1V_1 - P_2V_2$$

or $$E_2 + P_2V_2 = E_1 + P_1V_1 \tag{25}$$

or, finally,

$$H_2 = H_1 \tag{26}$$

This analysis shows that the throttling process is one which operates at constant enthalpy. A more exact statement of the results of a Joule-Thomson type of experiment is that it gives $(\partial T/\partial P)_H$. It is customary to define the Joule-Thomson coefficient μ_{JT} as

$$\mu_{JT} = \left(\frac{\partial T}{\partial P}\right)_H \tag{27}$$

and it is this quantity which has been exhibited in Table 4-2.

The data for μ_{JT} show that a gas may either cool down in an expansion, when μ_{JT} is positive, or may heat up, when μ_{JT} is then negative. At room temperature all gases except hydrogen and helium have positive values for μ_{JT} and are therefore cooled by expansion. At temperatures below $-80°C$ the coefficient for hydrogen becomes positive, and below about $-220°C$ that for helium becomes positive. We shall see later that these data have considerable practical importance.

4-12. Adiabatic Processes. Frequently, one deals with a process which, either from the insulation around the system or from the speed of the reaction, occurs with no appreciable heat exchange between the system and the surroundings. Such processes, with

$$q = 0 \quad \text{and} \quad \Delta E = -w \tag{28}$$

are known as *adiabatic processes*.

In the following chapter particular use will be made of such a process that involves an ideal gas, and here the equations that show how an ideal gas behaves under adiabatic conditions are developed.

For an infinitesimal process that acts on n moles of an ideal gas the internal-energy change can, according to the discussion of Sec. 4-9, be expressed as

$$dE = nC_v \, dT \tag{29}$$

The work, which is that of expansion, is

$$dw = P \, dV$$

which, on insertion of the ideal-gas-law expression for P, is

$$\notdw = nRT \frac{dV}{V} \tag{30}$$

Eqs. (29) and (30) can be inserted into Eq. (28) to give

$$nC_v \, dT = -nRT \frac{dV}{V}$$

or

$$\frac{C_v}{R} \frac{dT}{T} = -\frac{dV}{V} \tag{31}$$

For a process that takes the gas from a volume V_1 at a temperature T_1 to a new volume V_2 at a temperature T_2 one has

$$\frac{C_v}{R} \int_{T_1}^{T_2} \frac{dT}{T} = -\int_{V_1}^{V_2} \frac{dV}{V}$$

or

$$\frac{C_v}{R} \ln \frac{T_2}{T_1} = -\ln \frac{V_2}{V_1} \tag{32}$$

On rearrangement, and after antilogarithms have been taken, this result can be written as

$$V_1 T_1^{C_v/R} = V_2 T_2^{C_v/R} \tag{33}$$

A frequently more useful arrangement is obtained by substituting for T_1 and T_2 the ideal-gas-law expression $T = PV/nR$ and $C_p = C_v + R$ to get

$$P_1 V_1^{C_p/C_v} = P_2 V_2^{C_p/C_v} \tag{34}$$

The ratio of the two specific heats frequently occurs and is given the designation

$$\gamma = \frac{C_p}{C_v} \tag{35}$$

With this notation the variation of pressure and volume of an adiabatic process involving an ideal gas is given by

$$P_1 V_1^\gamma = P_2 V_2^\gamma \tag{36}$$

or

$$PV_1^\gamma = \text{const} \tag{37}$$

On plots of P versus V, curves for adiabatic processes are steeper than are those for isothermal processes, as is indicated in Fig. 4-6. When a gas expands isothermally, heat is absorbed to make up for the work done by the gas. For an adiabatic expansion the work of expansion uses up the thermal energy of the gas. As a result the temperature falls, and the pressure change, for a given expansion, is greater than in the corresponding isothermal expansion.

4-13. Molecular Interpretation of the Internal Energy and Enthalpy. Two of the thermodynamic properties that have been introduced so far are the internal energy and the enthalpy. These are state functions; i.e., they are properties of the system. It should be possible, therefore, if our understanding of the detailed nature of the molecular world is sufficient, to calculate these properties. Such calculations are, in fact, possible but are difficult and rather unsatisfactory for other than ideal gases and even then are only for the thermal part of the internal energy and enthalpy. The behavior of liquids and all but the simplest solids is still too little understood to allow us to extend such calculations. In spite of these limitations, the calculation of thermodynamic properties for ideal-gas systems on the basis of the molecular model will lead to a better general appreciation of these quantities. It must be emphasized again,

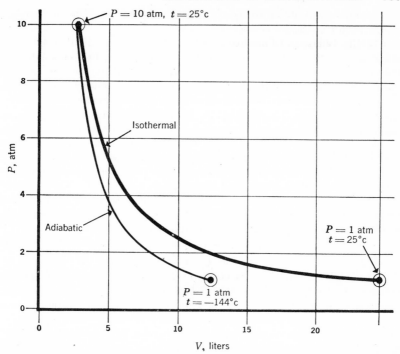

Fig. 4-6. Isothermal and adiabatic expansions of 1 mole of N_2 from 10 atm and 25°C to 1 atm. (For N_2 at 25°C, $\gamma = 1.40$.)

however, that the thermodynamic development does not require this molecular interpretation.

In the previous chapter, it was pointed out that in the molecular approach it is helpful to divide the energy of a molecule into two terms. The first of these terms represents the energy of the system for all molecules in their lowest allowed energy level. In anticipation of the introduction of the internal-energy property, this was denoted by E_0. The second term gives the thermal energy, denoted by $E - E_0$, which represents the thermal, or excitation, energy. For an ideal-gas system, the interpretation of E_0 and $E - E_0$ indicates that the sum of these two quantities is a complete description of the energy content of the system. The use of the symbols E_0 and $E - E_0$, the sum of which must be E, is, therefore, in keeping with the use of this symbol for the thermodynamic internal energy.

The enthalpy function can also be written for molecular interpretation. A subtraction of E_0 from each side of the defining equation for the enthalpy gives

$$H - E_0 = (E - E_0) + PV \tag{38}$$

For ideal gases, furthermore, this expression becomes

$$(H - E_0) = (E - E_0) + nRT$$

or

$$H = E_0 + (E - E_0) + nRT \tag{39}$$

The thermal contribution to the enthalpy can be calculated if the thermal-energy term $E - E_0$ can be obtained.

4-14. The Vibrational Contribution to $E - E_0$. The contributions of translation and rotation to the thermal energy of a molecule and the elimination of the electronic contribution were satisfactorily handled by the classical and qualitative treatments of the previous chapter. The vibrational contribution is the only one that need be worked out by a detailed application of Boltzmann's distribution. In order that the total thermal energy of a molecule, as outlined in Sec. 3-15, can be calculated, it is now necessary to obtain an expression for the thermal vibrational energy of an Avogadro's number of molecules distributed throughout a vibrational-energy-level scheme.

The Schrödinger-equation solution for a single vibrational mode of molecule shows that a set of equally spaced energy levels are allowed. The details of the solution will be treated in Chap. 10; it is now necessary only to investigate the pattern of the allowed vibrational energies. These energy levels are shown in Fig. 4-7 and are given by the expression

$$\epsilon_v = \epsilon(v + \tfrac{1}{2}) \tag{40}$$

where v is the vibrational quantum number and can have the values 0, 1, 2, 3, ... The quantity ϵ_v is the energy of the v level, and here ϵ is the spacing between the levels. The separation ϵ between the levels can frequently be determined, as will be shown in Chap. 10, by spectroscopic studies. For a diatomic molecule, only one such set of energy levels exists; while, for a polyatomic molecule with n atoms, there are $3n - 6$ (or $3n - 5$ for a linear molecule) such sets, each with its own value of ϵ.

We now find a formula for the average energy above that of the $v = 0$ level

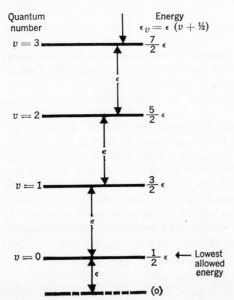

Fig. 4-7. The first four vibrational-energy levels of a vibrational degree of freedom.

for an Avogadro's number of molecules distributed over such a set of allowed vibrational energies.

The energies of the levels above that of the lowest level are given by

$$\epsilon_v - \epsilon_0 = (v)(\epsilon) \qquad v = 0, 1, 2, \ldots \tag{41}$$

Of a total of N molecules let n_0 be the number with $v = 0$, n_1 the number with $v = 1$, and so forth. Then

$$N = n_0 + n_1 + n_2 + \cdots \tag{42}$$

Boltzmann's-distribution law allows us to write

$$n_1 = n_0 e^{-\epsilon/kT}$$
$$n_2 = n_0 e^{-2\epsilon/kT} \tag{43}$$

and so forth. The notation is simplified by letting

$$x = \frac{\epsilon}{kT} \tag{44}$$

which leads to the expressions

$$N = n_0 + n_0 e^{-x} + n_0 e^{-2x} + \cdots$$
$$= n_0(1 + e^{-x} + e^{-2x} + \cdots) \tag{45}$$

This series, whose value will be needed later, can be summed by the trick of multiplying both sides by e^{-x} to give

$$N e^{-x} = n_0(e^{-x} + e^{-2x} + e^{-3x} + \cdots) \tag{46}$$

Subtraction of the last two equations, with term-by-term cancellation of the exponential series, gives

$$N(1 - e^{-x}) = n_0 \tag{47}$$

The total number of molecules is thereby related to the number in the lowest energy level and the energy-level spacing term $x = \epsilon/kT$.

The total vibrational energy of the N molecules can now be obtained by adding up the terms for the number of molecules in each level times the energy of that level. Thus

$$(E - E_0)_{\text{vib}} = n_1(\epsilon) + n_2(2\epsilon) + n_3(3\epsilon) + \cdots$$
$$= n_0\epsilon(e^{-x} + 2e^{-2x} + 3e^{-3x} + \cdots) \tag{48}$$

Again, the trick of multiplication by e^{-x} is effective and gives

$$(E - E_0)_{\text{vib}}e^{-x} = n_0\epsilon(e^{-2x} + 2e^{-3x} + 3e^{-4x} + \cdots) \tag{49}$$

Subtraction of the last two equations leads to

$$(E - E_0)_{\text{vib}}(1 - e^{-x}) = n_0\epsilon(e^{-x} + e^{-2x} + e^{-3x} + \cdots) \tag{50}$$

The value of the series is given by Eq. (46), and with that result we obtain

$$(E - E_0)_{\text{vib}}(1 - e^{-x}) = n_0\epsilon \frac{Ne^{-x}}{n_0}$$

or

$$(E - E_0)_{\text{vib}} = \frac{N\epsilon e^{-x}}{1 - e^{-x}} = \frac{N\epsilon}{e^x - 1}$$

and thus

$$(E - E_0)_{\text{vib}} = \frac{N\epsilon}{e^{\epsilon/kT} - 1} \tag{51}$$

This result gives the vibrational energy of an Avogadro's number of molecules for each vibrational degree of freedom. The vibrational-level spacing ϵ must be determined, usually spectroscopically, for each vibrational mode. If ϵ has the units of ergs per molecule, $N\epsilon$ will be in ergs per mole. Division by 4.184×10^7 will convert these units to the most frequently used units of calories per mole for $E - E_0$. The units of ϵ in the exponential term must, of course, correspond to the units of kT. Equation (51) is plotted in Fig. 4-8 for several temperatures so that the contribution for a vibrational degree of freedom at these temperatures can be readily determined for a given value of the vibrational-level spacing ϵ.

A typical value of the vibrational-energy spacing is 2×10^{-13} erg. For this value

$$N\epsilon = \frac{6.023 \times 10^{23}(2 \times 10^{-13})}{4.18 \times 10^7} = 2880 \text{ cal/mole} \tag{52}$$

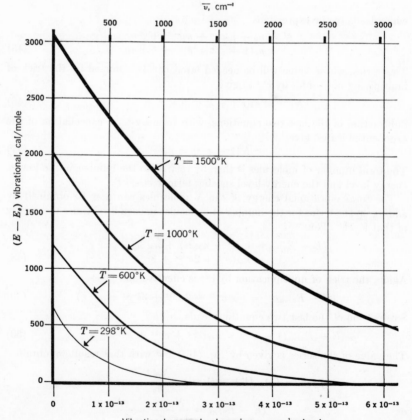

Fig. 4-8. The thermal vibrational energy of a vibrational mode as a function of the vibrational-energy-level spacing.

and at 25°C

$$x = \frac{\epsilon}{kT} \frac{2 \times 10^{-13}}{1.38 \times 10^{-16}(298)} = 5 \tag{53}$$

The average vibrational energy for this set of energy levels is

$$(E - E_0)_{\text{vib}} = \frac{2,880}{e^5 - 1} = 20 \text{ cal/mole} \tag{54}$$

Classically, where no quantum restrictions apply, an average kinetic energy of $\frac{1}{2}RT$ or about 300 cal/mole would be expected. A vibration, both a molecular one and one for ordinary-sized weights and springs, has both kinetic and potential energy. These energies, moreover, are generally equal, and, in this case, the total classical energy per degree of freedom would be

$$2(\tfrac{1}{2}RT) = 600 \text{ cal/mole}$$

at 25°C. The classical situation corresponds to small values of the energy-level spacing compared to kT. The limit of $(E - E_0)_{\text{vib}}$ given by Eq. (51) when $\epsilon \ll kT$ and the exponential in the denominator can be approximated by the first two terms $1 - \epsilon/kT$ of the exponential expansion is seen to be $NkT = RT$. This result agrees, therefore, with that deduced classically on the basis of $\frac{1}{2}RT$ kinetic and $\frac{1}{2}RT$ potential energy.

The difference between 600 cal/mole and the value obtained in Eq. (54) is attributable to the effect of the rather widely spaced vibrational quantum levels.

We are now in a position to perform a complete calculation of the thermal energies of simple ideal-gas molecules.

4-15. Calculation of the Internal-energy and Enthalpy Functions. A calculation of the functions $E - E_0$ and $H - E_0$ for NO_2 will illustrate the molecular approach to thermodynamic quantities. For this molecule, which will later be shown to be nonlinear, there will be 3 translational degrees of freedom, 3 rotational degrees, and $3n - 6 = 3$ vibrational degrees. A spectroscopic study shows that the three vibrational modes have energy-level schemes with spacings of 750, 1,323, and 1,616 cm^{-1}, or 1.49, 2.63, and 3.21×10^{-13} ergs per molecule.

The contributions to $E - E_0$ at 25°C are calculated as

Translational		$\frac{3}{2}RT =$	888 cal/mole
Rotational		$\frac{3}{2}RT =$	888 cal/mole
Vibrational			
$\epsilon = 1.49 \times 10^{-13}$	$x = 3.63$	$\dfrac{N\epsilon}{e^x - 1} =$	60 cal/mole
$\epsilon = 2.63$	$x = 6.40$	$\dfrac{N\epsilon}{e^x - 1} =$	7
$\epsilon = 3.21$	$x = 7.80$	$\dfrac{N\epsilon}{e^x - 1} =$	2
Electronic		$=$	0
		$E - E_0 =$	1845 cal/mole

$$(55)$$

The enthalpy function $H - E_0$ is obtained, by reference to Eq. (29), as

$$H - E_0 = (E - E_0) + RT$$
$$= 1,845 + 592$$
$$= 2437 \text{ cal/mole} \tag{56}$$

At first, it is perhaps more informative to write

$$E = E_0 + 1845 \text{ cal/mole}$$
$$H = E_0 + 2437 \text{ cal/mole} \tag{57}$$

In this form the breakdown of the internal energy and the enthalpy into a "zero-point" energy and a thermal-energy component is more apparent.

Table 4-3 shows values of $H - E_0$ for some other fairly simple molecules. For very light molecules some error is introduced by the classical treatment of the rotational contribution, and other methods have then been used to obtain the tabulated values. The calculated results, furthermore, apply only to ideal gases, and some of the compounds listed behave ideally only at fairly low pressures.

It was previously pointed out that for ideal gases the internal energy and enthalpy are functions only of the temperature. The present molecular interpretation of both these functions should further emphasize this aspect by the occurrence of the variable T and the absence of P and V in the calculations of this section.

Use of these functions for problems of chemical interest will be postponed until the following chapter. There the procedure for dealing with the E_0 term, which our molecular approach has introduced but failed to treat, will be developed.

4-16. Molecular Interpretation of C_v and C_p. Explicit formulas for the internal energy and enthalpy of ideal gases as a function of temperature, the quantity

Table 4-3. The Enthalpy Function $H - E_0$ at Various Temperatures
(The internal-energy function $E - E_0$ is obtained by subtracting RT from the tabulated values)

	$H - E_0$ (cal/mole)			
	298.16°K	600°K	1000°K	1500°K
H₂..................	2023.8	4,128.6	6,965.8	10,694.2
O₂..................	2069.8	4,279.2	7,497.0	11,776.4
CO..................	2072.6	4,209.5	7,256.5	11,358.8
CO₂..................	2238.1	5,322.4	10,222	17,004
H₂O..................	2367.7	4,882.2	8,608	13,848
CH₄..................	2397	5,549	11,560	21,130
Ethane..............	2856	8,016	18,280	34,500
Ethylene............	2525	6,732	14,760	27,100
Acetylene...........	2392	6,127	12,090	20,547
Benzene.............	3401	12,285	30,163	57,350

* National Bureau of Standards, "Tables of Selected Values of Chemical Thermodynamic Properties."

E_0 being temperature-independent, have been obtained in the preceding section. As shown by Eqs. (13) and (20), the heat capacities C_v and C_p can be obtained by differentiating these expressions with respect to temperature.

A vibrational mode contributes, according to the differentiation of Eq. (51), to the heat capacity by

$$C_{\text{vib}} = \frac{Rx^2e^x}{(e^x - 1)^2} \quad \text{where } x = \frac{\epsilon}{kT} \tag{58}$$

A graphical representation of the vibrational-heat-capacity contribution is shown in Fig. 4-9. Since, unlike the expression for $(E - E_0)_{\text{vib}}$, only x appears in the heat-capacity function, it is possible to plot the heat-capacity curve against $x = \epsilon/kT$ and have this single curve serve for all values of ϵ and T.

The contributions to the heat capacity C_v can now be listed as

Translation	$\frac{3}{2}R$
Rotation	$\frac{3}{2}R$ (or R for linear molecules)
Vibration ($x = \epsilon/kT$)	$\dfrac{Rx^2e^x}{(e^x - 1)^2}$
Electronic	0

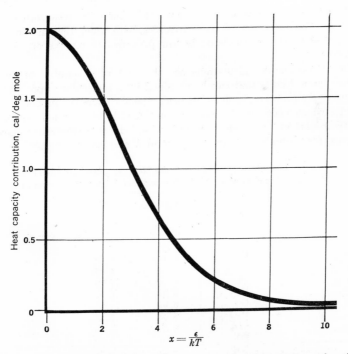

Fig. 4-9. The heat-capacity contribution from a vibrational mode as a function of $x = \epsilon/RT = h\nu/RT = 1.44\bar{\nu}/T$.

The constant-pressure heat capacity C_p, as shown in Sec. 4-10, is obtained for ideal gases from C_v by the expression [Eq. (22)]

$$C_p = C_v + R$$

Again, NO_2 vapor can be used as an example. The contributions to C_v are evaluated as

Translation $\qquad\qquad\qquad$ $\frac{3}{2}R = 2.98$
Rotation $\qquad\qquad\qquad\;\;$ $\frac{3}{2}R = 2.98$
Vibration

$\epsilon = 1.49 \times 10^{-13}$ $\qquad$ $x = 3.63$ $\qquad$ $\dfrac{Rx^2e^x}{(e^x - 1)^2} = 0.74$

$\epsilon = 2.63$ $\qquad\qquad\;\;$ $x = 6.40$ $\qquad$ $\dfrac{Rx^2e^x}{(e^x - 1)^2} = 0.14$

$\epsilon = 3.21$ $\qquad\qquad\;\;$ $x = 7.80$ $\qquad$ $\dfrac{Rx^2e^x}{(e^x - 1)^2} = 0.05$

Electronic $\qquad\qquad\qquad\qquad\qquad\qquad\qquad\;\; = 0$

$\qquad\qquad\qquad\qquad\qquad\qquad\qquad\qquad\;\; C_v = \overline{6.89}$ cal/deg mole

With this result,

$$C_p = C_v + R$$
$$= 6.89 + 1.99 = 8.88 \text{ cal/deg mole}$$

Table 4-4 shows the results for such calculations for some other simple molecules. The experimental heat capacities, with which they are compared, are measured values extrapolated to low pressures to remove any nonideal contribution.

These heat-capacity calculations are the first of a number of valuable thermodynamic results that can be obtained by a molecular approach. The calculation of a property, such as the heat capacity, from the properties of the molecules which make up the gas is a considerable feat. Such calculations, furthermore, are of very great practical value. Heat capacities at high temperatures, for example, are frequently needed and are not easily measured.

Table 4-4. Comparison of Constant-pressure Heat Capacities Calculated from Molecular Properties with Values Obtained from Thermal Measurements

Gas	C_p (cal/mole deg) at 25°C	
	Calculated	Observed
H_2	6.90	6.93
N_2	6.96	6.86
O_2	7.02	6.99
HCl	6.96	6.89
CO	6.97	6.90
H_2O	8.03	7.97
CO_2	8.89	8.90
SO_2	9.51	9.52
NH_3	8.52	8.47
CH_4	8.54	8.45

The molecular calculation, however, often provides a fairly easy way of obtaining otherwise inaccessible values of C_v and C_p.

The state of our knowledge of liquids and most solids is illustrated by the fact that calculations of heat capacities for these phases cannot yet be made. Gases which are not ideal likewise provide difficulties that are not easily surmounted.

Problems

1. Calculate the work that can be done by a mass of 400 g falling a distance of 275 cm. How much heat would be produced if this mass were allowed to fall freely this distance?

2. What is the heat of vaporization in calories per mole of benzene if 1.34 amp of current passing through an electrical heater of 50 ohms resistance for 5.62 min vaporizes 78.1 g of benzene?   *Ans.* 7250 cal/mole.

3. One mole of an ideal gas is allowed to expand against a piston that supports 0.4 atm pressure. The initial pressure is 10 atm, and the final pressure is 0.4 atm, the temperature being kept constant at 0°C.

(*a*) How much work is done by the gas during the expansion?

(*b*) What is the change in internal energy and in the enthalpy of the gas?

(*c*) How much heat is absorbed?

$\qquad$ *Ans.* (*a*) $w = +521$; (*b*) $\Delta E = \Delta H = 0$; (*c*) $q = +521$ cal.

4. One mole of an ideal gas is allowed to expand reversibly, i.e., against a confining pressure that is at all times infinitesimally less than the gas pressure, from an initial pressure of 10 atm to a final pressure of 0.4 atm, the temperature being kept constant at 0°C.

(*a*) How much work is done by the gas?

(*b*) What is the change in E and in H?

(*c*) How much heat is absorbed?

$\qquad$ *Ans.* (*a*) $w = 1,910$; (*b*) $\Delta E = \Delta H = 0$; (*c*) $q = +1,910$ cal.

5. A chemical reaction in a gas mixture at 500°C decreases the number of moles of gas, which can be assumed to behave ideally, by 0.347. If the internal-energy change is 5.70 kcal, what is the enthalpy change?

6. The densities of ice and water at 0°C are 0.9168 and .0.9998 g/cc, respectively. Calculate the difference between ΔH and ΔE of fusion for 1 mole under atmospheric pressure. The density of liquid water at 100°C is 0.9584 and of water vapor at 100°C and 1 atm is 0.000596 g/cc. Calculate the difference between ΔH and ΔE for the vaporization of water at atmospheric pressure.

7. A cylinder containing 1 mole of liquid water at 100°C is heated until the liquid is converted to vapor. The cylinder is fitted with a piston which just resists a pressure of 1 atm. How much work is done by the expanding gas? If the heat of vaporization of water is 9700 cal, what is the change in internal energy?

$\qquad$ *Ans.* $w = +730$; $\Delta H = +9,700$; $\Delta E = +8,970$ cal.

8. Three-tenths mole of CO is heated at a constant pressure of 10 atm from 0 to 250°C. The molar heat capacity of CO at constant pressure is $C_p = 6.420 + 1.665 \times 10^{-3}T - 1.96 \times 10^{-7}T^2$. If CO can be assumed to behave ideally, calculate w, q, ΔE, and ΔH for the process.

9. Calculate w, q, ΔE, and ΔH when 3.45 g of liquid CCl_4 is heated from 0 to 25°C at a pressure of 1 atm. The coefficient of thermal expansion of CCl_4 is 0.00118 per

degree centigrade, the density at 20°C is 1.595 g/cc, and the molar heat capacity of liquid CCl_4 is 30.8 cal/deg mole.

10. Calculate w, q, and ΔE when 1 mole of liquid water is compressed adiabatically from 1 atm and 0°C to 1,000 atm. The compressibility of water is $\beta = -(1/V_0)(\partial V/\partial P) = 40 \times 10^{-6}$ per atmosphere.

11. Hydrogen gas is expanded reversibly and adiabatically from a volume of 1.43 liters, at a pressure of 3 atm and temperature of 25°C, until the volume is 2.86 liters. The heat capacity C_p of hydrogen can be taken to be 6.90 cal/deg mole.

(a) Calculate the pressure and temperature of the gas, assumed to be ideal, after the expansion. *Ans.* 1.137 atm, 226°K.

(b) Calculate q, w, ΔE, and ΔH for the gas.

Ans. $q = 0$; $w = +62.0$; $\Delta E = -620$; $\Delta H = -87.1$ cal.

12. Calculate the thermal contribution $E - E_0$ to the internal energy of Br_2 at 100°C and at 1000°C. Assume ideal-gas behavior, and use the vibrational-energy-level separation of 324 cm^{-1}.

What is the thermal contribution $H - E_0$ to the enthalpy? Calculate the heat capacity at several temperatures, and compare with the empirical expression $C_p = 8.4228 + 0.9739 \times 10^{-3}T - 3.555 \times 10^{-7}T^2$ cal/mole deg, where T is the absolute temperature. *Ans.* $(H - E_0)_{100°C} = 2,970$; $(H - E_0)_{1000°C} = 10,940$ cal.

13. Using the thermal-energy data of Prob. 12 and assuming ideal-gas behavior, calculate ΔE, ΔH, w, and q when 1 mole of Br_2 is heated at a constant pressure of 1 atm from 100 to 1000°C. Repeat the calculation, using the empirical heat-capacity expression.

14. Using the data of Table 4-3, determine the difference in ΔH for the reaction at 1500°K and at 298°K for the reactions:

(a) $2CO + O_2 \rightarrow 2CO_2$

(b) $2H_2 + O_2 \rightarrow 2H_2O$

15. Verify several points on the curves of Figs. 4-8 and 4-9 ,using various numerical values for the vibration separations and temperatures.

16. Calculate the number of Br_2 molecules that are in the $v = 0$, $v = 1$, $v = 2$, and $v = 3$ energy levels when 1 mole of Br_2 is held at 100°C. The vibrational-energy-level spacing is 324 cm^{-1}.

Calculate at this temperature the vibrational contribution to $E - E_0$ of the molecules in the $v = 1$, in the $v = 2$, and in the $v = 3$ levels. Compare the sum of these contributions with the total thermal vibrational energy obtained in Prob. 12.

Ans. $(E - E_0)_{vib} = 347$ cal (and 373 cal from Prob. 12).

17. The value of γ for CH_4 is 1.31, and near room temperature and at pressures less than about 1 atm the gas behaves ideally. An adiabatic and reversible expansion is performed which reduces the pressure of a CH_4 sample, initially at 100°C and with volume 3 liters, from 1 to 0.1 atm.

(a) What are the final temperature and volume of the gas?

(b) How much work is done by the gas?

(c) What is the difference between ΔH and ΔE for the process?

18. Compare the limits, at ϵ equal to zero, of the energy curves of Fig. 4-8 with the values that would be expected if a vibrational mode behaved classically.

19. Obtain the expression for the heat-capacity contribution of a vibrational degree of freedom given in Eq. (58) by differentiating the thermal vibrational energy [Eq. (51)] with respect to temperature.

Verify that the limit of C_{vib} as x goes to zero, i.e., for small ϵ or high T, is the value that would be expected classically.

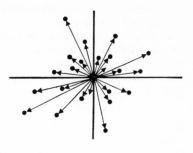

5

Thermochemistry

The specific application of the first law of thermodynamics to the study of chemical reactions is referred to as *thermochemistry*. Thermochemistry deals with the measurement or calculation of the heat absorbed or given out in chemical reactions. The subject has therefore great immediate practical importance. Thermochemistry also provides the data from which the relative energy or enthalpy contents of chemical compounds can be deduced. This aspect implies that thermochemistry is basic to the study of chemical bonding, and, as we shall see, it also provides data necessary for the thermodynamic study of chemical equilibria.

5-1. Measurements of Heats of Reaction. It will make some of the approaches used in thermochemistry more understandable if some of the methods and the scope of the more common experimental techniques are first considered.

Only a very few of the many possible chemical reactions are such that their heat of reaction can be accurately determined. To be suitable for a precise calorimetric study, a reaction must be fast, complete, and clean. A fast reaction is required so that the heat of the reaction will be given out or absorbed in a short period of time. It is then easier to prevent heat from flowing away from the reaction system or into it from the surroundings while the measurement of the temperature change of the system is being made. The completeness of the reaction is required so that difficult corrections for unreacted material need not be made. Finally, a clean reaction implies one that goes completely to a given set of products with no complicating side reactions. These stipulations are rather severe and rule out all but a few types of reactions.

In the field of organic chemistry the combustion reactions are of outstanding suitability. The burning of a compound containing only carbon, hydrogen, and oxygen usually leads to the nice formation of the sole products CO_2 and H_2O. For organic compounds containing other elements the products are not always so well defined, but combustion reactions are frequently practical.

113

Most of the available thermochemical data for organic compounds come from combustion experiments.

The heat of combustion is usually determined in a "bomb calorimeter." Figure 5-1 shows an apparatus used at the National Bureau of Standards. A weighed sample is placed in the cup within the reaction chamber, or bomb, and the bomb is then filled with oxygen under a pressure of about 20 atm. A fine wire dipping into the sample is heated by an electrical current to start the reaction. Once started, the reaction proceeds rapidly with the evolution of a large amount of heat. This heat is determined by the temperature rise of the water around the calorimeter. It is customary to calibrate the apparatus by the measurement of the temperature rise resulting from the combustion of a sample with a known heat of combustion. The bomb and water chamber are carefully insulated from the surroundings so that as little heat as possible is lost. Such an arrangement where the reaction chamber is insulated so that no heat can flow into or out of it is called an *adiabatic* calorimeter.

Heats of combustion are usually very large, of the order of hundreds of kilocalories per mole, and with careful work these can be measured with an accuracy of better than 0.01 per cent. A disadvantage of the use of heats of combustion is that, if one is interested in the difference in energy contents of two compounds, one must make use of the small difference between two large numbers.

Table 5-1 shows some heats of combustion of a number of organic compounds.

A second important type of reaction that is occasionally suitable for organic compounds is hydrogenation. Unsaturated materials, such as those with a carbon-carbon double bond or triple bond, can sometimes be made to pick up hydrogen in a reaction that is suitable for calorimetric study. This reaction gives out less heat than oxidation reactions and is, therefore, more useful in giving information on small energy differences between compounds. This technique has been developed primarily by G. B. Kistiakowsky at Harvard.

The heats of inorganic reactions, in aqueous solution, for instance, can frequently be measured in a calorimeter that is essentially an isolated container

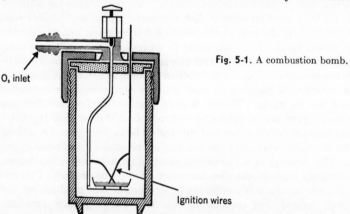

Fig. 5-1. A combustion bomb.

O₂ inlet

Ignition wires

Table 5-1. Heats of Combustion ΔH at 25°C
[In kcal.   The products are $CO_2(g)$ and $H_2O(l)$]

$H_2(g)$..................	$-$ 68.317
C(graphite).............	$-$ 94.052
CO(g)..................	$-$ 67.636
$CH_4(g)$................	$-$ 212.80
$C_2H_6(g)$..............	$-$ 372.82
$C_3H_8(g)$..............	$-$ 530.61
n-Butane(g)...........	$-$ 687.98
i-Butane(g)............	$-$ 686.34
n-Heptane(g)..........	$-$1149.9
Ethylene(g)............	$-$ 337.23
Acetylene(g)...........	$-$ 310.62
Benzene(g).............	$-$ 789.08
Ethanol(l)..............	$-$ 326.71
Acetic acid(l)..........	$-$ 208.5

open to the atmosphere.   Heats of neutralization, solution, and complex formation can be so studied.   The same stringent requirements, as previously mentioned, still apply, of course, if accurate results are to be obtained.

5-2. Internal-energy and Enthalpy Changes in Chemical Reactions.   Thermochemistry deals with the particular process of a chemical reaction.   If such reactions are represented as

$$\text{Reactants} \rightarrow \text{products} \tag{1}$$

the internal-energy change and enthalpy change for the process are related to the energy and enthalpy contents of the reactants and products by

$$\Delta E = E_{\text{products}} - E_{\text{reactants}} \tag{2}$$

and
$$\Delta H = H_{\text{products}} - H_{\text{reactants}} \tag{3}$$

For example, the enthalpy change H for the reaction

$$C + \tfrac{1}{2}O_2 \rightarrow CO \tag{4}$$

gives the enthalpy of 1 mole of CO compared with 1 mole of C plus $\frac{1}{2}$ mole of O_2; that is,

$$\Delta H = H_{CO_2} - H_C - \tfrac{1}{2}H_{O_2} \tag{5}$$

When chemical reactions are dealt with, the Δ notation, which previously signified any change, means the difference of some property for the products and the reactants.

If heat is absorbed in the reaction and the products contain more energy than the reactants, ΔE, if the process is at constant volume, and ΔH, if the process is at constant pressure, are positive; that is, H and E increase as a result of the reaction.   Such reactions are called *endothermic*.   Reactions for which ΔE and ΔH are negative proceed with a decrease in E and H.   Heat is therefore given out and the reaction is said to be *exothermic*.

To summarize:

ΔH or ΔE	positive	heat absorbed	endothermic
ΔH or ΔE	negative	heat given out	exothermic

The combustion experiments previously mentioned are, for example, all exothermic, and therefore for these reactions ΔH and ΔE are negative.

Toward the end of the last century a large number of heats of reaction were determined, principally by J. Thomson and M. Berthelot. It was their hope that such data would explain the tendency of reactions to occur. In comparison with ordinary mechanical systems they were led to expect that the energy or heat given off in a reaction was a measure of the "affinity" of the reagents.

It is true that in general the reactions that proceed rapidly and completely are those, like the combustion reaction, that give out a large amount of heat. The principle that the heat of reaction is a measure of the driving force of the reaction, as Thomson and Berthelot assumed, is, however, incorrect. Reactions that are endothermic do occur and are not at all unusual. It is apparent that this simple energy criterion is not adequate to provide a thermodynamic explanation of the tendency of reactions to occur. In the following chapter we shall meet the other factor that must be considered.

5-3. Relation between ΔE and ΔH. A measurement of a heat of reaction usually gives directly either the internal-energy change or the enthalpy change. Either datum can, however, be used to calculate the other. If the reaction is performed in a constant-volume apparatus, such as the bomb calorimeter, no work of expansion is performed and the heat of the reaction is equal to the internal-energy change. If a constant-pressure system is used, the heat of the reaction, as was pointed out in Sec. 4-10, is equal to the enthalpy change.

The difference between ΔH and ΔE for a reaction depends on the volume change that occurs when the reaction is performed at constant pressure and on this pressure. If both the reactants and products are composed only of solids and liquids, the change in volume for a reaction will be quite small. Since 1 mole of a typical simple compound is likely to have a volume of no more than 100 cc, it is unlikely that a reaction would cause a volume change of more than about 10 cc. At ordinary pressures the PV term corresponding to this volume change is only

$$\Delta(PV) = P \, \Delta V = (1)(10) = 10 \text{ cc/atm} = 0.2 \text{ cal}$$

The enthalpy change would be greater or less than the internal-energy change by this amount. A fraction of a calorie is, however, invariably negligible compared with the experimental error of a measured heat of reaction.

If gases are involved in the reaction, an appreciable value of $\Delta(PV)$ can occur and ΔH and ΔE will be significantly different. Suppose that the reaction produces a net amount of Δn moles of gas. To the accuracy of the ideal-gas laws and neglecting the volumes of liquids and solids, the PV term will be greater for the products than for the reactants by an amount

$$\Delta(PV) = \Delta(nRT) = RT \, \Delta n \tag{6}$$

The enthalpy change for the reaction will therefore be greater than the internal-energy change by $RT \, \Delta n$, or, for the reaction,

$$\Delta H = \Delta E + RT \, \Delta n \tag{7}$$

If there are more moles of gas in the reactants than in the products, Δn will, of course, be negative and ΔH will be less than ΔE.

Consider, as an example, the reaction

$$2C(s) + O_2(g) \rightarrow 2CO(g) \tag{8}$$

where s stands for solid and g for gas. A bomb-calorimetric study gives the heat of this reaction, i.e., the combustion of 2 moles of graphite, as 53,412 cal given out. Since this is a constant-volume experiment, we have immediately

$$\Delta E = -53,412 \text{ cal} \tag{9}$$

The product contains 2 moles of gas, and the reactants contain 1 mole. The value of Δn is $+1$, and at 25°C the enthalpy change is calculated as

$$\begin{aligned} \Delta H &= \Delta E + RT \, \Delta n \\ &= -53,412 + (1.987)(298) \\ &= -53,412 + 592 = -52,830 \text{ cal} \end{aligned} \tag{10}$$

It has now been pointed out that the heats of some reactions can be measured and that ΔE and ΔH for these reactions can be calculated.

5-4. Thermochemical Equations. An elaboration of the usual form in which chemical-reaction equations are usually written is sometimes advisable in thermochemical work.

Since the heat of a reaction depends on whether a reagent is solid, liquid, or gas, it is necessary to specify the state of the reagents. This is usually done by adding s, l, or g after the compound. Occasionally a more careful description is necessary. When carbon is involved in a reaction, for instance, it is necessary to state whether it is graphite or diamond. One must be specially careful with water, which can quite reasonably be involved as a gas or a liquid, and with carbon, which can be involved as diamond or graphite.

Another characteristic of thermochemical equations is the appearance of fractional numbers of moles of some of the reactants or products. If one is interested in the heat of a reaction which produces 1 mole of water, for instance, one would write the reaction and the enthalpy change for the reaction

$$H_2(g) + \tfrac{1}{2}O_2(g) \to H_2O(l) \qquad \Delta H = -68,317 \text{ cal} \tag{11}$$

The reaction written with integers corresponds to the formation of 2 moles of water, and one would then have twice as much heat evolved. Such a reaction would be written as

$$2H_2(g) + O_2(g) \to 2H_2O(l) \qquad \Delta H = -136,634 \text{ cal} \tag{12}$$

Similarly, the combustion reaction is usually written so that the heat of combustion of 1 mole of material is explicitly shown. For the combustion of benzene one would usually write

$$C_6H_6(g) + \tfrac{15}{2}O_2(g) \to 6CO_2(g) + 3H_2O(l) \qquad \Delta H = -789,083 \text{ cal} \tag{13}$$

One additional comment is necessary. Unless the information is otherwise given, it is convenient to indicate the temperature and pressure at which the reported enthalpy applies. A superscript degree sign indicates that the pressure is 1 atm, a usual reference or standard state. (This superscript, meaning standard state, must be distinguished from the previously used subscript zero, meaning the lowest energy-level quantity.) The temperature is indicated by a subscript giving the absolute temperature. The equation for the formation of water would then be

$$H_2(g) + \tfrac{1}{2}O_2(g) \to H_2O(l) \qquad \Delta H^\circ_{298} = -68,317 \text{ cal} \tag{14}$$

5-5. Indirect Determination of Heats of Reaction. Many reactions whose enthalpy change would be of interest are not suitable for direct calorimetric study.   Fortunately the internal-energy or enthalpy changes of such reactions can often be obtained by an indirect method.   This was originally suggested by Hess in 1840 and is often known as *Hess's law of heat summation*.   We shall see, however, that it is merely an application of the first law of thermodynamics.

The determination of the enthalpy change when carbon is converted from graphite to diamond, i.e.,

$$C(graphite) \rightarrow C(diamond) \qquad \Delta H = ? \tag{15}$$

will illustrate the method.   Although this reaction can be made to occur, it is certainly very unsuitable for any direct calorimetric study.

The combustion of both graphite and diamond can be conveniently studied, and these reactions and the heats of combustion are

$$C(graphite) + O_2(g) \rightarrow CO_2(g) \qquad \Delta H^{\circ}_{298} = -94,030 \text{ cal} \tag{16}$$
$$C(diamond) + O_2(g) \rightarrow CO_2(g) \qquad \Delta H^{\circ}_{298} = -94,480 \text{ cal} \tag{17}$$

The enthalpy changes of these reactions are clearly different as a result of the different enthalpies of graphite and diamond.   Analytically this can be written as

$$-94,030 = H_{CO_2} - H_{C(graphite)} - H_{O_2} \tag{18}$$
$$-94,480 = H_{CO_2} - H_{C(diamond)} - H_{O_2} \tag{19}$$

Subtraction of these algebraic equations with cancellation of the enthalpies of CO_2 and O_2 gives, on rearrangement,

$$H_{C(diamond)} - H_{C(graphite)} = -94,030 + 94,480$$
$$= +450 \text{ cal} \tag{20}$$

The result of $+450$ cal is the enthalpy change of the original graphite to diamond reaction.

It is important to notice that this same result could have been obtained by subtracting the two combustion-reaction equations [Eqs. (16) and (17)] as though they were algebraic equations.   Canceling the O_2 and CO_2 terms and moving the C(diamond) term to the right side with a change of sign gives

$$C(graphite) \rightarrow C(diamond) \qquad \Delta H = -94,030 - (-94,480)$$
$$= +450 \text{ cal} \tag{21}$$

This treatment of the reaction equation is always possible and saves writing out the heat contents of each of the species before the subtraction is made.

Combining reactions by either of these methods is equivalent to calculating ΔH for the desired reaction by an indirect but experimentally more feasible path.   The previous example can be illustrated as

$$CO_2$$
$$\Delta H = -94,030 \nearrow \qquad \searrow \Delta H = +94,480$$
$$C(graphite) + O_2 \rightarrow C(diamond) + O_2$$

The fact that the enthalpy is a thermodynamic property requires ΔH to be the same by the indirect path, that is, $-94,030 + 94,480 = +450$, as by the direct path.   It is this fact which allows the previous reaction subtractions to be performed.

One additional example can be given.   The heat of the reaction by which a compound is formed from its elements is, as we shall see, of special interest.   In few cases can such reactions be directly studied.   Consider, for example, the formation of methane according to the equation

$$C(graphite) + 2H_2(g) \rightarrow CH_4(g) \tag{22}$$

Again combustion reactions can be used and give

(a)	$CH_4(g) + 2O_2(g) \rightarrow CO_2(g) + 2H_2O(l)$	$\Delta H^\circ_{298} = -212,800$
(b)	$H_2(g) + \frac{1}{2}O_2(g) \rightarrow H_2O(l)$	$\Delta H^\circ_{298} = -68,317$
(c)	$C(graphite) + O_2(g) \rightarrow CO_2(g)$	$\Delta H^\circ_{298} = -94,050$
$-(a) + 2(b) + (c)$	$C(graphite) + 2H_2(g) \rightarrow CH_4(g)$	$\Delta H^\circ_{298} = -17,884$ cal

5-6. Standard Heats of Formation.   Methods for obtaining, either directly or indirectly, the enthalpies of many reactions have been given.   Although it is not at all practical to compile a table of all the reactions for which such data are available, it would be feasible to tabulate information for each of the compounds for which thermal data have been obtained.   The *standard heats of formation* provide a means of making such a table.   Furthermore, from these data it is possible to work out the heats of any reactions involving the listed compounds.

The enthalpy of an element or compound is meaningful only when it is compared with some reference or standard state.   Methods have been given, it should be recognized, for obtaining only enthalpy *differences*.   If, for the moment, we consider only the elements, we are at liberty to choose some state for each element and to calculate the enthalpy of that element in terms of that state.   It is customary to take this *reference or standard state as that of 1 atm pressure and 25°C with the element in the physical state and stable form under these conditions*.   The enthalpy of the elements in the standard state is arbitrarily given the value zero.   Thus the standard enthalpy of H_2 at 1 atm and 25°C is zero.   At higher temperatures the enthalpy, referred to the zero value at 1 atm and 25°C, will be some positive quantity; at lower temperatures it will be some negative quantity.   Enthalpies based on this reference state are called *standard enthalpies*.   The assignment of the arbitrary value of zero for the standard enthalpy at 1 atm and 25°C to all elements is allowed because no chemical reaction converts one element into another.

Once reference enthalpies are assigned to the elements it is possible to determine standard enthalpies for compounds.   These enthalpies are usually called *standard heats of formation*.   Consider, for example, the reaction

$$C(graphite) + O_2(g) \rightarrow CO_2(g) \qquad \Delta H^\circ_{298} = -94,030 \tag{23}$$

The enthalpy change for the reaction is equal to the standard enthalpy of CO_2 less the standard enthalpies of C and O_2.   Since the latter are elements in their standard state, their standard enthalpies are zero.   The standard enthalpy, or standard heat of formation, of CO_2 must therefore be $-94,030$.   The enthalpy of the reaction by which the compound is formed from its elements is seen to be equal to the standard heat of formation of the compound.   As a result of this, one uses the symbol ΔH°_f for this standard heat of formation.

By combining reactions one can frequently deduce the enthalpy of formation

Table 5-2. Standard Heats of Formation [with C(graphite) as the Standard State for Carbon]
(Kcal/mole)

Substance	$(\Delta H_f^\circ)_{298.15^\circ K}$	Substance	$(\Delta H_f^\circ)_{298.15^\circ K}$
C(graphite)	0	$H_2O(g)$	-57.789
C(diamond)	0.453	$H_2O(l)$	-68.317
CO	-26.416	$NH_3(g)$	-11.04
CO_2	-94.052	HF	-64.2
CH_4	-17.889	HCl	-22.06
C_2H_2	54.194	HBr	-8.66
C_2H_4	12.496	HI	6.20
C_2H_6	-20.236	NO_2	8.091
C_3H_8	-24.820	S(rhombic)	0
n-Pentane(g)	-35.00	S(monoclinic)	0.071
n-Pentane(l)	-41.36	$S(g)$	53.25
Neopentane, $(CH_3)_4C(g)$	-39.67	SO_2	-70.96
Benzene	19.820	SO_3	-94.45
Toluene	11.950	H_2S	-4.815
Ethanol(l)	-66.356	NaCl(s)	-98.321

of a compound from its elements, as was illustrated for CH_4. Furthermore, when the standard enthalpies of some compounds have been determined, they can be used in the working out of the standard enthalpies of other compounds. Table 5-2 shows standard heats of formation of some simpler molecules. Such a table of enthalpies can be used to determine the enthalpy for any reaction, at 1 atm and 25°C, involving the elements and any of the compounds appearing in the table.

The heat of hydrogenation of ethylene can be calculated as an illustration. One writes

$$H_2C{=}CH_2(g) + H_2(g) \rightarrow CH_3CH_3(g)$$

at 25°C $\Delta H_f^\circ = 12{,}496$ $\Delta H_f^\circ = 0$ $\Delta H_f^\circ = -20{,}236$ (24)

The enthalpy of the reaction is the difference in enthalpy of the products and the reactants. Thus

$$\Delta H_{298}^\circ = \Delta H_f^\circ(CH_3CH_3) - \Delta H_f^\circ(H_2) - \Delta H_f^\circ(H_2CCH_2)$$
$$= -20{,}236 - 0 - 12{,}496$$
$$= -32{,}732 \text{ cal} \tag{25}$$

The calculated enthalpy for the reaction has, of course, no necessary connection with the assignment of zero enthalpy to the elements in their standard states. It is the enthalpy change occurring when 1 mole of ethylene is hydrogenated.

A table of standard heats of formation is a very convenient way of presenting thermochemical data. Enthalpies of reactions can be calculated as needed from such data.

5-7. Temperature Dependence of Heats of Reaction.
The enthalpies of reactions calculated from a table of standard heats of formation apply to a temperature of 25°C. For these data to be of appreciable value, a means for determining the heats of reactions at other temperatures must be available. This can be done by writing the enthalpy of the reaction as

$$\Delta H = H_{\text{products}} - H_{\text{reactants}} \tag{26}$$

and differentiating with respect to temperature to get

$$\left(\frac{\partial \Delta H}{\partial T}\right)_p = \left(\frac{\partial H_{\text{products}}}{\partial T}\right)_p - \left(\frac{\partial H_{\text{reactants}}}{\partial T}\right)_p \tag{27}$$

The change in enthalpy with respect to temperature at constant pressure was shown in Sec. 4-10 to be the heat capacity at constant pressure, so that we can write

$$\left(\frac{\partial \Delta H}{\partial T}\right)_p = (C_p)_{\text{products}} - (C_p)_{\text{reactants}} = \Delta C_p \tag{28}$$

and, in a similar manner,

$$\left(\frac{\partial \Delta E}{\partial T}\right)_V = \Delta C_v \tag{29}$$

It is necessary, therefore, to know only the difference in the heat capacities of the products and the reactants in order to determine how the enthalpy of a reaction changes with temperature. For small ranges of temperature ΔC_p can be taken as constant, and integration gives

$$\Delta H_2 - \Delta H_1 = \Delta C_p(T_2 - T_1) \tag{30}$$

A diagrammatic derivation of this result is perhaps more revealing. Consider a constant-pressure reaction that proceeds with an enthalpy change ΔH_1 at temperature T_1 and an enthalpy change ΔH_2 at temperature T_2, as in Fig. 5-2. If the reactants are heated from T_1 to T_2, the heat absorbed, or enthalpy

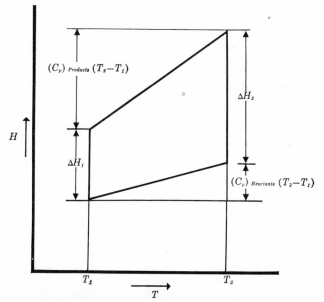

Fig. 5-2. The temperature dependence of the heat of reaction (assuming that C_p of products and reactants are independent of T in the temperature interval T_1 to T_2).

change, would be $(C_p)_{\text{reactants}}(T_2 - T_1)$. If the products are similarly heated, the enthalpy change would be $(C_p)_{\text{products}}(T_2 - T_1)$. Now one can equate the enthalpy involved in going from state a to state b of Fig. 5-2 by the two different paths to get,

$$\Delta H_1 + (C_p)_{\text{products}}(T_2 - T_1) = \Delta H_2 + (C_p)_{\text{reactants}}(T_2 - T_1)$$

or
$$\Delta H_2 - \Delta H_1 = \Delta C_p(T_2 - T_1) \qquad (31)$$

as previously obtained.

If heats of reaction over a wide range of temperatures are needed, it is necessary to take into account the dependence of the heat capacities themselves on temperature. Experimental heat capacities are usually expressed by an empirical relation such as

$$C_p = a + bT + cT^2 + \cdots \qquad (32)$$

and values of a, b, and c are given, as is done in Table 5-3. If each of the C_p's of the products and the reactants are so written, one can see that ΔC_p will have the same form as that shown for C_p. The previous differential equation, which corresponds to the integral form

$$\Delta H_{T_2} - \Delta H_{T_1} = \int_{T_1}^{T_2} \Delta C_p \, dt \qquad (33)$$

can then be integrated. If all the reagents behave as ideal gases and are not very large molecules, it is often possible to calculate the heat capacities of each reagent from molecular properties, as was indicated in Sec. 4-16.

5-8. Heats of Reaction and the Molecular Model. It has been shown in the previous chapter that the enthalpy of a compound can be treated as being composed of a temperature-independent part called E_0 and a temperature-dependent part $H - E_0$. The former depends on the zero-point energy and reflects the strength of the chemical binding in the compound, while the latter measures the thermal excitation of the compound. This more detailed understanding of molecular energies is now carried over to chemical reactions.

If the molecules involved are not too complex, it is possible to calculate

Table 5-3. Heat Capacities at Constant Pressure of Some Gases
(According to the Expression $C_p = a + bT + cT^2$)
(Valid for the temperature range 300 to 1500°K)

Substance	a	b	c
H₂.............	6.9469	-0.1999×10^{-3}	4.808×10^{-7}
O₂.............	6.148	3.102	$-\ 9.23$
N₂.............	6.524	1.250	$-\ 0.01$
Cl₂............	7.5755	2.4244	$-\ 9.650$
CO............	6.420	1.665	$-\ 1.96$
CO₂...........	6.214	10.396	$-\ 35.45$
H₂O...........	7.256	2.298	2.83
NH₃...........	6.189	7.887	$-\ 7.28$
CH₄...........	3.381	18.044	$-\ 43.00$
C₂H₆...........	2.247	38.201	-110.49
C₂H₄...........	2.830	28.601	$-\ 87.26$
Benzene........	-0.409	77.621	-264.29

$H - E_0$ for each of the product molecules and each of the reactant molecules. The difference $\Delta(H - E_0)$ can then be formed. The enthalpy difference for the reaction depends on this term through the relation

$$\Delta H = \Delta E_0 + \Delta H - \Delta E_0$$

or
$$\Delta H = \Delta E_0 + \Delta(H - E_0) \tag{34}$$

If the $H - E_0$ terms can be calculated and if a heat of reaction ΔH is known at some temperature, the zero-point-energy difference ΔE_0 can be calculated. This term gives the energy change for the reaction when all reactants and products are in the lowest energy levels.

If we are interested in the reagents in their standard state of 1 atm pressure, the enthalpy of the reaction can be written as

$$\Delta H° = \Delta E_0° + \Delta(H° - E_0°) \tag{35}$$

For ideal gases the pressure has no effect on the enthalpy or energy, and this designation of the standard state does not affect any of the terms. The table of standard enthalpies can be used directly for ideal gases to determine the ΔH term of Eq. (34), which is identical to the $\Delta H°$ term of Eq. (35).

An immediate practical use of this splitting up of ΔH is the determination of values of ΔH for temperatures other than those at which measured C_p's are available. The thermal term $\Delta(H - E_0)$ can be calculated at any temperature, and once ΔE_0, the temperature-independent term, is known, the value of ΔH can be obtained at any temperature.

A molecular interpretation of the heat of the reaction

$$N_2(g) + 2O_2(g) \rightarrow 2NO_2(g) \tag{36}$$

can be given as an illustration. The thermal contributions to the enthalpy of the three species, assumed to behave as ideal gases, can be calculated as illustrated previously for NO_2. The terms of these calculations are shown in Table 5-4. From these data one obtains

$$\Delta(H - E_0)_{298} = 2(H - E_0)_{NO_2} - 2(H - E_0)_{O_2} - (H - E_0)_{N_2}$$
$$= (2)(2438) - (2)(2072) - 2070$$
$$= 4876 - 4144 - 2070 = -1338 \text{ cal} \tag{37}$$

The heat of the reaction at 298°K can be calculated from the standard heats of formation listed in Table 5-2. These give

$$\Delta H_{298} = 2\,\Delta H_f(NO_2) - \Delta H_f(N_2) - 2\,\Delta H_f(O_2)$$
$$= (2)(8091) - 0 - (2)(0)$$
$$= 16{,}182 \text{ cal} \tag{38}$$

The results of Eqs. (37) and (38) can be inserted into a rearranged form of Eq. (34) to give

$$\Delta E_0 = \Delta H_{298} - \Delta(H - E_0)_{298}$$
$$= 16{,}182 - (-1338)$$
$$= +17{,}520 \text{ cal} \tag{39}$$

In this way, the energy change that would occur when the reagents in their lowest allowed energy state reacted to form the product molecules, also in their lowest energy state, is obtained. One can now write

$$\Delta H = 17{,}520 + \Delta(H - E_0) \tag{40}$$

where ΔH is the enthalpy change of the reaction at the same temperature and $\Delta(H - E_0)$ is the calculable thermal-enthalpy term at that temperature. With Eq. (40) it is a relatively simple matter to calculate the heat of reaction for the formation of NO_2 at some new and even experimentally difficult temperature. The terms for the N_2 oxidation reaction at 1500°K, for example, are also given in Table 5-4 and yield

$$\Delta(H - E_0)_{1,500} = (2)(16,690) - (2)(11,700) - 11,210$$
$$= -1230 \text{ cal} \tag{41}$$

with which we obtain

$$\Delta H_{1500°} = +17,520 - 1230$$
$$= +16,290 \text{ cal} \tag{42}$$

It is clear that the heat of the reaction can be calculated by this method at any temperature for which the thermal-energy terms $H - E_0$ can be calculated. At high temperatures, usually above 1500°K, it is necessary also to take into account electronic excitation; i.e., electronic energy states other than the ground state become appreciably populated.

Calculations such as this can give the heats of reactions at any temperature if a single heat of reaction is known. Great use of this approach has been made, particularly in the field of hydrocarbon reactions. Predictions of the heats of rearrangements, of combustion, and so forth, of petroleum-fraction molecules can be made at temperatures at which actual measurements would be very difficult. This type of calculation, based on our knowledge of the energies of molecules, can be extended, as we shall see, to give important information on the equilibrium of reacting molecules.

5-9. Bond Energies. So far our thermochemical study has been concerned with the practically important matter of the heats of reactions. In addition to being useful for their own sakes, these results are necessary for further thermodynamic treatments. Thermochemical data are also important in helping us to understand the nature of the bonds that hold atoms together in molecules.

The previous section suggests that use should be made of ΔE_0 values, which are uncomplicated by thermal energies, for the study of chemical-bond energies. At 25°C, however, the thermal-excitation term is relatively quite small. It is, therefore, customary to make use of the more available enthalpies of reactions at 25°C.

Chemists usually focus their attention on the bonds that join together the atoms in a molecule. The energy of a molecule can be attributed primarily to the energies of these chemical bonds. It is a great help in understanding some aspects of chemical reactions and compounds to have some idea of the strengths, i.e., the energies, of the chemical bonds.

For diatomic molecules the bond energy is easily defined and frequently directly measurable. For a molecule AB the bond energy is defined as the energy required to break the molecule into two atoms A and B. The process by which a bond or molecule is ruptured into fragments is called *dissociation*.

Table 5-4. The Thermal Contributions $H - E_0$ to the Enthalpy of the Ideal-gas Systems N_2, O_2, and NO_2
(Cal/mole)

	N_2		O_2		NO_2	
298°K:						
Translation..............	$\frac{3}{2}RT =$	890	$\frac{3}{2}RT =$	890	$\frac{3}{2}RT =$	890
Rotation................	$\frac{2}{2}RT =$	590	$\frac{2}{2}RT =$	590	$\frac{3}{2}RT =$	890
Vibration...............	$(\nu = 2,360 \text{ cm}^{-1})$	0	$(\nu = 1,580 \text{ cm}^{-1})$	2	$(\nu = 750 \text{ cm}^{-1})$	60
					$(\nu = 1,323 \text{ cm}^{-1})$	6
					$(\nu = 1,616 \text{ cm}^{-1})$	2
PV term...............	$RT =$	590	$RT =$	590	$RT =$	590
$(H - E_0)_{298}$.........		2070 cal		2072 cal		2438 cal
1500°K:						
Translation..............	$\frac{3}{2}RT =$	4,470	$\frac{3}{2}RT =$	4,470	$\frac{3}{2}RT =$	4,470
Rotation................	$\frac{2}{2}RT =$	2,980	$\frac{2}{2}RT =$	2,980	$\frac{3}{2}RT =$	4,470
Vibration...............	$(\nu = 2,360 \text{ cm}^{-1})$	780	$(\nu = 1,580 \text{ cm}^{-1})$	1,270	$(\nu = 750 \text{ cm}^{-1})$	2,030
					$(\nu = 1,323 \text{ cm}^{-1})$	1,480
					$(\nu = 1,616 \text{ cm}^{-1})$	1,260
PV term...............	$RT =$	2,980	$RT =$	2,980	$RT =$	2,980
$(H - E_0)_{1,500}$.......		11,210 cal		11,700 cal		16,690 cal

Table 5-5. Bond Energies*
(Kcal/mole)

Diatomic molecules

H—H	104	Br—Br	45
H—F	135	I—I	36
H—Cl	102	Li—Li	26
H—Br	87	Na—Na	18
H—I	71	Na—Cl	98
F—F	41	O_2	117
Cl—Cl	57	N_2	225

Bonds of polyatomic molecules

C—C	80 (85)	C—O	79
C=C	145	C=O	173
C≡C	198	C—H	98
N—N	37	N—H	92
N≡N	225	O—H	109
O—O	34		

* Data mostly from K. S. Pitzer, *J. Am. Chem. Soc.*, **70**: 2140 (1948). (The value of 85 kcal for C—C corresponds to the bond in diamond.)

The bond energies of diatomic molecules are, therefore, equal to the dissociation energies of the molecules. Table 5-5 shows some results.

The bond energies of polyatomic molecules are less definite quantities. First consider the C—H bond energy of the bonds in methane. The standard heat·of formation, from Table 5-2, gives

$$\text{C(graphite)} + 2\text{H}_2(g) \rightarrow \text{CH}_4(g) \qquad \Delta H^\circ_{298} = -17,890 \qquad (43)$$

Experimental results are also available for the reactions

$$\text{C(graphite)} \rightarrow \text{C}(g) \qquad \Delta H = 170,400 \qquad (44)$$

and

$$\text{H}_2(g) \rightarrow 2\text{H}(g) \qquad \Delta H = 103,200 \qquad (45)$$

The second equation is the sublimation of carbon, while the third gives the dissociation of hydrogen. Combination of these three equations gives

$$\text{C}(g) + 4\text{H}(g) \rightarrow \text{CH}_4(g) \qquad \Delta H = -394,690 \text{ cal} \qquad (46)$$

This reaction forms four C—H bonds from the atoms, and since the·four bonds are identical, one-quarter of this energy can be attributed to the formation of each bond. The C—H bond energy is thus calculated as 98.7 kcal.

It should be mentioned that in other books a variety of values will be found for bond energies of bonds involving a carbon atom. These discrepancies arise from the varied history that the value for the heat of sublimation of carbon has undergone. It should not be surprising, in view of the high temperatures that carbon must be taken to in order to study the solid-to-vapor process, that the determination of the heat of sublimation is difficult and that a value for the heat of sublimation cannot be obtained by a direct thermal measurement. The value of 170.4 kcal now seems generally accepted.

Just as for the C—H bond energy, one can obtain the bond energies for the H—O, H—N, H—S bonds from the molecules H_2O, NH_3, and H_2S.

A more difficult situation arises for a molecule such as methyl alcohol. The heat of formation of methyl alcohol from the gaseous atoms can be calculated from previously given data and the value for the heat of vaporization of 8.42 kcal as

$$C(g) + 4H(g) + O(g) \rightarrow CH_3OH(g) \qquad \Delta H = -482,800 \text{ cal} \qquad (47)$$

The methyl alcohol molecule is made up of three CH bonds, a CO bond, and an OH bond. The energies of each of these types of bonds cannot be sorted out from the observed formation energy without some simplifying assumption. It is customary to assume that the CH and OH bonds have the same energy as they do in the CH_4 and H_2O molecules. With this assumption the result

$$3(C—H) + (C—O) + (O—H) = 482.8 \text{ kcal} \qquad (48)$$

can be made to give

$$C—O = 482.8 - (3)(98.7) - 109.4 = 77.3 \text{ kcal} \qquad (49)$$

This type of procedure can give the bond energies for a large number of bonds, some of which are shown in Table 5-5. The values shown are "best" values. The values deduced for the C—C and C—H bond for one hydrocarbon molecule may not be exactly the same as for another hydrocarbon. It is necessary then to select some suitable average bond energies. In this way the values of Table 5-5 have been obtained.

One should appreciate that the assumption that bond energies can be transferred from one molecule to another is not necessarily valid. The magnitude of the error that might be involved can be illustrated by noticing that both

$$CH_3CH_2CH_2CH_2CH_3$$
$$n\text{-pentane}$$

and

$$
\begin{array}{c}
CH_3 \\
| \\
CH_3—C—CH_3 \\
| \\
CH_3
\end{array}
$$
2,2-dimethylpropane

have 4 C—C bonds and 12 C—H bonds. The standard heats of formation of these compounds, however, are $-30,150$ and $-34,150$ cal; that is, they differ by about 4000 cal.

For most molecules, it appears that the tabulated bond energies can be used to calculate the heat of formation of a molecule and that this value will be within a few kilocalories of the observed value.

In a later chapter more use will be made of this table of bond energies in relation to some problems in molecular bonding. In particular, special attention will be paid to molecules whose heats of formation are not what would be expected from the bond energies. In such molecules some unusual bonding or steric effect must be occurring. For the present, it is sufficient that the qualitative aspect of bond energies be appreciated and that the approximate magnitude of these energies be learned.

Problems

1. When 0.532 g of benzene is burned at 25°C in a constant volume system with an excess of oxygen, 5.33 kcal of heat is given out and the products are $CO_2(g)$ and $H_2O(l)$. What is the heat of combustion of benzene? For this combustion process what are q, w, ΔH, and ΔE per mole of benzene?

2. A sample of liquid acetone weighing 0.5680 g is burned in a bomb calorimeter for which the net heat capacity, including the sample, is 1348 cal/deg. A temperature rise from 22.87 to 24.56°C is observed. What is the heat of combustion in calories per gram of the sample? What are the values, per mole of ΔH and ΔE, for the combustion of acetone?

$Ans.$ $\Delta H_{comb} = -4010$ cal/g $= -233$ kcal/mole; $\Delta E_{comb} = -232$ kcal/mole.

3. Deduce values for ΔE for the combustion reactions for which enthalpies are listed in Table 5-1. Assume that all gases behave ideally.

4. Deduce the enthalpy change for the reaction

$$2CH_4(g)CH_3CH_3(g) + H_2(g)$$

by combining the equations and the heats for the combustion reactions of the three reagents. $Ans.$ $\Delta H = +15.54$ kcal.

5. The standard heat of formation of carbon monoxide cannot be determined conveniently from the reaction of carbon and a limited supply of oxygen. Show how the heat of formation of carbon monoxide from the elements can be deduced from conveniently measurable heats of combustion.

6. A flow process converts 0.5 mole of acetylene per minute into benzene by passing acetylene gas over a catalyst bed. At what rate must heat be added or removed in order to keep the catalyst bed and the exit benzene vapor at the same temperature as the incoming acetylene? $Ans.$ 23.84 kcal removed per minute.

7. Calculate the heat of combustion of neopentane from the standard heats of formation given in Table 5-2.

8. Calculate the standard heat of formation of n-butane from the heat-of-combustion data of Table 5-1. $Ans.$ -29.81 kcal.

9. The heat of combustion of cyclopropane has been reported as 499.8 kcal/mole. Calculate the standard heat of formation at 25°C.

10. Combustion of diborane, B_2H_6, proceeds according to the equation

$$B_2H_6(g) + 3O_2(g) \rightarrow B_2O_3(s) + 3H_2O(g)$$

and 464 kcal is liberated per mole of B_2H_6. Combustion of boron metal also proceeds to the product B_2O_3 and gives out 283 kcal/g atom. What is the standard heat of formation of diborane?

11. Deduce the heat of the reaction whereby ethyl alcohol is formed from ethylene and water. Use (a) the heats of combustion of Table 5-1 and (b) the heats of formation of Table 5-2. $Ans.$ $\Delta H = -10.52$ kcal.

12. Calculate, from the heats of combustion in Table 5-1 and the results of Prob. 10, the heat per pound that can be released by the reagents of the following reactions (ΔH_{vap} of O_2 is 1629 cal/mole):

$$C_7H_{16}(n\text{-heptane})(g) + 11O_2(l) \rightarrow 7CO_2(g) + 8H_2O(g)$$
$$B_2H_6(g) + 3O_2(l) \rightarrow B_2O_3(s) + 3H_2O(g)$$

13. Calculate the maximum flame temperature, i.e., the adiabatic value that corresponds to all the heat of reaction going into the product molecules, when H_2 is burned in just sufficient oxygen to lead to the product H_2O.

Make use of the heat-capacity data of Table 5-3 but note that the data are not really applicable to the temperature range of the problem.   *Ans.* 4350°K.

14. Using the data of Tables 5-2 and 5-3, calculate the heat of the reaction $C_2H_4(g)$ + $H_2(g) \rightarrow C_2H_6(g)$ at 1500°K.

15. The heat of sublimation of NaCl can be estimated to be 181 kcal/mole at 25°C. Using a vibrational-level spacing for NaCl vapor molecules of 380 cm^{-1}, calculate the enthalpy of NaCl at 1000°C compared with the crystal at 25°C.

16. The enthalpy change of the reaction $Cl_2(g) \rightarrow 2Cl(g)$ at 25°C is about 57 kcal. Calculate what the internal-energy change and the enthalpy change would be for all reagents in their lowest allowed quantum states. The vibrational energy-level spacing for Cl_2 is found spectroscopically to be 565 cm^{-1}. What would the internal-energy change and the enthalpy change for the dissociation of Cl_2 be at 2000°K?

Ans. $\Delta E_0 = +56.2$; $\Delta H_{2000°K} = +58.9$ kcal.

17. At high temperatures all molecules tend to break up into smaller fragments. Do the energy considerations of the Cl_2 example in Prob. 16 explain this?

18. Draw to scale a diagram like that of Fig. 5-2 for the reaction $CO(g) + \frac{1}{2}O_2(g) \rightarrow CO_2(g)$ showing the enthalpies of reaction at 25°C and at 1500°K. Make use of the data of Tables 5-1 and 5-3.

Read off other values of $\Delta H°$, and plot $\Delta H°$ as a function of temperature over this temperature range.

19. Plot curves showing $H° - E_0°$ CO, $\frac{1}{2}O_2$, and CO_2 over the temperature range 25°C to 1500°K. The vibrational spacings for CO and O_2 are 2,168 and 1,580 cm^{-1}, respectively. CO_2 is a linear molecule and has four modes of vibration with the spacings 668, 668, 1,320, and 2,168 cm^{-1}. Plot $\Delta(H° - E_0°)$ for the reaction $CO(g) + \frac{1}{2}O_2(g) \rightarrow CO_2(g)$ versus temperature. Using the standard heats of formation, calculate $\Delta E_0°$ for the reaction. Using values of $\Delta(H° - E_0°)$ and the value of $\Delta E_0°$, obtain values of $\Delta H°$, and plot against temperature. Compare with the curve obtained in Prob. 18.

20. Using data from the text, calculate the heat capacity of NO_2 at various temperatures between 298 and 1500°K. Fit these values with an expression of the form $Cp = a + bT^2 + cT^3$.

21. Using the data of Prob. 9, calculate a value for the C—C bond energy for cyclopropane.   *Ans.* 73 kcal.

22. Verify the value given for the —N—H bond energy in Table 5-5.

23. Verify the $>C=C<$ bond energy of Table 5-5. If, instead of assuming that the C—H bond of methane had the same energy as that in ethylene, it were assumed that a C=C had exactly twice the energy of a —C—C— single bond, what would be the deduced value for the energy of the C—H bond in ethylene?

24. If the C—H bond energy of Table 5-5 is assumed to apply to both n-pentane and 2,2-dimethylpropane, what values of the C—C bond energy are obtained from the reported standard heats of formation of these compounds?

25. From the bond-energy data of Table 5-5 deduce $\Delta H_f°$ for propane, and compare with the value in Table 5-2.   *Ans.* −18 kcal.

26. Explain why the C—C bond energy in diamond is half the value of the heat of sublimation of diamond.

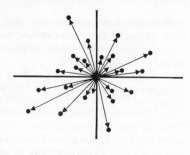

6

Entropy and the Second and
Third Laws of Thermodynamics

A very large part of chemistry is concerned, in one way or another, with the state of equilibrium and the tendency of systems to move in the direction of the equilibrium state. Thermodynamics is the basic approach for the study of equilibria. It has been mentioned in the previous chapter that the enthalpy and internal-energy changes in reactions are not reliable indications of the tendency of a reaction to proceed; i.e., they do not indicate where the equilibrium lies. The thermodynamic and molecular treatments that we now take up are concerned with the questions:

1. Can the equilibrium state of a chemical system be determined by the use of some new thermodynamic function?

2. If so, can this function, and therefore the equilibrium state, be understood in terms of the properties of the molecules involved?

After a preliminary discussion of the general statements of the second law of thermodynamics, a new thermodynamic function will be, rather arbitrarily, introduced. This function will allow the second law to be applied to chemical systems, and it will be seen that the second law and the new function are concerned with the equilibrium state and the tendency of processes, or reactions, to occur spontaneously. A molecular interpretation of the new thermodynamic function will then be suggested.

Not until the following chapter will the thermodynamic study of equilibria be completed by the introduction of another, more convenient function.

6-1. General Statements of the Second Law of Thermodynamics. Although the second law can be stated in a number of different ways, all statements can ultimately be shown to generalize our knowledge that natural processes tend to go to a state of equilibrium. The second law sums up our experiences with equilibria, just as the first law summed up our experience with energy. The general statements of the second law, like the conservation-of-energy statement of the first law, are not immediately applicable to chemical problems. After the law is introduced in general terms, it will be shown that it can be expressed in a chemically useful form.

Two important statements of the second law have been given. One due to Lord Kelvin is that "it is impossible by a cyclic process to take heat from a reservoir and convert it into work without at the same time transferring heat from a hot to a cold reservoir." Another statement, given by Clausius, is that "it is impossible to transfer heat from a cold to a hot reservoir without at the same time converting a certain amount of work into heat."

The first of these two statements is illustrated by the fact that a ship cannot derive work from the energy in the sea on which it moves. A moment's thought about all types of engines will show that there is always a hot and a cold source. A steam engine, for example, could not be made to produce work if it were not for the high pressure and high temperature of the steam *compared* with the surroundings.

This statement of the second law is related to equilibria when it is realized that work can be obtained from a system only when the system is not already at equilibrium. If a system is at equilibrium, no process tends to occur spontaneously and there is nothing to harness to produce work. A more mechanical example is the production of hydroelectric power. Here work is obtained when the spontaneous tendency of water to flow from a high to a low level is used. Lord Kelvin's statement recognizes that the spontaneous process is the flow of heat from a high to a lower temperature and that only from such a spontaneous process can work be obtained.

The second statement is readily illustrated by the operation of a refrigerator. Again we have the recognition that the spontaneous flow of heat is from a high to a low temperature and that the reverse is possible only when work is expended.

A rather more sophisticated approach than will be used here concerns itself with how the high and low temperatures referred to in these statements are defined. The statements of Kelvin and Clausius, in fact, provide fundamental definitions for temperature. Temperature so defined, however, can be shown to be identical with the temperature scale that makes the relation $PV = nRT$ hold for ideal gases.

The chemist's interest in the second law of thermodynamics is aroused by the possibility of this law saying something about the position of equilibrium in a chemical process. As a preliminary to this application we consider in detail a simple process that involves the transformation of heat into work.

6-2. The Carnot Cycle. Although chemists are not necessarily interested in the conversion of heat into work, it will be found that the consideration of a particularly simple engine for doing this leads us to a step of great chemical importance.

A hypothetical engine provides a specific example on the basis of which the second law of thermodynamics can be put in a chemically useful form. More particularly the cycle of the engine shows that a new and very valuable thermodynamic function can be introduced.

The engine that we consider operates with 1 mole of an ideal gas as the working substance and was analyzed originally by the French engineer Sadi Carnot in 1824. This engine is very convenient for analysis, but although the pattern of operation is not entirely different from that of a steam, or internal-combustion, engine, it is not a practical device. One cycle of this engine has the net effect of using up heat from a hot reservoir, producing work, and giving some heat to a cold reservoir. The engine would operate by continually repeating this cycle.

A diagram of a Carnot engine is shown in Fig. 6-1. Heat can be supplied at the higher temperature T_h and removed at the lower temperature T_l. The dotted lines indicate the possibility of sliding in heat conductors or insulators so that heat can be transferred or not, as desired. The piston is connected to some device, such as a system of pulleys and weights, such that work can be done by the gas on this device or such that the device can do work on the gas. Any material could be assumed to be present in the cylinder, but the analysis is greatly simplified if the working material in the cylinder is 1 mole of an ideal gas.

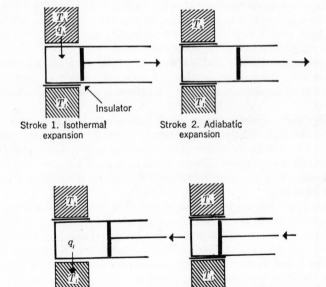

Stroke 1. Isothermal expansion

Stroke 2. Adiabatic expansion

Stroke 3. Isothermal compression

Stroke 4. Adiabatic compression

Fig. 6-1. The four strokes of the Carnot engine.

The Carnot cycle consists of four steps, which are shown in Fig. 6-2. Each step is performed reversibly; i.e., the pressure of the gas is only infinitesimally different from that of the piston and the heat flows across an infinitesimal temperature gradient. The heat and work of each step will be investigated, and the contributions will then be added together to find the net effect of the complete cycle.

Step 1. The gas is expanded isothermally at a temperature T_h from an initial volume V_1 to a volume V_2. An amount of work w_1 is done by the gas, and an amount of heat q_h flows from the hot reservoir to the gas.

Since the gas is ideal and the temperature is constant, $\Delta E = 0$ and

$$q_h = w_1 = \int P \, dV = RT_h \int_{V_1}^{V_2} \frac{dV}{V} = RT_h \ln \frac{V_2}{V_1} \tag{1}$$

Step 2. The gas is expanded adiabatically from a volume V_2 to a volume V_3 while the temperature drops to a value T_l. An amount of work w_2 is done by the gas, and since the insulators are in place for this adiabatic step, no heat is transferred.

Since $q = 0$, the first law and the fact that the working substance is an ideal gas gives

$$w_2 = -\Delta E_2 = -C_v(T_l - T_h) = C_v(T_h - T_l) \tag{2}$$

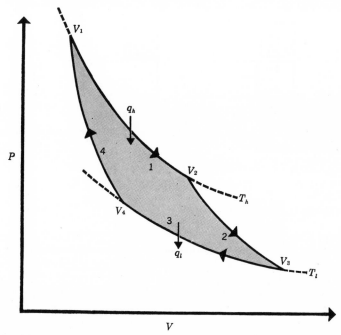

Fig. 6-2. The Carnot cycle on a PV diagram. (The four strokes are numbered as in Fig. 6-1.)

Step 3. The gas is compressed isothermally at the lower temperature T_l from the volume V_3 to a volume V_4. An amount of work w_3 is done on the gas by the piston, and an amount of heat q_l flows from the gas to the cold reservoir.

Since the gas is ideal and the temperature is constant, $\Delta E = 0$ and

$$q_l = w_3 = \int P \, dV = RT \int_{V_3}^{V_4} \frac{dV}{V} = RT \ln \frac{V_4}{V_3} \qquad (3)$$

We note that, since V_4 is less than V_3, the term $\ln (V_4/V_3)$ is negative and, therefore, q_l and w_3 are both negative. This corresponds to work being done *on* the gas and heat being given off from the gas.

Step 4. The gas is compressed adiabatically from the volume V_4 to the original volume V_1 while the temperature rises to the higher temperature T_h at which the cycle was started. An amount of work w_4 is done on the gas during this compression, and no heat is absorbed.

Again, as in step 2, we have $q = 0$, and the first law gives

$$w_4 = -\Delta E_4 = -C_v(T_h - T_l) \qquad (4)$$

Here also it can be noted that, corresponding to work being done on the gas, w_4 is negative.

That the entire cycle obeys the first law of thermodynamics can first be checked. The net work performed by the gas is

$$w = w_1 + w_2 + w_3 + w_4 \qquad (5)$$

where w_1 and w_2 are positive quantities and w_3 and w_4 are negative. Furthermore, w_2 and w_4 are numerically equal and cancel each other. The net work is, therefore,

$$w = w_1 + w_3$$
$$= RT_h \ln \frac{V_2}{V_1} - RT_l \ln \frac{V_3}{V_4} \qquad (6)$$

where both logarithm terms are so written that they are positive quantities. The net heat absorbed is

$$q = q_h + q_l$$
$$= RT_h \ln \frac{V_2}{V_1} - RT_l \ln \frac{V_3}{V_4} \qquad (7)$$

Furthermore, the process is cyclic,

$$\Delta E = 0 \qquad (8)$$

and the first law is obeyed since the net heat absorbed by the gas is equal to the work done by the gas. The next section will show that the cycle corresponds to an engine cycle in that work is obtained from heat.

6-3. The Efficiency of the Transformation of Heat into Work. The performance of an engine is usually computed on the basis of the net work produced for a given consumption of heat from the hot reservoir. In an internal-combustion engine, for example, one measures the work produced from a given amount of fuel, which is the counterpart of heat from the hot reservoir. The efficiency of the Carnot engine is defined, therefore, as

$$\text{eff} = \frac{w}{q_h} \tag{9}$$

where w, as above, equals the net work $w_1 + w_3$.

The previous relation for w can be simplified by the recognition that the adiabatics of steps 2 and 4 relate the four volumes according to equations

$$(T_h)^{C_v/R} V_2 = (T_l)^{C_v/R} V_3$$

and
$$(T_h)^{C_v/R} V_1 = (T_l)^{C_v/R} V_4 \tag{10}$$

Division of the first of these by the second gives

$$\frac{V_2}{V_1} = \frac{V_3}{V_4} \tag{11}$$

The previous expression [Eq. (6)] for the net work then reduces to

$$w = R(T_h - T_l) \ln \frac{V_2}{V_1} \tag{12}$$

Since this is a positive quantity, a net amount of work is produced per cycle and, therefore, work is indeed being obtained from heat.

As before

$$q_h = RT_h \ln \frac{V_2}{V_1} \tag{13}$$

and the efficiency is calculated as

$$\text{eff} = \frac{w}{q_h} = \frac{R(T_h - T_l) \ln (V_2/V_1)}{RT_h \ln (V_2/V_1)} = \frac{T_h - T_l}{T_h} \tag{14}$$

This formula represents the results of the analysis of the operation of the Carnot engine. The relation of this particular result to the previously given general statements of the second law can now be investigated.

That the Carnot cycle immediately illustrates Lord Kelvin's statement is apparent when it is recognized that a cold reservoir at absolute zero is never available. All engines using a cold reservoir at a temperature above absolute zero have efficiencies, according to Eq. (14), less than unity. Such engines take heat from a hot reservoir, convert only part of it into work, and must, therefore, give the remainder out as heat to the cold reservoir.

The Clausius statement requires us to think of a Carnot cycle that is run in the reverse direction to that of the preceding derivation. Since all the steps in the cycle are reversible, this could occur if the temperatures of the heat reservoirs were changed by infinitesimal amounts. We now have a refrigerator in which an amount of work w is expended, heat q_l is taken from the cold reservoir, and heat q_h is delivered to the hot reservoir. Clausius' statement says that the flow of heat will not occur unless w has some nonzero value. The Carnot-cycle efficiency expression shows that w can be zero only when T_h and T_l are equal, a result that is in accordance with the Clausius statement of the second law.

Any other device for developing work from heat would also serve to illustrate the second law. The calculation of a quantitive value for the efficiency would, however, be rather more difficult than for the Carnot cycle operating on 1 mole of an ideal gas. The Carnot cycle has the advantage also of showing the efficiency of an engine that operates between a fixed high-temperature reservoir and a fixed low-temperature reservoir.

One can, furthermore, show that any other reversible engine operating between these two temperatures and with any other working substance will have an efficiency equal to that calculated for the reversible Carnot cycle. The Carnot-cycle efficiency can, therefore, be used to make an estimate of the maximum conversion of heat to work that can be expected for a real engine.

A steam engine, for instance, can be taken as operating between some high temperature around 120°C and a condenser temperature of about 20°C. For such an engine the efficiency can be estimated as

$$\text{eff} = \frac{393 - 293}{393}\,(100) = 25\% \tag{15}$$

Thus, for every 4 cal of heat supplied in the steam, the equivalent of 1 cal of work can be obtained, and 3 cal of heat is given off at the low temperature. This efficiency is the maximum that could be expected if there were no other inefficiencies in the operation. In addition, of course, there is a mechanical efficiency that limits the available work to some fraction of this theoretically possible amount.

Such a calculation indicates the desirability of operating an engine with as high a value of T_h and as low a value of T_l as possible. In working engines this is done as much as possible.

6-4. Entropy. The efficiency of the Carnot cycle, and similar but more practical engines, is of special interest in several engineering areas. The Carnot cycle also gives a concrete example for investigating the second law of thermodynamics. The principal interest to the chemist results from the fact that the derivation suggests that a new and, as we shall see, a very useful thermodynamic function is suggested.

Since the net work of the cycle is equal to the difference between the heat absorbed and the heat given out, we can write

$$\text{eff} = \frac{q_h + q_l}{q_h} \tag{16}$$

which, when compared with Eq. (14), gives

$$\frac{q_h + q_l}{q_h} = \frac{T_h - T_l}{T_h} \tag{17}$$

(The q_l term is a negative quantity corresponding to heat being given out.) Equation (17) can be rearranged to give

$$\frac{q_h}{T_h} + \frac{q_l}{T_l} = 0 \tag{18}$$

or

$$\sum \frac{q}{T} = 0 \tag{19}$$

The special significance of this result follows from the fact that any reversible cycle involving an ideal gas can be thought of as being made up of a large number of Carnot cycles, as illustrated by Fig. 6-3. A grid of isotherms and adiabatics is drawn through the heavy curve, which represents any reversible

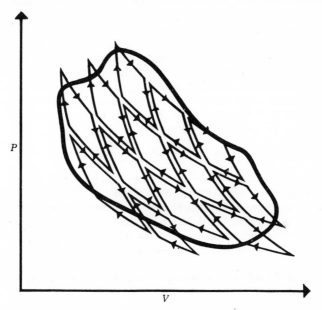

Fig. 6-3. A cyclic process approximated by a set of Carnot cycles.

process. The grid can be used to construct a set of Carnot cycles so that the outer parts of the set trace out a curve that approximates that of the general process. If one were to perform all the Carnot cycles in the set, the net result would be almost the same as performing the general process. This results from the fact that all the Carnot-cycle steps that are inside the boundary are canceled out because each is traced in both a forward and a reverse direction. If one goes to the limit of an infinitely closely spaced grid, one can obtain an exact reproduction of any process. As a result one can write *for any cyclic reversible process* performed on an ideal gas

$$\sum \frac{q}{T} = 0$$

Here q represents the various heats absorbed, divided by the temperatures at which the absorption occurs. This result can be written more generally as

$$\oint \frac{dq_{rev}}{T} = 0 \qquad (20)$$

where the sign $\oint$ signifies integration around a complete cycle and the subscript has been added to q to emphasize the fact that this relation holds only when the process is performed reversibly.

Detailed considerations of cyclic processes of any type with any substance would be found to lead to a similar result. No proof that Eq. (20) is generally applicable can be given. It can be stated, however, that analysis of any cyclic process will, like that presented here for the Carnot cycle, lead to the conclusion of Eq. (20).

In the previous discussion of internal energy it was pointed out that a zero value for a cyclic integral implied that the function being integrated was independent of the path over which the integration was made. In other words, *such a function is a state function or thermodynamic property.*

We are, therefore, at liberty to define a function, which is generally denoted by S and called entropy, such that changes in this function are given by

$$dS = \frac{dq_{rev}}{T} \tag{21}$$

and

$$S_b - S_a = \Delta S = \int_a^b \frac{dq_{rev}}{T} \tag{22}$$

The Carnot-cycle argument, leading to Eq. (19), has shown that the entropy differences which are defined by Eq. (22) are functions that depend only on the initial and final states of the system and not on how a process is carried out.

The entropy function is, therefore, a state function or thermodynamic property. One should recognize that the definition of entropy changes in terms of dq_{rev}/T not only defines the function but also shows us how to calculate changes in it.

Again, it would not be so necessary to emphasize that entropy is a thermodynamic property if it were defined in a way that showed how it could be calculated for a given temperature and pressure from molecular properties. Later it will be seen that such calculations can, in fact, be made. The present definition, however, involves q, which depends on the path. There are usually a number of reasonable ways of performing a process reversibly, each way having a different value of q_{rev}. The results of the Carnot-cycle discussion, however, illustrate that for all reversible paths dq_{rev}/T will be the same.

Before showing some of the uses of this new thermodynamic function and the ways it can be understood in terms of molecular properties, we shall illustrate how changes in entropy can be calculated for some simple processes. Practice with such calculations is necessary for one to obtain familiarity with this new function.

6-5. Entropy Changes in Reversible Processes. For the present, examples are drawn from rather nonchemical systems. Except for the electrochemical reactions to be studied later most chemical reactions are performed irreversibly and do not provide suitable examples.

First, it must be emphasized that in entropy calculations it is important to distinguish between the system and the surroundings of the system. The system is that part on which we focus our attention. It may be part of a mechanical system or, more chemically, a gas, liquid, or solid or a reaction mixture. The surroundings constitute all other parts which might interact with the system. The surroundings will most frequently consist of heat reservoirs that can add to or subtract heat from the system or of mechanical devices which can do work on or accept work from the system.

The entropy change, not only of the system but also of the surroundings, will be of interest. The combination of the system and its surroundings cor-

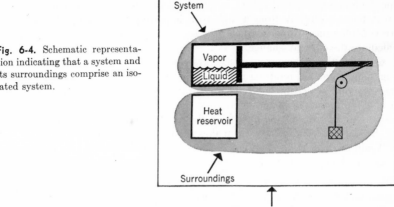

Fig. 6-4. Schematic representation indicating that a system and its surroundings comprise an isolated system.

responds to an "isolated system," as suggested in Fig. 6-4, since the process being considered affects nothing outside of the system and its surroundings.

Example 1.   Consider the entropy changes involved in the conversion of 1 mole of liquid water at 100°C to vapor at 100°C and 1 atm.

The system consists of the 1 mole of water, and the surroundings consist of a heat reservoir at 100°C, as illustrated in Fig. 6-4.   Since there is only an infinitesimal temperature gradient between the heat reservoir and the water, the system can absorb the necessary heat reversibly.   From the defining equation for entropy changes [Eq. (21)], we calculate

$$\Delta S_{\text{system}} = \int \frac{dq_{\text{rev}}}{T} = \frac{1}{T} \int dq_{\text{rev}} = \int_{n=0}^{n=1} \frac{\Delta H_{\text{vap}}}{T} \, dn$$
$$= \frac{\Delta H_{\text{vap}}}{T} = \frac{9{,}720}{373} = 26 \text{ cal/deg} \tag{23}$$

The integration is easily performed because T is constant.

At the same time the surroundings, i.e., the heat reservoir, experience a change in entropy due to the loss of an amount of heat ΔH_{vap}.   Thus

$$\Delta S_{\text{surroundings}} = -\frac{\Delta H_{\text{vap}}}{T} = -26 \text{ cal/deg} \tag{24}$$

For the systems plus the surroundings, i.e., for everything involved,

$$\Delta S_{\text{total}} = 0 \tag{25}$$

The result of the calculation is that the entropy of the water increases by 26 cal/deg.   The surroundings suffer an equal but opposite change so that the total entropy change of the isolated combination of system plus heat reservoir is zero.

Example 2.   Consider the entropy change for the transfer of an amount of heat q from a hot body at temperature T_h to a body at lower temperature T_l.

A reversible way of performing this heat transfer must be devised since then the defining equation [Eq. (21)] can be used to calculate the entropy change. Heat flowing directly from a high to a low temperature corresponds to an irreversible process, and for such processes we have no direct way in which to calculate the entropy change.

Consider the arrangement of the system and surroundings represented by Fig. 6-5b. The hot reservoir is at a temperature infinitesimally lower than T_h, and the cold reservoir at a temperature infinitesimally higher than T_l. The heat flows indicated in the figure give the net result, as far as the system is concerned, of transferring heat from the hot to the cold body. The addition of the heat reservoirs, however, makes the process reversible.

Again the heat transfers occur at constant temperatures so that the integrations for the calculation of ΔS give terms of the type q/T. Thus

$$\Delta S_{\text{system}} = \Delta S_{\text{hot body}} + \Delta S_{\text{cold body}}$$
$$= -\frac{q}{T_h} + \frac{q}{T_l} = \text{a positive quantity} \qquad (26)$$

For the surroundings

$$\Delta S_{\text{surroundings}} = \Delta S_{\text{hot res}} + \Delta S_{\text{cold res}}$$
$$= \frac{q}{T_h} - \frac{q}{T_l} = \text{a negative quantity} \qquad (27)$$

Again the system is seen to gain entropy, and the combination of everything involved in the heat transfers maintains a constant entropy.

The entropy has been calculated by means of the arrangement of Fig. 6-5b,

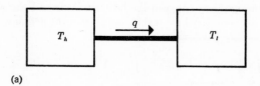

(a)

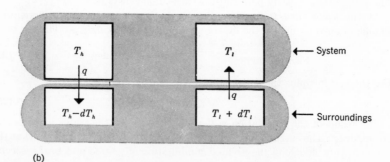

(b)

Fig. 6-5. Irreversible and reversible paths for the transfer of heat from a body at a high temperature T_h to a low temperature T_l. (a) Irreversible heat transfer. (b) Reversible heat transfer.

but it must be remembered that the entropy change of the *system* is independent of the way in which the process is performed and depends only on the initial and final states.   Equation (26) gives, therefore, the entropy change of the system when heat q is transferred from the hot end to the cold end by any process.   The process involving the heat reservoirs was introduced only so that we would have a way in which to calculate this entropy change.

Example 3.   Determine the entropy change for the isothermal expansion of n moles of an ideal gas at temperature T from a volume V_1 to a volume V_2.

The expansion can be performed irreversibly by simply opening a stopcock and allowing the gas to rush into the previously evacuated compartment as represented by Fig. 6-6a.   We have no method for analyzing this process directly to find the entropy difference between the expanded gas and the initial gas.   It is necessary to think of a process that can be carried out reversibly and that takes the system from the same initial to the same final state.   Figure 6-6b shows how this might be done.

For this isothermal expansion, the internal energy does not change, and the heat absorbed can be calculated from the first-law expression as

$$dq = dw = P\,dV = nRT\frac{dV}{V} \tag{28}$$

This expression for the heat absorbed allows the entropy change of the system to be calculated as

$$\Delta S_{\text{system}} = \frac{dq_{\text{rev}}}{T} = \int_{V_1}^{V_2} \frac{nRT}{T}\frac{dV}{V} = nR\ln\frac{V_2}{V_1}$$
$$= \text{a positive quantity} \tag{29}$$

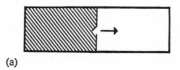

(a)

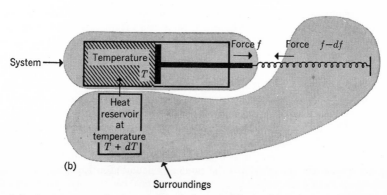

(b)

Surroundings

Fig. 6-6. Arrangements for irreversible and reversible isothermal expansions of a gas. (*a*) Irreversible expansion.   (*b*) Reversible expansion.

The entropy change of the surroundings, i.e., the heat reservoir and the mechanical device, is similarly calculated from the heat that flows out of the reservoir. This entropy is an amount of equal magnitude but opposite sign to that in Eq. (29). Thus

$$\Delta S_{\text{surroundings}} = -nR \ln \frac{V_2}{V_1} \tag{30}$$

Again the important result is obtained that, if everything involved is considered, the entropy change, as is seen from the sum of Eqs. (29) and (30), is zero.

These three examples illustrate a completely general result. *For a reversible process, the entropy change of the system and the surroundings together is always zero.* This can also be stated as: the entropy change in an isolated system is always zero for a reversible process.

We have, therefore, arrived at one important qualitative property of the new function. Another property, discussed in the next section, will suggest the usefulness of entropy.

6-6. Entropy Changes in Irreversible Processes. An irreversible process, as has been mentioned, is one that occurs when a lack of balance exists in a system. The flow of heat directly from a high to a low temperature and the expansion of a gas into a vacuum are examples of irreversible processes. Likewise, the sparking of a mixture of hydrogen and oxygen results in the irreversible process that forms water.

All natural processes are more or less irreversible. Only in the idealized world of weightless and frictionless systems can processes occur when only an infinitesimal lack of balance exists. *The driving force that causes reactions to proceed spontaneously is the lack of balance or the irreversibility of the process.*

In the previous section an important generalization was drawn regarding processes that occur reversibly. That is, if an irreversible process is replaced by a reversible one involving both the system and some associated surroundings, the total entropy change is found to be zero. Now we shall seek a generalization about the entropy change that is associated with irreversible processes.

Irreversible processes are those which have a natural tendency to occur; i.e., they are spontaneous processes. Chemical terminology would have it that irreversible processes are those in which there is a driving force that tends to make the reaction or process occur. The study of any property that might be associated with the tendency of processes, or chemical reactions, to proceed is of obvious chemical interest.

Examples 2 and 3 of Sec. 6-5 have readily visualizable irreversible paths. The entropy change when these processes occur irreversibly can be immediately obtained when it is recognized that the entropy change of a *system* depends only on the initial and final states and not on the path of the reaction.

The irreversible transfer of heat from the hot to the cold body, as in Fig. 6-5a, allows the heat to flow directly, and no surroundings are involved. The entropy change for the system is the same as calculated in Eq. (20); i.e.,

$$\Delta S_{\text{system}} = -\frac{q}{T_h} + \frac{q}{T_l}$$

Now, however,

$$\Delta S_{\text{surroundings}} = 0$$

and
$$\Delta S_{\text{total}} = -\frac{q}{T_h} + \frac{q}{T_l} = \text{a positive quantity} \tag{31}$$

The irreversible expansion of the ideal gas of Example 3 of Sec. 6-5 can be performed by allowing the gas to rush from volume V_1 to a total volume V_2 by opening a stopcock connecting an evacuated section, as suggested in Fig. 6-6a. Again the initial and final states are the same as those in Sec. 6-5, and, therefore, the entropy change of the system is that obtained there; i.e.,

$$\Delta S_{\text{system}} = nR \ln \frac{V_2}{V_1}$$

Now, however, no heat is absorbed, nor is any work done, and we have

$$\Delta S_{\text{surroundings}} = 0$$

and
$$\Delta S_{\text{total}} = nR \ln \frac{V_2}{V_1} = \text{a positive quantity} \tag{32}$$

These two examples illustrate another completely general result. When a spontaneous process occurs, it will always be found that, if the total entropy change for everything involved is calculated, a positive quantity is obtained. *In all irreversible, i.e., spontaneous, processes the entropy of the system and its surroundings increases. Alternatively, all irreversible processes of isolated systems occur with an increase of entropy.*

Some of the importance attached to entropy, as a result of this deduction, can be seen by its position alongside energy in the famous maxim of Clausius: "The energy of the universe is constant; the entropy of the universe tends always toward a maximum." Since all natural processes are spontaneous, they must occur with an increase of entropy and, therefore, the sum total of the entropy in the universe is continually increasing. Recognition of this trend leads to some interesting philosophical discussions as, for example, Sir Arthur Eddington's idea that "entropy is time's arrow."

We are now in a position to summarize the results of this and the preceding section and thereby to indicate the use that can be made of the function called entropy. Suppose that one wishes to investigate the possibility of a reaction, either chemical or physical, proceeding from one state a to another state b. If one can calculate the entropy difference

$$\Delta S_{\text{total}} = (S_b - S_a)_{\text{total}} \tag{33}$$

for the system and any of its surroundings that might be involved one can make use of the statements that result from our two entropy generalizations of this and the preceding section:

If ΔS_{total} is positive, the reaction will tend to proceed spontaneously from state a to state b.

If ΔS_{total} is zero, the system is at equilibrium and no spontaneous process will occur.

If ΔS_{total} is negative, the reaction will tend to go spontaneously in the reverse direction, i.e., from b to a.

These statements, together with the definition of the state-function entropy, constitute a formulation of the second law of thermodynamics that is more applicable to chemical problems than the statements previously given.

That these properties of entropy sum up our experiences with naturally occurring phenomena can be illustrated by the simple example of the flow of heat in Example 2 of Sec. 6-5. The entropy calculation given above shows that when heat flows irreversibly, i.e., directly, from the hot end to the cold end the entropy increases. This corresponds, according to the three italicized statements preceding, to a spontaneous process and illustrates that these entropy statements are equivalent to the second law as stated by Clausius (Sec. 6-1).

For the type of process used in this example it is certainly cumbersome and unnecessary to introduce the entropy function; the Clausius statement of the law is itself adequate. On the other hand, when one is dealing with a chemical reaction

$$\text{Reactants} \rightarrow \text{products}$$

one would be greatly aided by a thermodynamic property that could be determined for the reactants and the products and that would tell whether or not the reaction would tend to proceed spontaneously.

The early thermochemists incorrectly assumed that all that needed to be considered was the energy of a reaction and that the energy given out by a reaction was a measure of the driving force. We now see that in an isolated system, where energy cannot be gained or lost, the entropy change is the driving force. In a more general system, as we shall see in the next chapter, both the energy and entropy factors must be considered in order to deduce what processes will tend to occur spontaneously. By way of comparison, the student may recall that the spontaneous processes and the equilibrium state of mechanical systems, such as weights and pulleys, can be calculated on essentially an energy basis. Chemical reactions are less simple. A molecular interpretation of entropy will make understandable the role of an entropy factor as well as an energy factor in determining the spontaneity of chemical reactions.

6-7. The Molecular Basis of Entropy. In the development of thermodynamics it is quite unnecessary to attempt to lead the student to any further "explanation" of entropy. The definition of entropy shows how changes in this function can be calculated, and the discussion of the previous section has, at least qualitatively, shown how entropy changes are related to the spontaneity of reactions. With this information one understands entropy as well, for instance, as one understands a familiar quantity like work. One might notice that one's appreciation of work is pretty well limited to its definition as force times distance and to a familiarity with some of its qualitative features. Entropy differs only in that it is a less familiar function.

It is very natural and, for our investigation of the molecular world, very profitable to attempt to find a molecular interpretation of entropy. One can ask, for example: What is it about an expanded gas which makes it have more entropy than the same gas when it is compressed? Or: Why is it that a vapor has more entropy than it would have if condensed to a liquid? A more chemical question might arise if a reaction $A \rightarrow B$ were investigated and it were found that the entropy of B was greater than that of A.   One then not only can, but should, ask: What is it about the molecules of B that makes them have more entropy than the same number of molecules of A?   In this section, qualitative answers to such questions will be given.   It is convenient to leave a more detailed and quantitative explanation until the next chapter.

It is not immediately obvious, as it was in the molecular study of internal energy, what molecular phenomenon is responsible for the entropy of a system. Some idea of what it is that should be calculated can be obtained by trying to discover some quantity that might tend to increase when an isolated system moves spontaneously toward the equilibrium position.   A very nonchemical example will reveal such a quantity.

Consider a box that contains a large number of pennies.   Suppose further-more that these pennies are initially arranged such that they all have heads showing.   If the box is now shaken, the chances are very good that some arrangement of higher probability, with a more nearly equal number of heads and tails, will result.   This system of pennies has, therefore, a natural or spontane-ous tendency to go from a state of low probability to one of high probability. The system can be considered to be isolated since no heat is transferred, and the shaking process could be almost eliminated by using some other objects that could more easily turn over.   The driving force that operates in this isolated system is seen to be the probability.   The system tends to change toward its equilibrium position, and this change is accompanied by an increase in the probability.   Such an example suggests that the entropy might be identified with some function like the probability.   The next chapter will show in a more rigorous manner that the entropy is, in fact, related to the probability.

No general definition of probability is necessary here.   An example showing the probabilities of various arrangements of 4 pennies in a box will be sufficient to illustrate that a quantitative interpretation can be given to the term *prob-ability*.   When a box containing 4 pennies is shaken, each penny has an equal chance of showing a head or a tail.   The number of ways, and therefore the probability, of getting a total of 1, 2, 3, or 4 heads can be calculated as shown in Table 6-1.   The probability of getting 2 heads is seen, for example, to be 6 times as great as of getting no heads.   If a very large number of such boxes were shaken, the number of boxes showing 2 heads would be very nearly 6 times as great as the number showing no heads.   The larger number of boxes

Table 6-1. Number of Arrangements of Four Pennies
(H implies a head showing, T a tail showing)

Description	Arrangements	No. of arrangement
4 heads, 0 tails........	HHHH	1
3 heads, 1 tail.........	HHHT, HHTH, HTHH, THHH	4
2 heads, 2 tails........	HHTT, HTHT, HTTH, THHT, THTH, TTHH	6
1 head, 3 tails.........	TTTH, TTHT, THTT, HTTT	4
0 heads, 4 tails........	TTTT	1

showing 2 heads is due to the larger number of arrangements or the greater probability of the 2-head result and does not depend in any way on an energy factor.

The molecular equivalent of the number of arrangements that correspond to various numbers of heads showing is the number of quantum states, or the number of energy levels, that are available and that, when occupied, correspond to a given description of the system. The equilibrium of A and B in which B has the higher entropy, for example, can be understood in terms of the fact that there are, for some reason, more energy states available for B and, therefore, more ways of distributing the atoms in these states so that a molecule of the type B is formed than there are ways of arranging the atoms in the energy states so that a molecule of the type A is formed. The tendency for A to change over to B, even if no energy driving force exists, is understood, therefore, to be due to the driving force that takes the system from a state of lower probability, i.e., of few energy levels and few possible arrangements, to one of higher probability, i.e., one of many available energy levels and more possible arrangements. The qualitative result from this discussion is: *For states of equal energy, the state with more available energy levels has the higher probability and therefore the higher entropy.* On this basis, it is clear that for isolated systems the spontaneous process is that which moves to a state of higher entropy.

A previous example showed that the isothermal expansion of a gas was accompanied by an increase in the entropy of the gas. It might be of interest here to show that this increase is understandable on the basis of the relation of entropy to probability. The isothermal expansion of an ideal gas, in a box fitted with a piston, affects only the translational energy levels of the molecules. The qualitative effect can be understood on the basis of the one-dimensional translational-energy-level expression

$$\epsilon_n = n^2 \frac{h^2}{8ma^2} \tag{34}$$

where a is the dimension of the container affected by the moving piston. Expansion corresponds to an increase in one of the dimensions of the container and, therefore, according to Eq. (34), to a decrease in the spacing between the available energy levels. The average translational energy remains $\frac{1}{2}RT$ in each degree of freedom, and the occupancy of the available translational energy states can be depicted for the compressed and expanded states, as in Fig. 6-7. It is clear that more energy levels are available for the molecules of the gas when the volume is large than when the volume is small. More ways of arranging the molecules, i.e., of distributing them throughout the levels, exist for the expanded volume; and it is therefore this state that has the higher probability and higher entropy. By a molecular treatment we have come, therefore, to the same qualitative conclusion as we did by the direct application of thermodynamics in Sec. 6-5. It is interesting to note that the expansion of gas, by the opening of the stopcock of Fig. 6-6, for example, occurs, according to this molecular interpretation, only because there are more available translational energy levels for the larger volume.

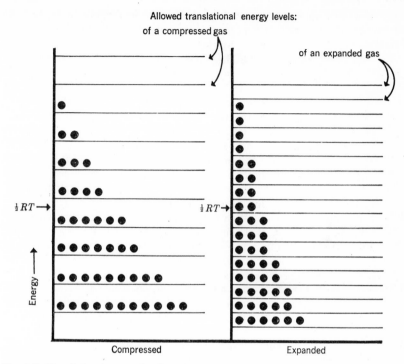

Fig. 6-7. Translational-energy levels (schematic) for a one-dimensional compressed and expanded gas, showing the increased number of levels available and therefore the higher probability for the expanded state.

The molecular explanation of the entropy change in a process is basically quite simple.   In practice, of course, it is not always easy to see which of two states has the more available quantum states, or energy levels.   Thus, for the liquid-to-vapor transition, it was found that a large entropy increase occurs. The difficulties encountered in a molecular understanding of the liquid state makes it very difficult to evaluate this entropy increase from the molecular model.   A further complexity, about which more will be said in the following chapter, surrounds the "availability" of quantum states when their energy levels are at various energies above the ground state.   In such cases, the Boltzmann-distribution expression will have to be used to tell how available the higher energy states are.

These difficulties in applying the molecular approach to entropy determinations are mentioned here so that this approach can be compared with the thermodynamic method.   In Sec. 6-5, for example, the entropy changes were deduced for processes from other observable thermodynamic quantities, and no detailed investigation of the systems was necessary.   It is such deductions of thermodynamic quantities that characterize the pure thermodynamic method.   The two approaches powerfully complement each other in that frequently a fuller understanding of the molecular nature of a system is obtained as a result of attempts to calculate on a molecular basis some thermodynamic quantity that has been obtained by the pure thermodynamic method.

6-8. The Unattainability of Absolute Zero. The third and final of the great summations of our experiences with nature on which all the deductions of thermodynamics are based must now be introduced. Full use of thermodynamics can then be made in our subsequent studies of chemical systems.

The second law of thermodynamics has introduced entropy, and this function has been shown to be important when the directions of spontaneous changes are investigated. The second law, moreover, shows how differences in entropy of two states of a system can be determined. The third law gives a method for obtaining the absolute value of the entropy of a system. As with the first two laws, the third is an expression of our experiences with nature. The basic experiences for this law come about from attempts to achieve very low temperatures. Such activity is not as readily undertaken as are the experiments that form the basis of the first and second laws, and for this reason the third law will appear to be a less general principle. All attempts that have been made to obtain lower and lower temperatures, however, lead to the general statement that *the absolute zero of temperature is unattainable*. It is this statement that can be used as a basis for the expression in the next section for the third law of thermodynamics. First, however, it may be of interest to mention briefly some of the steps that have been taken in the direction toward absolute zero.

It is not the mere attainment of low temperatures that stimulates attempts to achieve such temperatures. It will be shown that the measurement of absolute values for entropies requires measurements at temperatures approaching absolute zero. Furthermore, as absolute zero is approached, the reduction of thermal energy leads to the appearance of a number of very interesting phenomena that are obscured or nonexistent at higher temperatures. Interest in such effects has led to the production of lower and lower temperatures.

The principal refrigeration technique is based on the cooling resulting from a Joule-Thomson expansion, as discussed in Sec. 4-11. It will be recalled that, when a gas is below its inversion temperature, an expansion produces a cooling effect as a result of work being done by the gas to overcome the mutual attraction of the molecules of the gas.

The countercurrent arrangement, introduced by Siemans in 1860, whereby the expanded and, therefore, cooled gas is passed back over the compressed gas, leads to cooling which can be continued until condensation occurs. By such a process liquid air can be formed. The liquid air so produced can be distilled to give oxygen, boiling point 90°K, and nitrogen, boiling point 77°K. Liquid nitrogen can now be readily obtained commercially, and the attainment of a temperature of about 77°K presents no problem to the research worker.

Still lower temperatures are obtained by performing such a Joule-Thomson expansion on hydrogen. This gas must first, however, be cooled below its inversion temperature of 193°K, by means, for example, of liquid nitrogen. Expansion then allows liquid hydrogen, boiling point 22°K, to be formed.

Finally, liquid hydrogen can be used to cool helium below its inversion temperature, and subsequent expansion produces liquid helium, which boils at 4°K. Temperatures of somewhat less than 1°K can be produced by reducing the pressure over the helium, but this technique is limited by the large amounts of vapor that must be pumped off. For many low-temperature research problems the temperatures reached by liquid hydrogen or helium are satisfactory and can be reached with commercially available liquid helium or a helium liquefier.

Temperatures considerably below the 1°K obtainable with liquid helium can be attained by a magnetic cooling method, proposed independently by P. Debye and W. F. Giauque in 1926 and known as *adiabatic demagnetization*.

A brief description of the method and its molecular basis can be given. The method consists in cooling a salt, of a type called *paramagnetic*, to liquid-helium temperatures in the presence of a magnetic field. This type of salt is characterized by the presence of unpaired electrons. These spinning, unpaired electrons behave as little magnets, and in the presence of the magnetic field they line themselves up so that their axis of spin, which is the direction of their magnetic moment, lies in the direction of the field. At this stage it is convenient to think of the crystal as having a system consisting of the unpaired, spinning electrons, called the *spin system*, and the remainder of the crystal, called the *lattice system*. When the electron spins, or magnets, are lined up all in the same direction, they are in a state of low probability and, therefore, low entropy. Once the crystal has been cooled and magnetized, it is thermally isolated and the magnetic field is turned off. The crystal spontaneously loses its magnetism. This means that the electron spins are taking up random orientations as they go over into more probable arrangements. For this spontaneous process to occur, the entropy of the spin system must increase, and, therefore, according to Eq. (21), heat must be absorbed by the spin system. This heat is taken from the thermal vibrational energy of the crystal lattice, and this results in a temperature drop of the crystal. By this technique temperatures within 1/1,000° from absolute zero have been obtained.

Low-temperature, or *cryogenic*, work shows that temperatures very near absolute zero can be obtained. It appears, however, that, in spite of the remarkably close approaches to absolute zero that have been achieved, absolute zero cannot be reached. In addition to direct attempts in this direction, one draws on other evidence, such as that provided by the molecular interpretation of matter, to support this generalization.

The chemist's interest in the unattainability of absolute zero stems primarily from the implication of this generalization on the entropy of crystals as the temperature approaches absolute zero.

6-9. Entropy and the Third Law of Thermodynamics. In the magnetic-cooling method a difference in entropy is used to draw heat from the crystal lattice and so reduce its temperature. More generally, one could make use of any difference of entropy between two systems to perform such a cooling. Furthermore, if any such entropy differences existed down to absolute zero, one might expect to be able to use these entropy changes to reduce the temperature to absolute zero. The generalization that absolute zero is unattainable means that it must be concluded that the entropies of all materials at absolute zero are the same. Furthermore, partly on the basis of the molecular interpretation of this result, one sees that the value to be taken for the entropy at absolute zero is zero. Although a more careful statement will need to be made later, the chemically useful deduction from the unattainability of absolute zero can now be stated as the third law of thermodynamics: *The entropy of all materials at absolute zero can be taken as zero.*

The third law makes it possible to obtain absolute entropies of chemical compounds from calorimetric measurements. The difference in entropy between $0°K$ and a temperature T can be deduced from the defining equation for entropy

$$S_T - S_0 = \int_0^T \frac{dq_{rev}}{T} \tag{35}$$

The third law states that the S_0 can be assigned the value of zero. The integral can be evaluated from measured heat capacities and heats of transitions.

If a given phase is heated from T_1 to T_2, it gains entropy according to the expression

$$\int_{T_1}^{T_2} \frac{dq_{rev}}{T} = \int_{T_1}^{T_2} \frac{C_p \, dT}{T} = \int_{T_1}^{T_2} C_p \, d(\ln T) \tag{36}$$

The integration can be performed if the necessary values for C_p are available. The integration is usually performed graphically, and in Fig. 6-8 the areas under the continuous parts of the curve correspond to the value of the integral. Since heat-capacity measurements are usually not taken down below about $15°K$, attainable with liquid hydrogen, an extrapolation to absolute zero is necessary. The basis for the extrapolation, which introduces a comparatively small term in the total entropy, will be given when the nature of solids is studied.

In taking a compound from near absolute zero to some temperature, such as $25°C$, a number of phase transitions are generally encountered. At each of these transitions the heat capacity will, for the most part, change abruptly, and heat will be absorbed. The entropy change corresponding to such transitions can be calculated from the measured enthalpy change for the transition by the expression

$$\Delta S_{trans} = \frac{\Delta H_{trans}}{T_{trans}}$$

The entropy obtained by adding up all the contributions from absolute zero is usually reported at $25°C$. Table 6-2 shows the terms that go into such a determination for nitrogen, and Table 6-3 gives the results that have been obtained for a number of compounds.

Such third-law entropy values are of interest to the chemist in two important areas. First, they provide the data with which molecular calculations of entropy can be compared. Second, they comprise, along with values for the enthalpies of reactions, the thermodynamic basis for treating chemical equilibria. The following chapter will introduce one further, but very important, thermodynamic function which is defined in terms of entropy and enthalpy.

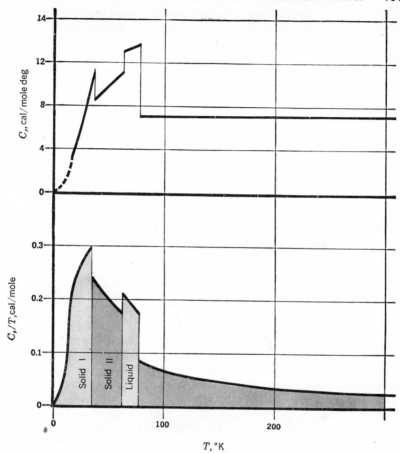

Fig. 6-8. Graphs of C_p and C_p/T (for the integration $\int \frac{C_p}{T}\,dT$) for N_2. [*Data of W. F. Giauque and J. O. Clayton, J. Am. Chem. Soc.,* **55**: 4875 (1933).]

Table 6-2. The Entropy of Nitrogen from Heat-capacity Data*

	Cal/deg mole
0–10°K extrapolation	0.458
10–35.61°K (graphical integration)	6.034
Transition 54.71/35.61	1.536
35.61–63.14°K (graphical integration)	5.589
Fusion 172.3/63.14	2.729
63.14–bp (graphical integration)	2.728
Vaporization 1,332.9/7,732	17.239
Correction for gas imperfection	0.22
Ideal gas 77.32–298.2°K (from spectroscopic data)	9.37
Entropy of ideal gas at 298.2°K and 1 atm	45.90

* From W. F. Giauque and J. O. Clayton, *J. Am. Chem. Soc.,* **55**: 4875 (1933).

Table 6-3. Entropies for the Standard State at 298.16°K

Substance	S (cal/deg mole)	Substance	S (cal/deg mole)
		Solids	
Al	6.75	NaCl	17.3
BaO	16.8	Ag	10.21
Ca	9.95	Pb	15.51
C(graphite)	1.36	Li	6.70
C(diamond)	0.6	Si	4.47
Fe	6.47	Sn	12.3
I_2	27.9		
		Liquids	
Br_2	36.4	Hg	18.5
H_2O	16.72		
		Gases	
Cl_2	53.31	Methane	44.50
F_2	48.58	Ethane	54.85
He	30.13	Propane	64.51
H_2	31.21	Ethylene	52.45
O_2	49.00	Acetylene	48.00
H_2O	45.11	Benzene	64.34
HBr	47.44	Toluene	76.42
HCl	44.61	Cyclohexane	71.28
N_2	23.025		
NO	50.34		
NH_3	46.01		
CO	47.30		
CO_2	51.06		

This new function will allow chemical equilibria to be more conveniently studied and molecular explanations of thermodynamic quantities to be more quantitatively given.

Problems

1. Compare the theoretical efficiency of a steam engine operating at 5 atm pressure, at which pressure water boils at 152°C, with one operating at 100 atm, at which pressure water boils at 312°C. The condenser in each case is at 30°C.

Ans. 29 per cent at 5 atm, 48 per cent at 100 atm.

2. A Carnot cycle uses 1 mole of an ideal gas, for which $C_v = 6.0$ cal/mole deg, as the working substance and operates from a most-compressed stage of 10 atm pressure and 600°K. It expands isothermally to a pressure of 1 atm, and then adiabatically reaches a most-expanded stage at a temperature of 300°K.

(a) Obtain numerical values for the heat and work of each stroke.

Ans. $w_1 = +2{,}750$; $w_2 = +1{,}800$; $w_3 = -1{,}375$; $w_4 = -1{,}800$ cal; $q_h = +2{,}750$; $q_l = -1{,}375$ cal; eff. = 50 per cent.

(b) What is the efficiency with which heat is converted to work in this engine?

(c) Repeat the calculation for a maximum compression of 100 atm at 600°K and a maximum expansion of 1 atm at 300°K. Compare the efficiency with that of the first calculation.

3. Plot the Carnot cycle of Prob. 2 on a graph of P versus V.

4. The net work of a Carnot cycle is the summation of $\int P\ dV$ for all strokes. Obtain this by graphical integration on the figure of Prob. 3, and compare with the value calculated in Prob. 2.

5. On a graph of T versus S:

(a) Sketch a typical Carnot cycle.

(b) Sketch the Carnot cycles of Prob. 2.

6. Since the relation $dq = T\ dS$ holds for reversible processes, the net heat absorbed in a Carnot cycle is the cyclic integral $\oint T\ dS$. Obtain this value by graphical integration on the figure of Prob. 5, and compare with the value calculated in Prob. 2.

7. Show the system and the surroundings that can be used to perform the reversible conversion of 1 mole of benzene from solid to liquid, the temperature staying constant at the freezing point of benzene, 5.4°C. What is the entropy change of the benzene and of the surroundings? (ΔH_{fusion} of benzene is 30.2 cal/g.)

8. What is the entropy of vaporization of:

	Bp (°C)	ΔH_{vap} (kcal/mole)
Argon.....................	−185.7	1.88
Mercury..................	356.6	15.50
Carbon tetrachloride.........	76.7	7.17
Benzene...................	80.1	7.35

9. Calculate the change in entropy of 5 moles of an ideal gas when the gas is expanded reversibly and isothermally from 2 to 1 atm pressure at 25°C. What would be the entropy change of the surroundings? What would be the entropy changes of the system and the surroundings if the expansion were performed adiabatically?

$Ans.\ \Delta S_{\text{gas}} = +6.89$ cal/deg.

10. Ten grams of ice at 0°C is added to 20 g of water at 90°C in a Dewar flask. The heat of fusion of water is 1430 cal/mole, the specific heat of water can be taken as independent of temperature, and the heat capacity of the Dewar can be ignored.

(a) What is the final temperature of the water?

(b) How could the process be performed reversibly, and what would the entropy changes of the system and of the surroundings then be?

(c) What is the entropy change of the system for the direct addition?

(d) What is the entropy change of the surroundings for the direct addition?

$Ans.$ (a) 33.5°C; (b) $\Delta S_{\text{system}} = +0.70$ cal/deg; $\Delta S_{\text{surroundings}} = -0.70$ cal/deg; (c) $+0.70$ cal/deg.

11. A 276-cc gas bulb at 25°C holding 0.046 mole of hydrogen is connected by a tube with a stopcock to an evacuated bulb with a volume of 500 cc. Calculate the entropy change when the stopcock is opened. Assume that hydrogen behaves ideally.

12. If the entropy of 1 mole of N_2 at 1 atm and 25°C is denoted by S°_{298}, what would be the entropy of 1 mole of N_2 at 1 atm and 150°C if the heat capacity per mole could be taken to have the value 6.9 cal/deg?

13. Calculate the increase in entropy of 3 moles of methane, CH_4, when the temperature is raised from 300 to 1000°K, the pressure remaining constant at 1 atm. The heat capacity is given in Table 5-3. $Ans.$ 44.24 cal/deg.

14. By a suitable graphical integration determine the entropy of metallic silver at 25°C from the following heat-capacity per gram atom data, which have been reported by Meads, Forsythe, and Giauque [J. Am. Chem. Soc., **63**: 1902 (1941)].

$T°K$	C_p (cal/deg)	$T°K$	C_p (cal/deg)
15	0.160	170	5.644
30	1.141	190	5.757
50	2.784	210	5.837
70	3.904	230	5.911
90	4.573	250	5.911
110	5.010	270	6.050
130	5.289	290	6.080
150	5.490	300	6.095

Assume that the heat capacity approaches absolute zero according to a T^3 relation; that is, $C_p = (\text{const})T^3$, and $C_p = 0$ at $T = 0$.

Ans. $S°_{298.1} = 10.21$ cal/deg per gram atom.

15. At 25°C and 1 atm the entropy of 12.01 g of diamond is 0.585 cal/deg and that of 12.01 g of graphite is 1.365 cal/deg. If equilibrium could be established in an isolated system, which implies that there be no heat of reaction, which form of carbon would result?

The heat of combustion of diamond is 94,484 cal/mole and of graphite is 94,030 cal/mole. If equilibrium could be established and energy and not entropy considerations were important, which form of carbon would result?

16. Calculate the heat capacity of N_2 over the temperature range 77 to 298°K. Only the translational and rotational contributions are significant at such temperatures. Using this heat-capacity data, calculate the entropy gained by 1 mole of N_2 as the temperature is increased from 77 to 298°K, and compare with the value shown in Table 6-2. *Ans.* 9.41 cal/deg.

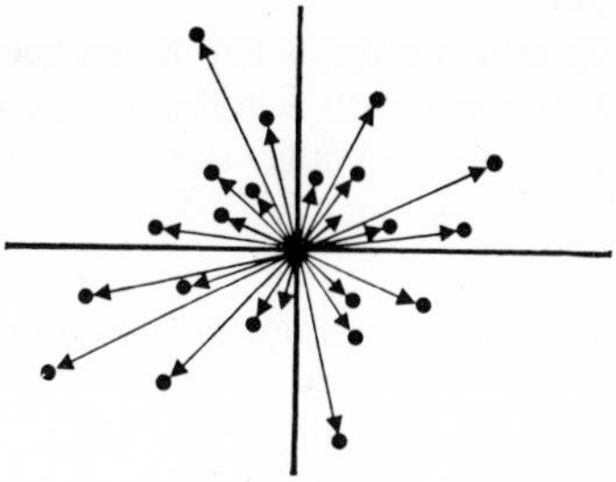

7

Free Energy and Chemical Equilibria

In the previous chapters two thermodynamic functions that have a bearing on the position of the equilibrium state in a chemical system have been considered. The supposition of the early thermochemists that equilibrium was always approached with a decrease in the internal energy of the system—a principle which applies to macroscale mechanical systems—has been shown to be inadequate for chemical systems. A more careful statement of the role of the internal energy or enthalpy is that *in systems of constant entropy the equilibrium position is that of lowest energy.* The preceding chapter, furthermore, has shown that *in systems of constant energy the equilibrium position is that of highest entropy.*

In most chemical processes neither the energy nor entropy is held constant. It is now necessary to find some way of determining how the energy and entropy factors act together to drive a system to equilibrium. To do this, a new thermodynamic function is introduced. This function, as we shall see, shows the compromise that is struck when both energy and entropy change. To limit the discussion, only the function that is particularly applicable to constant-pressure processes is introduced, and a similar function that is rather more convenient for processes at constant volume is not considered here.

7-1. The Free-energy Function. The new function, called *free energy* or Gibbs free energy, and denoted by G, is defined by

$$G = H - TS \tag{1}$$

Since H and TS are properties of the system, so also is G.

The relation between the free-energy function and the equilibrium state of a system can now be shown by deriving the free-energy change for a rather restricted process. First the defining equation of H is substituted in Eq. (1) to give

$$G = E + PV - TS \tag{2}$$

For a general change in G one now has

$$dG = dE + P\,dV + V\,dP - T\,dS - S\,dT \tag{3}$$

These many terms can be reduced by considering a process occurring at constant temperature and pressure and under conditions that keep the system only infinitesimally away from a state of balance. These restrictions make $T \, dS = dq$, $S \, dT = 0$, $V \, dP = 0$ and leave

$$dG = dE + P \, dV - dq \tag{4}$$

The first law can now be used to replace $dE - dq$ by dw. Since it is important to remember that a balanced process has been stipulated and that for such reactions a maximum amount of work is done by the system, the work term is written as dw_{max}. The free-energy change is then

$$-dG = dw_{max} - P \, dV \tag{5}$$

Since $P \, dV$ corresponds to the work "wasted" against the confining pressure and dw_{max} gives the maximum work that could conceivably be harnessed from the constant-pressure reaction, we recognize that

$$-dG = dw_{useful} \tag{6}$$

where w_{useful} is the net work that the system could provide over and above that of expansion. The result is obtained that, for the type of reaction considered, the decrease in the free energy during the process is equal to the useful, or net, work that might in principle be obtained from the process.

This property of the free-energy change is very revealing. At least in principle, any process that tends to proceed spontaneously can be made to do useful work. In fact, this is, of course, usually impractical, but the presence of a drive to a new state can, in principle, be harnessed. Since the free-energy change measures the useful work that might be obtained from a constant-pressure process, it is a measure of the spontaneity of the process. We have the very important result that *the decrease in free energy of a constant-pressure process is the measure of the tendency of the process to proceed spontaneously.*

If a system undergoes a change which is accompanied by a large value of $-\Delta G$, that is, if the free energy decreases, the reaction will proceed spontaneously and work, in principle, could be obtained from the process. If no path is available for which the free energy would decrease, no spontaneous process can occur and the system is in a state of equilibrium. If a process is considered and it is calculated that the process would be accompanied by an increase in free energy, the process will not proceed spontaneously in the direction considered.

The qualitative relations, for constant-pressure processes, of free energy to spontaneity and equilibrium can be summarized as follows: For

$\Delta G = -$, *the process tends to proceed spontaneously*

$\Delta G = 0$, *the system is at equilibrium*

$\Delta G = +$, *the process tends to proceed spontaneously in the opposite direction*

One should notice that in these statements the free-energy change is that for the system and the role of the surroundings need not be included.

The statement that a system is at equilibrium means only that it is in equilibrium with respect to the reactions or processes that are being considered. For chemical systems there will frequently be reactions which are thermodynamically possible but which will not occur for the particular conditions of the systems and therefore need not be considered.   A careful statement will always say that a system is in equilibrium with respect to certain specified processes.

For the chemist the free energy is probably the most important of the thermodynamic quantities.   Many problems can be understood in terms of this function.   Moreover, it will be found that frequently our interest in enthalpy and entropy is due to their appearance in the defining equation for the free energy.

It can only be mentioned that, while the free-energy function G, the Gibbs free energy, is suitable for direct application to constant-pressure processes, another free-energy function is more convenient for constant-volume processes. This function, known as the *Helmholtz* free energy, is represented by A and is defined as

$$A = E - TS$$

A development, such as is performed on G in this section, would show that in a constant-volume process the decrease in A corresponds to the driving force of the reaction.   Thus H and G are functions that are convenient for constant-pressure processes, while E and A are more convenient for constant-volume processes.   In the introduction to thermodynamics that is presented here it will be sufficient to develop the applications of H and G.

7-2. Some Free-energy Calculations.   The use of free energy can be illustrated by some simple examples.

Example 1. Calculate the free-energy change for the process of converting 1 mole of water at 100°C and 1 atm to steam at the same temperature and pressure.

We return to the defining equation for the free energy, $G = H - TS$, and calculate the free-energy change from the enthalpy and entropy contributions. For a constant-temperature process the change in free energy is given by

$$\Delta G = \Delta H - T \, \Delta S \tag{7}$$

Since the process is carried out at constant pressure, the enthalpy change is equal to the heat absorbed.   This heat is the heat of vaporization ΔH_{vap}, and thus

$$\Delta H = \Delta H_{\text{vap}} \tag{8}$$

The entropy change is also calculated from its defining equation, $dS = dq_{\text{rev}}/T$. Since T is constant, the integration is simply

$$\Delta S = \frac{1}{T} \int dq = \frac{\Delta H_{\text{vap}}}{T} \tag{9}$$

and
$$T \, \Delta S = \Delta H_{\text{vap}} \tag{10}$$

The free energy for the process is, therefore,

$$\Delta G = \Delta H_{\text{vap}} - \Delta H_{\text{vap}} = 0 \tag{11}$$

This result, in view of the previous discussion, could have been written down immediately.   Since water and steam are in equilibrium at 100°C and 1 atm, the free-energy change for the conversion of one to the other must be zero.

The equilibrium can be pictured as resulting from the fact that the formation of water from steam is favored by the energy term ΔH but that the higher entropy of the steam works to favor the formation of steam. At 100°C and 1 atm these effects just balance, and water and steam are in equilibrium. The free-energy equation shows how the two factors reach a compromise.

Example 2. Calculate the difference in free energy of n moles of an ideal gas at pressure P_1 and n moles of the gas at a lower pressure P_2. The temperature remains constant.

The necessary enthalpy and entropy terms are calculated with reference to a cylinder and piston arrangement that can take the gas reversibly from P_1 to P_2. Since the temperature is constant, ΔE and ΔPV are zero and, therefore, so also is ΔH. Furthermore, as in the example of Sec. 6-5, since $\Delta E = 0$,

$$q = w = \int_{V_1}^{V_2} P\,dV = nRT \ln \frac{V_2}{V_1} \tag{12}$$

which, with $P_1 V_1 = P_2 V_2$, gives

$$q = nRT \ln \frac{P_1}{P_2} \tag{13}$$

With this result for the heat of this isothermal reversible process, the entropy can be calculated as

$$\Delta S = \int \frac{dq}{T} = \frac{1}{T} \int dq = nR \ln \frac{P_1}{P_2} \tag{14}$$

The free-energy change is now calculated as

$$\begin{aligned} \Delta G &= \Delta H - \Delta(TS) \\ &= \Delta H - T\,\Delta S \\ &= 0 - nRT \ln \frac{P_1}{P_2} \\ &= nRT \ln \frac{P_2}{P_1} \end{aligned} \tag{15}$$

Since P_1 is greater than P_2, ΔG has a negative value.

In the previous section it was shown that for a constant-pressure process the value of $-\Delta G$ was a measure of the tendency of the process to occur. This criterion cannot be applied directly to the pressure-varying process of the expansion of a gas. We can, however, return to Eq. (3) and obtain, for a balanced reaction,

$$dG = dE - dq + P\,dV + V\,dP$$
$$\text{or} \qquad -dG = dw_{\max} - d(PV) \tag{16}$$

For the constant-temperature expansion of an ideal gas being dealt with here $d(PV) = d(nRT) = 0$, and the decrease in free energy is equal to the maximum work that could be obtained from the system. It follows, therefore, that, since ΔG for the isothermal expansion of an ideal gas is negative, the expansion will tend to proceed spontaneously. Again a rather powerful method has been used to obtain an obvious answer. The value of such a method when applied to chemical systems should, however, be apparent.

It is convenient to recognize that this result [Eq. (16)] gives a quantitative expression for the fact that a gas at high pressure is capable of doing more useful work than one at low pressure.   A gas at a high pressure has a high free energy, and spontaneous processes, with their accompanying decreasing free energy, can occur.   This result will be mentioned again later in the chapter.

Example 3.   Calculate the free-energy change when 1 mole of water is formed from its elements at 25°C and 1 atm pressure.

The reaction to be considered is

$$H_2 + \tfrac{1}{2}O_2 \rightarrow H_2O(l) \tag{17}$$

The heat of this reaction, ΔH, is the standard heat of formation of water, which is given in Table 5-2 as $-68,320$ cal.   The entropies of the three reagents are given by the third law of thermodynamics and are listed in Table 6-3. These values lead to

$$\Delta S = S_{H_2O(l)} - \tfrac{1}{2}S_{O_2} - S_{H_2}$$
$$= 16.72 - (\tfrac{1}{2})(49.00) - 31.21 = 38.99 \text{ cal/deg} \tag{18}$$

Since the process is at constant temperature, the change in free energy is

$$\Delta G = \Delta H - T\,\Delta S \tag{19}$$

which gives

$$\Delta G = -68,317 - (298.16)(-38.99) = -56,690 \text{ cal} \tag{20}$$

The reaction proceeds with a large decrease in free energy, and this agrees with the known fact that the reaction tends to proceed spontaneously.   The fact that mixtures of oxygen and hydrogen do not react appreciably until a spark or flame starts the reaction is a matter of the rate of the reaction and is no concern of thermodynamics.   Thermodynamics tells us that if equilibrium is established it will be far over in the direction of the water.

7-3. Standard Free Energies.   The previous examples of free-energy calculations show that changes in free energies can be calculated and that these changes correlate with the tendency of the system to proceed to a state of equilibrium.   In view of this fact, it would be very useful to have a tabulation of free energies of chemical compounds so that the free-energy change of a possible reaction could be easily calculated.

Free energies, like any other energies, must have some reference point. The same procedure is followed as was done for enthalpies.   A zero value is assigned to the free energies of the stable form of the elements at 25°C and 1 atm pressure.   These, and the free energies of compounds based on these references, are known as *standard free energies of formation*.   These data can be determined from free energies of reactions in exactly the same way as were standard heats of formation.   Example 3 of Sec. 7-2, for example, gives the standard free energy of formation of liquid water as $-56,690$ cal.   Table 7-1 shows the standard free energies of a number of compounds.

Table 7-1. Standard Free Energies of Formation at 25°C
(Kcal/mole)

$HCl(g)$	-22.778	$C_2H_6(g)$	-7.860
$H_2O(g)$	-54.635	$C_2H_4(g)$	16.282
$H_2O(l)$	-56.690	$C_2H_2(g)$	50.000
$CO(g)$	-32.808	$C_6H_6(g)$	30.640
$CO_2(g)$	-94.260	$NH_3(g)$	-3.903
$CH_4(g)$	-12.09	$NaCl(s)$	-91.894

A use of the data of this table can be indicated by applying them to the question of whether or not it would be worthwhile to look for a catalyst to promote the hydrogenation of ethylene at 25°C and 1 atm. One writes

$$H_2C{=}CH_2(g) + H_2(g) \rightarrow CH_3CH_3(g) \tag{21}$$
$$\Delta G_f^\circ (25°C) + 16{,}282 \qquad 0 \qquad -7{,}260$$

and calculates

$$\Delta G_{298}^\circ = -7{,}860 - (+16{,}282) = -24{,}142 \text{ cal} \tag{22}$$

The large negative free-energy change shows that the reaction tends to proceed spontaneously, and if a way is found to make it proceed fast enough, i.e., if a catalyst is available, the reaction will occur.

7-4. The Dependence of Free Energy on Pressure and Temperature. The standard free energies, such as appear in Table 7-1, allow predictions to be made of the possibility of a reaction for the single conditions of 25°C and 1 atm. For these free-energy data to be of real use, a means must be available for calculating free energies at other pressures and temperature.

The defining equations of G and H give

$$G = H - TS$$
$$= E + PV - TS \tag{23}$$

and for a general change,

$$dG = dE + P\,dV + V\,dP - T\,dS - S\,dT \tag{24}$$

If the process is reversible, $T\,dS = dq$ and if no work other than that of expansion occurs, $P\,dV = dw$. The first-law expression $dE - dq + dw = 0$ cancels out three of the terms of Eq. (24) and leaves

$$dG = V\,dP - S\,dT \tag{25}$$

Furthermore, if P is held constant, one obtains the important result

$$\left(\frac{\partial G}{\partial T}\right)_P = -S \tag{26}$$

whereas if T is held constant, the second important result

$$\left(\frac{\partial G}{\partial P}\right)_T = V \tag{27}$$

is obtained. These two results show how the free energy of a chemical compound depends on the pressure and on the temperature. For the present, only the pressure dependence is considered.

If it is stipulated that the temperature is constant, the free-energy dependence on pressure can be written as

$$dG = V\,dP \tag{28}$$

It perhaps should be emphasized that the development has so far made no stipulations as to the type of system under consideration and Eqs. (26) to (28) are therefore quite general.

Since liquids and solids are quite incompressible, the free-energy change corresponding to an increase in pressure, ΔP, for some not too large pressure change can be written, according to Eq. (28) and the assumption of a constant volume, as $V\,\Delta P$. This change in free energy resulting from the application of ordinary pressures to liquids and solids is relatively small, and for many purposes the free-energy change experienced by liquids and solids can be neglected.

For gases the dependence of free energy on pressure is appreciable and important. For an ideal gas, P and V are related by the ideal-gas law, and the integration of Eq. (28) can be performed to give the free-energy change when the pressure is changed from P_1 to P_2. Thus

$$G_2 - G_1 = \int V\,dP = nRT \int_{P_1}^{P_2} \frac{dP}{P}$$

$$= nRT \ln \frac{P_2}{P_1} \tag{29}$$

This result is that obtained in Example 2 of Sec. 7-2, in which the separate enthalpy and entropy changes were calculated.

Of particular interest is the way in which the free energy changes from its standard state value when the pressure changes from 1 atm. If state 1 is the standard state, then

$$P_1 = 1 \text{ atm} \quad \text{and} \quad G_1 = G°$$

State 2 now corresponds to some general pressure other than 1 atm, and the subscripts on state 2 can be dropped.

With this notation for states 1 and 2, Eq. (29) can be rewritten as

$$G - G° = RT \ln \frac{P}{1}$$

or
$$G = G° + RT \ln P \tag{30}$$

where P must be expressed in atmospheres. This expression is strictly applied to ideal gases, but until the details of nonideal behavior are treated in Chap. 17, it will be assumed to apply approximately to all gases.

Equation (30) shows that the free energy of a gas at pressure P is made up of the free energy that it has at 1 atm plus an additional term that is positive for P larger than 1 atm and negative for P less than 1 atm.

7-5. Quantitative Relation of ΔG and the Equilibrium Constant. Methods are now available for the determination of the free-energy change accompanying a chemical reaction, and qualitative arguments have been given for deciding, on the basis of the free-energy change, whether a reaction will proceed in one direction or the other. Chemical experience tells us, however, that a reaction will proceed in a given direction only until the system reaches a state of equilibrium. It will now be shown that free energies can be used to show not only the direction in which a reaction tends to proceed but also the equilibrium state to which this reaction carries the system.

Consider a reaction involving four gases A, B, C, and D,

$$aA + bB \rightarrow cC + dD \tag{31}$$

where a, b, c, and d are the numbers of moles of each reagent involved. The free energies of a moles of A at a pressure P_A, b moles of B at P_B, and so forth, can be written, in view of Eq. (30), as

$$\begin{aligned}
&\text{Free energy of } a \text{ moles of } A = aG_A = aG_A° + aRT \ln P_A \\
&\text{Free energy of } b \text{ moles of } B = bG_B = bG_B° + bRT \ln P_B \\
&\text{Free energy of } c \text{ moles of } C = cG_C = cG_C° + cRT \ln P_C \\
&\text{Free energy of } d \text{ moles of } D = dG_D = dG_D° + dRT \ln P_D
\end{aligned} \tag{32}$$

The free-energy change for the reaction, when the pressures of the four species are P_A, P_B, P_C, and P_D, can now be calculated as

$$\Delta G = G_{\text{products}} - G_{\text{reactants}}$$
$$= cG_C + dG_D - aG_A - bG_B$$
$$= cG_C^\circ + dG_D^\circ - aG_A^\circ - bG_B^\circ + RT \ln \frac{(P_C)^c(P_D)^d}{(P_A)^a(P_B)^b}$$

or
$$\Delta G = \Delta G^\circ + RT \ln \frac{(P_C)^c(P_D)^d}{(P_A)^a(P_B)^b} \tag{33}$$

This equation relates the free-energy change of the reaction for the reagents at the pressures P_A, P_B, P_C, P_D to a term involving the free energies of all reagents at 1 atm pressure and a term for the free-energy pressure dependence.

If the reaction system is allowed to proceed to a state of equilibrium, with respect to this reaction, it will reach a position for which no further driving force is operative. The free energy will be a minimum, and any small change in the state of the system must be accompanied by a zero free-energy change. For the reaction proceeding at this equilibrium state, therefore, $\Delta G = 0$, and Eq. (33) can be rearranged to give

$$\Delta G^\circ = -RT \ln \left(\frac{P_C{}^c P_D{}^d}{P_A{}^a P_B{}^b}\right)_{\text{equilibrium}} \tag{34}$$

where the subscript "equilibrium" is added to remind us that the relation holds only when the pressures are those of the system at equilibrium.

This expression constitutes a thermodynamic derivation of the familiar equilibrium constant expression. Since ΔG° for a particular reaction at a given temperature is a fixed quantity, the exhibited pressure term must have some constant value that is independent of the individual pressures. It is customary to call this set of pressures the equilibrium constant and to denote it by the symbol K. Thus

$$K = \left[\frac{(P_C)^c(P_D)^d}{(P_A)^a(P_B)^b}\right]_{\text{equilibrium}} \tag{35}$$

and Eq. (34) becomes with this notation

$$\Delta G^\circ = -RT \ln K \tag{36}$$

This equation represents one of the most important results of thermodynamics. By it the equilibrium constant of a reaction is related to a thermochemical property. The immediate and obvious value of the equation is that it allows the calculation of not only the direction in which a reaction will proceed but also the equilibrium state which the reacting system will finally attain. For many systems it is much easier to measure or calculate the thermodynamic property of free energy than it would be to measure the equilibrium constant. On the other hand, it is sometimes easier to determine an equilibrium constant and from it to calculate the free-energy change, which frequently is of interest for molecular-structure arguments.

This quantitative relationship can readily be seen to be consistent with the previous qualitative statements about the significance of the free-energy change. If ΔG° is very negative, for instance, the argument of Sec. 7-1 leads to the expectation of a spontaneous reaction. The above equation confirms this by showing that the equilibrium constant would be a large positive quantity. The reaction, therefore, would proceed until a large concentration of products was built up.

Confusion sometimes arises because Eq. (34) or (36) involves $\Delta G°$, which corresponds to pressures of 1 atm, and K, which involves the equilibrium pressures. One might look at the equation as showing that the equilibrium state corresponds to pressures of the reagents that give a free-energy term that can balance the standard free-energy term.

The above derivation applies strictly only to ideal gases. For nonideal gases the free energy will not differ from its standard value exactly according to the equation $G = G° + RT \ln P$. In a later chapter these nonideal effects will be dealt with. For the present no great error will be introduced by applying the present equations to any gaseous reagents.

Since many equilibria are studied in solution, it is very desirable to have a result that can be applied to the concentrations of reagents in addition to one that treats gaseous reagents. Only a minor extension of the present treatment is needed to obtain the corresponding equation with the equilibrium constant expressed in terms of concentrations. This will, however, also be postponed to a later chapter.

As an example of the use of the free-energy–equilibrium relation, the industrially important process of the formation of ammonia from its elements can be considered. The reaction is

$$N_2 + 3H_2 \rightarrow 2NH_3 \tag{37}$$

and the standard free-energy terms are

$$
\begin{array}{lll}
N_2 & \Delta G°_{298} = 0 & \\
3H_2 & \Delta G°_{298} = 0 & \\
2NH_3 & \Delta G°_{298} = (2)(-3,940) = -7880 \text{ cal}
\end{array} \tag{38}
$$

Thus, for the reaction

$$\Delta G°_{298} = -7880 \text{ cal} \tag{39}$$

and Eq. (36) gives

$$\log K = -\frac{\Delta G°_{298}}{2.303\ RT} = \frac{7,880}{(2.303)(1.987)(298)} = 5.78$$

and

$$K = \frac{(P_{NH_3})^2}{(P_{N_2})(P^3_{H_2})} = 6 \times 10^5 \tag{40}$$

at 25°C.

It should be pointed out that, if the reaction had been written as

$$\tfrac{1}{2}N_2 + \tfrac{3}{2}H_2 \rightarrow NH_3 \tag{41}$$

the value of $\Delta G°_{298}$ would have been -3940 cal and the equilibrium constant that would have been calculated from Eq. (36) would have been

$$K_{Eq.\ (41)} = \frac{P_{NH_3}}{(P_{N_2})^{\frac{1}{2}}(P_{H_2})^{\frac{3}{2}}} = 7.7 \times 10^2 \tag{42}$$

This result is essentially that obtained previously, both sides being the square root of those of Eq. (40).

The synthesis of ammonia would seem to be indicated as certainly feasible by this calculation. It turns out, however, that it is very difficult to get the reagents to react fast enough, i.e., to come to the calculated equilibrium position fast enough, to make the process feasible. To increase the speed of the reaction, it is usually run at higher temperatures, and it is necessary, therefore, that we be able to calculate the equilibrium constant at temperatures other than 25°C.

Such an interest in reactions at various temperatures is sufficiently general so that it is now necessary that a method be developed for finding the temperature dependence of the equilibrium constant.

7-6. Temperature Dependence of the Free Energy of a Reaction and the Equilibrium Constant. The free energy of each compound that is involved in a reaction is dependent on the temperature, according to Eq. (26), by the relation

$$\left(\frac{\partial G}{\partial T}\right)_P = -S$$

For a chemical reaction it is the free energy of the products less that of the reactants that is of interest. Application of Eq. (26) to each reagent allows the expression

$$\left(\frac{\partial \Delta G}{\partial T}\right)_P = -\Delta S \tag{43}$$

to be written, where

$$\Delta G = G_{products} - G_{reagents} \tag{44}$$

and

$$\Delta S = S_{products} - S_{reagents} \tag{45}$$

At any given temperature the change of free energy for the reaction is related to the enthalpy and entropy change by

$$\Delta G = \Delta H - T \Delta S \tag{46}$$

which can be rearranged to

$$\Delta S = \frac{\Delta H - \Delta G}{T} \tag{47}$$

This expression can be used to eliminate ΔS from Eq. (43) to give

$$\left(\frac{\partial \Delta G}{\partial T}\right)_P = \frac{-\Delta H + \Delta G}{T} \tag{48}$$

which, if constant pressure is separately stated, can be rearranged to

$$\frac{d \Delta G}{dT} - \frac{\Delta G}{T} = -\frac{\Delta H}{T} \tag{49}$$

The two terms on the left side of Eq. (49) can be verified to be equal to

$$T \frac{d}{dT}\left(\frac{\Delta G}{T}\right)$$

since, on differentiation, this expands to

$$T \frac{d}{dT}\left(\frac{\Delta G}{T}\right) = T\left[\frac{T(d \Delta G/dT) - \Delta G}{T^2}\right] = \frac{d \Delta G}{dT} - \frac{\Delta G}{T}$$

With this expression, Eq. (49) becomes

$$T \frac{d}{dT}\left(\frac{\Delta G}{T}\right) = -\frac{\Delta H}{T} \tag{50}$$

It is particularly convenient to write this result for all the reagents in their standard states.   This is expressed as

$$T \frac{d}{dT}\left(\frac{\Delta G^{\circ}}{T}\right) = -\frac{\Delta H^{\circ}}{T} \tag{51}$$

Finally the relation between ΔG° and the equilibrium constant [Eq. (36)] can be inserted to give

$$\frac{d(\ln K)}{dT} = \frac{\Delta H^{\circ}}{RT^2} \tag{52}$$

This important formula is the goal of the derivation.   The variation of the equilibrium constant with temperature is seen to depend on the standard heat of the reaction.

It is sometimes more convenient to write the equation in the form

$$\frac{d(\ln K)}{d(1/T)} = -\frac{\Delta H^{\circ}}{R} \quad \text{or} \quad \frac{d(\log K)}{d(1/T)} = -\frac{\Delta H^{\circ}}{2.303R} \tag{53}$$

The integrated form of these equations, on the assumption that H° is essentially temperature-independent, is

$$\log K = -\frac{\Delta H^{\circ}}{2.303R}\left(\frac{1}{T}\right) + \text{const} \tag{54}$$

Both the integrated and differential forms show that a plot of $\log K$ versus $1/T$ should give a straight line with a slope equal to $-\Delta H^{\circ}/2.303R$.   The linearity shown by good measurements can be judged by the example of Fig. 7-1.   The straight line has, furthermore, been drawn with the slope $\Delta H^{\circ}/R$, with a value of ΔH° from the data of Table 5-2.

One frequently uses a measured value of ΔH° to calculate the equilibrium constant at various temperatures.   It is, of course, also possible to use measurements of the equilibrium constant at a number of temperatures to evaluate the heat of the reaction.

When ΔH is itself an appreciable function of temperature, the integration of the differential form of the temperature dependence must recognize this quantity as a variable.   This dependence of ΔH on temperature has been treated in Sec. 5-7.   For many purposes it is satisfactory to assume a constant value of ΔH that corresponds to an average value over the temperature range of the equilibrium-constant measurements.

7-7. Molecular Interpretation of Equilibria.   The great importance of free energy stems from its immediate relation to the equilibrium constant of a reacting system.   Since it is a straightforward matter to determine, in principle, the equilibrium constant from molecular properties, it is convenient to do so and then to use the information so obtained to understand the molecular basis for free energy.

Consider an equilibrium such as is established between two isomers of a compound.   If the isomers are represented by A and B, the equilibrium is

$$A \rightleftarrows B$$

To determine the equilibrium constant for an actual reaction from the molecular properties of the reagents, it would be necessary to have complete information on the allowed translational, rotational, vibrational, and electronic

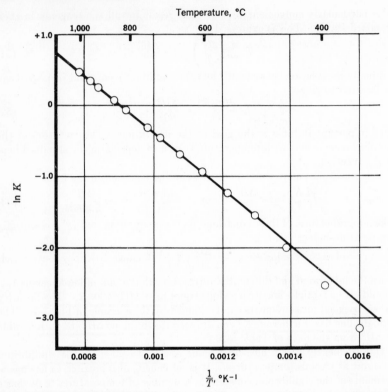

Fig. 7-1. The temperature dependence of the equilibrium constant for the reaction $CO_2 + H_2 \rightarrow CO + H_2O$. (*From Louis P. Hammett, "Introduction to the Study of Physical Chemistry," McGraw-Hill Book Company, Inc., New York, 1952.*)

energy levels of each of the molecules. It is sufficient, at first, to represent the complicated pattern of energy levels by simple sets of levels, as in Fig. 7-2. For the determination of an equilibrium constant, as will appear, the essential features of the molecular energy patterns are the spacings between the energy levels, represented here by ϵ_A and ϵ_B, and the difference in the energy of the lowest available energy levels of the two molecules, represented by $\Delta\epsilon_0$. The second quantity, of course, has already been introduced in Chap. 5 as the molar zero-point energy difference ΔE_0. It is now possible, with the assumed energy-level patterns of Fig. 7-2, to show that the equilibrium constant for the reaction can be determined.

On a molecular basis the question of the position of the equilibrium between A and B is phrased in this way: If a large number of molecules are allowed to distribute themselves throughout the energy-level pattern of Fig. 7-2, how many will end up in an A level and how many in a B level? The question is answered by application of the Boltzmann-distribution expression.

Let N_0^A be the number of molecules which, at equilibrium, occupy the lowest energy level.   This happens to be an A level.

The total number of molecules N_A in the A levels can be calculated from the numbers N_i^A in the individual A levels as

$$N_A = N_0^A + N_1^A + N_2^A + \cdots$$
$$= N_0^A + N_0^A e^{-\epsilon_A/kT} + N_0^A e^{-2\epsilon_A/kT} + \cdots$$
$$= N_0^A(1 + e^{-\epsilon_A/kT} + e^{-2\epsilon_A/kT} + \cdots)$$

or
$$N_A = N_0^A \sum_{i=0}^{\infty} e^{-i\epsilon_A/kT} \qquad \text{where } i = 0, 1, 2, \ldots \qquad (55)$$

In a similar way, the number of molecules that occur in the B levels is

$$N_B = N_0^B + N_1^B + N_2^B + \cdots$$
or
$$N_B = N_0^B(1 + e^{-\epsilon_B/kT} + e^{-2\epsilon_B/kT} + \cdots)$$

$$= N_0^B \sum_{i=0}^{\infty} e^{-i\epsilon_B/kT} \qquad \text{where } i = 0, 1, 2, \ldots \qquad (56)$$

Since equilibrium is established between the distribution throughout the A

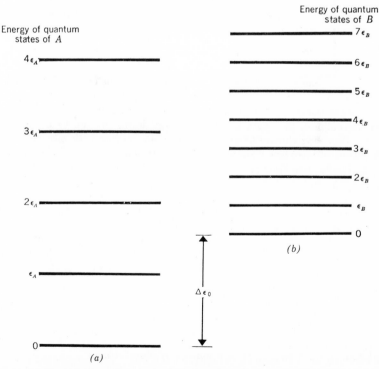

Fig. 7-2. The energy levels of the hypothetical molecules A and B.

levels and the B levels, the population of the lowest B level is related to the population of the lowest A level by the Boltzmann expression

$$N_0^B = N_0^A e^{-\Delta \epsilon_0 / kT} \tag{57}$$

and the total population of the B levels can be rewritten as

$$N_B = N_0^A e^{-\Delta \epsilon_0 / kT} \sum_{i=0}^{\infty} e^{-i\epsilon_B / kT} \tag{58}$$

The equilibrium constant for the reaction of A to B might be expressed in terms of the equilibrium pressure of A and B. If both A and B are assumed to behave as perfect gases and the equilibrium system is in some volume V, then one has

$$P_A = n_A \frac{RT}{V} \quad \text{and} \quad P_B = n_B \frac{RT}{V} \tag{59}$$

The pressures of the two reagents are seen to be proportional to the number of moles or the number of molecules of each present. The equilibrium constant can, therefore, be written as

$$K = \frac{P_B}{P_A} = \frac{N_B}{N_A} = e^{-\Delta \epsilon_0 / kT} \frac{\Sigma e^{-i\epsilon_B / kT}}{\Sigma e^{-i\epsilon_A / kT}} \tag{60}$$

If the difference in zero-point energies is written in terms of 1 mole instead of one molecule, $\Delta \epsilon_0$ is replaced by ΔE_0 and k by R. This gives

$$K = e^{-\Delta E_0 / RT} \frac{\Sigma e^{-i\epsilon_B / kT}}{\Sigma e^{-i\epsilon_A / kT}} \tag{61}$$

This important result shows that the equilibrium constant can be related to two types of molecular-energy terms. The first, ΔE_0, depends only on the difference in the zero-point energies, while the second type, involving ϵ_A and ϵ_B, depends only on the spacings of the energy levels for the two molecules. Before discussing this result and applying it to more realistic situations it is convenient to introduce a simplification in notation.

7-8. The Partition Function.   The result of the previous section is more neatly written if a symbol is introduced for each of the summation terms. One sum of Eq. (61) can be recognized as a property of the compound B, while the other is a property of compound A. Similar summations would have appeared even if a more realistic pattern had been used for the energy levels. Such summations over the energy levels of a molecule frequently occur in calculations of thermodynamic properties and are called *partition functions*. The partition functions, denoted by Q, for the molecules A and B of Fig. 7-2 are defined as

$$\begin{aligned} Q_A &= \sum_{i=0}^{\infty} e^{-i\epsilon_A / kT} \\ Q_B &= \sum_{i=0}^{\infty} e^{-i\epsilon_B / kT} \end{aligned} \tag{62}$$

and with this notation the equilibrium expression becomes

$$K = e^{-\Delta \epsilon_0 / kT} \frac{Q_B}{Q_A} \tag{63}$$

Again, if the zero-point energy difference is expressed in calories per mole, that is, ΔE_0, and R is expressed in calories per mole degree, one writes

$$K = e^{-\Delta E_0/RT} \frac{Q_B}{Q_A} \qquad (64)$$

Two further comments are necessary to make this result, derived for the simple energy patterns of Fig. 7-2, more generally applicable.

It is sometimes important to recognize that some of the allowed energy levels result from more than one quantum state, and such energy levels will then really consist of two, three, or more levels on top of each other. Such multiple levels are said to have a *multiplicity*, or *degeneracy*, of 2, 3, 4, ... The multiplicity of the ith level is usually denoted by g_i. The ith energy level then corresponds to g_i quantum states and will be populated g_i times as much as if it were a single level. In view of such multiple levels, the Boltzmann-distribution expression can be written as

$$N_i = g_i N_0 e^{-\epsilon_i/kT} \qquad (65)$$

Second it must be recognized that in an actual gas-phase molecule the energy levels—translational, rotational, vibrational, and possibly electronic—do not form anything like a simple equispaced pattern as in the illustrative example used here. The previous results are, however, completely applicable to a real system if the more general expression is used that designates the ith level as having energy ϵ_i, above the lowest level for the molecule. This notation has already been used in Eq. (65) and corresponds to a partition function for a molecule

$$Q = \sum_{i=0}^{\infty} g_i e^{-\epsilon_i/kT} \qquad (66)$$

In practice, of course, the determination of the complete energy-level pattern that allows the summation of Eq. (66) to be performed may be a difficult task.

The calculation of the change in any thermodynamic function for a chemical reaction can be shown to involve nothing more than the determination of the partition function and a statement of the ΔE_0 value. The summation represented by this function often is, of course, difficult to calculate on account of the complicated energy-level pattern. In many cases, particularly for solids and liquids, such a calculation is as yet impossible. It is important to notice, however, that the partition function of a gaseous molecule depends only on the energy-level spacing of the molecule and can, at least in principle, be calculated from a knowledge of the translational, rotational, vibrational, and electronic energy levels. For many systems, liquids, for example, where the quantum states and the allowed energy levels are insufficiently understood for such a calculation, the molecular interpretation is helpful in that it provides a qualitative understanding of the thermodynamic properties in terms of a concrete model.

A qualitative appreciation of the partition function is very helpful and can be easily acquired. A large value of Q will result, for example, if the g's are large and if the energy levels are closely spaced. We deduce, therefore, that the partition function is a measure of the number of available energy levels.

It follows then that the *partition function measures the probability*. A molecule with a large partition function has therefore a high probability. This general discussion of the partition function now permits the molecular expression [Eq. (64)] for the equilibrium constant to be further investigated.

Thermodynamics has already revealed that the equilibrium constant for a reaction depends on two factors: an energy effect and an entropy effect. These two factors are therefore recognized in the molecular expression, where they enter in the energy term ΔE_0 and the probability term Q_B/Q_A. The equilibrium constant will tend to be large if the energy term favors the reaction, i.e., if ΔE_0 is small or negative, and if the entropy or probability term favors the reaction, i.e., if Q_B is greater than Q_A.

7-9. Molecular Interpretation of Free Energy. The molecular interpretation of the equilibrium constant can be compared with the thermodynamic relation of the free energy and the equilibrium constant. The logarithm of Eq. (64) gives

$$\ln K = -\frac{\Delta E_0}{RT} + \ln \frac{Q_B}{Q_A}$$

or

$$-RT \ln K = \Delta E_0 - RT \ln \frac{Q_B}{Q_A} \qquad (67)$$

Comparison with the thermodynamic relation $\Delta G^\circ = -RT \ln K$ leads to the result

$$\Delta G^\circ = \Delta E_0 - RT \ln \frac{Q_B}{Q_A} \qquad (68)$$

This molecular interpretation of the free-energy change for the reaction cannot be rigorously resolved into contributions from each of the components since in the formation of the difference term ΔG° some terms may have canceled out. In fact a more detailed derivation shows that an RT term belongs with the free energy of each component. This term is just the same PV, or RT for an ideal gas, term that occurs in the definition of the enthalpy and again represents an ability of the system to do work as a result of the volume occupied by the system. The division of the ΔE_0 term can be made, as has been done in treatments of heats of reactions. Thus, one can write $\Delta E_0 = (E_0)_B - (E_0)_A$ and express the free energies of the separate components A and B as

$$\begin{aligned} G_A^\circ &= (E_0)_A - RT \ln Q_A + RT \\ G_B^\circ &= (E_0)_B - RT \ln Q_B + RT \end{aligned} \qquad (69)$$

These very important expressions show how the free energy is to be understood in terms of molecular energies. For example, a compound can have a high free energy and tend to be reactive as a result of having a large value of E_0 or a low value of Q. The reactivity can, therefore, stem from a high energy base or a low probability. The energy and probability can, of course, work against each other. The free-energy function gives the net effect of these terms. Again, even if calculations cannot be made, these factors will operate and recognition of the energy and probability terms provides a more concrete understanding of free energy.

The quantity that is calculated and frequently tabulated is the *free-energy function*

$$G° - E_0 = -RT \ln Q + RT \tag{70}$$

or

$$\frac{G° - E_0}{T} = -R(\ln Q - 1) \tag{71}$$

If such functions can be calculated for all the reagents in the reaction, one can calculate $\Delta(G° - E_0)$ for the reaction and write

$$\Delta G° = \Delta E_0 + \Delta(G° - E_0) \tag{72}$$

The temperature-independent term ΔE_0 can be obtained from thermal measurements, as was discussed in Sec. 5-8. Calculated values of $\Delta(G° - E_0)$ at various temperatures can then be used to obtain $\Delta G°$ and the equilibrium constant of the reaction at these temperatures. Alternatively one sometimes uses the measured equilibrium constant at one temperature to obtain $\Delta G° = -RT \ln K$ at that temperature. A calculated value of $\Delta(G° - E_0)$ then gives the value of ΔE_0. Again values of $\Delta(G° - E_0)$ at various temperatures can be used with Eq. (72) to obtain $\Delta G°$ and K for the reaction at these temperatures.

The calculation of values for $\Delta G°$ and K for various temperatures from either one thermal result ΔE_0 or one measured equilibrium constant is a step of considerable practical importance. Something of the practical as well as the conceptual value of the molecular interpretation of thermodynamic properties should be apparent as a result of the above deductions.

A very simple example involving highly artificial energy-level schemes can be used to illustrate these results. Consider now the molecules A and B each to have only one allowed energy level. That for A consists of a level of multiplicity 2, that for B, of multiplicity 3, as shown in Fig. 7-3. Furthermore, the multiple energy level of B is taken as 300 cal/mole higher than that for A; that is, ΔE_0 for the reaction A to B is 300 cal/mole. The free-energy difference between A and B and the equilibrium constant for the system can be calculated at two temperatures, say, 25 and 1000°C.

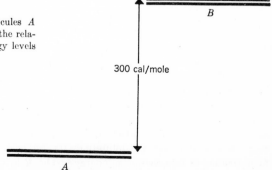

Fig. 7-3. Hypothetical molecules A and B for the illustration of the relation between molecular energy levels and equilibrium constants.

300 cal/mole

B

A

The partition functions are very simply calculated as

$$Q_A = \left(\sum_i g_i e^{-\epsilon_i/kT}\right)_A = g_0^A e^{-0/kT} = (2)(1) = 2$$
$$Q_B = \left(\sum_i g_i e^{-i/kT}\right)_B = g_0^B e^{-0/kT} = (3)(1) = 3 \tag{73}$$

Now Eq. (68) can be used to give

$$\Delta G^\circ_{298} = 300 - (1.987)(298)(2.303) \log \tfrac{3}{2}$$
$$= 300 - 240$$
$$= 60 \text{ cal} \tag{74}$$

and
$$\Delta G^\circ_{1273} = 300 - (1.987)(1{,}273)(2.303) \log \tfrac{3}{2}$$
$$= 300 - 1{,}025$$
$$= -725 \text{ cal} \tag{75}$$

These values of ΔG° could be used to calculate the equilibrium constants at the two temperatures. Alternatively, we can start over again and calculate the equilibrium constant directly from Eq. (64); i.e.,

$$K = e^{-\Delta E_0/RT} \frac{Q_B}{Q_A}$$

Thus
$$K_{298} = e^{-300/(1.987)(298)}(1.5) = 0.90$$
$$K_{1,273} = e^{-300/(1.987)(1,273)}(1.5) = 1.34 \tag{76}$$

It is well worthwhile, even for this artificial example, to notice how the energy and entropy, or probability, factors combine to determine the equilibrium constant. At the lower temperature, the energy term ΔE_0 dominates and leads to the favoring of A over B. At higher temperatures, this factor becomes less important, and the larger number of states that comprise B swings the equilibrium over to the side of B.

7-10. Molecular Interpretation of Entropy. The previous chapter gave the qualitative result that the entropy of a state is to be related to its probability. It is now possible to be a little more quantitative.

The standard free energy of a compound is given both by the thermodynamic relation

$$G^\circ = H^\circ - TS^\circ \tag{77}$$

and the molecular expression, of the previous section,

$$G^\circ = E_0 - RT \ln Q + RT \tag{78}$$

These two interpretations of G° can be equated and, with $H^\circ = E^\circ + RT$, rearranged to give

$$S^\circ = \frac{E^\circ - E_0}{T} + R \ln Q \tag{79}$$

This result provides a means by which the entropy of a chemical compound can be obtained from a knowledge of its energy-level pattern. It has been shown in Secs. 4-13 and 4-15 that the term $E^\circ - E_0$ is just the thermal energy and that this can be calculated from the energy-level pattern. This difference $E^\circ - E_0$ can be obtained absolutely and is not, as E° itself is, dependent on an arbitrary choice of a reference energy. The $R \ln Q$ term has been shown in the previous section to be likewise calculable from the energy-level pattern.

These qualitative ideas that are derived from Eq. (79) lead to the recognition that, at least in principle, an absolute value of the entropy of a compound can be calculated. Calculations for some simple molecules will be carried out in Secs. 7-12 to 7-14. The agreement of entropy values calculated from molecular properties by the use of Eq. (79) with the third-law results is generally good. Some comparisons are shown in Table 7-2. A molecular interpretation of the third law in the following section leads, moreover, to an understanding of the cases of poor agreement and allows a better statement of the third law to be made.

Some appreciation of the molecular interpretation of entropy that is given by Eq. (79) can be reached by first considering two states of a system that happen to have equal thermal energies or are such that they both have zero thermal energies. For such special states A and B, the entropy difference is simply

$$S = S_B - S_A = R \ln \frac{Q_B}{Q_A} \tag{80}$$

It was shown in Sec. 7-8 that the partition function was to be interpreted as a measure of the number of available quantum levels of a state or as the probability of a state. Equation (80) leads again, as did our qualitative discussions of Sec. 6-7, to the understanding of entropy in terms of probabilities and more specifically to the statement that *entropy is proportional to the logarithm of the probability of the state.*

A more thorough interpretation of the molecular basis of thermodynamic functions than can be given here would, in fact, choose as a starting point the statement that the entropy is the logarithm of the probability. Such an approach, however, requires rather more of a statistical interpretation of probability than seems necessary for our purposes. Furthermore, it is perhaps well for a chemist to emphasize the importance of free energy and to look to the equilibrium-constant expression [Eq. (64)] and the closely related free-energy

Table 7-2. Comparison of Entropies Calculated from Molecular Properties with Their Third-law Values

Gas	Entropy (cal/deg mole) of the ideal gas at 1 atm and 298°K		
	Calculated	Third law	Deviation
Cl_2...............	53.31	53.3	0.0
CO................	47.31	46.2	1.1*
HCl...............	44.62	44.5	0.1
HBr...............	47.48	47.6	0.1
H_2O..............	45.11	44.3	0.8*
N_2O..............	42.58	51.4	1.1*
NO (at 121.4°K)......	43.75	43.0	0.8*
CH_4..............	44.50	44.3	0.2
C_2H_4.............	52.45	52.5	0.0

* Accounted for by disorder at absolute zero.

expressions [Eqs. (69)] as the basis for molecular interpretations of free energy and entropy.

7-11. Molecular Interpretation of the Third Law. These molecular deductions of the preceding section have led to the same conclusion as that stated in the third law of thermodynamics, namely, that an absolute value can be assigned to the entropy of a chemical compound. The absolute values obtained from considerations of the details of molecular energies are compared with those from calorimetric third-law measurements in Table 7-2. It is apparent that some discrepancies exist between the third-law entropy values and the calculated values and that these disagreements are outside the experimental error of about 0.2 cal/deg. These discrepancies arise because of the loose statement that has been used for the third law in Sec. 6-9. A molecular interpretation of the third law shows what the source of these difficulties is and leads to a better statement of the third law. Attempts to provide a molecular understanding of entropy have led to the identification of entropy with the logarithm of the probability of the state of the system. For solid and liquid systems it is usually not possible to calculate a value for the entropy. For perfect crystals near absolute zero, however, the situation is particularly simple.

For a molecule of a crystal a set of allowed energy levels will exist which can qualitatively be described as related to the twistings and the vibrations of the molecule about its equilibrium position. The quantitative aspects of the entire energy-level pattern are generally not known. As the temperature approaches absolute zero, it will be true, however, that no matter what the energy pattern is like, the molecules will occupy only the lowest available level. If there is only one available lowest energy state, as is usually the case, the assignment of each molecule to that state corresponds to forcing the system into a state of very low probability. There are, it should be mentioned, a variety of states due to nuclear behavior in a molecule, but these contribute equally at absolute zero and all other temperatures and can be left out of consideration. The situation at absolute zero can be compared with that of requiring all the pennies in the box of Sec. 6-7 to show heads. More quantitatively, the expression for the entropy obtained in Sec. 7-10, that is, $S = R \ln Q$ when $E - E_0$ is zero, can be used to show that, since Q approaches unity for a perfect crystal at absolute zero, the entropy S must approach zero. It is the perfectly ordered state of the crystal, with all the molecules in the same lowest energy level, that is the molecular basis for the third-law result that the entropy is zero at absolute zero.

The positive values for the entropies of all compounds at temperatures above absolute zero result from the fact that, as the temperature is raised, more and more energy levels become available to the molecules. The entropies at such temperatures are, of course, very characteristic of the individual molecule since each molecule, particularly in the solid or liquid state, will have its own particular energy-level pattern.

The reason for the discrepancies between the calculated and third-law entropies of Table 7-2 can now be given.

The molecule CO, for example, shows a third-law entropy which is 1.11 cal/deg greater than the value calculated molecularly. Such a discrepancy would result if the entropy of carbon monoxide at absolute zero was not, in fact, zero but had a positive value of about 1 cal/deg. This would imply that the state of the crystal at absolute zero is not perfectly ordered, i.e., does not have the lowest possible probability.

The explanation for the disorder of such a crystal at absolute zero is that the two ends of the molecule are very similar and a crystal might form, not with the perfect order (CO CO CO $\cdots$) but, possibly, with a disordered pattern, such as (CO CO OC CO $\cdots$). A crystal formed in this way will have insufficient energy at very low temperatures to reorient the molecules. Since the probability of each molecule occupying a site in the crystal and being correctly oriented is unity, the probability of a molecule occupying a site and having either orientation is twice that. The entropy of such a crystal might be expected to be greater than the generally expected value of zero by $R \ln 2 = 1.38$ per degree. The discrepancy found for CO is approximately this value.

Other types of disorder can now be expected to persist at absolute zero and to lead to apparent discrepancies in the third law. A glassy material at absolute zero, for example, will not have the necessary molecular order to guarantee an entropy of zero at absolute zero. In view of difficulties such as these a more careful statement of the third law becomes necessary. One such statement, which is suitable for chemical applications, is: *The entropy of all pure, ordered crystalline solids may be taken as zero at the absolute zero of temperature.*

*7-12. The Translational Entropy of an Ideal Gas. It is particularly important to obtain a qualitative understanding of the molecular basis for entropy and energy and, furthermore, an appreciation of how these factors determine the free-energy difference and the equilibrium constant for reacting species. It is, however, satisfying also to see that the molecular expressions that have been obtained here in a rather simple manner can lead to quantitative values for thermodynamic functions. In particular, it can be shown that a value can be calculated for the entropy of an ideal gas and that such calculated values agree with the thermodynamic third-law values. It should be pointed out that in this and the following several sections the treatment of a number of complications that are present is avoided. The more detailed treatment of the molecular interpretation of thermodynamic functions depends on a more thorough discussion of probability. Advanced texts on statistical mechanics or statistical thermodynamics can be consulted for this material.

The calculation of entropy from molecular properties makes use of Eq. (79),

$$S^\circ = \frac{E^\circ - E_0^\circ}{T} + R \ln Q$$

Although, as we shall see, a special complication enters into the calculation of the translational contribution to the entropy, it seems well to start with this term since the calculated value of S°_{trans} can be immediately compared with the third-law values for the entropies of the inert gases.

The translational energy of an Avogadro's number of molecules has been shown on both classical and quantum-mechanical grounds to be $\frac{3}{2}RT$. This value can be substituted for the first term of Eq. (79) to give

$$S^{\circ}_{\text{trans}} = \tfrac{3}{2}R + R \ln Q_{\text{trans}} \tag{81}$$

The partition-function term involves a summation over the allowed translational energy levels. For a particle of mass m in a cubic container of dimension a the allowed energy levels, which were obtained in Sec. 3-11, are given by

$$\epsilon = (n_x^2 + n_y^2 + n_z^2) \frac{h^2}{8ma^2} \tag{82}$$

where n_x, n_y, and n_z are the quantum numbers for the 3 translational degrees of freedom. The partition function for such a set of levels is

$$
\begin{aligned}
Q &= \sum_{n_x,n_y,n_z=1}^{\infty} e^{-(n_x{}^2+n_y{}^2+n_z{}^2)\,h^2/8ma^2kT} \\
&= \left(\sum_{n_x=1}^{\infty} e^{-n_x{}^2h^2/8ma^2kT} \right) \left(\sum_{n_y=1}^{\infty} e^{-n_y{}^2h^2/8ma^2kT} \right) \left(\sum_{n_z=1}^{\infty} e^{-n_z{}^2h^2/8ma^2kT} \right)
\end{aligned} \tag{83}
$$

Since the translational energy levels are, as shown in Sec. 3-10, very closely spaced, each summation can be replaced by an integration. Thus the first summation of Eq. (83) becomes

$$\int_0^{\infty} e^{-n_x{}^2h^2/8ma^2kT} \, dn_x$$

The substitution

$$\alpha^2 = \frac{n_x^2 h^2}{8ma^2kT}$$

rearranges the integral to

$$\frac{a}{h} (8mkT)^{\frac{1}{2}} \int_0^{\infty} e^{-\alpha^2} \, d\alpha$$

This definite integral has the value $\sqrt{\pi/2}$, and the entire translational partition function is obtained as

$$Q = \left[\frac{(2\pi mkT)^{\frac{1}{2}}a}{h} \right]^3 \tag{84}$$

Substitution of $a^3 = V$ gives the result

$$Q = \frac{(2\pi mkT)^{\frac{3}{2}}V}{h^3} \tag{85}$$

A subtlety that has so far been ignored now arises as a result of the Avogadro's number of molecules having to accommodate themselves in the set of energy levels that, as it were, belongs to the container in which the molecules are put.

Suppose, for comparison with the problem of interest, that we first consider the system to consist of an Avogadro's number of particles each in its own box of volume V. The partition function for each box is Q as given by Eq. (85). The contribution to the entropy of the system from each set of energy levels will be $k \ln Q$ so that the total entropy contribution from the Avogadro's number of boxes will be $N(k \ln Q)$ or $R \ln Q$, in agreement with the partition-function term of Eq. (79).   For a system with N particles in N sets of energy levels the entropy contribution term can be written, therefore, as $N(k \ln Q)$ or $k \ln Q^N$, where the Q^N term is the product of the partition functions for each of the energy-level patterns.   For N separate energy-level patterns the second term in the entropy expression of Eq. (79) is, therefore, k times the natural logarithm of the product of the partition functions calculated for each energy-level pattern.

Now the effect of requiring all N particles to distribute themselves in one set of energy levels must be investigated.   The problem is simplified by the fact that there are very many more translational energy levels than there are molecules and therefore it is unlikely that an energy level will be occupied by more than one molecule.   The difference between the case of a single box and that of separate boxes is indicated by a particular distribution of 3 particles in Fig. 7-4. If each particle were in a separate box, these distributions would be counted as contributing 6 different arrangements.   In one box, on the other hand, *since the particles are not numbered and are indistinguishable,* the 6 arrangements that were different when different containers were imagined become identical and should be counted only once.   For this example of 3 particles the number

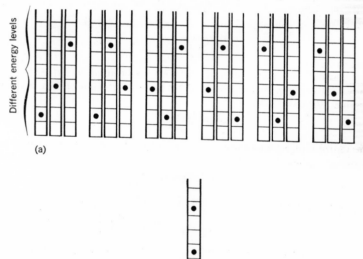

(a)

(b)

Fig. 7-4. A schematic illustration that 6, or 3!, different arrangements of 3 particles with 1 to an energy-level pattern lead to only one arrangement if all particles are identical and are put in a single energy pattern.   (For N particles the number of different arrangements is decreased by a factor of $N!$.)   (a) Each particle in a separate box, or energy-level pattern.   (b) All three particles accommodated by a single energy-level pattern.

of distributions for the single box is $1/3!$ times that for separate boxes. For an Avogadro's number of particles the total partition-function term Q^N, appropriate when there are N separate energy-level patterns, must be divided by $N!$ to remove these meaningless interchanges of particles.

For translation, therefore, the general $R \ln Q$ term of Eq. (79), which can be written as $k \ln Q^N$, should be replaced by the special expression

$$k \ln \frac{Q^N}{N!} \tag{86}$$

where Q is given by Eq. (85). It should be recognized that the use of $Q^N/N!$ rather than a term Q^N arises from the fact that, for translation, there is just one set of translational energy levels into which all the molecules must go. Rotation, vibration, and electronic energy levels are different in that each molecule "owns" its own levels.

The $N!$ term can be handled by the Stirling approximation

$$\begin{aligned} \ln N! &= N \ln N - N \\ &= N \ln N - N \ln e \end{aligned} \tag{87}$$

which can be written as

$$N! = \left(\frac{N}{e}\right)^N \tag{88}$$

Substitution of this approximation in expression (86) gives

$$k \ln \left(\frac{Qe}{N}\right)^N = R \ln \frac{Qe}{N} \tag{89}$$

The translational partition-function term to be used in Eq. (81) for the entropy is, therefore, finally obtained by the substitution of Eq. (85) in the expression (89) as

$$R \ln \frac{(2\pi m k T)^{\frac{3}{2}}}{Nh^3} eV \tag{90}$$

The entropy of a monatomic ideal gas is therefore given, according to Eq. (81), as

$$S^0_{\text{trans}} = \tfrac{3}{2}R + R \ln \frac{(2\pi m k T)^{\frac{3}{2}} eV}{Nh^3} \tag{91}$$

Recognition that $\ln e = 1$ leads finally to the important result

$$S^0_{\text{trans}} = R \left[\frac{5}{2} + \ln \frac{(2\pi m k T)^{\frac{3}{2}}}{Nh^3} V \right] \tag{92}$$

This equation was obtained by Sackur and Tetrode by an early and rather unsatisfactory derivation. It has now been frequently checked against third-law entropies and can be relied on to give the translational contribution to the entropy of an ideal gas.

The experimental third-law entropy of argon gas at 1 atm pressure and $87.3°K$, its normal boiling point, has been reported as 30.85 cal/mole deg. The values necessary for the calculation of S^0_{trans} from Eq. (92) are

$$m = 6.63 \times 10^{-23} \text{ g} \qquad h = 6.62 \times 10^{-27} \text{ erg-sec}$$

$$k = 1.38 \times 10^{-16} \text{ erg/deg} \qquad V = \frac{87.3}{273}(22,400) = 7,160 \text{ cc}$$

$$T = 87.3°K$$

The calculated entropy is, therefore,

$$S° = R(\tfrac{5}{2} + 2.303 \log 4.61 \times 10^5)$$
$$= 1.987(2.500 + 13.045)$$
$$= 30.89 \text{ cal/deg mole} \tag{93}$$

The calculated value agrees nicely, therefore, with that based on the third-law calorimetric method.

Such agreement of calculated and third-law entropies can be taken as support either for the molecular postulate of Schrödinger and Boltzmann or for the thermodynamic choice of a zero entropy at absolute zero.

*7-13. The Rotational Entropy of the Diatomic Molecules of an Ideal Gas. As was pointed out in Sec. 3-15, a rotating molecule has a set of rotational energy levels. For a diatomic, or any linear, molecule, the allowed rotational energies of a molecule of moment of inertia I will be shown in Chap. 10 to be given by

$$\epsilon_{rot} = \frac{J(J+1)h^2}{8\pi^2 I} \qquad J = 0, 1, 2, \ldots \tag{94}$$

Furthermore, the rotational energy level corresponding to a given value of J will be found to have a multiplicity of $2J + 1$. These features of the rotational energy patterns allow the rotational partition function and then the rotational contribution to the entropy to be obtained.

The partition function is, according to Eq. (66), the summation

$$Q_{rot} = \sum_{J=0}^{\infty} g_J e^{-\epsilon_J/kT}$$

$$= \sum_{J=0}^{\infty} (2J+1)e^{-J(J+1)h^2/8\pi^2 IkT} \tag{95}$$

The rotational energy levels are sufficiently close together so that this summation may be replaced by an integration to give

$$Q_{rot} = \int_0^{\infty} (2J+1)e^{-J(J+1)h^2/8\pi^2 IkT} \, dJ \tag{96}$$

This integral can be put in a recognizable form by writing β for the terms $h^2/8\pi^2 IkT$ and introducing the variable z for $J(J+1)$. Thus

$$z = J(J+1) \qquad \text{and} \qquad dz = (2J+1) \, dJ$$

With this notation the integral is simply

$$\int_0^{\infty} e^{-\beta z} \, dz$$

The value of this definite integral is $1/\beta = 8\pi^2 IkT/h^2$. The desired result for the rotational partition function is, therefore,

$$Q_{rot} = \frac{8\pi^2 IkT}{h^2} \tag{97}$$

This result, it should be mentioned, is correct only for heteronuclear diatomic and for unsymmetric linear polyatomic molecules. For molecules such as H_2, N_2, CO_2, and acetylene, $H—C\equiv C—H$, the symmetrical nature of the molecule makes some of the rotational states whose energy levels are given by Eq. (94) not allowed. The rotational partition function is then somewhat different from that obtained here. We need not, however, become involved in this complexity.

The rotational energy of a molecule was shown in Sec. 3-15 to be $\frac{1}{2}RT$ per degree of freedom. For a linear molecule, which has just 2 rotational degrees of freedom, the value of $E - E_0$ for rotation is therefore RT. With this result and Eq. (79), the rotational entropy of a heteronuclear diatomic molecule can be written as

$$S_{\text{rot}} = \frac{(E° - E_0°)_{\text{rot}}}{T} + R \ln Q_{\text{rot}}$$

$$= R\left(1 + \ln \frac{8\pi^2 I kT}{h^2}\right) \tag{98}$$

For CO, for example, as will be shown in Sec. 10-1 the bond length is 1.128 A, and the moment of inertia is 14.48×10^{-40} g/sq cm. The rotational-entropy contribution at 25°C can therefore be calculated as

$$\begin{aligned} S_{\text{rot}} &= R(1 + 2.303 \log 107.5) \\ &= R(1 + 4.680) \\ &= 11.29 \text{ cal/deg mole} \end{aligned} \tag{99}$$

For comparison, the translational entropy of CO at 1 atm and 298°K can be calculated from Eq. (91) as

$$S_{\text{trans}} = 35.75 \text{ cal/deg mole} \tag{100}$$

The much greater translational- than rotational-entropy contribution can be understood in terms of the much closer spacing of the translational energy levels and, therefore, the much larger number of translational states throughout which the molecules are distributed.

*7-14. The Vibrational Entropy of the Diatomic Molecules of an Ideal Gas. The vibrational energy levels for a diatomic molecule form, as discussed in Sec. 4-14, a pattern with equally spaced energy levels that are given by the expression

$$\epsilon_{\text{vib}} = (v + \tfrac{1}{2})\epsilon \tag{101}$$

where ϵ is the spacing between adjacent levels. The quantum state corresponding to the quantum number v is, therefore, at an energy $v\epsilon$ above the state with $v = 0$. The partition function is then simply

$$Q_{\text{vib}} = \sum_{v=0}^{\infty} e^{-v\epsilon/kT}$$

or $$Q_{\text{vib}} = 1 + e^{-\epsilon/kT} + e^{-2\epsilon/kT} + \cdots \tag{102}$$

Unlike the translational- and rotational-energy summations, the vibrational-energy summation presents discrete terms since the levels are appreciably spaced compared with kT; this series cannot, therefore, be replaced by an integral. The series can be summed, however, by the trick used in Sec. 4-14. Thus, multiplication of Eq. (102) on the left and on the right by $e^{-\epsilon/kT}$ gives

$$Q_{\text{vib}}e^{-\epsilon/kT} = e^{-\epsilon/kT} + e^{-2\epsilon/kT} + e^{-3\epsilon/kT} + \cdots \tag{103}$$

Subtraction of Eq. (103) from Eq. (102) leads, after term-by-term cancellation of the series terms, to

$$Q_{\text{vib}}(1 - e^{-\epsilon/kT}) = 1$$

or $$Q_{\text{vib}} = \frac{1}{1 - e^{-\epsilon/kT}} \tag{104}$$

The vibrational-entropy contribution can be obtained by use of this result and Eq. (4-51), which gives the $E - E_0$ term as

$$E - E_0 = \frac{N\epsilon}{e^{\epsilon/kT} - 1}$$

Thus Eq. (79) can give, for each vibrational degree of freedom,

$$S^\circ_{vib} = \frac{N\epsilon/T}{e^{\epsilon/kT} - 1} + R \ln \frac{1}{1 - e^{-\epsilon/kT}} \tag{105}$$

For CO, for example, the vibrational levels are found to be spaced by 2,168 cm^{-1}, or 4.31×10^{-13} erg. The vibrational contribution to the entropy at 25°C can then be shown by substitution of values in Eq. (105) to be insignificant.

Qualitatively it can be recognized that such a small fraction of the molecules are in vibrational states other than the lowest available vibrational level that the entropy contribution from the vibrational states is effectively zero. In general the vibrational-entropy contribution is small but, except for wide vibrational spacings as in CO, not negligible.

It follows, therefore, that the total entropy of CO at 1 atm and 298°K is calculated, according to the expression given here, as

$$\begin{aligned} S^\circ &= S^\circ_{trans} + S^\circ_{rot} + S^\circ_{vib} + S^\circ_{elec} \\ &= 35.75 + 11.29 + 0.00 + 0.00 \\ &= 47.04 \text{ cal/deg mole} \end{aligned} \tag{106}$$

Calculations that allow for the fact that the rotational-energy term $E - E_0$ is not exactly the classical value give the calculated result 47.31 cal/deg mole.

The third-law value of 46.2 is expected, in view of the discussion of Sec. 7-11, to be too small by the amount $R \ln 2 = 1.38$ owing to residual randomness at absolute zero. Thus, the corrected third-law result of 47.6 is in satisfactory agreement with the value obtained from molecular properties.

The calculation of the entropy of CO is an example of the results that can be deduced for thermodynamic functions from a knowledge of molecular properties. For larger gas-phase molecules, the procedure is usually limited by the difficulty in deducing the energy-level spacings for the $3n - 6$ vibrational modes. For liquids and solids so little is known about the allowed energy-level patterns that it is not generally possible to perform the summations over energy levels and obtain values for thermodynamic properties.

Problems

1. The values of ΔH and ΔS for a chemical reaction are -22.6 kcal and -45.2 cal/deg, respectively, and these values are not changed much by temperature changes.
    (a) What is ΔG for the reaction at 300°K?   *Ans.* $-9,040$ cal.
    (b) What is ΔG for the reaction at 1000°K?   *Ans.* $+22,600$ cal.
2. Calculate ΔH, ΔS, and ΔG when 1 mole of water is converted from liquid at 100°C and 1 atm to vapor at the same temperature and pressure. Discuss the influence of the entropy and energy factors on the spontaneity of the reaction.
3. What is the free-energy change when 4.50 g of water is converted from liquid at

25°C to vapor at 25°C and a pressure of 0.1 mm Hg. (The equilibrium vapor pressure of water at 25°C is 23.8 mm Hg, and the vapor can be assumed to behave ideally.) Will the process from liquid to this vapor tend to proceed spontaneously?

Ans. −810 cal.

4. Express ΔH, ΔS, and ΔG for a system consisting of two large blocks, at different temperatures, and a process in which a small amount of heat Q is transferred:

(a) From the high-temperature to the low-temperature block

(b) From the low-temperature to the high-temperature block

5. Using data of previously given tables, confirm the value of the standard free energy given in Table 7-1 for CO_2 at 25°C.

6. Calculate the free energies at 25°C, based on the standard free energies of Table 7-1, of:

(a) Ethylene at 10^{-5} atm pressure

(b) Hydrogen at 10^{-5} atm pressure

(c) Ethane at 10^5 atm pressure

What would be the free-energy change for the formation of ethane from hydrogen and ethylene if the reagents are at these partial pressures?

Compare with the value obtained in Eq. (22), and comment on the spontaneity of the reaction in each situation.

7. Calculate the free energies at 25°C, based on the standard heats of Table 5-2 and the entropies of Table 6-3, for C_2H_4, H_2, and C_2H_6 at 1 atm and at the pressures indicated in Prob. 6. Calculate ΔH, ΔS, and ΔG for the reaction $H_2 + C_2H_4 \rightarrow C_2H_6$ for the reagents at 1 atm pressure and for the pressure conditions of Prob. 6 and for standard states. Comment on the factors that affect the spontaneity of the reaction in the two situations.

8. The standard heat of formation and the entropy of *n*-pentane, $CH_3CH_2CH_2$-CH_2CH_3, at 25°C and 1 atm are −35.00 kcal/mole and 83.40 cal/deg mole, respectively. The values for neopentane, $(CH_3)_4C$, are −39.67 kcal/mole and 73.23 cal/deg mole.

(a) What is the free-energy difference for these compounds at 25°C and 1 atm pressure?

(b) What pressure would neopentane be taken to in order to have the same entropy as *n*-pentane has at 1 atm and the same free energy as *n*-pentane has at 1 atm?

Ans. 6.0×10^{-3} atm.; 16 atm.

(c) An amount of n-pentane to produce 1 atm pressure is put in a reaction chamber with a catalyst that brings about equilibrium with neopentane. What are the pressures of the two isomers at equilibrium, the temperature being held at 25°C?

Ans. $P_{n\text{-pentane}} = 0.059$; $P_{\text{neopentane}} = 0.941$ atm.

9. What is the equilibrium constant at 25°C for the formation of benzene from acetylene by the reaction $3(C_2H_2) \rightarrow C_6H_6$? What would be the equilibrium pressures in a reaction vessel which initially held acetylene at 1 atm pressure at 25°C?

10. Assuming that ΔH for the reaction of Prob. 9 is essentially constant over the temperature range 25 to 500°C, obtain an expression for the equilibrium constant as a function of temperature in this range. What is the equilibrium constant at 500°C?

Ans. $K_P = 1.3 \times 10^{23}$.

11. Calculate the logarithm of the equilibrium constant at 25°C for the reaction $CO_2(g) + H_2(g) \rightarrow CO(g) + H_2O(g)$, using the free-energy data of Table 7-1.

Obtain an expression for the heat of the reaction as a function of temperature from the standard heats of formation and the heat-capacity data of Table 5-3.

Deduce an expression for log K as a function of temperature in the temperature range

300 to 1000°K. Plot and compare with the experimental results shown in Fig. 7-1 (note that Fig. 7-1 is in terms of natural logarithms).

12. What is the equilibrium constant at 25°C for the reaction of oxygen and hydrogen to form water vapor? Equal volumes of oxygen and hydrogen are mixed and put in a constant volume container. If the initial total pressure is 0.01 atm, what will be the pressures of all reagents if a spark is passed through the mixture and equilibrium is established?

13. At 3000°K the equilibrium pressures of CO_2, CO, and O_2 are 0.6, 0.4, and 0.2 atm, respectively.

(a) Calculate the equilibrium constant for the reaction $2CO_2 \rightarrow 2CO + O_2$.

(b) What is the value of $\Delta G^{\circ}_{3000°K}$ for this reaction?   *Ans.* +14,570 cal.

14. The equilibrium constant at 400°C for the reaction $\frac{3}{2}H_2 + \frac{1}{2}N_2 \rightarrow NH_3$ is 0.0129.

(a) Calculate $\Delta G^{\circ}_{673°K}$ for this reaction.

(b) Using the standard heats of formation of Table 5-2 and the heat capacities of Table 5-3, obtain an expression for the heat of reaction as a function of temperature.

(c) Deduce the equilibrium constant and ΔG° at 298°K.

(d) With the result of (c) and the standard heats of formation of the reagents calculate ΔS° for the reaction at 298°K.

(e) Compare this value of ΔS° from the measured equilibrium constant and thermal data with the value given by the third-law results of Table 6-3.

15. Calculate the free-energy differences and the equilibrium constants at 25 and 1000°C for hypothetical molecules A and B such as in Fig. 7-3, but with A having a single level and B having a doubly degenerate one 500 cal/mole higher than that of A.
          Ans. $\Delta G^{\circ}_{298} = +89$; $\Delta G^{\circ}_{1273} = -1255$ cal.

16. Consider a hypothetical molecule that, instead of having real translational, rotational, and vibrational energy levels, has only two allowed energy levels and that these levels are separated by an amount 600 cal/mole. Over the temperature range 0 to 2000°K, and with the assumption of ideal-gas behavior, plot:

(a) The thermal contribution to the internal energy

(b) The thermal contribution to the enthalpy

(c) The thermal contribution to the free energy

(d) The entropy

(e) The heat capacity at constant pressure

Comment on the low- and high-temperature limiting values of each function.

17. Calculate ΔH, ΔS, ΔG, and K at 298 and 1500°K for the reaction forming 1 mole of B from 1 mole of A. A molecule of A is characterized by a series of levels spaced by the constant amount 1000 cal/mole and a molecule of B by a similar series with a constant spacing of 2000 cal/mole. The lowest B level is 200 cal/mole above the lowest A level. (The series that must be summed can be handled by a term-by-term numerical summation.)

18. Show by substitution of the summation expression for the partition function that the internal-energy function $E - E_0$ can be related to the partition function by the equation $E - E_0 = RT^2(d \ln Q/dT)$.

19. If the translational, rotational, and vibrational energies of a molecule can be written as separate terms, the sum of which is the total energy, show that the total partition function is the product of the partition functions for each type of energy. Show further that the entropy as given by Eq. (79) can be written as the sum of the translational, rotational, and vibrational contributions.

*20. Calculate the entropy of helium at 25°C and 1 atm pressure. Compare this result with the third-law entropy value of 29.8 cal/deg.

*21. Plot the entropy contribution to a molecule from a vibrational degree of freedom as a function of the vibrational-level spacing. Prepare plots for 298 and 1500°K. (Vibrational levels are found spectroscopically to be spaced by energies up to about 4,000 cm^{-1}.)

Compare these curves with the qualitative statement that the entropy increases as the number of available states increases.

*22. Plot the entropy contribution to a molecule from a rotational degree of freedom as a function of the moment of inertia of the molecule. Prepare plots at 298 and 1500°K. (Moments of inertia of relatively simple molecules to which the equations developed here apply are in the range 3×10^{-40} to about $1,000 \times 10^{-40}$ g/sq cm.)

*23. Calculate the entropy of N_2O at 25°C and 1 atm pressure. The molecule is linear and has a moment of inertia of 66.9×10^{-40} g/sq cm. The four vibrational modes have spacings 2,224, 1,285, 589, and 589 cm^{-1}. Compare the calculated value with the third-law result, corrected for $R \ln 2$ residual entropy at absolute zero, of 52.6 cal/deg.

8

Introduction to the Theory of
Chemical Bonding

The subject of atomic and molecular structure has been introduced in Chap. 3 only in sufficient detail to allow a molecular interpretation to be given to the thermodynamic functions. A further direct look into the molecular world will now be taken.

One of the most exciting endeavors in man's investigation of the world in which he lives has been his attempts to understand the basic units of matter that make up the material world. For the chemist the basic units are the molecules and the atoms of which they are composed. Even when these particles have been identified, the questions of why and how atoms are held together into molecules remain. Some of the long-sought-for answers to these questions can now be given, and, in this respect, the description of the nature of chemical bonding represents the culmination of one aspect of man's efforts to unravel the secrets of matter.

An attempt will be made to present here the approaches used by current theoretical studies of molecular structure. It should be mentioned that not only is the scope of the present chapter limited to a few simple molecules but the present state of the theory itself is likewise limited. The molecules that can be considered to have yielded to quantitative theoretical analyses can, in fact, be taken to include only the single example of the hydrogen molecule. One must at times, however, allow oneself to be impressed with the fact that the source of attraction between two hydrogen atoms to form a hydrogen molecule has been discovered, for it is this calculation that reveals the nature of chemical binding. A tremendous increase in our understanding of all chemistry results. The awkwardness with which the theory tackles larger molecules should not conceal this triumph.

It is not necessary for us to become involved in the mathematical complexities to which molecular theory inevitably leads. The goal of the chapter will be to provide an appreciation of the modern approaches to molecular structure. Such an appreciation will provide a foundation for further studies of molecular theory and also will present the necessary information and attitudes for its more qualitative use in other branches of chemistry. It should be pointed out, furthermore, that the understanding of molecular structure and bonding that results from the approaches of this and the following chapter has been in a large measure responsible for tremendous advances in many branches of chemistry and biochemistry since 1900. It now is necessary to have at least a qualitative appreciation of molecular theory to keep up with the developments in any part of chemistry and related fields.

The present chapter deals with theoretical approaches to molecular bonding. The following chapter considers some of the extensions that have been made to larger molecules. The complementing experimental studies are treated in Chap. 10. The theory of molecular bonding is so dependent on that of atomic structure that it is first necessary to extend atomic theory beyond the stage reached in Chap. 3.

ATOMIC STRUCTURE

8-1. The Solution of the Schrödinger Equation for the Hydrogen Atom. The previous introduction to wave mechanics, as represented by the Schrödinger equation, pointed out that it provided a method of solving for the electronic energy and the electron position in a system of atomic or molecular dimensions. The use of the equation was illustrated only by very simple potential-energy functions. Problems involving such functions, however, are representative of many applications of the Schrödinger equation. It is well, at first, to keep in mind that, although the mathematical details of an atomic problem are more complicated, the procedure of the calculation is just that followed in Secs. 3-9 to 3-11.

One might have felt that all problems in atomic and molecular structure were solved when the Schrödinger equation was suggested and accepted. They are solved "in principle" according to the famous statement by the physicist Dirac. It is true, however, that only the very simplest atomic and molecular systems can be handled in a straightforward and reasonably exact manner. Molecular systems that interest chemists are usually of such complexity that the Schrödinger equation serves as little more than a guide to a semiempirical understanding. The basis of almost all quantum-mechanical studies of atoms and molecules is the description of the hydrogen atom provided by wave mechanics. For this reason it is not possible to overemphasize the importance of appreciating the qualitative aspects of the wave functions deduced for the electron of a hydrogenlike atom.

The Schrödinger equation can be set up for the electron moving in the electric field of the nucleus. If the nuclear charge is $+Ze$, where Z is the atomic number, and the electronic charge is $-e$, the potential energy of the electron at a distance r from the nucleus is $-Ze^2/r$.   Substitution of this potential-energy function in the three-dimensional Schrödinger equation (Sec. 3-11) gives

$$-\frac{h^2}{8\pi^2 m}\left(\frac{\partial^2\psi}{\partial x^2} + \frac{\partial^2\psi}{\partial y^2} + \frac{\partial^2\psi}{\partial z^2}\right) - \frac{Ze^2}{r}\,\psi = \epsilon\psi \qquad (1)$$

The spherical symmetry of the potential-energy function about the nucleus suggests that solutions of the equation will be more readily found if it is written in the spherical coordinates shown in Fig. 8-1.   The three coordinates in this system are r, θ, and ϕ.   These are related to the cartesian coordinates, as can be seen by inspection of Fig. 8-1, by the equations

$$\begin{aligned} x &= r\sin\theta\cos\phi \\ y &= r\sin\theta\sin\phi \\ z &= r\cos\theta \end{aligned} \qquad (2)$$

The mathematical steps by which Eq. (1) is transformed to spherical coordinates and solutions are found for the resulting equation are rather lengthy and will not be followed through here.   It is sufficient for our purposes to recognize that the problem is the same, in principle, as that which was worked through in Sec. 3-11 for a particle in a three-dimensional square-well-type

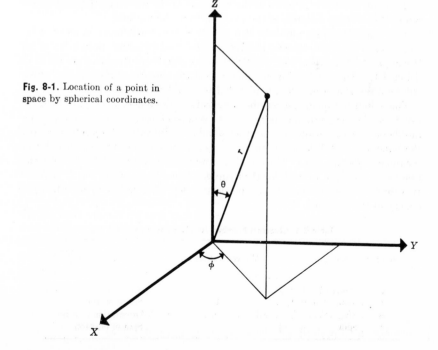

Fig. 8-1. Location of a point in space by spherical coordinates.

potential. It is found that solution functions exist for the spherical-coordinate form of Eq. (1) only for energies given by the expression

$$\epsilon = -\frac{2\pi^2 m e^4 Z^2}{h^2 n^2} \quad \text{where } n = 1, 2, 3, \ldots \quad (3)$$

The Schrödinger-equation approach, therefore, leads to exactly the same allowed energies as those previously deduced from the Bohr model of the atom.

The functions that solve the Schrödinger equation can, like those found for the three-dimensional square potential in Sec. 3-11, be written as the product of three functions, each function involving only one of the three coordinates r, θ, and ϕ. The solutions can therefore be represented as

$$\psi(r,\theta,\phi) = R(r)\Theta(\theta)\Phi(\phi) \quad (4)$$

The solutions represented by Eq. (4) contain three quantum numbers; i.e., a given solution is designated by assigning three integers to the general solution function. These quantum numbers are also analogous, and appear in an analogous way, to those of the particle-in-a-box problem.

One of the three quantum numbers is represented by n, and only this quantum number shows up in the energy expression [Eq. (3)] as well as in the wave function. It plays a role that is very similar to that of the rather arbitrarily introduced Bohr-atom quantum number. It determines the electronic energy and, as will be shown, appears in the $R(r)$ part of the wave function and determines the average distance of the electron from the nucleus.

Two other quantum numbers also appear in the Schrödinger-equation solutions. The symbols, names, possible values, and principal properties of all three quantum numbers that the Schrödinger equation introduces are listed in Table 8-1. An additional quantum number, the spin quantum number, which will be discussed in Sec. 8-3, is included to complete the table.

The azimuthal quantum number l appears in the θ dependence of the wave function; the magnetic number m, in the ϕ dependence. These two quantum numbers, like the principal quantum number n, introduce themselves in just the same way as did the quantum numbers in the solutions of Secs. 3-9 and 3-11 for the particle in a box. The quantum numbers l and m are different from the number n, however, in that, for the hydrogen atom, they specify the wave function that describes the position of the electron but their values do not affect the energy of the electron.

Table 8-1. Quantum Numbers for Electrons in Atoms

Symbol	Name	Allowed values	Property principally determined
n	Principal	$1, 2, 3, \ldots$	Size and energy of orbit
l	Azimuthal	$0, 1, 2, \ldots, n-1$	Shape of orbit
m	Magnetic	$-l, -l+1, \ldots, 0, \ldots, l-1, l$	Orientation of orbit
s	Spin	$\frac{1}{2}, -\frac{1}{2}$	Spin of electron

The significance of the quantum numbers is better appreciated by considering the wave functions that the Schrödinger equation produces as descriptions of the positions that an electron can assume when it is held to a nucleus of charge Ze.

8-2. The Hydrogen-atom Wave Functions. The mathematical form of some of the wave functions that are solutions to the hydrogen atom wave equation are shown in Table 8-2. The inclusion of variable nuclear charge Z makes these wave functions appropriate to any one electron system, and they are, therefore, "hydrogenlike" wave functions. Again, one should remember that these expressions represent the same kind of results as did the trigonometric functions of the particle-in-a-box problem. In particular, the square of these functions gives the probability of the electron being in a volume element at some position designated by r, θ, and ϕ. The electron configurations implied by the functions of Table 8-2 are best shown by diagrams that give separately the radial and the angular parts of the wave functions.

The radial distribution of the wave functions is controlled primarily by the quantum number n. The principal factor affecting the radial extent of a wave function, or *orbital*, is the exponential factor, which has the form e^{-Zr/na_0}, where Z is the atomic number of the nucleus and a_0 is the collection of constants that equals 0.529 A and is called the *Bohr radius*. This exponential term is such that for larger values of the principal quantum number n the wave function falls off less rapidly with the distance from the nucleus. With the larger nuclear charges, which will be encountered when atoms other than hydrogen are considered, the fall-off is more rapid, and the electron is held more closely to the nucleus. The radial part of the wave function and the square of this function are shown for the three lowest energy orbits $n = 1$, $n = 2$, and $n = 3$

Table 8-2. The Hydrogenlike-atom Wave Functions $\psi = R(r)\Theta(\theta)\Phi(\phi)$ **for the $n = 1$ and $n = 2$ Shells**

($a_0 = 0.529$ A. Z is the effective nuclear charge, which for the hydrogen atom has the value 1)

n	l	m	$R(r)$	$\Theta(\theta)\Phi(\phi)$	Wave-function symbol
1	0	0	$2\left(\dfrac{Z}{a_0}\right)^{\frac{3}{2}} e^{-Zr/a_0}$	$\left(\dfrac{1}{4\pi}\right)^{\frac{1}{2}}$	$1s$
2	0	0	$\left(\dfrac{Z}{2a_0}\right)^{\frac{3}{2}}\left(2 - \dfrac{Zr}{a_0}\right) e^{-Zr/2a_0}$	$\left(\dfrac{1}{4\pi}\right)^{\frac{1}{2}}$	$2s$
2	1	0	$\dfrac{1}{\sqrt{3}}\left(\dfrac{Z}{2a_0}\right)^{\frac{3}{2}}\left(\dfrac{Zr}{a_0}\right) e^{-Zr/2a_0}$	$\left(\dfrac{3}{4\pi}\right)^{\frac{1}{2}} \cos\theta$	$2p_z$
2	1	+1	$\dfrac{1}{\sqrt{3}}\left(\dfrac{Z}{2a_0}\right)^{\frac{3}{2}}\left(\dfrac{Zr}{a_0}\right) e^{-Zr/2a_0}$	$\left(\dfrac{3}{4\pi}\right)^{\frac{1}{2}} \sin\theta\cos\phi$	$2p_x$
2	1	−1	$\dfrac{1}{\sqrt{3}}\left(\dfrac{Z}{2a_0}\right)^{\frac{3}{2}}\left(\dfrac{Zr}{a_0}\right) e^{-Zr/2a_0}$	$\left(\dfrac{3}{4\pi}\right)^{\frac{1}{2}} \sin\theta\sin\phi$	$2p_y$

in Fig. 8-2a. The detailed form is seen to depend on l but the over-all extension to depend on n.

A better picture of the radial distribution of the electron orbits is obtained by showing the relative probabilities of the electron being at various distances from the nucleus rather than, as has been done in Fig. 8-2a, the relative probabilities of it being in unit volumes at various distances. A distinction exists because an annular volume element, a distance r from the nucleus, is proportional to the area $4\pi r^2$ of a sphere of radius r. The probability of the electron being at a distance between r and $r + dr$ from the nucleus is, therefore, given by $4\pi r^2\ dr$ times the probability of it being in a unit volume at a distance r from the nucleus. Figure 8-2b shows the *radial-distribution functions* that include the r^2 factor. It is interesting to note that the average distance of the electron from the nucleus, as can be determined by integrating over the positions taken up in accordance with the graphs of Fig. 8-2, is equal to the radius of the corresponding orbit calculated by the Bohr theory.

The actual wave function for the electron of the hydrogen atom is given by the product of the radial part and the two angular parts as shown in Eq. (3). It is now necessary to show the effect of the angular parts of the wave function. For the present it is important to visualize the forms of the $l = 0$ and $l = 1$ wave functions. The wave function with $l = 0$ is known as an *s orbit*, and that with $l = 1$ is known as a *p orbit*.

As the wave functions of Table 8-2 show, the s wave functions, i.e., those with $l = 0$, $m = 0$, have no dependence on either of the angles. The wave function varies in the same way for all directions from the nucleus, and the radial-distribution curves of Fig. 8-2 are, therefore, complete descriptions. The constancy of the angular factor can, however, be represented as the sphere of Fig. 8-3, so that the total wave function is the radial function times a factor that is independent of the angles.

The p wave functions, i.e., those with $l = 1$, can have $m = +1$, $m = 0$, or $m = -1$. Inspection of the mathematical expressions of Table 8-2 shows that the shape of the orbit is determined by the fact that $l = 1$, while the orientation of this orbit is dependent on the value of m. Consider first the wave function with $l = 1$ and $m = 0$. The absence of dependence on ϕ shows that for all positions around the z axis the function is the same; i.e., it is symmetric about this axis. Consideration of a few values of θ will lead to the recognition that the angular part of this $l = 1$, $m = 0$ wave function has the form of a dumbbell extended along the z axis. The complete wave function will also have large values, i.e., will project most, along the z axis as indicated in Fig. 8-3. It is for this reason that the p function with $m = 0$ is labeled as p_z.

The dependence of the remaining two p orbits on θ and ϕ can likewise be found by inspection of the expressions of Table 8-2. These two orbits, labeled as p_x and p_y, are found to have the same dumbbell shape but to project along the x and y axes.

The origin of the name magnetic quantum number attached to m can now be appreciated. When an atom is in a magnetic field, the energy of the atom

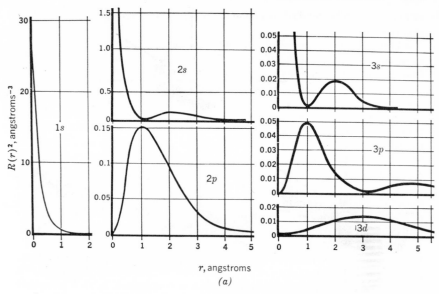

r, angstroms

(a)

Fig. 8-2a. The square of the radial part of the wave function for the hydrogen atom.

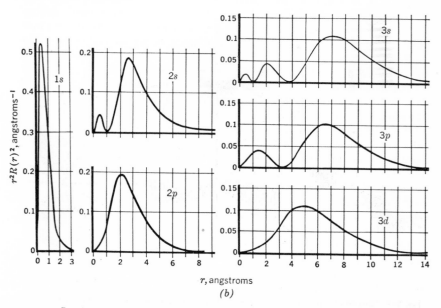

r, angstroms

(b)

Fig. 8-2b. The radial-distribution function $r^2R^2(r)$ for the hydrogen atom.

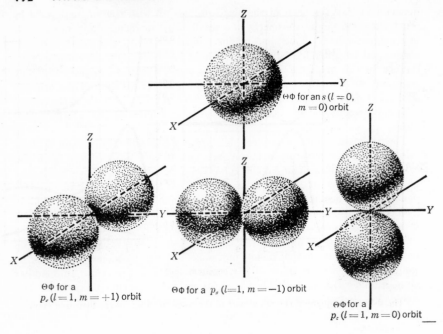

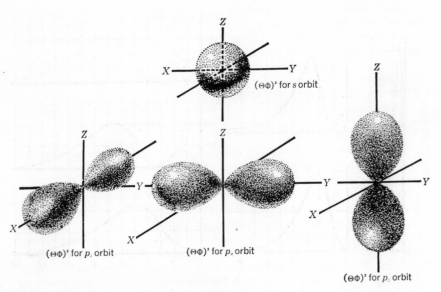

Fig. 8-3. The angular part of the hydrogen-atom wave functions for $l = 0(s)$ and $l = 1(p)$ orbits.

depends on how the orbit of the electron lines up with the magnetic field in much the same way as the energy of a small magnet depends on its orientation in a magnetic field. Thus, in a magnetic field the p_x, p_y, and p_z orbits, which correspond to different values of m, would have different orientations with respect to the magnetic field and would have, therefore, slightly different energies.   In the absence of a magnetic field, the orientation of the orbit in space is of no consequence, and the p_x, p_y, and p_z orbits have the same energy as is indicated by the absence of m in the energy expression [Eq. (3)] for a free atom.

The quantum number l has been described as giving the shape of an electron orbit. For some purposes it is important to recognize that l also gives the orbital angular momentum, in units of $h/2\pi$, of an electron in an orbit with that value of l.   Thus an s electron has zero orbital angular momentum, while a p orbital has one unit of orbital angular momentum.   The corresponding interpretation of the quantum number m is that it measures, also in units of $h/2\pi$, the component of angular momentum along any defined direction.   The three p orbitals p_x, p_y, and p_z result therefore from the fact that the orbital can be oriented in space so that its one unit of orbital angular momentum gives the components of $+h/2\pi$, 0, or $-h/2\pi$ along a specified direction.   In a similar manner an electron in a d orbital has an angular momentum of $2(h/2\pi)$.   The five values that m can take on for a d orbital correspond to angular momentum components along a direction in space of $+2h/2\pi$, $+h/2\pi$, 0, $-h/2\pi$, and $-2h/2\pi$.

It must always be remembered that Figs. 8-2 and 8-3 are intended to show the two parts, radial and angular, of the wave function and that the wave function is given by the product of these two parts.   The diagram of the angular factor, for instance, does not imply an abrupt boundary to the wave functions. These descriptions of the behavior of the electron of an atom produced by the Schrödinger equation must be understood.   Quantitative developments in atomic and molecular theory make use of these functions to describe more complicated systems.   Furthermore, in all branches of chemistry it is now customary to explain the behavior of molecular systems on the basis of wave functions of the hydrogen atom.

It will be necessary to assume that even in larger atoms with many electrons the electrons occupy wave functions of the type obtained by wave mechanics for the one-electron atom hydrogen.   This procedure is, of course, an approximate one in that it generally ignores the mutual interactions of the electrons. The increase in the nuclear charge of the atom over that for the hydrogen atom can, however, be allowed for.   The wave functions of Table 8-2 have been written for a nuclear charge of Z to allow for the extension of these functions to other atoms.   In practice it is found advantageous, in treating the outermost electrons of an atom, to assume that they "see" an *effective nuclear charge.* This quantity is somewhat less than the actual nuclear charge and allows for the fact that electrons in inner orbits shield the nuclear charge from the outer electron. More will be said about this subject when many-electron atoms are treated in more detail.

One further aspect of the general behavior of electrons in atoms must, however, be considered before the Schrödinger-equation results for a one-electron atom can be extended to many-electron atoms.

8-3. Electron Spin and the Pauli Exclusion Principle. The description of an electron of an atom provided by the three quantum numbers introduced by the Schrödinger equation is not quite a complete one. Spectroscopic evidence, for example, shows that each of the allowed energy levels of some atoms that are calculated as single levels by the Schrödinger equation is, in effect, split into two levels. An explanation for this additional splitting was given by G. E. Uhlenbeck and S. Goudsmit. They proposed that, in addition to the usual properties ascribed to an electron, as by the Schrödinger equation, it is necessary to consider the electron itself to be spinning about its axis and thereby to have a spin angular momentum. The spectroscopic results are explained by associating with the electron a spin angular momentum which can have a contribution along a direction in space of $s(h/2\pi)$, where s is the spin quantum number that can have only the values of $+\frac{1}{2}$ or $-\frac{1}{2}$. An energy level of an electron, previously described by n, l, and m, now may have slightly different values depending on whether s is $+\frac{1}{2}$ or $-\frac{1}{2}$. The spectroscopic quantum states of an atom are, therefore, determined by the values assigned to the quantum numbers n, l, m, and s.

Now that the states available to the electrons can be described, it remains to find a rule for assigning the electrons to these states. A rule that satisfactorily explains the electron structures of atoms in a manner that is consistent with their chemical behavior, i.e., with their place on the periodic table, was stated by W. Pauli. This rule, known as the *Pauli exclusion principle*, states that, *in a single atom, no two electrons can have the same values for the four quantum numbers n, l, m, and s.* On the basis of this statement and the wave functions of the preceding section, it is possible to give an approximate description of the electronic structures of many-electron atoms. The Boltzmann distribution operates, of course, to require that all the electrons be in the lowest allowed energy levels at ordinary temperatures.

8-4. Electronic Structure and the Periodic Table. Electrons can now be assigned to the available orbits, i.e., quantum numbers can be assigned to the electrons, of each of the elements of the periodic table. The electronic structures so obtained will be used later as a basis for theories of how atoms bind themselves together to form molecules.

The principle that is followed is that electrons are placed in the lowest available energy levels in a way that is consistent with the exclusion principle of Pauli. The energy levels of the one-electron atom treated by the Schrödinger equation form the basis for the assignments, but modifications of these energies must be made for many-electron atoms.

The single electron of the hydrogen atom is expected, normally, to occupy the $n = 1$ state, which is that of lowest energy. The values of l and m are then both necessarily zero, and the spin quantum number s can be $+\frac{1}{2}$ or $-\frac{1}{2}$. Both the electrons of the helium atom can be accommodated in the $n = 1$ level, frequently called the K shell. One electron will have $n = 1$, $l = 0$, $m = 0$, $s = +\frac{1}{2}$; the other, the values $n = 1$, $l = 0$, $m = 0$, $s = -\frac{1}{2}$. At this stage the K shell is filled since no more than two electrons can be assigned $n = 1$ without violating the exclusion principle. Such a completed shell, as is assigned to the helium atom, is resistant to chemical reaction, as is shown by the inert nature of helium.

A convenient notation for the electron configurations is illustrated by writing $1s^1$ for the hydrogen atom and $1s^2$ for the helium atom. The first number gives the principal quantum number; the s indicates that the electrons have $l = 0$, and the superscript tells how many electrons are in this state, which in this example is the $1s$ state.

Before assigning the electrons to the available orbits of atoms of the second row of the periodic table, it is necessary to point out the effect of the inner shells of electrons. For atoms with more than two electrons, the nuclear charge will be shielded from the outer electrons by the two K-shell electrons. The effect of this completed K shell and also similar larger completed shells of electrons is to make the energy of an orbit dependent on the quantum number l, as well as on n, in a manner indicated in Fig. 8-4a. This dependence on l

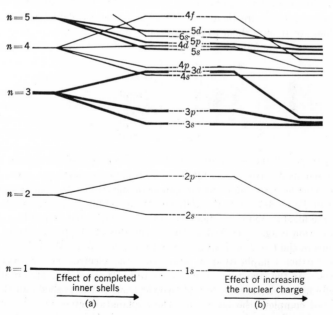

Fig. 8-4. The effect of inner shells and increased nuclear charge on atomic energy levels. (a) Effect of completed inner shells. (b) Effect of increasing the nuclear charge.

can be attributed to the fact that s electrons, for instance, penetrate near the nucleus within the inner shell, as Fig. 8-2 shows, and are, therefore, less effectively shielded from the nuclear charge. They experience more of the full unshielded effect of the nuclear charge.

On the basis of a lower energy for the $2s$ electrons than for the $2p$ electrons lithium can be assigned the structure $1s^2 2s^1$ and beryllium the structure $1s^2 2s^2$. At this stage the $2s$ level is filled and further electrons must be added to the $2p$ orbits. There is here, with $l = 1$, a choice of $m = +1, 0,$ or -1. For a free atom the orientation of the orbit in space does not affect the energy, and the three values of m therefore correspond to equal energy states. Including the two spin quantum-number possibilities for each value of n, l, and m, there are a total of six p states which can be diagramed as follows:

(1)	$l = 1$	$m = +1$	$s = \frac{1}{2}$	p_x
(2)	$l = 1$	$m = +1$	$s = -\frac{1}{2}$	p_x
(3)	$l = 1$	$m = 0$	$s = +\frac{1}{2}$	p_z
(4)	$l = 1$	$m = 0$	$s = -\frac{1}{2}$	p_z
(5)	$l = 1$	$m = -1$	$s = +\frac{1}{2}$	p_y
(6)	$l = 1$	$m = -1$	$s = -\frac{1}{2}$	p_y

All these states have the same energy, but once an electron is added to the p_x orbit, for example, another electron will preferentially go in the p_y of the p_z orbit. This repulsion results in the lowest energy state being that in which the electrons distribute themselves throughout the available orbits in a way that does not require them to pair up their spins.

The six elements following beryllium can be described as

B	$1s^2 2s^2 2p^1$
C	$1s^2 2s^2 2p^2$
N	$1s^2 2s^2 2p^3$
O	$1s^2 2s^2 2p^4$
F	$1s^2 2s^2 2p^5$
Ne	$1s^2 2s^2 2p^6$

At this stage, all the possibilities in the $n = 2$, or L, shell have been used up. The closed shell corresponds, furthermore, to another inert gas, neon.

The remainder of the elements can be assigned electron configurations as shown in Table 8-3. For the elements from sodium to argon the $3s$ and $3p$ orbits are filled in analogous manner to that of the $2s$ and $2p$ orbits. An inert configuration is again reached at argon even though the possibility of putting electrons in the $l = 2$ or d orbits exists for the $n = 3$, or M, shell.

One further complication in tabulating the electron configurations now appears. As the structures of elements 19 to 28 show, it is apparently energetically favorable, at first, to add two electrons to the $4s$ shell and then to go back and complete the $3d$ level. The explanation given for this order, as illustrated in Fig. 8-4b, is that at potassium and calcium the energy of the $4s$ orbit is lower than that of the $3d$. The increased nuclear charge of the next elements, however, is such that the $3d$ level is pulled down and can then be filled. Similar behavior is shown at higher atomic numbers by both the d and f ($l = 4$) orbits. The further comment should be made that, when available orbits with nearly equal energy levels exist, the electron configuration will not

Table 8-3. Electronic Configurations of the Elements as Free, Gaseous Atoms*

Z	Element	1 s	2 s	2 p	3 s	3 p	3 d	4 s	4 p	4 d	4 f	5 s	5 p	5 d	5 f	6 s	6 p	6 d	6 f	7 s
1	H	1																		
2	He	2																		
3	Li	2	1																	
4	Be	2	2																	
5	B	2	2	1																
6	C	2	2	2																
7	N	2	2	3																
8	O	2	2	4																
9	F	2	2	5																
10	Ne	2	2	6																
11	Na	2	2	6	1															
12	Mg	2	2	6	2															
13	Al	2	2	6	2	1														
14	Si	2	2	6	2	2														
15	P	2	2	6	2	3														
16	S	2	2	6	2	4														
17	Cl	2	2	6	2	5														
18	A	2	2	6	2	6														
19	K	2	2	6	2	6		1												
20	Ca	2	2	6	2	6		2												
21	Sc	2	2	6	2	6	1	2												
22	Ti	2	2	6	2	6	2	2												
23	V	2	2	6	2	6	3	2												
24	Cr	2	2	6	2	6	5	1												
25	Mn	2	2	6	2	6	5	2												
26	Fe	2	2	6	2	6	6	2												
27	Co	2	2	6	2	6	7	2												
28	Ni	2	2	6	2	6	8	2												
29	Cu	2	2	6	2	6	10	1												
30	Zn	2	2	6	2	6	10	2												
31	Ga	2	2	6	2	6	10	2	1											
32	Ge	2	2	6	2	6	10	2	2											
33	As	2	2	6	2	6	10	2	3											
34	Se	2	2	6	2	6	10	2	4											
35	Br	2	2	6	2	6	10	2	5											
36	Kr	2	2	6	2	6	10	2	6											
37	Rb	2	2	6	2	6	10	2	6			1								
38	Sr	2	2	6	2	6	10	2	6			2								
39	Y	2	2	6	2	6	10	2	6	1		2								
40	Zr	2	2	6	2	6	10	2	6	2		2								
41	Nb	2	2	6	2	6	10	2	6	4		1								
42	Mo	2	2	6	2	6	10	2	6	5		1								
43	Tc	2	2	6	2	6	10	2	6	6		1 ... ?								
44	Ru	2	2	6	2	6	10	2	6	7		1								
45	Rh	2	2	6	2	6	10	2	6	8		1								
46	Pd	2	2	6	2	6	10	2	6	10										
47	Ag	2	2	6	2	6	10	2	6	10		1								
48	Cd	2	2	6	2	6	10	2	6	10		2								
49	In	2	2	6	2	6	10	2	6	10		2	1							
50	Sn	2	2	6	2	6	10	2	6	10		2	2							

Table 8-3. Electronic Configurations of the Elements as Free, Gaseous Atoms* *(Cont.)*

Z	Element	1 s	2 s	2 p	3 s	3 p	3 d	4 s	4 p	4 d	4 f	5 s	5 p	5 d	5 f	6 s	6 p	6 d	6 f	7 s
51	Sb	2	2	6	2	6	10	2	6	10		2	3							
52	Te	2	2	6	2	6	10	2	6	10		2	4							
53	I	2	2	6	2	6	10	2	6	10		2	5							
54	Xe	2	2	6	2	6	10	2	6	10		2	6							
55	Cs	2	2	6	2	6	10	2	6	10		2	6			1				
56	Ba	2	2	6	2	6	10	2	6	10		2	6			2				
57	La	2	2	6	2	6	10	2	6	10		2	6	1		2				
58	Ce	2	2	6	2	6	10	2	6	10	2	2	6			2	… ?			
59	Pr	2	2	6	2	6	10	2	6	10	3	2	6			2	… ?			
60	Nd	2	2	6	2	6	10	2	6	10	4	2	6			2				
61	Pm	2	2	6	2	6	10	2	6	10	5	2	6			2	… ?			
62	Sm	2	2	6	2	6	10	2	6	10	6	2	6			2				
63	Eu	2	2	6	2	6	10	2	6	10	7	2	6			2				
64	Gd	2	2	6	2	6	10	2	6	10	7	2	6	1		2				
65	Tb	2	2	6	2	6	10	2	6	10	9	2	6			2	… ?			
66	Dy	2	2	6	2	6	10	2	6	10	10	2	6			2	… ?			
67	Ho	2	2	6	2	6	10	2	6	10	11	2	6			2	… ?			
68	Er	2	2	6	2	6	10	2	6	10	12	2	6			2	… ?			
69	Tm	2	2	6	2	6	10	2	6	10	13	2	6			2				
70	Yb	2	2	6	2	6	10	2	6	10	14	2	6			2				
71	Lu	2	2	6	2	6	10	2	6	10	14	2	6	1		2				
72	Hf	2	2	6	2	6	10	2	6	10	14	2	6	2		2				
73	Ta	2	2	6	2	6	10	2	6	10	14	2	6	3		2				
74	W	2	2	6	2	6	10	2	6	10	14	2	6	4		2				
75	Re	2	2	6	2	6	10	2	6	10	14	2	6	5		2				
76	Os	2	2	6	2	6	10	2	6	10	14	2	6	6		2				
77	Ir	2	2	6	2	6	10	2	6	10	14	2	6	7		2				
78	Pt	2	2	6	2	6	10	2	6	10	14	2	6	9		1				
79	Au	2	2	6	2	6	10	2	6	10	14	2	6	10		1				
80	Hg	2	2	6	2	6	10	2	6	10	14	2	6	10		2				
81	Tl	2	2	6	2	6	10	2	6	10	14	2	6	10		2	1			
82	Pb	2	2	6	2	6	10	2	6	10	14	2	6	10		2	2			
83	Bi	2	2	6	2	6	10	2	6	10	14	2	6	10		2	3			
84	Po	2	2	6	2	6	10	2	6	10	14	2	6	10		2	4	… ?		
85	At	2	2	6	2	6	10	2	6	10	14	2	6	10		2	5	… ?		
86	Rn	2	2	6	2	6	10	2	6	10	14	2	6	10		2	6			
87	Fr	2	2	6	2	6	10	2	6	10	14	2	6	10		2	6			1 … ?
88	Ra	2	2	6	2	6	10	2	6	10	14	2	6	10		2	6			2
89	Ac	2	2	6	2	6	10	2	6	10	14	2	6	10		2	6	1		2 … ?
90	Th	2	2	6	2	6	10	2	6	10	14	2	6	10		2	6	2		2
91	Pa	2	2	6	2	6	10	2	6	10	14	2	6	10	2	2	6	1		2 … ?
92	U	2	2	6	2	6	10	2	6	10	14	2	6	10	3	2	6	1		2
93	Np	2	2	6	2	6	10	2	6	10	14	2	6	10	4	2	6	1		2 … ?
94	Pu	2	2	6	2	6	10	2	6	10	14	2	6	10	5	2	6	1		2 … ?
95	Am	2	2	6	2	6	10	2	6	10	14	2	6	10	7	2	6			2 … ?
96	Cm	2	2	6	2	6	10	2	6	10	14	2	6	10	7	2	6	1		2 … ?
97	Bk	2	2	6	2	6	10	2	6	10	14	2	6	10	8	2	6	1		2 … ?
98	Cf	2	2	6	2	6	10	2	6	10	14	2	6	10	9	2	6	1		2 … ?
99	E	2	2	6	2	6	10	2	6	10	14	2	6	10	10	2	6	1		2 … ?
100	Fm	2	2	6	2	6	10	2	6	10	14	2	6	10	11	2	6	1		2 … ?
101	Mv	2	2	6	2	6	10	2	6	10	14	2	6	10	12	2	6	1		2 … ?

* From Michell J. Sienko and Robert A. Plane, "Chemistry," McGraw-Hill Book Company, Inc., New York, 1957.

be easily decided and sometimes not even easily deduced from spectroscopic evidence.

8-5. Relation of Electronic Structure to the Chemistry of the Elements.   The relation of the chemistry of the elements to their electronic structure and position in the periodic table is not usually included in the scope of physical chemistry. One aspect, however, seems sufficiently close to the present discussion of atomic structure to warrant comment.

An atomic quantity of great importance in chemistry is the *ionization potential*.   This is a measure, usually expressed in electron volts (1 ev = 23.06 kcal/mole), of the energy required to remove an electron from a neutral atom.   It is the energy that is absorbed in reactions such as

$$Na(g) \rightarrow Na^+(g) + e^-(g)$$

Values for the ionization potential are most often obtained from spectroscopic studies, where, in effect, the limit to which an electron can be excited before ionization occurs is determined.   Table 8-4 shows the ionization potentials of some of the lighter atoms.   One should particularly notice the close relation between these numbers and the electronic structure or position in the periodic table of the atoms.

Table 8-4. Ionization Potentials of Some Atoms
(Ev)

Element	First ionization potential	Second ionization potential
H	13.60	
He	24.58	54.50
Li	5.39	75.62
Be	9.32	18.21
B	8.30	25.15
C	11.26	24.38
N	14.54	29.60
O	13.62	35.15
F	17.42	34.98
Ne	21.56	41.07
Na	5.14	47.29
Mg	7.64	15.03
Al	5.99	18.82
Si	8.15	16.34
P	10.55	19.65
S	10.36	23.4
Cl	12.96	23.80
A	15.76	27.62
K	4.34	31.81
Ca	6.11	11.87
Sc	6.56	12.80

A second chemically important atomic quantity is the *electron affinity*.   This is the energy, also usually expressed in electron volts, with which a neutral atom binds another electron.   It is, therefore, the energy *given out* in reactions such as

$$F(g) + e^-(g) \rightarrow F^-(g)$$

or, to make the quantity more comparable with the ionization potential, it is the energy *absorbed* in reactions such as

$$F^-(g) \rightarrow F(g) + e^-(g)$$

There are only a few atoms, in the gas phase, that bind an extra electron tightly enough so that the electron affinity has any value other than zero.   It is, moreover, a matter of considerable difficulty to deduce values for the electron affinity.   Some results that have been obtained are shown in Table 8-5.

The qualitative aspects of the variation of ionization potential and electron affinity and all the chemical consequences that these quantities imply can be understood in terms of the shielding of the nuclear charge by the electrons other than that being removed from the atom or added to the atom.   The chemistry of fluorine and sodium, for example, shows that the former readily gains an electron, while the latter readily loses one.   In this way, they both achieve a completed outer shell, the L shell, of electrons.   The tendency of atoms to form such completed shells must now be explained.   The outer, $n = 3$ electron of a neutral sodium atom is shielded from the nucleus by the other electrons of the atom, all of which are in inner orbits, i.e., have values of not less than 3.   Such electrons are effective in shielding the charge of the nucleus, and the outer electron is quite easily removed from the atom, as the data of Table 8-4 show.   The situation is very different in fluorine.   An available positon exists for an extra electron in the $n = 2$ level, and an electron in this positiion would be effectively shielded from the nucleus only by the two $n = 1$ electrons and relatively slightly shielded by the other seven $n = 2$ electrons. Fluorine, therefore, can strongly hold one electron more than it has as a neutral atom, and it, too, tends to go to the inert or completed shell configuration. It is, furthermore, clear that neon with a filled L shell can neither easily gain nor easily lose an electron.   An added electron would have to go in the $n = 3$ level and would be effectively shielded (and therefore loosely held) by all the

Table 8-5. Electron Affinities of Some Atoms
(Ev)

Element	Electron affinity
F	3.6
Cl	3.8
Br	3.5
I	3.2
O	2.2
S	2.4
H	0.7
Li	0.5
Na	0.7

10 electrons in the $n = 1$ and $n = 2$ shells.   Likewise, the electrons of the normal atom are tightly bound because they are shielded from the nucleus by only 2 inner-shell electrons and less effectively by the other electrons in the same shell.

Atomic structure has now been treated in sufficient detail to permit the study of the more chemically interesting subject of molecular structure.   It will be apparent, as the development of the current ideas of molecular structure are unfolded, that the basic material on atomic structure that has been presented is a necessary and often referred to basis.

MOLECULAR THEORY

The principal subject of this chapter can now be dealt with.   An understanding of atomic structure and the methods of wave mechanics provides the means for answering one of the fundamental questions of chemistry: What are the forces that bind atoms together into molecules?   This question has existed since the beginnings of chemistry, and it is the answer to this question that is the culmination of much of the theoretical work of chemistry.   The current solution will be illustrated by reference to the simplest molecule, H_2.   It will be seen that molecular bonding is at present only understood in principle and that our knowledge of wave mechanics, rather than terminating the study of chemical theory, leads to many new and exciting problems.

In this section of the chapter, the quantum-mechanical approach to chemical bonding will be shown by a detailed consideration, except for the evaluation of some integrals, of the bonding in the hydrogen molecule.   From this very simple molecule it will be possible to extend the theory of chemical bonding in a semiquantitative and semiempirical way to molecular structures of more chemical interest.   It is this extension which has become a basic and necessary part of the approaches and language in all branches of chemistry.   In introducing this important subject in its broader aspects it is also hoped that a basic understanding will result on which a physical chemist will later be able to build a more detailed and mathematical theory of molecular phenomena.

8-6. The Beginnings of Bonding Theory.   The introduction of the modern view of matter as made up of atoms and molecules by Dalton in 1808 led immediately to questions as to the nature of the forces that hold the atoms together when they are combined into a molecule.   At that time the contemporary studies of the effect of an electric current on chemical compounds by Davy probably contributed to the dominating theory of Berzelius that chemical union stems from an electrical attraction between particles of opposite charge.   This electrovalent theory persisted, in part at least, because of the lack of any alternative theory.   The recognition of molecules such as H_2 and N_2 and similar difficulties with many organic compounds led to the use of a schematic representation of chemical bonding and a tendency, particularly in the rapidly developing subject of organic chemistry, to a bypassing of the question of the source of chemical affinity.

It will be recalled that in the latter half of the nineteenth century, although no adequate theory of chemical bonding was available, the synthesis and structural studies of organic compounds rapidly proceeded. The theory and representation of aromatic systems by Kekule and the recognition of the tetrahedral carbon atom by Le Bel and by van't Hoff show the achievements that were made. Not only could compounds of very considerable complexity be synthesized and analyzed, but a representation of the geometric arrangement of all the atoms of the molecule could often be made. The development of this structural theory of organic compounds and the organization of the immense body of facts of organic chemistry must be ranked as one of the greatest accomplishments of science.

A similar development in inorganic chemistry occurred toward the end of the century in the work of Alfred Werner. His introduction of the idea of coordination number brought to inorganic chemistry a system that allowed for the same progress as structural theory had made possible for organic chemistry.

All these developments were made with little understanding of the chemical forces that, for instance, caused the four hydrogen atoms to arrange themselves tetrahedrally about a carbon atom in methane. All these chemical developments occurred before what logically would be prerequisite information had been unraveled. The chemists' curiosity about the nature of the chemical world could not wait for the work, around 1900, of J. J. Thomson and Rutherford to provide the logical starting point: an understanding of simple atomic structure.

The investigation at the turn of the century of the basic chemical units of matter, the electron and the nucleus, and their arrangement in atoms led to a renewed interest in the nature and source of the "affinities" exerted by atoms that were so successfully represented in structural theory. Knowledge that atoms consist of a nucleus with some outer arrangement of electrons was quickly coupled with the implications of the periodic table and led to some primitive but still valuable ideas on atomic and molecular structure. At this stage it is convenient to treat separately the two different types of chemical bonding that came to be recognized.

8-7. The Ionic Bond. The detailed interpretation of the electronic structure of the periodic arrangement of the atoms was not available in the early 1900s. The special stability of the inert gases, however, led to the idea that an outer shell of eight electrons was particularly stable. That electrons of atoms might be *transferred* from one atom to another so that they both could achieve inert-gas configurations was suggested at an early stage by J. J. Thomson and was developed by W. Kossel in 1916 into a theory of the ionic bond. Once the tendency for electrons to be transferred was postulated, the original theory of Berzelius could be resurrected to explain the binding of the ions that results. In Sec. 8-5 it was shown how our present knowledge of atomic structure leads to the expectation, for instance, that the sodium atom will easily lose an electron and that a chlorine atom can add one. In this way, although even now no completely theoretical, quantitative calculation of the energies involved can be made, one can expect that the NaCl gas-phase molecule will consist of the two ions Na^+ and Cl^- since each species would have completed outer shells with inert-gas configurations. The idea of the transferring of electrons to achieve such configurations leads to the understanding of many of the observed ionic species.

The ionic bond is most easily understood with reference to a gas-phase molecule, such as NaCl. At internuclear distances not far from the equilibrium distance it appears to be satisfactory to treat the molecule as a Na^+ ion bound to a Cl^- ion by the coulombic attraction of the opposite charges.

If the charges on the ions are q_1 and q_2 (for NaCl the value of q_1 is $+e$, and that of q_2 is $-e$), the electrostatic attraction leads to a potential-energy term, shown in Fig. 8-5, of $q_1 q_2/r$, where r is the internuclear separation. The effect of this term is to draw the ions together; i.e., the system tends toward the position of low potential. An opposing effect exists in the form of a repulsion between the nuclei and, for ions with inner shells, a more important repulsion between the inner-shell electrons of the two ions. The form of the variation of this potential-energy contribution with internuclear distance, also shown in Fig. 8-5, has been empirically shown by Born and Meyer to be satisfactorily represented by an equation of the form

$$U_{\text{rep}} = be^{-ar} \tag{5}$$

where a and b are empirical constants. Furthermore, to a quite good approximation, the constant a can be taken to be the same for all ionic molecules and is equal to 3.3×10^8 cm^{-1}. The total potential-energy function for an ionic bond can then be written as

$$U = \frac{q_1 q_2}{r} + be^{-3.3r \times 10^8} \tag{6}$$

For a univalent molecule, such as NaCl, the expression is

$$U = -\frac{e^2}{r} + be^{-3.3r \times 10^8} \tag{7}$$

The remaining empirical constant can be recognized as a measure of the size of the bonded ions. A value of b can be assigned for a given molecule so that the total potential-energy curve constructed from Eq. (7) will have a minimum at an internuclear separation equal to the experimentally determined equilibrium internuclear distance. Both the attractive and repulsive components of the potential energy and the net potential calculated from Eq. (7) are shown in Fig. 8-5.

The pure ionic or electrostatic bond is, as reference to the previous tables of ionization potentials and electron affinities shows, an oversimplification of the bonding in gas-phase molecules such as NaCl. At very long internuclear distances, i.e., for separate free sodium and fluorine particles, the energetically favored species are the atoms Na and Cl rather than the ions Na and Cl^-. Thus, for gas-phase reactions,

$$
\begin{array}{lll}
\text{Na} \to \text{Na} + e^- & \Delta H = 118 \text{ kcal} & \\
\text{Cl} + e^- \to \text{Cl}^- & \Delta H = -87 \text{ kcal} & (8) \\
\textbf{and therefore} \quad \text{Cl} + \text{Na} \to \text{Na}^+ + \text{Cl}^- & \Delta H = +31 \text{ kcal} &
\end{array}
$$

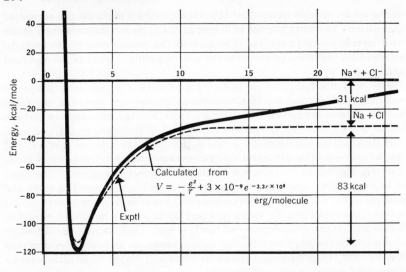

Fig. 8-5. The potential energy versus internuclear distance for an essentially ionic bond.

The equilibrium position, since the entropy of products and reactants is identical, is to the left, where the energy is lower.

At finite nuclear distances the coulombic energy that can be released from the coming together of ions, rather than atoms, makes the ionic description preferable until, at relatively short internuclear distances, such as the equilibrium internuclear distance, the ionic description is of dominant importance.

An experimental potential-energy curve for the NaCl molecule can be deduced by methods discussed in the following chapter. This experimental curve is shown in Fig. 8-5, for comparison with that deduced on the basis of a completely ionic system. This comparison shows that while the ionic description is adequate at short distances it should go over into some atomic description at very long distances if it is to represent the energy of the fragments of dissociation.

The nature of the forces that hold two atoms like Na and Cl together is, however, essentially understandable in terms of an ionic bond. Such bonding depends on the tendency for an electron to be transferred from one atom to the other. It is now necessary to investigate the source of attraction that is responsible for the stability of molecules such as H_2, where this electron transfer and an ionic description are not feasible.

8-8. Introduction to the Covalent Bond. Bonding in molecules such as H_2, N_2, and so forth, and in most organic molecules could not be reasonably treated as resulting from the formation and subsequent attraction of oppositely charged ions. Furthermore, even with the initial ideas on atomic structure and the inert-electron configurations, it was not immediately clear how atoms could be

held together in such molecules. The Bohr theory that had such a remarkable success in explaining the behavior of the hydrogen atom seemed of no
help in explaining even the hydrogen molecule. Simultaneously with the more
physical developments that led to the Bohr theory, G. N. Lewis at the University of California was developing a theory of the covalent bond from a more
chemical point of view.

Lewis was led to explain covalent bonds as resulting from the *sharing of
pairs of electrons* in such a way that the participating atoms all achieved the
stable inert-gas configuration. It is interesting to look back at the now-
primitive-looking model of the atom on which his theory was based. The
special stability of an outer shell of eight electrons suggested to Lewis that the
electrons might occupy corners of a cube about the nucleus. Although this
model is no longer accepted, the ideas of Lewis and the diagrams he developed
to represent the arrangement of the outer shell of electrons are still invaluable
in chemical theory.

Lewis diagrams illustrate the role of the electrons of the outer shell of an
atom. Both the inner shells and the nucleus are represented by the symbol of
the element. The sharing of the outer electrons to form chemical bonds can
then easily be depicted by writing a pair of electrons between the bonded
atoms. This pairing, according to Lewis, should lead to an inert-gas configuration about each atom. Thus hydrogen should have a share in two
electrons and most other atoms a share in eight electrons. In some cases the
sharing of two or three pairs of electrons in a bond is necessary to give the
desired inert configurations. A few examples will illustrate these useful diagrams; for covalent compounds

$$\cdot \overset{\displaystyle\cdot}{\underset{\displaystyle\cdot}{C}} \cdot \; + 4H \cdot \; \rightarrow \; H : \overset{\displaystyle\cdot\cdot}{\underset{\displaystyle H}{C}} : H$$

$$: \overset{\displaystyle\cdot\cdot}{\underset{\displaystyle\cdot}{O}} \cdot \; + 2H \cdot \; \rightarrow \; : \overset{\displaystyle\cdot\cdot}{\underset{\displaystyle H}{O}} : H$$

$$\cdot \overset{\displaystyle\cdot}{\underset{\displaystyle\cdot}{C}} \cdot \; + 4 : \overset{\displaystyle\cdot\cdot}{Cl} \cdot \; \rightarrow \; : \overset{\displaystyle\cdot\cdot}{Cl} : \overset{\displaystyle : \overset{\cdot\cdot}{Cl} :}{\underset{\displaystyle : \underset{\cdot\cdot}{Cl} :}{C}} : \overset{\displaystyle\cdot\cdot}{Cl} :$$

$$2 \cdot \overset{\displaystyle\cdot}{C} \cdot \; + 2H \cdot \; \rightarrow \; H : C ::: C : H$$

and for ionic compounds, where electron transfer leads to the desired inert-gas
configurations,

$$Na \cdot \; + \cdot \overset{\displaystyle\cdot\cdot}{\underset{\displaystyle\cdot\cdot}{Cl}} : \; \rightarrow \; Na^+ + : \overset{\displaystyle\cdot\cdot}{\underset{\displaystyle\cdot\cdot}{Cl}} :^-$$

Lewis diagrams and the bonding arrangements represented by these diagrams represent a considerable advance over the earlier representation of
molecular formulas, in which a line was drawn to represent the bond between
bonded atoms. The Lewis theory, for example, allows the number of covalent

bonds, or shared pairs of electrons, associated with an atom to be understood on the basis of its atomic number or its position in the periodic table.

Lewis diagrams are now still used as the most convenient and frequently, but not always, as an adequate representation of the electron configuration in a molecule. The sharing of electrons in covalent bonds as proposed by Lewis, however, is only a step in the direction of explaining the covalent bond. After Lewis's theory, published in 1916, it remained to show how the electrons were arranged in space about the atom or molecule, and particularly to do this in a way consistent with Bohr's theory of the hydrogen atom. Also left unanswered was the original question of why covalent bonds form; or, following Lewis, why the sharing of a pair of electrons should lead to a chemical bond.

Many attempts by Lewis and others to answer such fundamental questions were made in the years following 1916. With the appearance of the Schrödinger wave equation in 1926 and its immediate success in dealing with atomic problems, all attempts to understand more clearly the covalent bond were turned to this new approach. Within a year the results of Heitler and London threw new light on the nature of the covalent bond.

The complexity which develops when the Schrödinger equation is applied to molecular systems means that only the hydrogen molecule can be adequately treated. An understanding of this one example, however, allows the chemist to extend quantum-mechanical approaches in a qualitative manner to almost all chemical systems. It is, therefore, very worthwhile to appreciate the quantum-mechanical theory of the covalent bond as illustrated by the hydrogen molecule. The method of Heitler and London for handling this problem introduces a number of concepts that are now of general use in chemical theory. These concepts are used along with the Lewis theory to give greater insight into many chemical systems. Before this quantum-mechanical approach to the covalent bond can be indicated, it is necessary to recast the Schrödinger equation into a form more suitable for handling chemical systems.

8-9. The Use of Approximate Wave Functions. The Schrödinger equation has been introduced in Chap. 3. There the particle-in-a-box problem illustrated how the equation is used to solve for the electron position, in terms of ψ^2, and the electron energy in a system of atomic dimensions. It has, furthermore, been pointed out in Sec. 8-1 that the Schrödinger equation can be solved for the hydrogen atom. It is clear therefore that, if the energy and electron distribution of the hydrogen molecule can also be calculated, a theoretical treatment of at least the simplest of covalent bonds will have been achieved.

For the particle-in-a-box problem, it will be recalled, the Schrödinger equation was set up with the appropriate potential-energy term, and solutions to the resulting differential equation were sought. It was not difficult to solve the equation, i.e., to see that a trigonometric function would be a solution. In the hydrogen-molecule problem, which has two electrons moving in the potential field of two nuclei, one can again insert the appropriate coulombic potential-energy terms and again arrive at a differential equation. This equation, however, has no readily apparent solution. It is, in fact, very unlikely that any reasonably simple expression exists that solves this differential equation. To proceed with the hydrogen-molecule problem, it is necessary to have some way of finding an approximate solution to the equation. In almost all molecular applications of quantum mechanics a similar situation arises, and the technique of using approximate descriptions for chemical systems has become a basic part of modern chemical theory. Most often these approximate solutions or descriptions are based on the hydrogen-atom wave functions, which were given in Table 8-2.

The Schrödinger equation can be written in a compact form that allows approximate solutions to be more easily used. For one electron in a three-dimensional system the Schrödinger equation is

$$-\frac{h^2}{8\pi^2 m}\left(\frac{\partial^2 \psi}{\partial x^2} + \frac{\partial^2 \psi}{\partial y^2} + \frac{\partial^2 \psi}{\partial z^2}\right) + U(x,y,z)\psi = \epsilon\psi \tag{9}$$

It is now necessary to put this equation in a form so that a value of the energy ϵ can be obtained for a given potential function $U(x,y,z)$ when the equation is such that an exact solution function cannot be found. In such cases it can be assumed that a function that is a reasonable approximation to the expected solution can be invented.

The set of differentials is conveniently abbreviated as

$$\nabla^2 = \frac{\partial^2}{\partial x^2} + \frac{\partial^2}{\partial y^2} + \frac{\partial^2}{\partial z^2} \tag{10}$$

and this abbreviation allows the Schrödinger equation to be written as

$$-\frac{h^2}{8\pi^2 m}(\nabla^2 \psi) + U\psi = \epsilon\psi \tag{11}$$

where V is now understood to be a function of the three coordinates. The symbol ∇^2 is known as an *operator* and is said to operate on ψ. In a later connection it will be important to recognize that an operator does not in general *commute* with the function it operates on; that is, $\nabla^2 \psi$ is not the same as the meaningless quantity $\psi\nabla^2$.

The convenient operator notation can be extended if the symbol $\mathcal{3C}$, known as the *Hamiltonian*, is introduced for the terms,

$$\mathcal{3C} = -\frac{h^2}{8\pi^2 m}\nabla^2 + U \tag{12}$$

With this notation the Schrödinger equation is very compactly written as

$$\mathcal{3C}\psi = \epsilon\psi \tag{13}$$

One should recognize that nothing but a change of notation has been introduced up to this point.

Now this compact equation can be multiplied on the left by the function ψ that is expected to approximate the correct wave function for the system to give

$$\psi\mathcal{3C}\psi = \psi\epsilon\psi \tag{14}$$

Since ϵ is nothing more than a number giving the calculated energy of the system, the right side of Eq. (14) can be written as

$$\psi\epsilon\psi = \epsilon\psi^2 \tag{15}$$

(Care is being taken here because $\mathcal{3C}$, by comparison, does not commute and $\mathcal{3C}\psi \neq \psi\mathcal{3C}$.) Equation (14) can be rearranged to give

$$\epsilon = \frac{\psi\mathcal{3C}\psi}{\psi^2} \tag{16}$$

Equation (15) would yield a value of ϵ at each point in space for the trial function ψ. The average value of the energy of the system that is appropriate to the trial function is obtained by integrating over all of space. The average energy that is calculated for some approximate function ψ is, therefore, calculated as

$$\epsilon = \frac{\int \psi\mathcal{3C}\psi \, d\tau}{\int \psi^2 \, d\tau} \tag{17}$$

where $d\tau$ is the element of volume in whatever coordinate system is used.

It is this form of the Schrödinger equation, which gives ϵ in terms of $\mathcal{3C}$ and ψ, that allows the use of approximate wave functions. For a given system the potential-energy function can usually be written down, and therefore so can the Hamiltonian operator $\mathcal{3C}$, defined according to Eq. (12). If a well-behaved expression that is expected to approximate the true wave function for the system can be constructed, it can be inserted in the right side of Eq. (17). The necessary mathematical operations of differentiation and integration can be performed, and a value of ϵ will be obtained. In this way an approximate energy for the system can be calculated if a function that approximates the true wave function can be thought up.

This method of calculating the energy of a system would, however, be unduly hazardous if no way existed for checking the reliability of such energy calculations. An important theorem, known as the *variation theorem*, provides the desired criterion.

The theorem is stated, without proof, as showing that the *value of ϵ obtained from an approximate wave function is less negative, i.e., the system seems less stable, than the value obtained from the true wave function*. The best value of ϵ that can be obtained from various approximate wave functions is therefore the lowest value yielded by Eq. (17). The approach is to guess a wave function and to calculate a value of ϵ. Variations on this wave function that improve it will produce, when inserted in Eq. (17), a lower and better value of ϵ. The lowest value of ϵ that can be obtained is the best theoretical value for the energy of the system.

This approximate procedure seems rather devious and unsatisfactory. Although such criticism is justified, there exists at present no fundamentally better way of applying the Schrödinger equation to systems of any complexity and, in this regard, the H_2 molecule is already a complex system.

The dependence of chemical theory on this approximate approach will be apparent as specific examples are treated.

Six sections are now devoted to a somewhat mathematical treatment of the nature of the covalent bond, using the example of the H_2 molecule. A considerable amount of rather strange manipulations with wave functions is necessary, but none of the mathematical difficulties of the necessary integrations need be dealt with.   The explanation of the covalent bond that is obtained, although clearly an awkward and by no means final one, is basic to a real understanding of much of modern chemistry.   It is, therefore, a very necessary feature of physical chemistry.

It is also valuable to have a more pictorial view of the nature of bonding. For this reason, and for those who do not wish to delve more quantitatively into the source of the covalent-bond energy, a more general discussion is presented in the following chapter.   There the ideas that can be drawn from the more mathematical treatment are presented.   It should be possible, therefore, to proceed, omitting the remainder of this chapter, by relying on the introductory section of the following chapter to present a summary of the results.

*8-10. A Two-electron System: The Helium Atom.   Even the pre-Schrödinger theory of Lewis recognized the special role of pairs of electrons in almost all molecular systems.   The wave-mechanical interpretation of bonding bears out and clarifies the special role of pairs of electrons in chemical bonds.   To understand the basis of this bonding, it is therefore necessary to learn how to apply the Schrödinger equation to a system involving two electrons.   The helium atom provides a simple example which illustrates the new aspects that are encountered.

An approximate approach, similar to that which will be used for the hydrogen molecule, consists in recognizing that, since the two electrons of the normal helium atom are $1s$ electrons, the wave functions of these electrons can be approximated by the $1s$ wave functions of the one-electron atom listed in Table 8-2.   The nuclear charge of 2 is substituted for Z.   Each electron will require a wave function to describe its distribution about the nucleus, and if the electrons are labeled as 1 and 2, these wave functions, represented by $1s(1)$ and $1s(2)$, become

$$1s(1) = \frac{1}{\sqrt{\pi}} \left(\frac{2}{a_0}\right)^{\frac{3}{2}} e^{-2r_1/a_0}$$
$$1s(2) = \frac{1}{\sqrt{\pi}} \left(\frac{2}{a_0}\right)^{\frac{3}{2}} e^{-2r_2/a_0}$$

$$(18)$$

where r_1 and r_2 are the distances of electrons 1 and 2, respectively, from the nucleus.   An appropriate approximate wave function for the system can be constructed from these two wave functions and consists of the product

$$\psi = 1s(1)1s(2) \tag{19}$$

This function should be recognized as only approximate since it describes the positions of the electrons without regard for the fact that they will tend to repel one another.   The function is, however, satisfactory for an approximate treatment.

The Hamiltonian for the system consists of the differential terms, one for each electron, and all the potential-energy terms.   Upon recognizing that the nuclear charge is $+2e$ and the electronic charges are $-e$, the Hamiltonian is written as

$$\mathcal{H} = -\left(\frac{h^2}{8\pi^2 m}\right)\nabla_1^2 - \left(\frac{h^2}{8\pi^2 m}\right)\nabla_2^2 - \frac{2e^2}{r_1} - \frac{2e^2}{r_2} + \frac{e^2}{r_{12}} \tag{20}$$

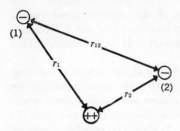

Fig. 8-6. Coordinates of the two electrons of the helium atom.

The differential operators ∇_1 and ∇_2 operate on the wave function, i.e., on the coordinates of electron 1 and electron 2, respectively. The coulombic potential terms correspond to the interactions shown in Fig. 8-6. Except for the electron repulsion term the Hamiltonian of Eq. (20) is seen to break down into two terms, one of which operates on the function of electron 1, and the other on the function of electron 2. It is convenient to abbreviate Eq. (20) to

$$\mathfrak{IC} = \mathfrak{IC}_1 + \mathfrak{IC}_2 + \frac{e^2}{r_{12}} \tag{21}$$

Equation (17) can now be used to calculate an approximate value for the energy of the helium atom. The denominator is

$$\int \psi^2 \, d\tau = \int [1s(1)1s(2)]^2 \, d\tau_1 \, d\tau_2$$
$$= \int [1s(1)]^2 \, d\tau_1 \int [1s(2)]^2 \, d\tau_2 \tag{22}$$

Since the $1s$ wave functions of Table 8-2 are normalized, i.e., the total probability of the particle being somewhere in space is unity, the integral over all space of the square of each electron wave function is unity and the complete denominator is therefore also unity.

The numerator is then equal to the energy ϵ and is written out as

$$\epsilon = \int [1s(1)1s(2)] \left(\mathfrak{IC}_1 + \mathfrak{IC}_2 + \frac{e^2}{r_{12}} \right) [1s(1)1s(2)] \, d\tau_1 \, d\tau_2$$

$$= \int 1s(1)1s(2)\mathfrak{IC}_1 1s(1)1s(2) \, d\tau_1 \, d\tau_2$$

$$+ \int 1s(1)1s(2)\mathfrak{IC}_2 1s(1)1s(2) \, d\tau_1 \, d\tau_2 + e^2 \int \frac{[1s(1)1s(2)]^2}{r_{12}} \, d\tau_1 \, d\tau_2 \tag{23}$$

The first two parts of the total integral will clearly give the same numerical values since they are identical except for the numbering of the electrons. Each of these terms can be simplified when it is realized that $\mathfrak{IC}_1$ operates only on $1s(1)$ and $\mathfrak{IC}_2$ only on $1s(2)$. The first term of Eq. (23) can be rearranged, for example, as

$$\int [1s(2)]^2 \, d\tau_2 \int 1s(1)\mathfrak{IC}_1 1s(1) \, d_1\tau = \int 1s(1)\mathfrak{IC}_1 1s(1) \, d\tau_1 \tag{24}$$

where the normalization condition has set the first part to unity. The energy of the system has now been reduced to

$$\epsilon = 2 \int 1s(1)\mathfrak{IC}_1 1s(1) \, d\tau_1 + e^2 \int \frac{[1s(1)1s(2)]^2}{r_{12}} \, d\tau_1 \, d\tau_2 \tag{25}$$

The two remaining integrals can both be solved. The first one involves nothing more than recognizing that the $1s$ wave function is the exact solution for the system whose Hamiltonian is $\mathfrak{IC}_1$. Thus

$$\mathfrak{IC}_1[1s(1)] = \epsilon'[1s(1)] \tag{26}$$

which, in its expanded form, is identical to the Schrödinger equation of the hydrogenlike atom [Eq. (1)].   Since ϵ' is just a number, the first integral term becomes

$$2\int 1s(1)\epsilon'1s(1)\,d\tau_1 = 2\epsilon'\int[1s(1)]^2\,d\tau_1 = 2\epsilon'$$

and the total energy can be written as

$$\epsilon = 2\epsilon' + \epsilon_{\text{elec rep}} \tag{27}$$

where $\epsilon_{\text{elec rep}}$ is written for the value of the second integral of Eq. (25).

The value for ϵ' is obtained from the one-electron energy expression [Eq. (3)], which, with the appropriate value $Z = 2$, gives the energy of the lowest $n = 1$ state compared with dissociation of the electron as

$$\epsilon' = -\frac{2\pi^2 me^4(2)^2}{h^2(1)^2} = -54.4 \text{ ev} \tag{28}$$

The electron-repulsion integral is harder to evaluate but leads to the result

$$\epsilon_{\text{elec rep}} = +33.9 \text{ ev} \tag{29}$$

The energy of the helium atom, compared with the three particles infinitely separated, is therefore calculated as

$$\epsilon = 2(-54.4) + 33.7 = -74.9 \text{ ev} \tag{30}$$

The numerical value of this result is not of particular importance at this stage. It is of value, however, to see how the approximate wave function for the two electrons can be used with Eq. (17) to obtain a final value for the energy of the system.

The helium-atom calculation gives an energy of -74.9 ev (1 ev = 23.03 kcal/ mole).   The experimental value, being the sum of the two ionization potentials, given in Table 8-4, is -78.98 ev.   The use of an approximate wave function has led therefore to a result which is not sufficiently negative by about 5 per cent.   The failure of the approximation can be attributed to the fact that the use of functions based on one-electron systems has not allowed the two electrons of the helium atom to keep away from each other as much as they would like.

A similar procedure can now be attempted for a system of two protons and two electrons, i.e., for the hydrogen molecule.   Before doing this, however, it is convenient first to point out that all the results can be reduced to five new integrals and to present values for these integrals.

*8-11. Integrals of the H₂ Calculation.   The similar manipulation that results from the use of Eq. (17) and $1s$ wave functions as a basis for the approximate solution of the hydrogen molecule leads to only five new integrals.   These present some mathematical difficulty, but the remainder of the problem consists in manipulating the wave functions as was done in the helium-atom example.   It is helpful initially to introduce the integrals and to report the values obtained for them.   The actual integration—being clearly nothing more than a mathematical step—will not be dealt with here but can be found in any of the standard texts on quantum mechanics.

The wave function that represents the behavior of the electrons in a hydrogen molecule will be approximated by the known wave functions for each of the electrons around a single atom.   Figure 8-7 shows the nuclei labeled as A and

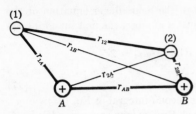

Fig. 8-7. Coordinates of the electrons of the hydrogen molecule.

B and the electrons as 1 and 2. An equally reasonable diagram shows electron 2 on nucleus A and electron 1 on nucleus B. If the internuclear distance r_{AB} is large, it will clearly be a good approximation to use the known $1s$ wave functions to describe the two separate atoms. At smaller internuclear distances the success of a treatment based on atomic orbitals is admittedly less certain.

The wave function describing the behavior of an electron in a normal hydrogen atom is given as the $1s$ wave function in Table 8-2. A compact notation represents such a function for electron 1 on atom A as $a(1)$, electron 2 on atom A as $a(2)$, electron 1 on atom B as $b(1)$, and electron 2 on atom B as $b(2)$. The notation $b(1)$, for example, implies the function

$$b(1) = \frac{1}{\sqrt{\pi}} \left(\frac{1}{a_0}\right)^{\frac{3}{2}} e^{-r_{1B}/a_0} \tag{31}$$

where r_{1B} is the distance of electron 1 from nucleus B.

In the following sections it will be shown that, on the basis of hydrogen-atom wave functions and with the notation of this section, three important integrals will result from the use of Eq. (17). These integrals are shown with their symbols, names, and values for various internuclear distances in Table 8-6.

The first integral, the *overlap integral*, derives its name from the fact that its value depends on the wave function for the electron on one atom overlapping with that of the second atom. At infinite internuclear separation, for example the product $a(1)b(1)$ or $a(2)b(2)$, would everywhere be zero because, for the region in space where $a(1)$ had a value, $b(1)$ would be zero, and vice versa, leading always to a zero value of the product. At zero internuclear distance, on the other hand, the two nuclei have merged into one, and the two wave functions are $1s$ functions of the same atom. Since they are normalized wave functions, the integral of their product would then be unity. At intermediate distances the integral must be evaluated, and the results obtained for some internuclear distances are reported in Table 8-6.

The second integral, called the *coulomb integral*, at infinite nuclear separation can be recognized as giving just the energy of a hydrogen atom. At infinite nuclear separation the electron on one of the nuclei experiences a potential function which is just that of its nucleus and is not at all affected by the other electron or nucleus. The function $a(1)$, for example, then is the exact solution for the Schrödinger equation; therefore

$$\mathfrak{IC}_1 a(1) = \epsilon_{\mathrm{H}} a(1) \tag{32}$$

where ϵ_{H} is the energy of the electron of a normal hydrogen atom. Recognizing that $a(1)$ commutes with ϵ and that $a(1)$ is normalized leads to the result that at infinite internuclear distance the coulomb-integral value ϵ_c is equal to ϵ_{H}, the hydrogen-atom energy. The value of 314 kcal in Table 8-6 is the ionization potential of H, given in Table 8-4, expressed in kilocalories per mole. At

Table 8-6. Integrals Arising in the Heitler-London Calculation of the Energy of the H₂ Molecule

(Values for integrals other than Δ are in kcal/mole; Δ is dimensionless.   Values for the nuclear repulsion e^2/r_{AB} are also included)

Integral	Name	Values at r_{AB} (in A, at multiples of a_0)						
		0	0.529	0.791	1.058	1.585	2.11	∞
$\Delta = \int a(1)b(1)\,d\tau_1$	Overlap integral	1.000	0.856	0.725	0.587	0.349	0.189	0
$\epsilon_c = \int a(1)\mathcal{H}_c a(1)\,d\tau_1$	Coulomb integral	-941	-770	-678	-610	-520	-470	-314
$\epsilon_x = \int a(1)\mathcal{H}_c b(1)\,d\tau_1$	Exchange integral	-941	-731	-578	-440	-234	-117	0
$R_c = e^2 \int\int \dfrac{a(1)a(1)b(2)b(2)\,d\tau_1\,d\tau_2}{r_{12}}$	Electron repulsion	$+393$	$+348$	$+307$	$+267$	$+200$	155	0
$R_x = e^2 \int\int \dfrac{a(1)a(2)b(1)b(2)\,d\tau_1\,d\tau_2}{r_{12}}$	Electron repulsion	$+393$	$+274$	$+186$	$+115$	$+37$	$+10$	0
e^2/r_{AB}	Nuclear repulsion	∞	$+628$	$+420$	$+314$	$+209$	$+157$	0

shorter internuclear distances the low potential of the second nucleus is effective and reduces the values of ϵ_c to those shown in Table 8-6.

The third integral derives its name, the *exchange integral*, in a manner that will be revealed in Secs. 8-13 and 8-16. As with the overlap integral it requires the two wave functions to overlap; otherwise it is identically zero. At zero internuclear distance the nuclei a and b merge and the exchange integral is seen to become identical with the coulomb integral. At intermediate internuclear distances it takes on the values indicated in Table 8-5.

Finally it is necessary to mention the two integrals that result from the terms for the repulsion of the two electrons of the system. These terms are frequently included in the previous coulomb and exchange integrals. The electron-repulsion integrals are similar to the coulomb and exchange integrals in the way in which the wave functions enter. Values for these integrals are also given for various values of r_{AB} in Table 8-6.

With these mathematical items tabulated it is now possible to proceed to an initial attempt to present a quantum-mechanical picture of the chemical bond.

*8-12. An Unsuccessful Treatment of the H_2 Molecule.

An attempt to understand the bond between the two hydrogen atoms might be made in a manner similar to that used for the helium atom. At large internuclear distances it is certainly a good approximation to represent the H_2 molecule as consisting of two hydrogen atoms. Even at shorter internuclear distances this approach might be a suitable approximation. A function that might be a satisfactory approximation to the correct wave function is, therefore,

$$\psi = a(1)b(2) \tag{33}$$

The energy of the system can be calculated from Eq. (17). First the Hamiltonian must be written. Recognizing, with the aid of Fig. 8-7, all the coulombic terms in the potential energy, we have

$$\mathcal{3C} = -\frac{h^2}{8\pi^2 m}\nabla_1^2 - \frac{h^2}{8\pi^2 m}\nabla_2^2 - \frac{e_2}{r_{1A}} - \frac{e^2}{r_{1B}} - \frac{e^2}{r_{2A}} - \frac{e^2}{r_{2B}} + \frac{e^2}{r_{12}}$$

$$= \left(-\frac{h^2}{8\pi^2 m}\nabla_1^2 - \frac{e^2}{r_{1A}} - \frac{e^2}{r_{1B}}\right) + \left(-\frac{h^2}{8\pi^2 m}\nabla_2^2 - \frac{e^2}{r_{2A}} - \frac{e^2}{r_{2B}}\right) + \frac{e^2}{r_{12}}$$

$$= \mathcal{3C}_1 + \mathcal{3C}_2 + \frac{e^2}{r_{12}} \tag{34}$$

The internuclear-repulsion term e^2/r_{AB} has been omitted and will be added explicitly when the total energy of the H_2 molecule is calculated.

The denominator of Eq. (17) is

$$\int [a(1)b(2)][a(1)b(2)]\,d\tau_1\,d\tau_2 \tag{35}$$

and since both $a(1)$ and $b(2)$ are normalized, the total integral is unity.

The numerator is then equal to the electronic binding energy and is written

$$\epsilon = \int a(1)b(2)\left(\mathcal{3C}_1 + \mathcal{3C}_2 + \frac{e^2}{r_{12}}\right)a(1)b(2)\,d\tau_1\,d\tau_2$$

$$= \int a(1)b(2)\mathcal{3C}_1 a(1)b(2)\,d\tau_1\,d\tau_2 + \int a(1)b(2)\mathcal{3C}_2 a(1)b(2)\,d\tau_2$$

$$+ e_2 \frac{a(1)b(2)a(1)b(2)}{r_{12}}\,d\tau_1\,d\tau_2 \tag{36}$$

Recognizing that the first and second integrals are identical, except for numbering of the electrons, and rearranging, as in the He atom example, converts Eq. (36) into

$$\epsilon = 2 \int [b(2)]^2 \, d\tau_2 \int a(1)\mathcal{K}_1 a(1) \, d\tau_1 + e^2 \int \frac{[a(1)b(2)]^2}{r_{12}} \, d\tau_1 \, d\tau_2$$

$$= 2\epsilon_c + R_c \tag{37}$$

The potential-energy curve corresponding to this result can be constructed from the data of Table 8-5 by combining the electronic-binding energy $2\epsilon_c + R_c$ with the nuclear-repulsion energy e^2/r_{AB}. Such a calculation gives the energy to dissociate the H_2 molecule into four separate particles. To obtain the dissociation energy of the molecule into two H atoms one must subtract the energy of two H atoms, i.e., add $(2)(314)$ kcal. When this is done, a curve as shown in Fig. 8-8 is obtained. While a minimum does appear in the curve, it has a depth of only about 15 per cent of the experimentally observed binding energy.

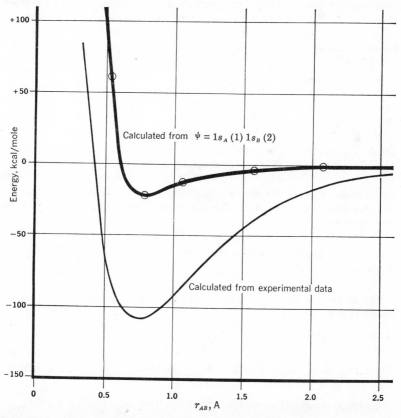

Fig. 8-8. The binding energy of the H_2 molecule based on the approximate wave function $\psi = 1s_A(1)1s_B(2) = a(1)b(2)$.

It appears, therefore, that this treatment has failed to reveal the principal source of the chemical-bond strength.

*8-13. The Heitler-London Treatment of the H_2 Molecule. Just a year after Schrödinger published his general method for treating problems of atomic and molecular dimensions, the method was successfully applied to the H_2 molecule by W. Heitler and F. London. Their treatment provided the long-sought-for-theoretical interpretation of the chemical bond. After their work it was no longer necessary to be mystified by the meaning of the line or pair of dots which were placed between two atoms to represent the chemical bond.

The basic difference between the treatment of Heitler and London and that of the preceding section stems from the recognition that the two electrons of the hydrogen molecule cannot, in fact, be distinguished. It is not in accord with our knowledge of the system, therefore, to suppose, as Eq. (33) does, that one electron can be recognized as electron 1 and that it is known to remain about a nucleus called nucleus A. Heitler and London pointed out that the approximate wave function for the molecule should recognize this indistinguishability of the electrons, and they suggested an approximate function which allows both arrangements of the electrons. Their approximation to the wave function for the electrons of the hydrogen molecule is

$$\psi = \frac{1}{\sqrt{2}} [a(1)b(2) + a(2)b(1)] \tag{38}$$

where the factor of $1/\sqrt{2}$ will be seen to partially normalize the function. With this function as an approximation, Eq. (17) can again be used to solve for the energy of the hydrogen molecule.

The denominator is

$$\int \psi^2 \, d\tau = \tfrac{1}{2} \int [a(1)b(2) + a(2)b(1)]^2 \, d\tau_1 \, d\tau_2$$
$$= \tfrac{1}{2} \int [a(1)b(2)]^2 \, d\tau_1 \, d\tau_2 + \tfrac{1}{2} \int [a(2)b(1)]^2 \, d\tau_1 \, d\tau_2 + \int a(1)b(1)a(2)b(2) \, d\tau_1 \, d\tau_2 \tag{39}$$

The normalization of the atomic functions $a(1)$ and $b(2)$ makes the first two integrals each equal to unity. The last of the three integrals of Eq. (39) can be written as

$$\int a(1)b(1) \, d\tau_1 \int a(2)b(2) \, d\tau_2$$

and recognized as the square of the overlap integral. The net result for the denominator therefore is

$$\int \psi^2 \, d\tau = 1 + \Delta^2 \tag{40}$$

The numerator can be expanded—the Hamiltonian being the same as that shown in Eq. (34)—to give

$$\int \psi \mathfrak{IC} \psi \, d\tau = \frac{1}{2} \int [a(1)b(2) + a(2)b(1)] \left(\mathfrak{IC}_1 + \mathfrak{IC}_2 + \frac{e^2}{r_{12}} \right)$$
$$\times [a(1)b(2) + a(2)b(1)] \, d\tau_1 \, d\tau_2 \tag{41}$$

The terms which result from $\mathfrak{IC}_1$ will be identical to those resulting from $\mathfrak{IC}_2$. The total integral can therefore be written

$$\int [a(1)b(2) + a(2)b(1)] \mathfrak{IC}_1 [a(1)b(2) + a(2)b(1)] \, d\tau_1 \, d\tau_2$$
$$+ \tfrac{1}{2} e^2 \int \frac{[a(1)b(2) + a(2)b(1)]^2}{r_{12}} \, d\tau_1 \, d\tau_2 \tag{42}$$

The first of these two integrals can be further simplified since the initial term $a(1)b(2)$ will be seen to lead to the same result, except for a different numbering, as the term $a(2)b(1)$.   Thus the first integral becomes

$2\int a(1)b(2)\mathfrak{K}_1[a(1)b(2) + a(2)b(1)] \, d\tau_1 \, d\tau_2$

$\qquad = 2\int a(1)b(2)\mathfrak{K}_1 a(1)b(2) \, d\tau_1 \, d\tau_2 + 2\int a(1)b(2)\mathfrak{K}_1 a(2)b(1) \, d\tau_1 \, d\tau_2$

$\qquad = 2\int b(2)b(2) \, d\tau_2\int a(1)\mathfrak{K}_1 a(1) \, d\tau_1 + 2\int a(2)b(2) \, d\tau_2\int a(1)\mathfrak{K}_1 b(1) \, d\tau_1$

$\qquad = 2\epsilon_c + 2\,\Delta\epsilon_x \qquad\qquad\qquad\qquad\qquad\qquad\qquad\qquad (43)$

The electron-repulsion integral, the second integral of Eq. (42), on expansion gives

$$\frac{e^2}{2} \int \frac{[a(1)b(2)]^2}{r_{12}} \, d\tau_1 \, d\tau_2 + \frac{e^2}{2} \int \frac{[a(2)b(1)]^2}{r_{12}} \, d\tau_1 \, d\tau_2$$

$$+ \, e^2 \int \frac{a(1)b(1)a(2)b(2)}{r_{12}} \, d\tau_1 \, d\tau_2$$

$$= \tfrac{1}{2}R_c + \tfrac{1}{2}R_c + R_x = R_c + R_x \quad (44)$$

Collection of all the results of Eqs. (40), (43), and (44) gives the total attractive electronic energy of the hydrogen molecule, according to the Heitler-London approximate function, as

$$\epsilon = \frac{2\epsilon_c + 2\,\Delta\epsilon_x + R_c + R_x}{1 + \Delta^2} \qquad (45)$$

The net binding energy of the molecule is its energy compared with two separate hydrogen atoms.   This net binding energy can be obtained from the result in Eq. (45) by a subtraction of twice the binding energy of an electron in a normal hydrogen atom, i.e., adding $(2)(+314) = 628$ kcal/mole, and subtracting the nuclear-repulsion e^2/r_{AB} term.   Figure 8-9 shows the calculated net binding energy according to the Heitler-London wave function.   Now the calculation has led to an appreciable strong bond, giving a bond energy of about 70 kcal at an internuclear distance of 0.80 A.   These values are to be compared with the observed results of 103.2 kcal/mole for the molecular-dissociation energy and 0.740 A for the equilibrium bond length.   One can conclude that the Heitler-London approach leads to a value for the chemical-bond energy that is in encouraging agreement, in view of the use of as simple a function as that of Eq. (38), with the observed value.

More elaborate approximate attempts than that described here have been made to calculate the properties of the H_2 molecule.   Most noteworthy of these is the calculation performed by James and Coolidge.   Using a wave function which contained 13 terms that could be varied to get the best, i.e., the lowest, calculated energy, they calculated a dissociation energy of 4.721 ev, or 102.6 kcal/mole, and an equilibrium nuclear separation of 0.741 A , in quite good agreement with the experimental results.

It is now necessary to look back and see what it is about the Heitler-London treatment which leads to an explanation of the chemical-bond strength.   Comparison with the attempt of the previous section shows that, in this approach, it is the *exchange phenomena* which lead to the stable arrangement of two electrons between the two nuclei.   It is the overlap of the wave functions on the two atoms which allows the exchange integral to take on a value, and it is

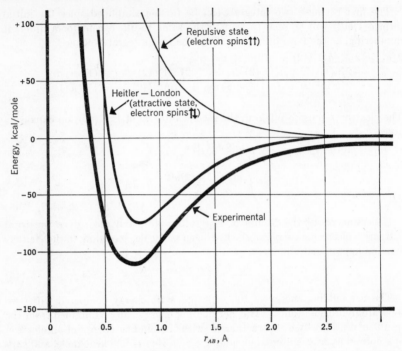

Fig. 8-9. The binding energy of the H_2 molecule based on the Heitler-London wave function $\psi = (1/\sqrt{2})[1s_A(1)1s_B(2) + 1s_A(2)1s_B(1)]$.

this term which contributes largely to the electronic-binding energy. This is the core of the quantum-mechanical explanation of Lewis's idea of a shared pair of electrons as given by the Heitler-London treatment.

In many larger molecules it will be satisfactory for some purposes to use the Lewis-diagram formulation but to recognize that, in principle, a Heitler-London type of calculation could be performed to show that the shared pair of electrons would form a chemical bond. Although this section has dealt directly only with the H_2 molecule, it has, therefore, great significance for our understanding of very many chemical bonds.

One caution should here be introduced. The result that a chemical bond is due to the exchange phenomena arises only because of the particular approximation method which has been used. Other methods depend on different approximate treatments. In such cases the exchange integral may not enter. It is true, however, that most chemists think of a chemical bond in terms of the atoms forming the bond, and the Heitler-London method with its introduction of the idea of exchange of electrons in the bond is in line with such an approach.

Finally, it should be mentioned that, when the Heitler-London approximation is used for larger molecules, it proceeds by treating each bond as consisting of a shared pair of electrons.   It is known then as the *valence-bond* approach in contrast to a second frequently used approximate method, which will be mentioned in Sec. 8-15.

*8-14. The Electron Spin in the Covalent Bond.   The atomic wave functions which have been used to construct the approximate wave function for the hydrogen molecule are $1s$ functions; that is, $n = 1$, and l and m are necessarily 0.   The spin quantum number, which can be $+\frac{1}{2}$ or $-\frac{1}{2}$ for each of the electrons, must now be decided.   In a form rather disguised from that in which it was introduced in Sec. 8-3, the *Pauli exclusion principle* enters here to require that for the wave function of Eq. (38) the two electrons must have their spins in opposite directions; i.e., they must not have the same spin quantum numbers.   This pairing of the spins of the electrons, as depicted in Fig. 8-10, is experimentally verified, as will be shown in studies of the magnetic properties of molecules in Chap. 10.

An approximate wave function for the H_2 molecule which can be written if the spins of the electrons are in the same direction is, again according to a requirement of the Pauli principle,

$$\psi = \frac{1}{\sqrt{2}} [a(1)b(2) - a(2)b(1)] \tag{46}$$

This can be used in the same way as was that of Eq. (38) to lead to energy values at various internuclear distances.   These results are shown in Fig. 8-10. No minimum occurs, and therefore no stable molecule of H_2 would result if the electron spins were in the same direction.   Such energy curves without minima are important, however, in spectroscopy and photochemistry, where molecules in excited electronic states are studied.

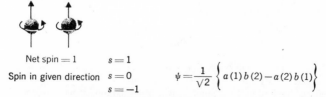

Net spin $= 0$ $s = 0$ $\psi = \frac{1}{\sqrt{2}} \left\{ a(1)\,b(2) + a(2)\,b(1) \right\}$
Spin in given direction

Net spin $= 1$ $s = 1$
Spin in given direction $\quad s = 0$ $\psi = \frac{1}{\sqrt{2}} \left\{ a(1)\,b(2) - a(2)\,b(1) \right\}$
$\qquad\qquad\qquad\quad s = -1$

Fig. 8-10. Spins of the pair of electrons in a chemical bond.

*8-15. The Molecular-orbital Method. To emphasize that the Heitler-London wave function is just one of many approximations which can be used and to introduce a method which will be useful in treating other properties of chemical bonds, it is helpful to consider a method developed principally by Hund, Mulliken, and Lennard-Jones. This method is known as the *molecular-orbital* method. It and the previously treated valence-bond method are the two most generally encountered approximate approaches.

The molecular-orbital method describes each electron separately as being distributed throughout the molecule. The descriptions of the electrons can still be based on hydrogen-atom wave functions, and in this way the wave function, not normalized, for electron 1 of the hydrogen molecule can be written as

$$\psi(1) = a(1) + b(1) \tag{47}$$

and the wave function for electron 2 is

$$\psi(2) = a(2) + b(2) \tag{48}$$

The wave function for the pair of electrons in the molecule is then

$$\begin{aligned}
\psi &= \psi(1)\psi(2) \\
&= [a(1) + b(1)][a(2) + b(2)] \\
&= [a(1)a(2) + b(1)b(2)] + [a(1)b(2) + a(2)b(1)]
\end{aligned} \tag{49}$$

The terms have been collected in the expanded form to show the comparison with the Heitler-London function. The final two terms are just those used by the Heitler-London function. The first two represent the possibility of both the electrons being on the same atom at the same time. While it seems reasonable that such configurations should be allowed for, further calculation shows that the molecular-orbital approach, in giving them equal importance with Heitler-London terms, rather overdoes it. A better approximation is certainly somewhere between these two simpler views, and more detailed calculations attempt to describe the situation more correctly.

The molecular-orbital wave function can also be used to calculate the energy of the chemical bond. Since the results are similar to those of the previous section and nothing new is introduced, this calculation need not be performed here.

In more elaborate chemical systems one finds that sometimes the valence-bond approach is better and, at other times, the molecular-orbital treatment is to be preferred. It is here necessary to note only that these represent two simple types of approximations which can be used in applying the Schrödinger equation to chemical systems.

Problems

1. If the outer electron of Na can be treated approximately as if it were in the $n = 3$ orbit of a Bohr atom with nuclear charge Z, what would the value of this effective nuclear charge have to be to account for the observed ionization potential?

Ans. 1.84.

2. Plot the relative probabilities of the electron being at various distances from the nucleus for the $1s$ wave function for the hydrogen atom, and see graphically that the most probable distance is the same as that obtained by the Bohr theory.

Confirm by differentiating the probability function that this maximum is at a_0.

3. The differential-volume element at a distance r from the nucleus is $4\pi r^2\, dr$. By a suitable integration find the average distance of a $1s$ electron of the H atom from the nucleus. $\left(\int_0^\infty x^3 e^{-x}\, dx = 6. \right)$ *Ans.* $\frac{3}{2}a_0$.

4. Plot, on the same graph, the electron density along the x axis and along a line at $45°$ to the x axis for the p_x orbit for $n = 2$ of a hydrogen-like atom.

5. From the expression for $\Theta\Phi$ of a p_x orbit given in Table 8-2 prepare graphs showing the values of $\Theta\Phi$ and $(\Theta\Phi)^2$ in the xz plane.

6. Show by a suitable integration that the $1s$ wave function of Table 8-2 is normalized.

7. Explain the trends found in the second ionization potentials of Table 8-4, in terms of the electronic shielding of the nucleus.

8. Assuming that the potential-energy function of Eq. (7) is satisfactory:

(a) Evaluate the constant b for KCl so that the minimum in the potential-energy curve occurs at the observed equilibrium internuclear distance of 2.8 A.

Ans. 0.915×10^{-8} erg.

(b) Prepare a plot of this potential versus internuclear separation.

(c) What energy does this potential function predict for the separation of KCl from its equilibrium internuclear distance into the ions K$^+$ and Cl$^-$?

Ans. 106 kcal/mole.

(d) According to the ionization-potential and electron-affinity values of Tables 8-4 and 8-5, how much energy is required for the reaction K + Cl → K$^+$ + Cl$^-$?

Ans. 12 kcal.

(e) What are the energetically favored products of the dissociation of KCl?

(f) Compare the value calculated for the dissociation to stable products from the results of (c) or (d) with the observed value of 4.42 ev = 102 kcal/mole.

Ans. 94 kcal.

9. Use Eq. (17) to calculate the energy of the lowest allowed state of an electron in a 10-A one-dimensional square-well potential function. Guess that a good wave function is the solution function of Sec. 3-9; that is, $\psi = A \sin (\pi x/a)$.

A well-behaved function that goes to zero at $x = 0$ and at $x = a$ and that might be used as an approximate solution to the square-well problem (if the exact solution could not be found) is $Bx(a - x)$, where B is some constant. Calculate the energy of the electron in the 10-A potential well on the basis of this approximate function.

Plot the energies, the wave functions, and the square of the wave functions for the exact and approximate solutions.

Does this example bear out the variation theorem?

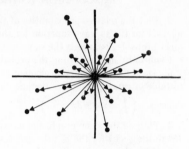

9

The Nature of the Chemical Bond

9-1. The Qualitative Basis for the Covalent Bond. In addition to the mathematical description of the covalent bond given in the preceding chapter, it is of value to have a more qualitative, pictorial idea of the basis for covalent-bond formation. One approach is to recognize that the Schrödinger equation allows the total energy of an atomic-size system to be calculated from the kinetic- and potential-energy contributions.

The Schrödinger-equation term that leads to the kinetic-energy contribution is the differential one, which, for a one-dimensional problem, can be interpreted as

$$-\frac{h^2}{8\pi^2 m}\frac{d^2\psi}{dx^2} = (\text{ke})\psi \tag{1}$$

With this identification the Schrödinger equation can be depicted as

$$(\text{ke})\psi + U\psi = \epsilon\psi \tag{2}$$

This equation is to be interpreted as the approach to be used to calculate the total energy ϵ, that is,

$$\text{ke} + U = \epsilon \tag{3}$$

in systems of atomic dimensions.

The kinetic energy in a quantum-mechanical system can most easily be appreciated from a consideration of a particle in square wells of different sizes, each with the same zero-potential-energy base. The variation in the lowest allowed energy state, as can be calculated from Eq. (34) of Chap. 3, and the corresponding change in the wave function are shown in Fig. 9-1. The narrower wells confine the particle to a smaller region in space, and a sharply curved wave function is produced. Since there is no potential-energy contribution, that is, $U = 0$ throughout the wells, the higher energy of the particle in the narrower wells is kinetic energy and this kinetic energy can be correlated with the curvature of the wave function. The important general result that this example illustrates is that, *the larger the region in space that is made available to a particle, the lower will be the kinetic energy of the particle.*

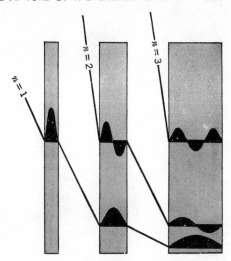

Fig. 9-1. The correlation between the curvature of the wave function and the kinetic energy of a particle confined to different regions in space. Note also that for higher quantum numbers in a given box the curvature increases.

The potential energy contributes to the total energy in atomic-dimension systems in a manner that is similar to the way in which it contributes in macroscopic systems.   The square of the wave function shows the probability of a particle being in a given region in space, and when regions of low potential are available, the calculation will show that the particle tends to have a high probability of being in that region.   In this way, however, the tendency to go to a small low-potential region in space, and thus to have a low-potential contribution, competes with the kinetic-energy requirement that the particle have low kinetic energy when it moves in a large region in space.

The net qualitative result from these two considerations is that *a particle will have low total energy if a large region of low potential energy is available.*

This statement can be applied, particularly in view of the background of the last sections of the previous chapter, to describe the chemical-bond formation between two hydrogen atoms.   At large internuclear distances the system consists of two hydrogen atoms, which can be represented by nuclei and associated electron wave functions.   This situation corresponds to the electron distributions of the separated atoms in Fig. 9-2.   The nature of the chemical bond is elucidated if it can be shown why, at shorter distances, the energy of the system decreases and a stable H_2 molecule is formed.

If the two atoms are thought of as being brought closer together and the wave functions describing the electrons left undisturbed, a slight gain in the potential energy of the system results since each electron now gets some of the benefit of the second nucleus.   Only about 10 per cent of the bond energy can be understood from this picture.

The description of the bond in terms of atomic orbitals needs the recognition that the two electrons are undistinguishable.   Since the electrons cannot be distinguished, it is meaningless to say that each electron must remain on its

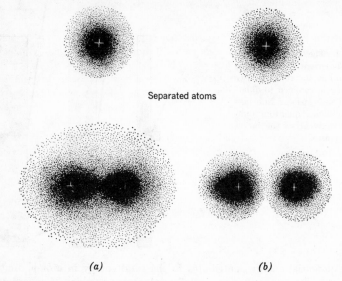

Separated atoms

(a) *(b)*

Fig. 9-2. The electron density in H_2 for the singlet state of the normal hydrogen molecule and the triplet excited state.

own nucleus.   If an *exchange* of places of the electrons is allowed, the region in space in which each electron can move is enlarged and a kinetic-energy contribution to the bond strength results.   This contribution is often referred to as a *delocalization* effect.   Furthermore, a large region in space, particularly between the two nuclei, of low potential is available to the electrons, and a potential-energy contribution to the bond energy also exists.

The mathematical approach of the previous chapter showed two of the ways in which the delocalization effect could be introduced.   In the Heitler-London method, the inadequacy of the wave function for the two electrons of the hydrogen molecule

$$\psi = 1s_A(1)1s_B(2) \tag{4}$$

which corresponds to keeping electron 1 in a $1s$ orbit on nucleus A and electron 2 in a $1s$ orbit on nucleus B, was recognized, and, except for a normalization factor, the electron description

$$\psi = 1s_A(1)1s_B(2) + 1s_A(2)1s_B(1) \tag{5}$$

was used.   With this approximate description for the wave function of the two electrons of H_2 a reasonable bond energy was obtained, and the idea of *exchange* of the electrons between the nuclei was introduced.   In the second approach, called the *molecular-orbital method*, the delocalization of each electron was immediately recognized, and the electron wave functions were written for electron 1 and electron 2 as

$$\varphi(1) = 1s_A(1) + 1s_B(1)$$
$$\varphi(2) = 1s_A(2) + 1s_B(2) \tag{6}$$

which were combined to give the complete two-electron wave function

$$\psi = \varphi(1)\varphi(2) \tag{7}$$

Both the Heitler-London and the molecular-orbital methods lead to satisfactory calculations of the electronic-binding energy. When the nuclear-repulsion term is subtracted, a reasonable potential energy, as shown in Fig. 8-9, is obtained. Both methods attempt to understand the hydrogen molecule in terms of the wave function appropriate to a hydrogen atom, i.e., a $1s$ wave function. Such approaches are followed only because of the mathematical difficulty of treating the H_2 molecule exactly.

It is shown explicitly by the calculations and can also be inferred from a qualitative argument that, for delocalization and bond formation to occur, the atomic orbitals for the electrons of the two nuclei must, to some extent, both occupy the region in space between the nuclei. One says that the wave functions must *overlap*. It is customary, therefore, when a somewhat more suggestive picture of bond formation is wanted than is provided by a line or a pair of dots between two nuclei, to draw a picture such as

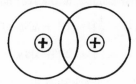

Such pictures become symbols for all the quantum-mechanical descriptions given in this section and the detailed treatments of the previous chapter.

The relative directions of the spins of the two electrons that make up the bond are important as a result of the Pauli exclusion principle. The previous statement that no two electrons in an atom can have all their quantum numbers the same can be rephrased to say that no two electrons can have their spatial quantum numbers the same; i.e., they cannot occupy the same region of space, unless they have opposite spins.

Two electrons can therefore make full use of the low-potential region of space between the nuclei only if they have opposite spins. The electron distribution that is calculated for such paired spins is illustrated in Fig. 9-2.

If the spins of the two electrons are in the same direction, the electrons are restricted from occupying together the space between the nuclei and advantage cannot be taken of the energy-lowering effects. The electron distribution that is found is also represented in Fig. 9-2. The energy of the system with electron spins in the same direction shows no minimum as the nuclei are brought closer together, and this energy curve has been indicated in Fig. 8-9. (This higher energy state has a total electron spin of unity, in contrast to the zero total electron spin when the two electron spins are opposed. Since unit spin can be oriented along any applied field to give the three states with quantized spin components of $+1$, 0, and -1, the unit spin state is known as a *triplet* state. The state with the electron spins opposed and zero net electron spin cannot be split up into components, and this state is known as a *singlet* state.)

Much progress has been made in chemistry and related fields on the basis of the qualitative ideas of covalent bonding that have been given in this section. Some of the uses to which such pictorial representations can be put will be brought out in the following sections.

9-2. Heteronuclear Bonds and the Ionic Character of Bonds. The ideas derived from our study of the H_2 molecule can be carried over qualitatively to all covalent bonds between like atoms. A new feature must, however, be introduced for heteronuclear bonds, such as that of the HCl molecule.

Any description of a heteronuclear bond should recognize the possibility of the bonding electrons being more closely associated with one nucleus than the other. In the HCl example, for instance, it is customary to think of the bonding pair of electrons as being more closely associated with the Cl atom than with the H atom.

The bond in HCl can be interpreted in terms of the distribution of the electron in a $1s$ orbital in the hydrogen atom and the unpaired electron in one of the $3p$ orbitals of chlorine. A suitable approximation to the distribution of each of these electrons, numbered 1 and 2, in the HCl bond can be written as

$$\varphi(1) = \frac{1}{\lambda}[1s_H(1)] + \lambda[3p_{Cl}(1)]$$

and
$$\varphi(2) = \frac{1}{\lambda}[1s_H(2)] + \lambda[3p_{Cl}(2)]$$

(8)

The form of these equations is important, but since no calculations will be carried through, a normalization factor need not be treated. Our expectation is that the factor λ is greater than unity; and therefore the $3p_{Cl}$ term is more important in the description than is the $1s_H$ term. The two-electron bond is then given by the wave function

$$\psi = \varphi(1)\varphi(2)$$
$$= \left\{\frac{1}{\lambda}[1s_H(1)] + \lambda[3p_{Cl}(1)]\right\}\left\{\frac{1}{\lambda}[1s_H(2)] + \lambda[3p_{Cl}(2)]\right\}$$
$$= \frac{1}{\lambda^2}[1s_H(1)1s_H(2)] + [1s_H(1)3p_{Cl}(2) + 1s_H(2)3p_{Cl}(1)]$$
$$+ \lambda^2[3p_{Cl}(1)3p_{Cl}(2)] \quad (9)$$

If the electrons are, in fact, held more closely by the Cl atom than by the H atom, the first term, which corresponds to both electrons being on the H atom, will be small on account of the $1/\lambda^2$ factor and can be ignored. The bond description can then be written as

$$\psi = [1s_H(1)3p_{Cl}(2) + 1s_H(2)3p_{Cl}(1)] + \lambda^2[3p_{Cl}(1)3p_{Cl}(2)] \quad (10)$$

which is usually written with the notation

$$\psi = \psi_{cov} + b\psi_{ionic} \quad (11)$$

where ψ_{cov} implies the equally shared description of the first term in Eq. (10) and ψ_{ionic} the description of the bond that puts both electrons on the more electron-attracting atom.

Thus the bonding electrons of a heteronuclear bond can be described in terms of a covalent factor and an ionic factor.   More pictorially, the bond in HCl is described in terms of wave-function terms corresponding to

$$\underset{\psi_{\text{cov}}}{H\!-\!Cl} \quad \text{and} \quad \underset{\psi_{\text{ionic}}}{H^+ :Cl^-}$$

Homonuclear bonds represent one extreme in that the electrons are shared equally and the covalent term alone is satisfactory.   For heteronuclear bonds, however, all degrees of importance of the ionic term are encountered, even up to the extreme of NaF-type molecules, where it is the covalent part of the description that has become negligible.

Since Eq. (11) is expected to be a better description of the bonding electrons than is ψ_{cov} itself, it follows, according to the variation theorem presented in Sec. 8-9, that the bond energy that corresponds to the more complete description should be greater than that which corresponds to the poorer, completely covalent description.   Unfortunately, molecules of interest, such as HCl, have far too many electrons to allow quantum-mechanical calculations to be made on the basis of the two different bond descriptions.

An important step was made by Pauling in showing that the extra energy corresponding to the better description of the bonding electrons can be deduced from the bond energies that were obtained from thermal data in Sec. 5-9.   In this method, the energy that a bond would have, if the electrons were equally distributed between the nuclei, is calculated from the average of the covalent-bond energies of the atoms of the bond.   Thus, this hypothetical bond energy is calculated for HCl, with D representing bond energies, as

$$
\begin{aligned}
D_{\text{Cl}_2} &= 57 \text{ kcal/mole} \\
D_{\text{H}_2} &= \underline{103} \\
& 2)\overline{160} \\
(D_{\text{HCl}})_{\text{cov}} &= 80 \text{ kcal/mole}
\end{aligned}
\qquad (12)
$$

It turns out generally to be better, for no satisfactory reason, to take the geometric mean, instead of the arithmetical average.   In this way one calculates

$$(D_{\text{HCl}})_{\text{cov}} = \sqrt{(57)(103)} = 77 \text{ kcal/mole} \qquad (13)$$

The actual bond energy is identified with the more complete description, and for HCl Table 5-5 gives

$$D_{\text{HCl}} = 102 \text{ kcal/mole} \qquad (14)$$

Comparison of the values 102 and 77 confirms our ideas that a covalent description for the bond of a heteronuclear molecule is inadequate and that a good description of a heteronuclear chemical bond must include an ionic term. For almost all heteronuclear bonds a similar result is found, namely, that the actual energy is greater than the calculated covalent value.

The energy difference Δ between the actual and covalent-bond energies can be taken as a measure of the ionic character of the bond.   For HCl one calculates

$$
\begin{aligned}
\Delta &= 102 - 77 = 25 \text{ kcal/mole} \\
&= 1.1 \text{ ev}
\end{aligned}
\qquad (15)
$$

where conversion to electron volts anticipates common usage.   Bonds in which the ionic term is important are expected to have large values of Δ, and vice versa. This correlation will be further developed in the following section and again when some additional experimental results are obtained.

9-3. Electronegativities. In view of the unequal sharing of bonding electrons revealed in the previous section, it seems desirable to try to assign to each atom a number which measures the tendency of the bonding electrons to be drawn toward that atom. *Electronegativity* is the name given to the index that attempts to represent this electron-attracting tendency. A large number of methods have been suggested to arrive at electronegativity values, but only two of these need be mentioned here.

A rather direct, but severely limited, method due to Mulliken makes use of the ionization potential and the electron-affinity data. The attraction that an atom, or really the ion, exerts on a pair of electrons that are in a bond between that atom and another atom can be expected to be some average of the attraction of the free ion for an electron, i.e., the ionization potential, and the attraction of the neutral atom for an electron, i.e., the electron affinity. Numerical values are obtained that coincide with values from other methods if electronegativities, designated as x, are calculated from

$$x = \frac{I + A}{5.6} \tag{16}$$

where I and A are the ionization potential and electron affinity and are in electron volts. The factor of 5.6 is an arbitrary scale factor. In this way, for example, one calculates

$$x_{\text{Cl}} = \frac{12.96 + 3.78}{5.6} = 3.0 \tag{17}$$

Similarly, values can be obtained for other elements for which ionization-potential and electron-affinity data are available.

A more generally applicable method, due to Pauling, makes use of the energy differences Δ obtained in the previous section. The value of Δ for a given bond is taken as a measure of the electronegativity difference of the two atoms of the bond. Pauling found that a self-consistent set of electronegativities could best be deduced if one used the relation

$$x_B - x_A = \sqrt{\Delta} \tag{18}$$

where Δ is expressed in electron volts. The use of the square root is quite arbitrary but leads, for example, to essentially the same value for $x_{\text{Cl}} - x_{\text{I}}$ from the data for ICl as from the data for HCl and HI.

Pauling's method allows differences in electronegativities to be deduced from bond-energy data, as shown in Table 9-1. To obtain values for the individual atoms, it is necessary to pick an arbitrary reference point. If x_{H} is taken as 2.1, the values of x_{Li} and x_{F} become 1.0 and 4.0 and this is considered a convenient range. Results obtained in this way are compared in Table 9-1 with values from Mulliken's method, and general agreement is noticed.

The electronegativity values for some elements arranged in the periodic-table form are shown in Fig. 9-3 and are of considerable interest. One should

Table 9-1. Electronegativity Differences and Electronegativities According to the Methods of Pauling and of Mulliken

Bond	Bond energies (kcal/mole)		Δ		$\sqrt{\Delta} = x_B - x_A$
	Hypothetical cov (geometric mean of covalent-bond energies)	Observed	In kcal	In ev	
H—F	65	135	70	3.0	1.7
H—Cl	76	102	26	1.1	1.0
H—Br	68	87	19	0.8	0.9
H—I	61	71	10	0.4	0.6
H—O	59	109	50	2.2	1.5
H—N	62	92	30	1.3	1.1
H—C	91	98	7	0.3	0.5
C—O	52	79	27	1.2	1.1
C—F	57	105	68	2.9	1.7

Atom	x_{Pauling}	x_{Mulliken}
H	(2.1)	2.5
F	3.8	3.8
Cl	3.1	3.0
Br	3.0	2.7
I	2.7	2.4

recognize that the electronegativity is at least a semiquantitative parameter that reflects much of the chemical behavior of the elements. Electronegativities have widespread and important uses in chemistry. It is important to

Li	Be	B		C	N	O	F
1.0	1.5	2.0		2.5	3.0	3.5	4.0
Na	**Mg**	**Al**		**Si**	**P**	**S**	**Cl**
0.9	1.2	1.5		1.8	2.1	2.5	3.0
K	**Ca**	**Sc**	**Ti–Ga**	**Ge**	**As**	**Se**	**Br**
0.8	1.0	1.3	1.7 ± 2	1.8	2.0	2.4	2.8
Rb	**Sr**	**Y**	**Zr–In**	**Sn**	**Sb**	**Te**	**I**
0.8	1.0	1.2	1.9 ± 3	1.8	1.9	2.1	1.5
Cs	**Ba**	**La–Lu**	**Hf–Tl**	**Pb**	**Bi**	**Po**	**At**
0.7	0.9	1.1	1.9 ± 0.4	1.8	1.9	2.0	2.2
Fr	**Ra**	**Ac**	**Th→**				
0.7	0.9	1.1	1.3→				

Fig. 9-3. Electronegativities of the elements arranged in periodic order. (*After Linus Pauling, "The Nature of the Chemical Bond," 3d ed., Cornell University Press, Ithaca, N.Y., 1960.*)

appreciate what it is that they are intended to represent and how they are deduced.

9-4. Directed Valence. So far chemical bonds have been treated for which no particular directional properties have been assigned to the atomic orbits that overlap to form the bond. When the bonding of atoms that have partially filled p orbitals is considered, important new features are encountered. This results from the fact that p orbitals are directed in space as shown in Fig. 8-3 and do not project equally in all directions as do s orbitals.

An attempt to describe the bonding in CH_4 brings us immediately to these new aspects. Chemical evidence, in the hands of Le Bel and van't Hoff, showed long ago that the four hydrogens are equivalent and, therefore, that they are placed in the most symmetric, tetrahedral arrangement about the central carbon atom, as shown in Fig. 9-4. An electronic picture of the bonding must at least lead to this tetrahedral structure.

Each of the four hydrogen atoms presents a $1s$ orbit containing one electron. Bonding to the carbon atom will occur, as it did in the H_2 example, when these orbits overlap with carbon-atom orbitals containing one electron.

The lowest energy state of a gaseous carbon atom has the electronic structure that can be represented as

Four bonds cannot be understood on the basis of this atomic configuration. It is observed spectroscopically, however, that an energy of 96.4 kcal/mole will excite one of the $2s$ electrons to the empty $2p$ orbit to give the structure

The expenditure of this *promotional energy* is allowed since the two extra bonds that can be formed will more than make up for the energy required to promote the electron. The chemical fact is that carbon tends normally to share four pairs of electrons as in CH_4 but that the methylene radical $:CH_2$, which does not need to expend any promotional energy, is also a species of considerable consequence.

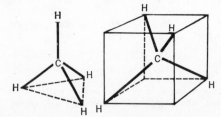

Fig. 9-4. Two representations of the tetrahedral structure of methane. The angle between any pair of bonds is $109\frac{1}{2}°$.

A difficulty still exists in that the atomic wave functions of carbon would seem to indicate one bond of one type, based on the $2s$ orbit, and three bonds of another type, based on the $2p$ orbits.   The solution to this dilemma was given by Pauling, who pointed out that, in the approximation that tries to explain the bonded system in terms of the free atom orbitals, the most suitable orbitals of the atom should be used as a basis for the description.   Furthermore, linear combinations of the $2s$ and $2p$ wave functions can be made to give four new wave functions that are satisfactory atomic functions for the description of the bonded system.   This procedure of combining orbitals to form new ones is called *hybridization*, and the new set are called *hybrid orbitals*.   The most suitable set, according to Pauling, consists of those wave functions which *project out farthest from the central atom* and can therefore concentrate in the region of low potential between two nuclei.   When the four orbitals that project farthest are constructed from the $2s$ and $2p$ orbitals, one finds, in fact, that these are concentrated along tetrahedral directions.   Their angular functions are indicated in Fig. 9-5.   Again the complete description requires a radial factor that shows a gradual fall-off of the function away from the nucleus. The overlap of these sp^3 hybrid orbitals with the $1s$ orbitals of the hydrogen atoms will lead to the observed tetrahedral geometry.

No further description of the bonding in molecules such as CH_4 will be given here.   The bonds can be understood, in principle, from the atomic orbitals and considerations of hybridization and ionic character.   The detailed exact, or nearly exact, calculation of the electron distribution and the bond energies in a molecule of even this complexity—the molecule that seems small to an organic chemist overwhelms the theoretician with its array of 5 nuclei and 10 electrons—is not yet possible.   For many chemical purposes, however, even diagrams of the type of Fig. 9-5 are a major step forward from the Lewis-diagram representation and the stick model of chemical bonds.

A similar but rather more subtle problem arises when one attempts to describe the bonding in a molecule such as H_2O.   The ground-state oxygen-atom configuration is represented as

$\qquad 1s \qquad\qquad\qquad 2s \qquad\qquad\qquad 2p$

and, as Fig. 9-6a shows, this atomic basis leads to a bonding description with a bond angle of 90° between the two O—H bonds.   In view of the CH_4 example, however, the possibility of hybridizing the orbitals in order to form better bonds must be considered as an alternative description.   If tetrahedral hybrid orbitals are formed, the bonded system is represented in Fig. 9-6b.   The better bonds are formed, however, at the expense of promoting a pair of electrons from the low-lying $2s$ orbit to the somewhat higher-energy sp^3 hybrid orbital.   The merits of the two descriptions of Fig. 9-6 cannot easily be decided by quantum-mechanical attacks, again because of the complexity of the system.   The experimental result that the bond angle in water is 105°, as

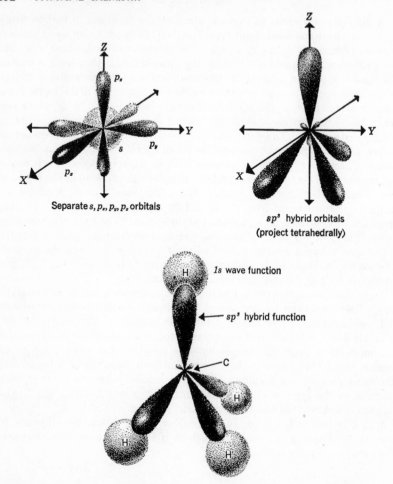

Fig. 9-5. The sp^3 hybrid orbitals that can be formed from linear combinations of the s and p orbits and the overlapping orbitals that lead to bonding in methane. (The angular part of the wave functions has been shown, and these have been distorted for clarity.)

we shall see in the following chapter, suggests that some intermediate description is preferable.

Finally it can be mentioned that in a molecule such as HF a similar difficulty arises. Two possible descriptions of the bonding are given in Fig. 9-7. No different nuclear arrangements are suggested by these different pictures, but different electronic distributions are implied. The electron positions, particularly those of the nonbonding electrons, create considerable havoc when attempts are made to interpret the dipole moment of a molecule simply in

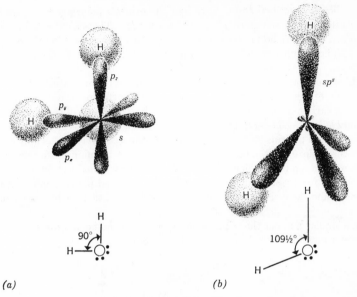

(a)   *(b)*

Fig. 9-6. Two descriptions of the bonding in H_2O.   The observed angle between the two O—H bonds is 105°.   *(a)* H_2O based on s, p_x, p_y, and p_z orbitals of oxygen.   *(b)* H_2O based on sp^3 hybrid orbitals of oxygen.

terms of its ionic character.   This problem will be encountered in the following chapter.

9-5. π Bonding.   The chemist's tendency to describe bonds in terms of atomic orbitals leads him to distinguish two ways in which a directed orbital, such as a p orbital, can overlap with a similar orbital of an adjacent atom.

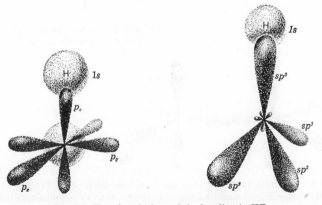

Fig. 9-7. Two descriptions of the bonding in HF.

Those bonds described so far have had the orbitals pointing at one another. Bonds that can be so described are called σ *bonds*. The second way in which a bond can be described in terms of atomic orbitals allows the orbitals to overlap in a parallel manner as indicated in Fig. 9-8. A bond so described is said to be a π *bond*.

The bonding in a compound such as ethylene can be most neatly described—there are, of course, any number of other ways of attempting a description—in terms of carbon-atom hybrids that combine the 2s and two of the 2p orbits into *trigonal hybrids*. These hybrids are planar arrangements, as shown in Fig. 9-8. Such trigonal hybrids on each of the carbon atoms can overlap, as indicated, to form the molecular skeleton from σ bonds. The remaining p orbitals on each carbon atom are perpendicular to the plane of the trigonal hybrid and are in a position to form a π bond. In this way, the observed planar configuration of ethylene and the resistance of the double bond to rotation are nicely accounted for.

In a similar manner the triple bond of acetylene can be described. Now the carbon atoms form σ bonds from the linear *sp* hybrid of the 2s and one of the

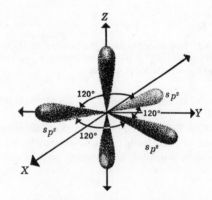

The *sp*² trigonal hybrids are in the *XY* plane
The *p_z* orbital is perpendicular to the *XY* plane

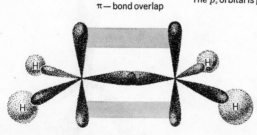

π — bond overlap

Fig. 9-8. *sp*³ trigonal hybrids and their use in a description of the bonding in ethylene $H_2C{=}CH_2$. (The distorted orbitals fail to show that the two p_z orbitals do overlap and form a π bond.)

$2p$ orbitals.   The remaining two $2p$ orbitals of each carbon atom are at right angles to this linear arrangement.   The observed linear structure of acetylene is accounted for by the bonding of σ bonds and two π bonds in perpendicular planes as indicated in Fig. 9-9.

The π-bond type of description of multiple bonds has the advantage for chemical interpretations and theoretical treatments of separating the electrons of the system into a set that forms the fairly ordinary σ bonds and a set that lends the characteristic unsaturation features to the system.   The advantages of this division will be seen in the following section and in later discussions on the mechanisms of reactions.

9-6. Aromatic Compounds and Resonance in Conjugated Systems.   Aromatic compounds present an area of great interest that has long drawn the attention of organic chemists and has likewise been an area of special interest to the

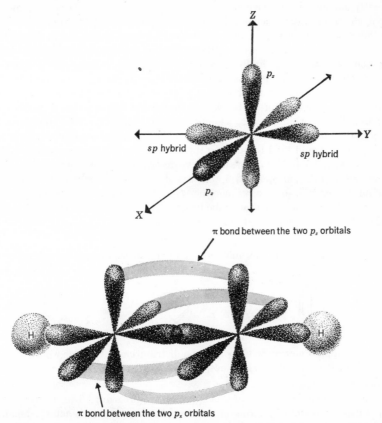

Fig. 9-9. sp^2 hybrid orbitals and their use in a description of the bonding in acetylene H—C≡C—H.

physical chemist. The preliminary task of the theoretician has been, since 1865, that of providing a quantum-mechanical basis for the Kekulé description of aromatic systems as *resonance hybrids* of the various bonded arrangements that can be drawn. The representation of benzene by Kekulé as

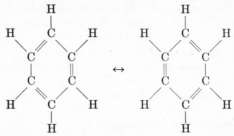

greatly advanced the chemistry of aromatics, and it is necessary now to analyze, in quantum-mechanical terms, the significance of this representation.

The π-bond description is here convenient because, as Fig. 9-10a shows, the benzene skeleton can be constructed from carbon sp^2 hybrids that form σ bonds to each other and to the hydrogen atoms. It remains to investigate the role of the six electrons in the six p orbitals perpendicular to the plane of the molecule. If we desire to describe the bonding in terms of the now familiar overlap of adjacent p orbitals to form π bonds, it is found that two different ways of overlapping the p orbitals exist, as indicated in Fig. 9-10b. An approximate description of the bonded system might make use of the overlap arrangement of ψ_I, which would tend to build up the electron density between atoms 1 and 2, 3 and 4, and 5 and 6. The alternative description ψ_{II}, which builds up electrons between 2 and 3, 4 and 5, and 6 and 1, is, however, equally good. It would be better, instead of using either ψ_I or ψ_{II}, to form an approximate wave function for the system that embodied the features of both I and II. One might try, as an approximate description,

$$\psi = \psi_I + \psi_{II} \tag{19}$$

An even better description would include wave-function terms corresponding to the overlap implied by the Dewar structures

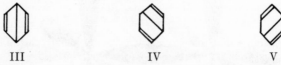

III   IV   V

A better approximation to the π electron distribution in benzene would then be

$$\psi = a\psi_I + a\psi_{II} + b\psi_{III} + b\psi_{IV} + b\psi_V \tag{20}$$

where b is presumably less than a.

The chemical description of this approximate procedure, which attempts to describe the system in terms of familiar, but not too satisfactory, bonding arrangements, is that the structures ψ_I to ψ_V are *resonance structures* and that the molecule is a *resonance hybrid* of these structures. The quantum-mechan-

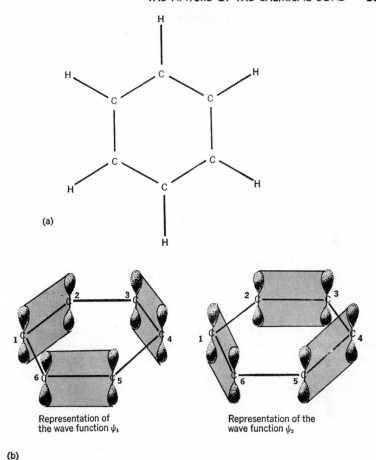

Fig. 9-10. A description of the bonding in benzene, using sp^2p_z orbitals on the carbon atoms and π-bond formation between adjacent p_z orbitals. (a) The σ bonded skeleton of benzene based on sp^2 trigonal hybrids of the carbon atoms. (b) Two ways of overlapping adjacent p orbitals to form π bonds in the benzene molecule.

ical approach shows that resonance structures are merely partial descriptions that can be used to build up a more complete description.

Our previous experience with improvements of electronic descriptions, in the Heitler-London treatment of the H_2 molecule and the introduction of ionic terms in heteronuclear-bond descriptions, has illustrated the variation-theorem result that better descriptions correspond to lower energies. This principle can again be checked, although a number of difficulties are present which cannot be dealt with here, by comparing the actual heat of formation of a molecule such as benzene with that which would be expected on the basis of the bonds drawn in one of the Kekulé structures. From Table 5-2 the heat of the formation reaction of benzene is given as

$$6C(\text{graphite}) + 3H_2(g) \rightarrow C_6H_6(g) \qquad \Delta H = 19.8 \text{ kcal} \qquad (21)$$

Furthermore

$$6C(\text{graphite}) + 6C(g) \qquad \Delta H = (6)(171) = 1026 \text{ kcal} \qquad (22)$$

and
$$3H_2(g) \rightarrow 6H(g) \qquad \Delta H = (3)(103) = 309 \text{ kcal} \qquad (23)$$

From these data the heat of formation of benzene from the gaseous atoms is obtained as

$$6C(g) + 6H(g) \rightarrow C_6H_6(g) \qquad \Delta H = -1{,}026 - 309 + 20 = -1315 \text{ kcal} \quad (24)$$

The energy of the hypothetical structure I or II is estimated from the bond energies of Table 5-5 as

$$
\begin{aligned}
6D_{C-H} &= (6)(98) &= 588 \\
3D_{C-C} &= (3)(80) &= 240 \\
3D_{C=C} &= (3)(145) &= \underline{435} \\
& & 1263 \text{ kcal}
\end{aligned}
$$

The difference, about 40 kcal, between these two results, known as the *resonance energy*, is in the direction expected from the variation theorem; i.e., more heat is evolved in the formation of benzene than would be expected on the basis of one of the Kekulé structures.

Although benzene offers the nicest and the classical example of resonance, the same phenomena can be recognized in other aromatic and unsaturated systems. It is necessary only that there be more than one reasonable way in which a bond diagram for the molecule can be drawn. This is always the case when the molecule can be said to have an alternating arrangement of multiple and single bonds, an arrangement that is known as *conjugation*. Butadiene, for example, can be described as the planar structure

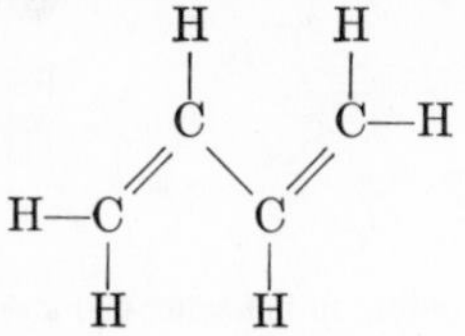

or less satisfactorily as

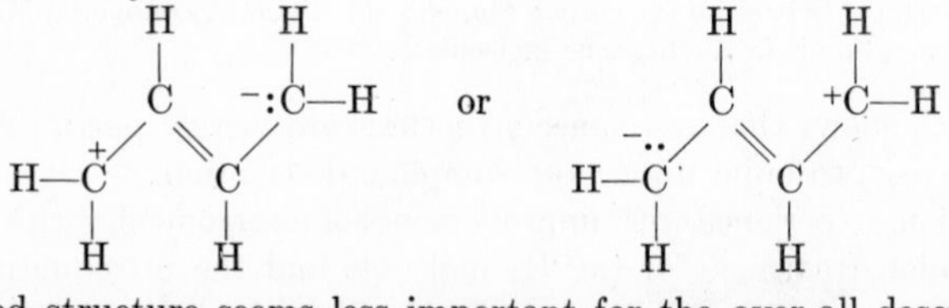

The charged structure seems less important for the over-all description but must be expected to make some contribution to the best complete description. Again it is found that more heat is evolved, for butadiene an amount equal to about 1 kcal, than would be expected on the basis of the bond strength of the noncharged representation.

In a similar way, many other molecules can be said to have resonance struc-

Table 9-2. Resonance Energies*

Substance	Formula	Resonance energy (kcal/mole)
Benzene		37
Naphthalene		75
Pyridine		43
Pyrrole	HC———CH HC CH N | H	31
Furan	HC———CH HC CH O	23
Thiophene	HC———CH HC CH S	31
Carboxylic acid	$R-C{\overset{O}{\overset{\|\|}{}}}-OH$	28
Amides	$R-C{\overset{O}{\overset{\|\|}{}}}-NH_2$	21
Carbon dioxide	CO_2	36
Phenol	⟨⟩—OH	7†
Benzaldehyde	⟨⟩—C${\overset{O}{\overset{\|\|}{}}}$—H	4†
Acetophenone	⟨⟩—C${\overset{O}{\overset{\|\|}{}}}$—CH₃	7†
Benzophenone	⟨⟩—C${\overset{O}{\overset{\|\|}{}}}$—⟨⟩	10†

* After Linus Pauling, "The Nature of the Chemical Bond," 3d ed., Cornell University Press, Ithaca, N.Y., 1960.

† Exclusive of resonance energy attributed to benzene ring.

tures and resonance energy. Some examples are listed in Table 9-2. In drawing resonance structures, one must remember that these are alternative electronic descriptions and that the nuclear positions must not be greatly different for the different structures. Furthermore, it is important to keep in mind that first-row elements can accommodate only a total of eight outer-shell electrons in their nonbonding and bonding orbitals.

It is instructive to consider a different approach to the description of the π electrons of conjugated, resonating systems. The previous approach has been of the valence-bond type since it has pictured bonds between adjacent atomic orbitals. The molecular-orbital approach recognizes immediately the delocalization of the double bonds in conjugated systems and is perhaps a more natural method for such systems. Again combinations of atomic orbitals can be used for this description, but the opportunity is taken here to illustrate the "free-electron" molecular-orbital method.

Consider a fairly long conjugated system such as β-carotene.

$$\left[\begin{array}{c} \mathrm{CH_3 \quad CH_3} \\ \diagdown \diagup \\ \diagup\diagdown \\ \diagdown \\ \diagdown \mathrm{CH_3} \end{array} \begin{array}{c} \mathrm{CH_3} \qquad\qquad \mathrm{CH_3} \\ | \qquad\qquad\quad | \\ \mathrm{CH{=}CH{-}C{=}CH{-}CH{=}CH{-}C{=}CH{-}CH} \end{array} \right]_2$$

If resonance structures are drawn, it will be noticed that each carbon-carbon bond along the chain has appreciable double-bond character. The π electrons are, therefore, not localized in one bond but are relatively free to move throughout the whole carbon skeleton. This suggests that the skeleton be considered as a roughly uniform region of low potential bounded, at the ends of the molecule, by regions of infinitely high potential. The diagram of Fig. 9-11 can then be drawn where the square potential well is to be the receptacle for the 22 π electrons. The allowed energies of these electrons, electron-electron repulsions being ignored, have been calculated in Sec. 3-9 and are given by the expression

$$\epsilon = \frac{n^2 h^2}{8ma^2} \qquad n = 1, 2, 3, \ldots \tag{25}$$

where a is the effective length of the molecule. Two electrons, one with each spin direction, can be placed in each quantum level. The electron description so obtained is shown in Fig. 9-11.

The chief merit of this treatment of conjugated systems is that it offers an easy approach to the calculation of the wavelength of light that is absorbed by such systems. In Fig. 9-11, for example, the transition indicated can be calculated as having an energy of

$$\Delta\epsilon = \epsilon_{12} - \epsilon_{11}$$
$$= 4.30 \times 10^{-12} \text{ erg}$$

which gives for the absorbed radiation

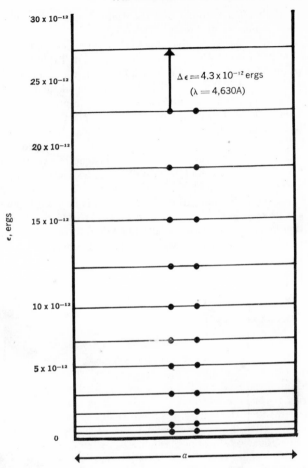

Fig. 9-11. The energy levels and the observed spectroscopic transition for the $22\,\pi$ electrons of β-carotene according to the free-electron or square-potential-well model.

$$\bar{\nu} = 21{,}600 \text{ cm}^{-1}$$

and $$\lambda = \frac{c}{\nu} = \frac{1}{\bar{\nu}} = 4.63 \times 10^{-5} \text{ cm} = 4{,}630 \text{ A} \tag{26}$$

Comparison with the observed absorption maximum of this compound of 4,510 A shows the success of the free-electron model.

9-7. Bonding with d Orbitals. In the preceding sections some of the approaches used to describe bonding between atoms that have partially filled s and p orbits have been described. These approaches are appropriate to organic compounds, except, perhaps, those involving sulfur and phosphorus. Inorganic compounds, on the other hand, frequently contain an atom, or atoms, that have partially filled d orbits. For the study of such compounds, an understanding of the geometry of d orbits is necessary.

Algebraic expressions can be given for the Schrödinger-equation atomic solutions with $l = 2$ in the same way as they were given in Table 8-2 for $l = 0$ and $l = 1$. For qualitative bond descriptions, however, the angular function diagrams, like those for $l = 0$ and $l = 1$ in Fig. 8-3, are adequate.

The d-orbital angular-wave-function factors are represented in Fig. 9-12. Six of the possible 10 d electrons can be accommodated by the first three orbitals that project between the selected cartesian axes. The remaining possible 4 d electrons are accommodated in orbitals that project along the axes. Simple dumbbell pictures lead to three instead of two diagrams, and it is customary, therefore, to combine two of these descriptions to give the two orbitals labeled as $d_{x^2-y^2}$ and d_{z^2} in Fig. 9-12. This representation, however, does give the false implication that one axis is necessarily unique.

One might proceed in a straightforward manner to describe bonding involving transition metals, where the partially filled d orbitals play a dominant role, in terms of the d-orbital atomic wave functions. There is, however, the possi-

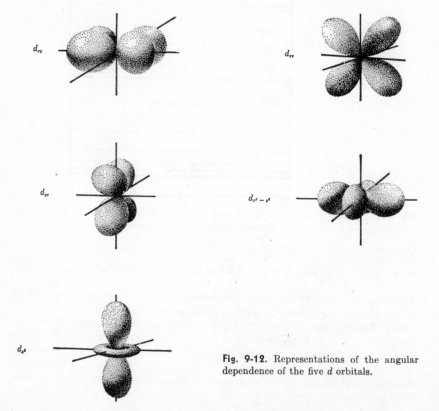

d_{xy}

d_{xz}

d_{yz}

$d_{x^2-y^2}$

d_{z^2}

Fig. 9-12. Representations of the angular dependence of the five d orbitals.

Table 9-3. Two Important Hybrids of s, p, and d Orbitals Used, According to Pauling, by Metals Forming Coordination Compounds

Orbitals involved	Geometry
dsp^2	Square planar
d^2sp^3	Octahedral

bility that hybrid orbitals provide a more suitable basis for describing bonded systems. It has often been assumed, but has never been satisfactorily demonstrated, that, as Fig. 8-4 indicates, the $3d$ orbital has approximately the same energy as the $4s$ and $4p$ orbitals and that some of these can be combined to form hybrid orbitals just as s and p orbitals were previously combined. Two of those which have been suggested as particularly suitable for bond formation are listed in Table 9-3.

The possible d-orbital building blocks, i.e., the d orbitals themselves, and the spd hybrids have now been outlined, and we can proceed to consider the nature of bonding in, what are of most interest, transition metal complexes.

9-8. Bonding in Coordination Compounds. The largest class of compounds in which d orbitals are involved in bonding is that of coordination compounds. Suitable representatives for our investigations of bonding in this class are the ferricyanide ion, as found in $K_3Fe(CN)_6$, and the ferrihexafluoride ion, as found, for example, in K_3FeF_6. Coordination compounds such as these consist of a central transition metal ion with attached, electron-rich groups called *ligands*. Transition elements are characterized by incompletely filled $3d$ orbits, and it is, therefore, the role of these d orbitals that must be understood if the bonding in coordination compounds is to be described. Two quite different approaches have been given. They both are of sufficient interest to merit our attention.

The earlier of the theories is due to Pauling and describes the bonding in much the same way, using covalent and ionic terms, as has already been done for bonds using s and p orbitals. If, according to Pauling, the covalent contribution is important, the metal atom will present empty, projecting orbits in the direction of the ligands so that overlap can occur and a good bond can be formed. The electron pair that enters the bonding orbital is that of the ligand as, for example, is suggested by the diagram

$$Fe^{3+}(:\bar{C}{\equiv}N)_6$$

The bonds so formed remove the formal charge and produce the structure

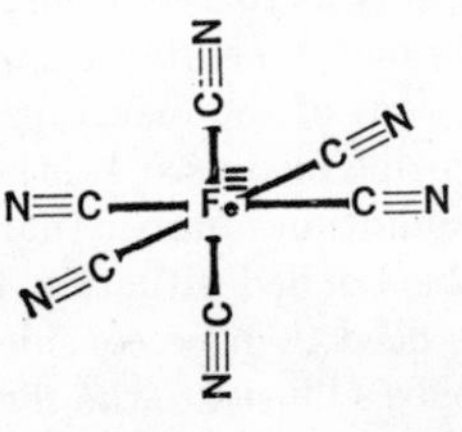

Such bonds are examples of coordinate or coordinate covalent bonds in contrast to the bonds previously studied, in which no formal charges are altered

when the bonds are formed. According to Pauling such ligand attachment can occur, and, when covalency is sufficiently important, the metal atom will present the suitable projecting hybrid orbitals to the ligands. Thus the example $Fe(CN)_6^{3-}$ is described in terms of an Fe^{3+} ion with outer electronic structure

where the five outer electrons are pushed back into three of the d orbitals to allow the formation of empty d^2sp^3 hybrid orbitals for covalent-bond formation with the ligands.

Alternatively, according to Pauling, each ligand may have less of a tendency to donate a pair of electrons to a covalent bond, and the ligands are then attracted to the central metal atom by essentially electrostatic, or ionic, forces. Such a situation appears to correspond to the ion FeF_6^{3-}, and in this case the most stable arrangement for the metal atom has the electrons unpaired and represented by

In the following chapter an experimental method will be presented that allows the deduction of the number of unpaired electrons in a compound. Such experiments assign one unpaired electron to $K_3Fe(CN)_6$ and five unpaired electrons to K_3FeF_6. It is with such data in mind that Pauling set up his theory of coordination compounds, and the explanation of the possible different numbers of unpaired electrons in different compounds of an element is seen to be neatly given.

A more recent theory, at least in this application, is known as the *crystal-field theory* or sometimes the *ligand-field theory*. This approach assumes that covalent-bond formation is not the important interaction of the ligands with the central metal ion. Attention is focused instead on the electrostatic interaction of the ligand groups, or their projecting pair of electrons, with the metal ion. The negative, or polar, ligands are assumed to be bound to the positive central metal ion by electrostatic forces. The geometry and electronic features of the system are imposed by the tendency of the electron-rich ligands to arrange themselves in such a way as to avoid the projecting filled d electrons of the metal ion. Alternatively one can state that for a given geometric arrangement of the ligands the electrons of the metal tend to occupy orbitals that do not point toward the electron-rich ligands. It is here assumed that the electron shell with greater principal quantum number than the partially filled d shell is of too high an energy in the bonded situation to contribute. Only the $3d$ orbits and not hybrid orbits need then be considered.

Again the two ferric complexes illustrate the theory. The Fe^{3+} ion itself has five electrons in the $3d$ orbit, and these electrons can be placed one in each of the five equal-energy $3d$ orbits of the free ion.   When, however, six negatively charged groups are brought up in octahedral positions, the geometry found for most hexacoordinate complexes, electrons in the different d orbitals take on different energies, depending on whether or not a ligand is brought up directly opposed to the orbital that the electron occupies.   This repulsion leads, as can be seen from Fig. 9-12, to three orbitals that are relatively undisturbed and two orbitals that are raised to higher energies.   The extent of splitting between these sets of orbitals depends on the nature of the ligands.

The experimental facts, in particular the number of unpaired electrons, suggests that for FeF_6^{3-} the splitting is relatively small and that the electrons can distribute themselves throughout all five orbitals and need not pair up.   For $Fe(CN)_6^{3-}$, on the other hand, the splitting of the d-orbital energies is apparently large, and the five d orbitals must put up with the electron repulsion that occurs when two electrons are in a single orbit.   This electron arrangement is consistent with the magnetic data that indicate one unpaired electron in $Fe(CN)_6^{3-}$.   The splitting of the d energy levels and the occupancy of the d orbitals by the electrons of the ferric ion in the two different types of octahedral coordination complexes are shown in Fig. 9-13.

A particular advantage of the crystal-field theory is that it allows the calculation, or interpretation, of the electronic transitions that give to coordination compounds their characteristic colors.   The transition that gives rise to

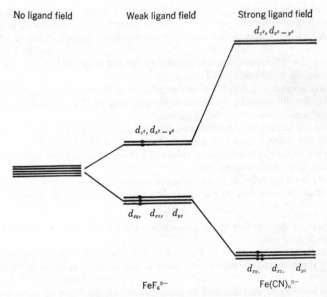

Fig. 9-13. The effect of octahedrally placed ligands on the energies of the five d orbitals of Fig. 9-12.   The orbitals occupied by the five d electrons of Fe^{3+} in the presence of weak and strong field ligands is indicated.

an absorption band, often in the visible region, is frequently one that takes a d electron from the lower energy set of d orbitals to the higher set. The energy separation between the two energy-level sets is a property of the ligand interaction with the central atom. It is possible, therefore, to correlate the frequency of light absorbed by the coordination compound with the nature of the ligands. Such correlations have been made and lead to a useful ordering of the ligands in terms of their interactions with a metal ion.

In spite of the great differences in the emphasis and approaches of the Pauling and the crystal-field theories, it should be recognized that they often, as in the present examples, lead to similar views of the bonded systems. Both approaches direct empty metal orbitals at the ligands, albeit for very different reasons. Likewise, the same predictions are made regarding the number of unpaired electrons.

It must be kept in mind that both approaches attempt to represent, in an approximate manner, the features of the bonded system in terms of descriptions that are directly appropriate only to the individual components. It will probably appear that the two approaches indicated here are the two limiting cases, one overemphasizing the role of covalent bonding and the other ignoring it completely, and that a better description is of some intermediate nature.

Problems

1. Calculate the kinetic-energy contribution to the binding energy of the H_2 molecule if each hydrogen atom is represented by a one-dimensional square-well potential of width 3 A and the hydrogen molecule by a corresponding potential, but of width 4 A.

Ans. 84.3 kcal/mole.

2. Verify the differences in electronegativity for the atoms of the bonds H—F and C—H, using the bond energy of Table 5-5.

Assigning a value of 2.1 to the electronegativity of H, calculate values for C and F.

Compare the difference in electronegativity obtained for C and F with the value that results from considerations of the C—F bond.

3. Using the ionization potentials and the electron affinities given in Tables 8-4 and 8-5, verify the electronegativities given in Table 9-1 for H, Cl, and F.

4. In view of the electronegativity values of Table 9-3 characterize metals by a statement about their electronegativities.

5. Verify from the drawing of a methane molecule in a cubic outline shown in Fig. 9-4 that the angle between any pair of bonds in a tetrahedral structure is $109\frac{1}{2}°$.

6. Represent the bonding in the molecules NH_3, BF_3, H—$\overset{\overset{\displaystyle O}{\|}}{C}$—H, and H—C≡N by:

(a) Lewis diagrams

(b) Diagrams, such as those of Figs. 9-5 to 9-9, which indicate the angular factor in the wave function and therefore something of the position in space occupied by the electrons.

7. The bonding in ethylene and in acetylene can be described in many ways other than that which uses sp^2 or sp orbitals forming σ bonds and p orbitals forming π bonds. A quite satisfactory description can be based on sp^3 hybrid orbitals. Show bonding pictures based on these hybrid orbitals for ethylene and for acetylene.

8. The heat liberated when 1 mole of hydrogen is added to 1 mole of cyclohexene is 28.8 kcal. The heat liberated when 3 moles of hydrogen is added to 1 mole of benzene is 49.8 kcal. What value do these data suggest for the resonance energy of benzene?
Ans. 36.6 kcal/mole.

9. Use a stick model to show the σ bonds in butadiene. Draw in the additional p orbitals on each carbon atom, and show how resonance requires the planarity of the molecule. Indicate the way in which the orbitals are occupied in each of the three most important resonance descriptions.

10. Using a stick-model description of the σ bonds, draw the most important resonance structures, and indicate the expected geometry for CO_2, CH_3COOH, $CH_3CO_2^-$,

$$O$$
$$\|$$

phenol, and acetamide, CH_3CNH_2.

11. The effective length of the conjugated molecule $CH_3{-}(CH{=}CH{-})_4{-}CH_3$ is about 9.8 A. Calculate and plot the energies of the first five allowed states, using a one-dimensional square-well potential to represent the molecular skeleton. Place the eight π electrons in the energy levels that would normally be occupied. Indicate the transition that would correspond to the absorption of radiation, and calculate the energy of quanta necessary to cause this excitation. Compare the wavelength of the radiation that has quanta of this energy with the wavelength of 3,000 A, which is the wavelength of the observed absorption band.

Ans. $\Delta\epsilon = 55.3 \times 10^{-13}$ erg; $\lambda = 3,590$ A.

12. Magnetic measurements indicate that in the ion $[Co(NH_3)_6]^{3+}$ there are no unpaired electrons while in the ion $[CoF_6]^{3-}$ there are four unpaired electrons. Describe the bonding of each of these ions so as to explain the observed numbers of unpaired electrons. Use both the Pauling method of description and that of the crystal-field theory. Both ions presumably have their ligands arranged octahedrally about the Co.

10

Experimental Study of Molecular Structure

Grouped together here are four general experimental methods that are directly concerned with the determination of the geometry and electronic structure of molecules. The difficulties that were encountered in the application of a completely theoretical approach to molecular bonding and structure lead one to refer frequently to experimentally determined properties in order to understand molecular phenomena. Knowledge of the size, shape, rigidity, and electronic structure of molecules deduced from the experimental methods that are treated here goes hand in hand with the theoretical approaches of the previous two chapters.

SPECTROSCOPY

Probably most used of all the experimental molecular-structure methods, if all its branches are included, is that of spectroscopy. The discrete nature of the energies of atomic and molecular systems has already been emphasized, and the quantized character of such energies has been used to give a molecular explanation of thermodynamic properties. Spectroscopy concerns itself with the transitions between such energy levels when the transition occurs with absorption or emission of electromagnetic radiation. The whole subject of molecular spectroscopy can be divided into different fields, depending on the type of molecular energy involved in the transition. The energy of a molecule can be described in terms of translational, rotational, vibrational, and electronic contributions. The spacing of the translational-energy levels, as has been pointed out in Chap. 3, is extremely small, and, furthermore, neutral molecules cannot interact with radiation and thereby change from one translational level to another. It follows that spectroscopic studies can, for the most part, be classified as rotational, vibrational, or electronic spectroscopy. In addition it should be mentioned that, if a sample is placed in an electric or magnetic field, it is possible to study transitions between energy levels resulting from the interaction of the molecules, or the atoms of the molecules, with the applied field. Nuclear magnetic-resonance spectroscopy and electron-spin spectroscopy are studies of this type which will be briefly treated.

A much more rigorous treatment than will be given here would show that it is not, in fact, strictly allowable to treat separately the different molecular energies. The nature of the vibrations of a molecule, for example, depends somewhat on the amount of rotational energy possessed by the molecule. Such *interactions*, however, are almost always of relatively minor importance.

10-1. Rotational Spectra. The rotational energies of a free molecule form the next most closely spaced pattern after the translational energies. A transition between two rotational-energy levels therefore involves a quantum of relatively little energy. These transitions absorb radiation, i.e., form a rotational spectrum, toward the long-wavelength end of the electromagnetic radiation. We shall see that radiation with wavelengths in the millimeter and centimeter range are affected. These wavelengths are in the *microwave region*, a region in which radar operates.

A straightforward procedure for approaching any type of spectroscopy is to apply the Schrödinger equation to the particular problem. This leads to a set of allowed energies, as was shown for the particle-in-a-box and the hydrogen-atom problems, and any observed absorptions of radiation can be correlated with transitions between pairs of these energy levels. Some mathematical complexity results when the Schrödinger equation is applied to the calculation of the rotational energy of a molecule. It serves our purpose better first to consider the problem of classical, i.e., not quantized, rotation and then to impose the quantum conditions in the same manner as did Bohr in his study of the hydrogen atom.

The kinetic energy of a particle of mass m moving around a fixed point, as illustrated in Fig. 3-5, with a velocity v is $\frac{1}{2}mv^2$. For rotary motion it is more convenient to introduce the angular velocity given by

$$\omega = \frac{v}{r} \tag{1}$$

where ω is in cycles per second, and the moment of inertia I defined as

$$I = mr^2 \tag{2}$$

In terms of these quantities the kinetic energy becomes

$$\epsilon = \tfrac{1}{2}mv^2 = \tfrac{1}{2}mr^2\left(\frac{v}{r}\right)^2 = \tfrac{1}{2}I\omega^2 \tag{3}$$

The moment of inertia of an assembly of i particles, such as the atoms of a molecule, is more generally defined as

$$I = \sum_i m_i r_i^2 \tag{4}$$

where r_i is the distance of the ith particle of mass m_i from the center of gravity of the system.

For a diatomic molecule, with which we shall be primarily concerned, the center of gravity, as shown in Fig. 10-1, is located such that $m_1r_1 = m_2r_2$. Combination with the relation $r_1 + r_2 = r$ gives

$$r_1 = \frac{m_2}{m_1 + m_2} r$$

and
$$r_2 = \frac{m_1}{m_1 + m_2} r \tag{5}$$

The moment of inertia of a general diatomic molecule can therefore be written as

$$I = \frac{m_1{}^2 m_2}{(m_1 + m_2)^2} r^2 + \frac{m_1 m_2{}^2}{(m_1 + m_2)^2} r^2 \tag{6}$$

which simplifies to

$$I = \frac{m_1 m_2}{m_1 + m_2} r^2$$

or
$$I = \mu r^2 \tag{7}$$

where the *reduced mass* μ defined as

$$\mu = \frac{m_1 m_2}{m_1 + m_2} \tag{8}$$

has been introduced.

Classically a system of particles with moment of inertia I can rotate with any angular velocity ω and can therefore have any energy $\frac{1}{2}I\omega^2$. For a system of molecular dimensions we should now expect, in view of the type of solutions that the Schrödinger equation has given for the problems to which it has been applied, that only certain rotational energies will be allowed. The Schrödinger equation automatically applies the quantum restrictions. Almost the same result can be obtained, however, by using Bohr's postulate that the angular momentum is quantized in units of $h/2\pi$. As shown previously in Sec. 3-8 for the rotation of an electron about a nucleus, the angular momentum is given by $I\omega$ and the Bohr quantum restrictions give the allowed angular momenta as

$$I\omega = \frac{h}{2\pi} J \qquad \text{where } J = 0, 1, 2, \ldots \tag{9}$$

This stipulation leads to the allowed rotational energies of

$$\epsilon = \tfrac{1}{2}I\omega^2 = \frac{1}{2}\frac{(I\omega)^2}{I}$$
$$= \frac{h^2}{8\pi^2 I} J^2 \tag{10}$$

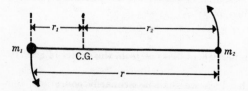

Fig. 10-1. The rotation of a diatomic molecule about its center of gravity.

The correct result, obtained from the Schrödinger-equation solution, is only slightly different, being

$$\epsilon = \frac{h^2}{8\pi^2 I} J(J+1) \qquad \text{where } J = 0, 1, 2, \ldots \qquad (11)$$

With this expression we have the desired result: an equation that relates the allowed rotational energies to a molecular property I and a quantum number. The allowed energies form an energy-level pattern as shown in Fig. 10-2. It remains to investigate what transitions among these levels can be stimulated by electromagnetic radiation and to compare the deduced absorptions of radiation with those observed.

A rotating molecule can withdraw energy from electromagnetic radiation or give up energy to the radiation if it can interact with the oscillating electric field that is associated with all electromagnetic radiation. The molecule can do this if it has dipole moment. The rotating dipole moment provides a coupling with the oscillating electric field of the radiation and allows energy to be transferred from the radiation to the molecule, or vice versa. It is concluded, therefore, that a molecule must have a dipole moment in order to give rise to a rotational spectrum. One observes, in fact, that molecules like H_2, N_2, and CO_2, which are linear, give rise to no absorptions that can be attributed to changes in the rotational energy of the molecules.

Even when a molecule has a dipole moment and can interact with the radia-

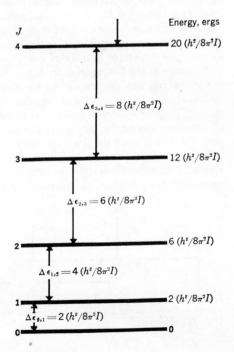

Fig. 10-2. The energies of the allowed rotational states of a linear molecule according to the expression $\epsilon = J(J+1)(h^2/8\pi^2 I)$ ergs.

Energy, ergs

J

4 ———— $20 \; (h^2/8\pi^2 I)$

$\Delta \epsilon_{3,4} = 8 \; (h^2/8\pi^2 I)$

3 ———— $12 \; (h^2/8\pi^2 I)$

$\Delta \epsilon_{2,3} = 6 \; (h^2/8\pi^2 I)$

2 ———— $6 \; (h^2/8\pi^2 I)$

$\Delta \epsilon_{1,2} = 4 \; (h^2/8\pi^2 I)$

1 ———— $2 \; (h^2/8\pi^2 I)$

$\Delta \epsilon_{0,1} = 2 \; (h^2/8\pi^2 I)$

0 ———— 0

tion, there is a restriction on the rotational transitions which can be induced. This restriction, an example of a *selection rule*, is that a molecule can increase or decrease its rotational energy by only one unit when it absorbs or emits a quantum of electromagnetic radiation. This selection rule is written as

$$\Delta J = \pm 1 \tag{12}$$

The restriction cannot be given any simple interpretation, but the existence of such a rule is easily recognized when the observed rotation spectra are investigated.

Rotational spectra are almost always studied by observing the radiation that is absorbed by the sample. For such *absorption spectra*, the only part of the selection rule that is of interest is that of $\Delta J = +1$.

Since, as a later calculation will show, the rotational-energy levels are closely spaced compared with kT, the molecules will be distributed throughout many of the lower allowed levels, such as those depicted in Fig. 10-2. The transitions which can occur, therefore, are between adjacent levels indicated by the $\Delta \epsilon$ terms of Fig. 10-2. These energy differences correspond, therefore, to the energies of quanta of radiation that can be absorbed to bring about a transition $\Delta J = +1$ or emitted in a transition $\Delta J = -1$.

It is more customary to deal with the frequency or wavelength of the absorbed radiation rather than the energy of the quanta. Recalling Planck's relation $\Delta \epsilon = h\nu$, we can convert the quantum energies to frequencies by dividing by h. Thus the radiation which would be absorbed could be expressed in terms of multiples of $h^2/8\pi^2 I$ ergs, as is done in Fig. 10-2, or in terms of multiples of radiation frequencies of $h/8\pi^2 I$ cycles/sec. Finally, the more customary frequency units of reciprocal centimeters can be introduced by division by c to give the factor as $h/8\pi^2 cI$ cm^{-1}.

A feature of the frequencies predicted for absorbed radiation (not the rotational energies but the transitions between them) that is apparent from Fig. 10-3 is that the values of $\Delta \epsilon$ are spaced by the constant factor of $2(h/8\pi^2 cI)$ cm^{-1}. Thus we expect to find in the microwave region a series of absorptions of radiation spaced by an equal amount, an amount that can be identified with $2(h/2\pi^2 cI)$ cm^{-1} for the molecule under investigation.

Many linear molecules have been studied in the microwave region of the spectrum and show absorptions which can be correlated with the previous formulas. The diatomic molecule that provides the nicest illustration is HCl.

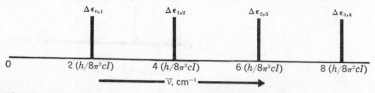

Fig. 10-3. The first few rotational transitions plotted as a function of frequency to show that a rotational spectrum of a linear molecule would show a set of lines with the constant spacing of $2(h/8\pi^2 cI)$ cm^{-1}.

Since this molecule, however, has a very low moment of inertia, the rotational-energy levels will be widely spaced compared with most other molecules.   The rotational transitions of HCl absorb at higher frequencies than the range usually attributed to the microwave region.   One observes in the far end of the infrared region the absorptions listed in Table 10-1.

The difference between successive absorptions is seen to be very nearly constant, as expected from the expressions for the allowed transitions shown in Figs. 10-2 and 10-3.   This frequency difference between successive lines of about 20.7 cm^{-1} is therefore identified with $2(h/8\pi^2 cI)$.   Knowledge of the value of this factor allows the J values of the levels involved in each transition to be assigned, as shown in the table.   It should be pointed out that the lack of data for the first few transitions results from the experimental difficulties in this region, i.e., the region between the accessible far infrared and the microwave.

From the frequencies of the rotational-absorption lines for HCl one obtains the result

$$2\,\frac{h}{8\pi^2 cI} = 20.7 \text{ cm}^{-1} \tag{13}$$

From this relation the internuclear distance of the HCl molecule can be obtained.   First the moment of inertia is calculated from Eq. (13) as

$$I = 2.70 \times 10^{-40} \text{ g/sq cm} \tag{14}$$

The reduced mass of the HCl molecule is

$$\mu = \frac{m_1 m_2}{m_1 + m_2} = \frac{(1.008)(35.46)}{1.008 + 35.46}\frac{1}{6.024 \times 10^{23}}$$
$$= 1.627 \times 10^{-24} \text{ gram} \tag{15}$$

Finally the desired molecular property, the bond length r, is obtained from

Table 10-1. Absorption of Radiation in the Far Infrared Attributable to Rotational-energy Changes of HCl*

$\bar{\nu}(cm^{-1})$	Assigned values of J for the transitions
......	$0 \rightarrow 1$
......	$1 \rightarrow 2$
......	$2 \rightarrow 3$
83.03	$3 \rightarrow 4$
104.1	$4 \rightarrow 5$
124.30	$5 \rightarrow 6$
145.03	$6 \rightarrow 7$
165.51	$7 \rightarrow 8$
185.86	$8 \rightarrow 9$
206.38	$9 \rightarrow 10$
226.50	$10 \rightarrow 11$

* From G. Herzberg, "Spectra of Diatomic Molecules," D. Van Nostrand Company, Inc., Princeton, N.J., 1950.

the relation $I = \mu r^2$ as

$$r = \sqrt{\frac{I}{\mu}} = \sqrt{\frac{2.70 \times 10^{-40}}{1.627 \times 10^{-24}}}$$
$$= 1.29 \times 10^{-8} \text{ cm} = 1.29 \text{ A} \tag{16}$$

This simple example illustrates the most important type of result obtained from studies of rotational spectra. For any linear molecule, with a dipole moment, a comparison of the spacing between the observed absorptions with the spacing term $2(h^2/8\pi^2 I)$ ergs or $2(h/8\pi^2 c I)$ cm^{-1} leads to a value for the moment of inertia of the molecule.

For diatomic molecules, as illustrated by the HCl example, a bond length can immediately be obtained. For a polyatomic linear molecule there will be several internuclear distances, and these cannot be directly evaluated from the one datum, the moment of inertia. In such cases the measurement of the spectra of different isotopically substituted molecules, whose internuclear distances can be assumed to be unaltered by isotopic substitution, provides additional data which often allow the sorting out of the individual bond lengths.

That rotational-energy levels usually have energy separations of less than kT can now be checked. The example HCl has one of the smallest molecular moments of inertia—only H_2 has an appreciably smaller moment—and, according to Eq. (11), HCl will have a more widely spaced rotational-energy-level pattern than other molecules. For HCl the energy-level spacing factor $h/8\pi^2 cI$ has the value 20.7 cm^{-1}, which corresponds to an energy factor of

$$\frac{h^2}{8\pi^2 I} = hc \frac{h}{8\pi^2 cI} = 6.62 \times 10^{-27}(3 \times 10^{10})(20.7)$$
$$= 0.405 \times 10^{-14} \text{ erg} \tag{17}$$

The $J = 1$ level is therefore 0.81×10^{-14} erg above the $J = 0$ level, and this value is small compared with the room-temperature value of kT of 4.14×10^{-14} erg. Higher levels, as Eq. (11) and Fig. 10-1 show, exhibit a wider spacing, which for HCl soon becomes comparable with kT at ordinary temperatures. The general result is, however, that most molecules have many rotational levels in the energy range zero to kT. It is this characteristic which allowed rotational energies to be treated classically in our previous thermodynamic studies.

The population of the various rotational-energy levels, when, for example, an Avogadro's number of molecules is considered, can be calculated from Boltzmann's distribution equation $N_J = N_0 e^{-\epsilon_J/kT}$ if allowance is made for the multiplicity of the levels. The Bohr-type derivation shows that the values of J designate the angular momentum, in units of $h/2\pi$. For a free molecule in space the direction of angular momentum has no energy consequence. If an electric field is applied, the direction of rotation relative to the applied field does have an effect on the energy. The quantum-mechanical result that can be looked upon as another example of the principle on which the Bohr-type postulate is based is that not only the total angular momentum but also the component of angular momentum in the direction of the applied field must be some integral multiple of $h/2\pi$.   In this way, as Fig. 10-4 shows, the multiplicity of a rotational level is found to be $2J + 1$.   Even in the absence of an electric field, this multiplicity exists, and the level is said to have a *degeneracy* of $2J + 1$.

The Boltzmann distribution can now be written to show explicitly the rotational-level multiplicity or degeneracy as

$$N_J = (2J + 1)N_0 e^{-\epsilon_j/kT} \tag{18}$$

Such an expression generally leads to a maximum in the population at some value of J other than $J = 0$.   The populations of the levels of HCl are shown diagrammatically in Fig. 10-5.   It is the information, in such a figure, the energies and populations of the rotational levels, that was used in Sec. 7-13 to deduce the rotational-entropy contribution.

The rotation of a general polyatomic molecule about any axis can be resolved into rotations about three mutually perpendicular axes.   Each of these rotations will have associated with it an energy-level pattern that depends on the moment of inertia about the axis for which the rotation occurs.   Thus each rotational degree of freedom will contribute information on the structure of the molecule, and in a manner similar to that illustrated for the diatomic molecule it is frequently possible to deduce the various internuclear distances of the molecule from the moment-of-inertia data.

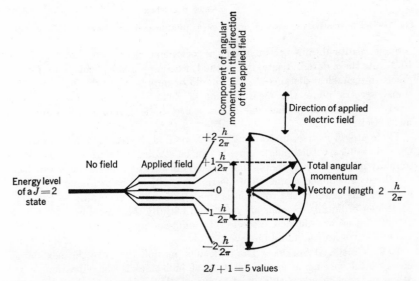

Fig. 10-4. The angular-momentum vector of $2(h/2\pi)$ of a $J = 2$ rotational level oriented relative to an applied electric field so that the component of the angular momentum in the field direction is also quantized.   An illustration that a rotational level has a multiplicity of $2J + 1$.

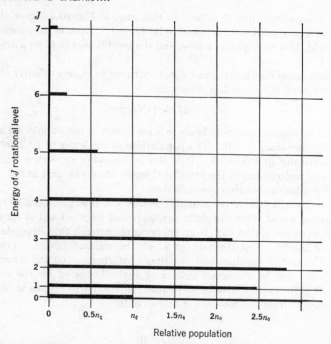

Fig. 10-5. The relative populations of the lower rotational-energy levels of HCl at 25°C.

Some results obtained from studies of rotational spectra are shown in Table 10-2. As these data indicate, the method, when applicable, leads to extremely precise internuclear distances. One should be impressed by the fact that rotational spectra allow the measurement of distances within molecules relatively more accurately than one can measure the length of a desk top with a meterstick.

There are, of course, limitations to this method of structure determination. Only molecules with dipole moments can be studied. Large molecules have so many internuclear distances that these quantities cannot be sorted out from the three determined moments of inertia. Finally, all measurements must be made on gases where the rotation is free and behaves according to Eq. (11). Molecules of liquids or solids are interfered with by their neighbors to such an extent that no well-defined, discrete rotational-energy levels exist and no rotational spectra are therefore observed.

10-2. Vibrational Spectra. The molecular motion that has the next larger energy-level spacing after the rotation of molecules is the vibration of the atoms of the molecule with respect to one another. It will be shown that the study of the absorptions of radiation that result from transitions among the vibrational-energy levels leads to further detailed insight into the nature of molecules.

Table 10-2. Some Molecular Dimensions from Analyses of Rotational Spectra*

	Molecule	Bond	Bond distance (A)
Diatomic..................	HF	H—F	0.917
	HCl	H—Cl	1.275
	HBr	H—Br	1.414
	HI	H—I	1.604
	CO	C≡O	1.128
	FCl	F—Cl	1.628
	NaCl	Na—Cl	2.361
	CsCl	Cs—Cl	2.904
Polyatomic linear............	HCN	C—H	1.064
		C≡N	1.156
	OCS	C≡O	1.164
		C≡S	1.558
	OCSe	C≡O	1.159
		C≡Se	1.709
	HCCCl	C—H	1.052
		C≡C	1.211
		C—Cl	1.632
Polyatomic nonlinear.........	CH₃Cl	H⌒C⌒H	110°20′ ± 1°
		C—H	1.103 ± 0.010
		C—Cl	1.782 ± 0.003
	CH₂Cl₂	H⌒C⌒H	112°0′ ± 20′
		Cl⌒C⌒Cl	111°47′ ± 1′
		C—H	1.068 ± 0.005
		C—Cl	1.7724 ± 0.0005

*From Gordy, Smith, and Trambarulo, "Microwave Spectroscopy," John Wiley & Sons, Inc., New York, 1953.

Although the vibrations of diatomic molecules will primarily be considered, it is convenient at first to consider the vibrations of a single mass attached by a flexible bond, i.e., by a spring, to a fixed point, as in Fig. 10-6. The vibrational characteristics of such a particle are determined by the mass of the particle and by the nature of the spring. For both ordinary-sized objects held by actual springs and for atoms held by chemical bonds it turns out to be quite a good approximation to make the simplest assumption about the spring or bond. This assumption, known as *Hooke's law*, is that the particle experiences a restoring force pulling or pushing it back to its equilibrium position and that this force is proportional to the distance to which the particle has been displaced from its equilibrium position. Since displacing the particle in one direction brings about a force in the opposite direction, Hooke's law is written

$$f = -kx \tag{19}$$

where f is the restoring force and x is the displacement from the equilibrium position. The proportionality constant k is known as the *force constant* and is a measure of the stiffness of the spring. The force constant is equal to the restoring force operating for a unit displacement from the equilibrium position. For molecular systems the force constant is usually given in the units of dynes per centimeter.

It is frequently more convenient to state Hooke's law in terms of the potential energy of the vibrating particle. The potential energy U at the equilibrium position can be arbitrarily taken as zero. Displacement of the particle from a position x to a position $x\,dx$ requires a force to be exerted to overcome that of the spring. The work done, all of which is stored in the system and is therefore potential energy, is equal to this applied force times the distance dx through which it acts. Thus

$$dU = \text{(applied force) } dx$$
$$= (-f)\,dx \tag{20}$$

which with Eq. (19) gives

$$dU = kx\,dx$$

Integration gives the potential as a function of distance, according to Hooke's law, as

$$U = \tfrac{1}{2}kx^2 \tag{21}$$

The potential energy therefore rises parabolically on either side of the equilibrium position, as illustrated in Fig. 10-6.

Once a potential function for the motion to be studied has been arrived at, it is possible to substitute this function in the Schrödinger equation and to solve

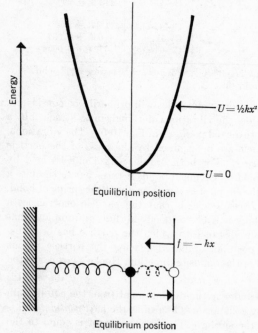

Energy

$U = \tfrac{1}{2}kx^2$

$U = 0$

Equilibrium position

$f = -kx$

x

Equilibrium position
$(x = 0)$

Fig. 10-6. Hooke's law of force for a single particle.

for the allowed energy-level pattern. Again this procedure is avoided, and some classical relations which are more easily visualized are obtained.

The classical motion of a particle, such as that of Fig. 10-6, can be deduced from Newton's law $f = ma$. If $f = -kx$ and $a = d^2x/dt^2$ are substituted, one obtains

$$m \frac{d^2x}{dt^2} = -kx$$

or
$$\frac{m}{k} \frac{d^2x}{dt^2} = -x \tag{22}$$

A solution to this equation can be seen by inspection and verified by substitution to be

$$x = A \sin \sqrt{\frac{k}{m}} t \tag{23}$$

A is a constant that is equal to the maximum value of x; that is, it is the vibrational amplitude. The position of the particle, therefore, varies sinusoidally with time. The time corresponding to one oscillation, or vibration, is $2\pi \sqrt{m/k}$ since every time t increases by $2\pi \sqrt{m/k}$ the quantity $\sqrt{k/m}\, t$ increases by 2π and the particle traces out one complete cycle. More directly useful is the reciprocal of this quantity, which is the frequency of vibration, i.e., the number of cycles performed per second. If this quantity is denoted by $\nu_{\text{classical}}$, we have

$$\nu_{\text{classical}} = \frac{1}{2\pi} \sqrt{\frac{k}{m}} \tag{24}$$

For a system of ordinary dimension there is, therefore, a natural frequency of oscillation that depends on the values of k and m. Any amount of energy can be imparted to the vibrating system, and this energy changes only the amplitude of the vibration.

The quantum-mechanical solution to this problem provided by the Schrödinger equation differs, of course, in that only certain vibrational levels are allowed. These can be calculated by the substitution of the potential-energy expression of Eq. (21) in the one-dimensional Schrödinger equation. Solutions to the differential equation will not be obtained here but can be shown to exist only for vibrational energies

$$\epsilon_{\text{vib}} = \left(v + \frac{1}{2}\right) \frac{h}{2\pi} \sqrt{\frac{k}{m}} \qquad \text{where } v = 0, 1, 2, \ldots \tag{25}$$

The quantum-mechanical result, therefore, indicates a pattern of energy levels with a constant spacing $(h/2\pi) \sqrt{k/m}$. It is this result that was assumed in Sec. 4-14 for the calculation of the average vibrational energy per degree of freedom.

It is interesting that the quantum-mechanical solution introduces the collection of terms $(1/2\pi) \sqrt{k/m}$ that correspond to the natural vibrational frequency of a classical oscillator. Equation (25) can, therefore, be written

$$\epsilon_{\text{vib}} = (v + \tfrac{1}{2})h\nu_{\text{classical}} \tag{26}$$

if the term $\nu_{\text{classical}}$ is interpreted according to Eq. (24).

It is now necessary to consider the vibration of the atoms of a molecule. Here the atoms vibrate against one another instead of against a fixed wall as in the one-particle problem of Fig. 10-6. It is adequate for our purposes to consider the simple example of a diatomic molecule. The coordinates that locate the positions of the atoms relative to the center of gravity of the molecule are those shown in Fig. 10-1. As the previous single-particle vibrational problem showed, it is necessary first to determine the form of the forces that restore the particles to their equilibrium position, or, what is equivalent, to specify the potential energy of the system as a function of the internuclear distance.

The difficulties encountered in the determination of the energy of molecular systems were seen in Chap. 8 to prevent potential-energy diagrams from being deduced for any but the simplest molecule. Figure 8-9 indicates the type of results that are obtained in such cases, and these can be taken as representative of the form of the potential-energy vs. internuclear-distance curves for molecular bonds. Vibrational energies, as we shall see, generally are sufficiently small so that the problem concerns itself with the portion of the potential-energy curve near the minimum. This portion, it turns out, can be satisfactorily approximated (Fig. 10-7) by a parabola, and the expression

$$U = \tfrac{1}{2}k(r - r_e)^2 \tag{27}$$

can be written. Here k is the force constant and measures the stiffness of the chemical bond, r is the variable internuclear distance, and r_e is the equilibrium internuclear distance.

The classical solution can again be obtained from Newton's $f = ma$ relation. If the bond is distorted from its equilibrium length r_e to a new length r, as indicated in Fig. 10-8, the restoring forces on each atom are $-k(r - r_e)$. These forces can be equated to the ma terms for each atom as

$$m_1 \frac{d^2 r_1}{dt^2} = -k(r - r_e)$$

and

$$m_2 \frac{d^2 r_2}{dt^2} = -k(r - r_e) \tag{28}$$

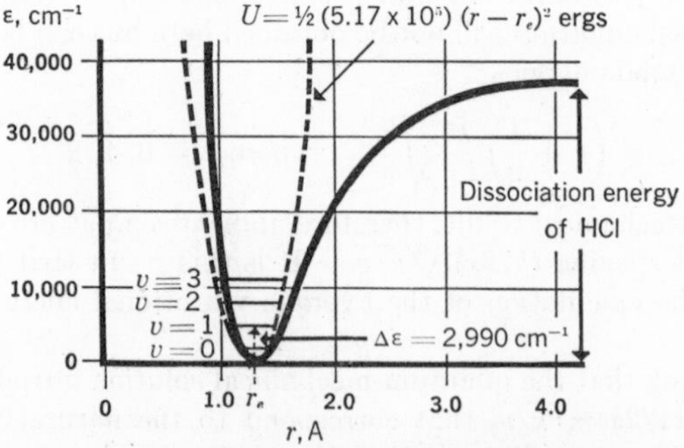

Fig. 10-7. Solid curve is the potential-energy curve for HCl deduced from a number of spectroscopic results (not all discussed here). The dashed curve is the Hooke's-law approximation which is satisfactory near the minimum where the first few vibrational-energy levels occur.

where r_1 and r_2 are the positions of atoms 1 and 2 relative to the center of gravity of the molecule. The relations between r_1, r_2, and r that keep the center of gravity fixed have been given by Eq. (5) as

$$r_1 = \frac{m_2}{m_1 + m_2} r$$

$$r_2 = \frac{m_1}{m_1 + m_2} r$$

Substitution in the $f = ma$ equation for particle 1, for example, gives

$$\frac{m_1 m_2}{m_1 + m_2} \frac{d^2 r}{dt^2} = -k(r - r_e) \tag{29}$$

which, since r_e is a constant, can also be written as

$$\frac{m_1 m_2}{m_1 + m_2} \frac{d^2(r - r_e)}{dt^2} = -k(r - r_e) \tag{30}$$

The term $r - r_e$ is the displacement of the bond length from its equilibrium position, and if the symbol x is introduced as $x = r - r_e$ and the reduced mass μ of Eq. (8) is inserted for the mass term, Eq. (30) becomes

$$\mu \frac{d^2 x}{dt^2} = -kx \tag{31}$$

This expression is identical to the corresponding equation for a single particle except for the replacement of the mass m by the reduced mass μ. It follows that the classical vibrational frequency for a two-particle system such as that of Fig. 10-8 is given by

$$\nu_{\text{classical}} = \frac{1}{2\pi} \sqrt{\frac{k}{\mu}} \tag{32}$$

and that the quantum-mechanical vibrational-energy-level result is

$$\epsilon = \left(v + \frac{1}{2} \right) \frac{h}{2\pi} \sqrt{\frac{k}{\mu}} \qquad v = 0, 1, 2, \ldots \tag{33}$$

or $$\epsilon = \left(v + \frac{1}{2} \right) h\nu_{\text{classical}} \tag{34}$$

The vibrational energies of a diatomic molecule consist of a set of levels as shown with the potential-energy functions in Fig. 10-7. If these allowed energies are expressed in the spectroscopically convenient units of reciprocal centimeters, they are found to be spaced by the amount

$$\Delta\epsilon = \frac{1}{hc} \frac{h}{2\pi} \sqrt{\frac{k}{\mu}} = \frac{1}{2\pi c} \sqrt{\frac{k}{\mu}} \qquad \text{cm}^{-1} \tag{35}$$

At room temperature the value of kT is sufficiently small compared with typical values of $\Delta\epsilon$ so that most of the molecules are in the lowest allowed vibrational state. In a spectroscopic study, therefore, one investigates the absorption of radiation by these $v = 0$ state molecules.

Electromagnetic radiation can induce transitions among the vibrational-energy levels. For energy to be transferred between the radiation and the vibrating molecule, an electrical coupling must be present. This coupling can occur if the vibrating molecule produces an oscillating dipole moment that can interact with the electric field of the radiation. It follows that homonuclear diatomic molecules like H_2, N_2, and O_2, which necessarily have a zero dipole moment for any bond length, will fail to interact. The dipole moment of molecules such as HCl, on the other hand, can be expected to be some function, usually unknown, of the internuclear distance. The vibration of such molecules leads to an oscillating dipole moment, and a vibrational spectrum can be expected.

Even when interaction between the vibrating molecule and the radiation occurs, a further selection rule applies. This rule restricts transitions resulting from the absorption or emission of a quantum of radiation by the relation

$$\Delta v = \pm 1 \qquad (36)$$

Vibrational spectra are usually determined by absorption spectroscopy, and then the rule $\Delta v = +1$ is the only part of this selection rule which is pertinent.

The experimental approach to the study of the $v = 0$ to $v = 1$ vibrational transitions is generally carried out with a spectrometer which has the same units as that indicated in Fig. 3-3.

The values of $\Delta \epsilon$ for vibrational-energy levels, however, are such that infrared radiation has quanta of this magnitude. For studies in the infrared region the source often consists of some ceramic element heated to a dull red, and the detector is a heat-sensitive element which frequently is a thermocouple. Since neither glass nor quartz is transparent to infrared radiation, other materials must be resorted to. The most frequently used material is rock salt. Large single crystals of NaCl are cleaved and polished to form prisms and windows for cells.

One use of vibrational spectra can now be illustrated by again using the example of HCl. One observes in the infrared region an absorption band centered at about 2,890 cm^{-1}. This absorption of radiation can be correlated with the vibrational transition $v = 0$ to $v = 1$, as shown in Fig. 10-7. It follows according to Eq. (35) that 2,890 cm^{-1} is the value of $\Delta \epsilon = (1/2\pi c) \sqrt{k/\mu}$ and, therefore, that

$$\begin{aligned} k &= 4\pi^2 c^2 \mu (2,890)^2 \\ &= 4\pi^2 (3 \times 10^{10})^2 (1.627 \times 10^{-24})(2,890)^2 \\ &= 4.84 \times 10^5 \text{ dynes/cm} \qquad (37) \end{aligned}$$

The theory of vibrational spectra, together with the observed absorption, has now led to a value for the force constant of a chemical bond. The force constant, it will be recalled, measures the force required to deform a bond by a given amount. The qualitative feature to be appreciated from results such as that worked out for HCl is that molecules are flexible. While it is at first difficult to appreciate the significance of the numerical values obtained for bond force constants, one can make interesting comparisons of the stiffness of different bonds. Some results for diatomic molecules and for bonds of polyatomic molecules are shown in Table 10-3. The increased stiffness of multiple bonds compared with single bonds is apparent and is in line with the greater strength of multiple bonds. It should be observed from the data of the table that the vibrational frequency, being determined by both the reduced mass and

Table 10-3. The Force Constants of Some Chemical Bonds*

Bond	Molecule	Force constant (dynes/cm)
H—F	HF	9.7×10^5
H—Cl	HCl	4.8
H—Br	HBr	4.1
H—I	HI	3.2
H—O	H_2O	7.8
H—S	H_2S	4.3
H—C	CH_3X	4.7–5.0
H—C	C_2H_4	5.1
H—C	C_2H_2	5.9
Cl—C	CH_3Cl	3.4
C—C	. . . . .	4.5–5.6
C=C	. . . . .	9.5–9.9
C≡C	. . . . .	15.6–17.0
N—N	. . . . .	3.5–5.5
N=N	. . . . .	13.0–13.5
N≡N	. . . . .	22.9
C—O	. . . . .	5.0–5.8
C=O	. . . . .	11.8–13.4

* From E. B. Wilson, Jr., J. C. Decius, and P. C. Cross, "Molecular Vibrations," McGraw-Hill Book Company, Inc., New York, 1955.

the force constant, according to Eq. (33), is not itself a simple measure of the bond stiffness.

In contrast to pure rotational spectra, only one vibrational-absorption band has been treated for a given diatomic molecule. This has followed from the assumption, which can now be checked, that almost all the molecules occupy the $v = 0$ level at ordinary temperatures and the fact that the vibrational-energy levels show an equally spaced set of levels. For HCl, for example, the absorption frequency, attributed to the $v = 0$ to $v = 1$ transition, is 2,890 cm⁻¹. The energy of a quantum of radiation of this frequency is

$$\Delta\epsilon = 2{,}890 \text{ cm}^{-1}$$
$$= 5.75 \times 10^{-13} \text{ erg} \tag{38}$$

This quantity is equal to the energy of a molecule in the $v = 1$ state compared with one in the $v = 0$ state. The Boltzmann distribution at 25°C gives the ratio of the populations of these two states as

$$\frac{N_1}{N_0} = e^{-\Delta\epsilon/kT}$$
$$= 8 \times 10^{-7} \tag{39}$$

This result confirms the statement that only a very small fraction of the molecules populate the higher vibrational levels at ordinary temperatures.

A closer look at the vibrational-absorption band of a molecule like HCl shows that it does not consist of an absorption region with a single maximum but

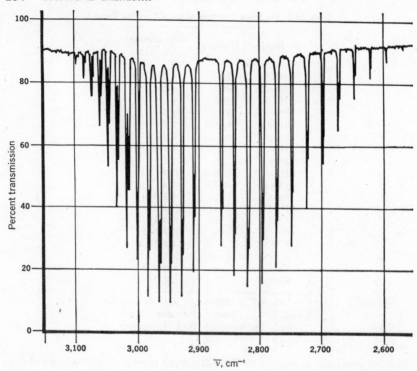

Fig. 10-8. The vibrational transition $v = 0$ to $v = 1$ for HCl vapor at high resolution, showing the vibration-rotation band structure (the very small splittings that also show up are due to the difference in vibrational frequencies of HCl^{35} and HCl^{37}). (*Spectrum courtesy of Dr. W. Kaltenegger, Case Institute of Technology.*)

rather has a number of closely spaced components as shown in Fig. 10-8. The presence of these components can be understood if it is realized that, as the molecule increases its vibrational quantum number from 0 to 1, it may well also change its rotational energy, subject to the rotational-selection rule $\Delta J = \pm 1$. Some of the rotation-vibration energy levels for the $v = 0$ and $v = 1$ states are shown in Fig. 10-9. The allowed transitions for absorption of energy are indicated by the arrows. The energies of these transitions show that the spectrum of this band should consist of a series of absorptions spaced by an amount $2(h^2/8\pi^2 I)$ ergs on either side of the band center. The center corresponds to the absent $v = 0$, $J = 0$ to $v = 1$, $J = 0$ transition. When such rotational spacing is resolved in a vibrational band, the moment of inertia and therefore the internuclear distance can be deduced, the spacing in the "fine structure" of the vibration-rotation spectra.

Polyatomic molecules exhibit vibrational spectra which can be interpreted as arising from transitions within each of a number of energy-level patterns like that of Fig. 10-7. Each energy-level pattern corresponds to one of the characteristic, or *normal*, vibrations of the molecule. Since a molecule of

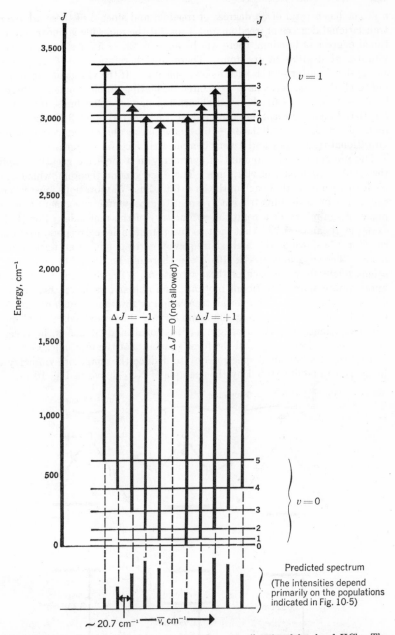

Fig. 10-9. The rotational levels of the $v = 0$ and $v = 1$ vibrational levels of HCl. The allowed transitions ($\Delta v = 1$, $\Delta J = \pm 1$) lead to the prediction of a vibration-rotation spectrum with spacing of about 20.7 cm^{-1}.

n atoms has a total of $3n$ degrees of freedom and since 3 of these are over-all translational degrees of freedom and 3 (or 2 if the molecule is linear) are rotational degrees of freedom, there will be $3n - 6$ ($3n - 5$ for a linear molecule) vibrational degrees of freedom. There are therefore $3n - 6$ (or $3n - 5$) energy-level patterns each with its own spacing. If the vibrations corresponding to all these patterns have associated oscillating dipole moments, there will be $3n - 6$ (or $3n - 5$) observed absorption bands. One finds, for example, for H_2O vapor, absorptions centered at 1,595, 3,652, and 3,756 cm^{-1}. For molecules with many atoms $3n - 6$ becomes large, and one expects very many vibrational transitions and a very complicated spectral pattern.

The presence of any amount of symmetry in a molecule greatly simplifies the study of its modes of vibration. There is a general theorem, which cannot be dealt with here, that each of the $3n - 6$ (or $3n - 5$) vibrations must be either symmetric or antisymmetric with respect to any symmetry element (such as a plane of symmetry or a center of symmetry) of the molecule. For H_2O, for example, it can be shown that the two lower frequencies correspond to symmetric vibrations, while the highest frequency corresponds to an antisymmetric mode. The diagrams of Fig. 10-10 can therefore be drawn to show how the atoms might move in each of these vibrations. The diagram is intended to approximate pure vibrational motions, and the arrows have therefore been drawn so that there is no over-all translation or rotation. Such diagrams can easily be drawn to represent the symmetry of the actual vibrational modes. The exact motion of the atoms in a vibrational mode depends, however, on the masses of the atoms and the force constants of the molecule.

The use of vibrational spectroscopy to deduce the shape or symmetry of a molecule can be illustrated by the example of NO_2 shown in Fig. 10-11. The

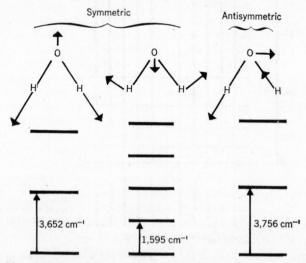

Fig. 10-10. The symmetry of the three modes of vibrations of the water molecule and the associated vibrational-energy-level patterns.

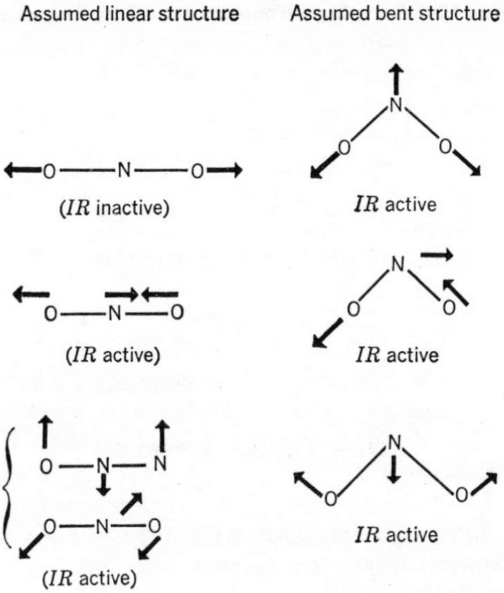

Assumed linear structure   Assumed bent structure

(*IR* inactive)   *IR* active

(*IR* active)   *IR* active

(*IR* active)   *IR* active

Fig. 10-11. The vibrations of NO_2 on the basis of linear and bent structures.

expected forms of vibration for a bent and a linear model are shown. The symmetric stretching vibration of the linear model cannot lead to absorption of energy because no oscillating dipole moment is associated with such a vibration. For the linear model only two absorption bands are expected, while for the bent model all three vibrations should absorb radiation in the infrared region, i.e., should be *infrared active*. Absorptions are observed, as mentioned in Sec. 4-15, at 750, 1,323, and 1,616 cm^{-1}, showing that NO_2 is a bent and not a linear molecule. Arguments such as this can be extended and can be applied to large molecules with various amounts of symmetry.

The principal direct applications of vibrational spectroscopy to molecular-structure problems have now been mentioned. The force constant of the bonds of a molecule can be evaluated, the moments of inertia can be deduced from the rotational structure of the vibrational band, and, finally, the molecular shape can sometimes be deduced from the number of observed absorptions.

A more practical use, and one of great value, particularly in the field of organic chemistry, is that in which the infrared absorption spectrum of a large molecule is used to identify the compound or to indicate the presence of certain groups in the molecule. Bonds or groups within a molecule sometimes vibrate with a frequency, i.e., have an energy-level pattern with a spacing, that is little affected by the rest of the molecule. Absorption at a frequency that is characteristic of a particular group can then be taken as an indication of the presence of that group in the compound being studied. Table 10-4 shows a few of the groups that have useful *characteristic frequencies*.

An even simpler use of vibrational spectra consists in verifying the identity of a compound by matching its infrared spectrum to that of a known sample.

Table 10-4. Some Characteristic Bond-stretching Frequencies

Group	$\bar{\nu}\ (cm^{-1})$
—O—H	3,500–3,700
—N̶—H	3,300–3,500
≡C—H	3,340
=C̶—H	3,000–3,120
—C̶—H	2,880–3,030
—C≡C—	2,200–2,260
—C≡N	2,250
\C=O⁄	1,660–1,870
\C=C⁄	1,600–1,680

Large molecules have such complicated spectra, as shown in Fig. 10-12, for example, that identical spectra can be taken as a sure indication of identical compounds. Thus, although for large molecules the complete vibrational spectrum can seldom be understood in terms of the nature of the $3n - 6$ vibrations, there are many uses to which such spectra can be put.

Brief mention can be made of the fact that vibrational transitions can be studied in a way other than that of infrared absorption spectroscopy. An arrangement such as that shown schematically in Fig. 10-13 is used. The sample is illuminated, at right angles to the spectrometer, by an intense source of monochromatic radiation, usually the 4,358 A visible line of a mercury-vapor lamp. One observes on the photographic plate of the spectrograph, as shown in Fig. 10-14, not only this 4,358 A line, which has been scattered into the spectrometer, but also a number of weaker lines, predominantly on the long-wavelength low-energy side of the 4,358 A line. These additional lines were first observed by C. V. Raman, and such spectra are now called *Raman spectra.*

The earlier prediction of the effect by Smekal explained these additional lines as resulting from the gain or, less likely, the loss of vibrational energy in a process depicted in Fig. 10-15. The quantum of visible light that is sent into the system is very large compared with the vibrational-energy spacings. The process can be understood by recognizing that the large energy quantum of radiation can interact with the sample molecules and can give up some of its energy to the vibrating molecules or can withdraw some of the vibrational energy. The difference between the frequency of a Raman line and that of the exciting line is therefore a measure of the vibrational-energy-level spacing. Both Raman and infrared spectroscopy therefore study the same molecular energy levels. Both methods have their special advantages, but one finds that the infrared absorption method is at present generally easier to use and is the more popular technique.

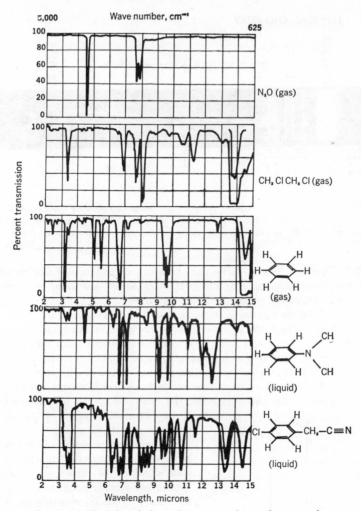

Fig. 10-12. The infrared absorption spectra of several compounds.

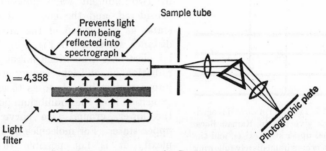

Fig. 10-13. Arrangement for Raman spectroscopy.

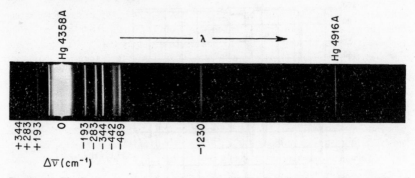

$\Delta\overline{\nu}\,(\mathrm{cm}^{-1})$

Fig. 10-14. The Raman spectrum of thionyl chloride ($SOCl_2$) showing the Raman shifts of the six vibrations. All six appear at longer wavelengths than the exciting line, while three can be seen at shifts to shorter wavelengths. (*Courtesy of Dr. D. A. Long, University of Wales, Swansea.*)

10-3. Electronic Spectra. The final type of energy levels of free molecules that lead to spectroscopically observable transitions are those in which the electron arrangement of the molecule is altered. The electronic spectra of atoms in which the electronic state, as described by the quantum numbers of the electrons of the atom, is changed have already been mentioned in connection with the spectra and Bohr theory of the hydrogen atom. In a similar manner, the electrons of a molecule can be excited to higher energy states, and the radiation that is absorbed in this process or the energy emitted in the return to the ground state can be studied. As with atomic systems, the energies involved are generally large, and electronic spectra are usually found in the ultraviolet region of the electromagnetic radiation.

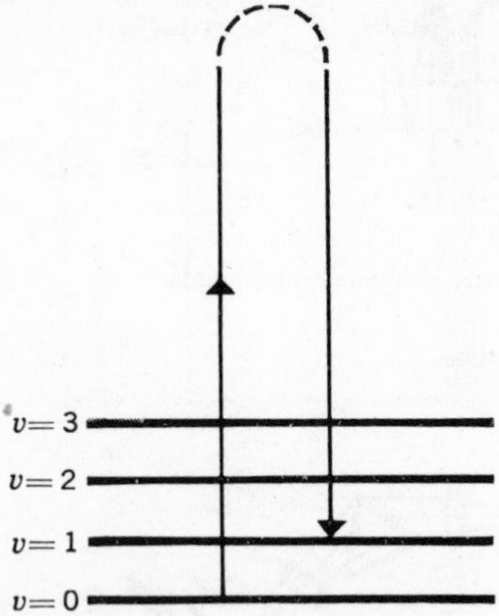

Some of the information which would be necessary for a theoretical approach to the understanding of molecular electronic spectra has already been introduced. In the theory of the H_2 molecule two different electronic configurations, as described by two different wave functions, were considered, and the energy of the two states as a function of the internuclear distance was shown in Fig. 8-9. Molecular electronic transitions might result if radiation of sufficient energy were sent into a system like H_2 so as to cause the transition from the equilibrium position in the lower, ground-state curve to the upper state. For molecules of any complexity it is not possible to deduce theoretically such energy curves for the

$v=3$

$v=2$

$v=1$

$v=0$

Fig. 10-15. The absorption and reemission that give rise to Raman lines. No actual upper state exists, and the emission occurs immediately following absorption.

states involved in the transition.   The electronic spectra of a number of molecules, however, can be interpreted as arising from transitions like that described for the hydrogen molecule.   The higher electronic energy state, lacking a minimum in the potential-energy curve, may lead to the formation of atoms, or fragments of the original molecule, and these fragments may be formed in some excited electronic state rather than in the ground atomic state indicated for H_2 in Fig. 8-9.   The more general situation is shown in Fig. 10-16a.

Other transitions occur to higher-energy electronic states which have a minimum in the potential-energy versus internuclear-distance curve.   Absorption of a quantum of radiation then leads to the formation of an excited molecule which need not instantaneously break up.   Figure 10-16b represents this situation.   In general, the bond strength in the excited state will be less than that in the ground state, and the equilibrium internuclear distance in the excited state will be longer than in the ground state.   The curves of Fig. 10-16b have been drawn to indicate this.   The electronic spectra of many

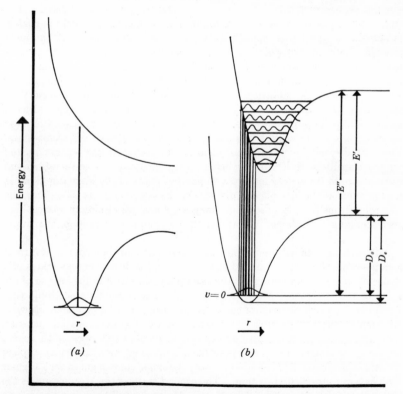

Fig. 10-16. Electronic energies as a function of internuclear distance for two typical situations.   (The vibrational-energy levels and the probability functions are indicated for the vibrational levels involved in the transitions.)

simple molecules can be explained in terms of a number of excited electronic states with potential-energy curves of one or the other of the types shown in Fig. 10-16.

The observed spectral transitions are related to such electronic-energy diagrams on the basis of the *Franck-Condon principle*. This principle stems from the idea that electrons move and rearrange themselves much faster than can the nuclei of molecules. For example, the time for an electron to circle a hydrogen nucleus can be calculated from Bohr's model to be about 10^{-16} sec, while a typical period of vibration of a molecule is a thousand times longer, or about 10^{-13} sec. Comparison of these times suggests that an electronic configuration will change in a time so short that the nuclei will not change their positions. The spectral transitions must be drawn vertically in Fig. 10-16 and not, as one might otherwise be tempted to do, from the potential minimum of the lower curve to that of the upper curve.

One further feature of the transitions between electronic-energy curves must be mentioned. Since a molecule vibrates, even when it is in the lowest vibrational-energy level, a range of internuclear distances must be considered. The quantum-mechanical solution for a vibrating molecule, as Fig. 10-16 indicates, shows that in the lowest energy state, contrary to classical ideas, the most probable internuclear distance is that corresponding to the equilibrium position. For the higher energy states, on the other hand, the quantum-mechanical result is more like the classical result that the most probable configuration is at the ends of the vibration, where the atoms must stop and reverse their direction. The transitions of Fig. 10-16 have been drawn with these ideas in mind. Transitions are expected to have greater probability of starting near the midpoint of the lowest vibrational level of the ground electronic state. The excited species, however, must have the same internuclear separation, and for the transitions to lead to probable arrangements it is necessary for them to be drawn to the energy levels for which the square of the wave function has a large value at the internuclear distance of the transition. It follows that an electronic transition, in absorption, may show a series of closely spaced lines corresponding to different vibrational and rotational energies of the upper state.

Although no detailed discussion can be given here of the types of electronic arrangements that can occur and that correspond to higher energy states of a molecule, it is worth pointing out the situation with regard to the pairing of the spins of the electrons. Most molecules have a ground-state electronic configuration in which the spin of each electron is opposed to, or paired up with, the spin of another electron which otherwise has the same spatial quantum numbers. Such ground states are known as *singlet states* since, with no net spin angular momentum, the imposition of a reference direction by an applied electric or magnetic field can produce only the single component of zero angular momentum in the field direction. The ground state of the H_2 molecule is the simplest example of such a singlet state. Molecules will have, in addition to a ground state that is usually a singlet state, a number of excited states that also have all the electrons paired and that are, therefore, also singlet states.

Whether or not the ground state is a singlet state, there will always be excited states in which two electrons have their spins in the same direction, giving the molecule a net spin angular momentum of $1(h/2\pi)$. Angular components along a specified direction can now have the values $1(h/2\pi)$, 0, and $-1(h/2\pi)$, and such an electronic configuration is known as a *triplet state*.

Electronic spectra of compounds containing no heavy atoms, i.e., most organic compounds, indicate that the absorption of electromagnetic radiation does not unpair the electrons of the molecule. The important selection rule that *transitions occur between states of like multiplicity* is obtained. This rule is a powerful guide to the deduction of the nature of excited electronic states.

For molecules exposed to strong magnetic fields or containing a high-atomic-number atom whose nucleus exerts such a field, this selection rule is broken down, and the spin coupling is readily broken down in an electromagnetic transition.

The assignment of the multiplicity to the state reached by an absorption of radiation and to the states that the molecule goes into as it loses its high energy is a matter of great importance in the study of fluorescence, phosphorescence, and photochemistry. These subjects will, however, be postponed until the following chapter.

The study of electronic spectra leads to a wealth of information about the electronic states and energies of molecules and to the bond distances and force constants of the molecule in excited electronic states. For small diatomic molecules it is frequently possible to assign quantum numbers to the various excited states in which the molecule can occur. For larger molecules, however, a more limited goal must be set. It is frequently sufficient to attempt to decide which of the electrons of the molecule are primarily responsible, i.e., which electron has its quantum number altered, for the observed transition.

The electrons in covalent single bonds, such as C—C and C—H, can be recognized as being very resistant to excitation. Saturated hydrocarbons absorb only very high-energy radiation, usually beyond 1,600 A, far in the ultraviolet. A simple olefin, however, has an absorption band at around 1,700 A, and this can be attributed to the excitation of the π electrons from the electron-paired bonding configuration to a high-energy, or antibonding, state. Such a transition is referred to as a $\pi \rightarrow \pi^*$ transition, the $*$ implying an excited state.

Some molecules have electronic configurations which can be altered in different ways to lead to an excited, or high-energy, electronic state. This situation arises, for example, with compounds containing a carbonyl group $C\!\!=\!\!\overset{..}{O}:$. For such a group the possibility of exciting the π electrons to the excited π^* state exists, as with an olefin, to give a $\pi \rightarrow \pi^*$ transition. Alternatively, the nonbonding electrons of the oxygen might be excited to the higher-energy π^*-electron state, and the absorption would then be characterized as an $n \rightarrow \pi^*$

transition, where the n signifies a nonbonding electron. The two types of transitions are represented in Fig. 10-17.

The recognition of the type of transition occurring on irradiation of a molecule is important for the understanding of the absorption process itself and is basic for the treatment of the behavior of the excited molecule. In spite of the difficulties in completely understanding the electron configurations involved in electronic transitions, it is frequently possible to deduce two important quantities from such studies. These quantities are the *dissociation energy* of a bond or molecule and the *ionization potential* of a molecule. The first quantity is shown as D_e and D_0 in Fig. 10-16. It is clear that, if the quantity E' of that figure can be deduced from the observed transitions and if the excess energy E'' of the dissociation fragments can be determined, one can evaluate the dissociation energy D_0 measured from the lowest vibrational state. Addition of $\frac{1}{2}h\nu_{\text{classical}}$ yields the total depth of the potential-energy curve. This dissociation energy, measured from the equilibrium position, is referred to as D_e. Some of the dissociation energies listed in Table 5-5 have been deduced from spectroscopic measurements of transition such as those of Fig. 10-16.

The ionization potential is the least energy, usually expressed in electron volts, which must be put into a molecule to remove an electron. This energy will generally be greater than the amounts that have been discussed and that lead merely to excited states. Any energy above the ionization potential can be absorbed by the molecule. The excess over that required to free the electron goes into the kinetic energy of the electron. By this process a continuous absorption, i.e., one which shows no discrete lines, should appear in the spectrum, and the onset of such a continuum can be taken as a measure of the

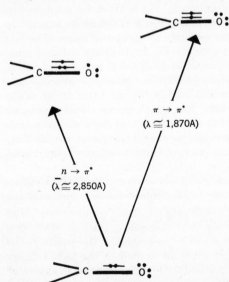

$\pi \rightarrow \pi^*$
$(\lambda \cong 1{,}870\text{A})$

$n \rightarrow \pi^*$
$(\lambda \cong 2{,}850\text{A})$

Fig. 10-17. Schematic representation of the $n \rightarrow \pi^*$ and $\pi \rightarrow \pi^*$ transitions such as those exhibited by a carbonyl group.

ionization potential of the molecule.   Ionization potentials of atoms have been mentioned previously and have been used in the deduction of electronegativities.   Ionization potentials of molecules are much more difficult to understand but are representative of the interesting data on the behavior of electrons in molecules that can be deduced from the study of electronic spectra.   A few values obtained spectroscopically and from the more direct measurements of the minimum energy required in an impinging electron beam to knock an electron out of a molecule are shown in Table 10-6.

Finally, it should be pointed out that not all electronic transitions occur in the ultraviolet region.   The occurrence of colored compounds indicates absorption of radiation in the visible spectrum.   Such absorption requires the electronic energy levels to be more closely spaced than in most molecules.   The most frequently encountered type of organic molecule that absorbs in the visible region, i.e., is colored, consists of a conjugated system frequently involving aromatic rings.   The qualitative explanation for the closer spacing that results from the delocalization of the conjugated electrons is most easily given by regarding such electrons as being free particles within the potential box of the molecule as discussed in Secs. 3-9 and 9-6.   For sufficiently long "boxes" the spacing is small enough to bring the absorption of radiation into the visible part of the spectrum.

ELECTRON DIFFRACTION

Much of the present information on the geometry and the bond lengths of molecules, other than the simpler ones which can be well-treated spectroscopically, comes from diffraction experiments.   The two principal diffraction techniques make use of the diffraction of X rays and the diffraction of electrons.   To these might be added the less general applied technique of neutron diffraction.   X-ray diffraction is most applicable to the study of crystal structures and to the structures of the molecules in crystal lattices.   It is convenient to leave this part of the subject until the general study of solids is undertaken.   For the present, the nature of diffraction experiments will be studied in terms of electron diffraction.   Such experiments are frequently performed on gases, and the net diffraction effect is the sum of the effects from the individual molecules.   The analysis of electron-diffraction results is, therefore, easier to present than is that for X-ray diffraction, where the effect is due to the collective action of all the atoms in the crystal.

10-4. The Interference Phenomenon.   The general principle of diffraction methods depends on the phenomenon of *interference*, which occurs when any wave motion is scattered from a number of centers.   This phenomenon, for example, is exhibited by visible radiation when a beam of light passes through a series of closely spaced slits, as illustrated in Fig. 10-18.   If the light is monochromatic, i.e., consists of radiation of only a single wavelength, the wave motions of the light emerging from the slits will add together in only certain directions.   In these directions *constructive interference* is said to occur, and at

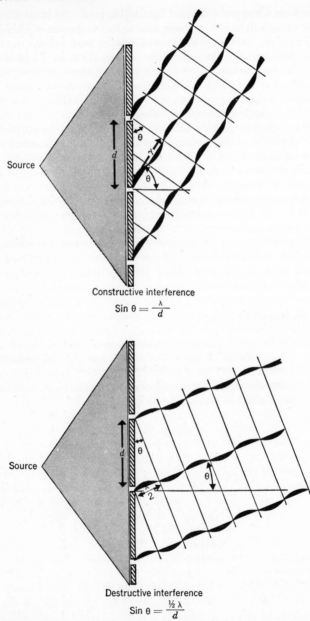

Constructive interference

$$\text{Sin } \theta = \frac{\lambda}{d}$$

Source

Destructive interference

$$\text{Sin } \theta = \frac{\frac{1}{2}\lambda}{d}$$

Fig. 10-18. Interference effects from an illuminated set of slits that act as sources. Illustration of the result that for constructive interference $\sin \theta = n\lambda/\alpha$, where $n = 0, 1, 2, \ldots$.

these directions a beam of diffracted light will appear.   At other directions the diffracted waves will be out of phase, *destructive interference* will occur, and no light will be seen.   More quantitative discussion easily shows, as Fig. 10-18 indicates, that the directions in which constructive interference occurs is related to the wavelength of the light and the distance between the slits by the expression $\sin \theta = n\lambda/d$.   The distance between the slits must be of the same order of magnitude as the wavelength of the light for this diffraction effect to lead to several reasonable values of θ for small integral values of n. Finally it can be pointed out, in anticipation of the use of diffraction techniques for structure determinations, that the diffraction relation of Fig. 10-18 can be turned around to $d = n\lambda/\sin \theta$ so that if the wavelength and angle for constructive interference are measured, the spacing, or "structure," of the slit assembly can be deduced from the observed diffraction pattern.   Thus, for a slit assembly of Fig. 10-19, for example, one could deduce the spacing between the slits from the regions of darkening on the photographic plate and the value of λ for the radiation.

The first use of diffraction techniques to investigate structures followed from the suggestion of Max von Laue in 1912 that the wavelengths of the then newly discovered X rays were in the angstrom range and that interference effects might be produced when a beam of such radiation passed through a crystal in which the crystal planes were known to be spaced by amounts of the order of angstroms.   That a similar interference effect might be observed with a beam of electrons followed from De Broglie's suggestion in 1924 that any particle moving with a momentum mv has associated with it a wavelength $\lambda = h/mv$.   That a beam of electrons has an associated wavelength implies that, if the wavelength is of the same order as the spacing between some set of slits or some set of centers that scatter electrons, interference effects can be observed with an electron beam also.

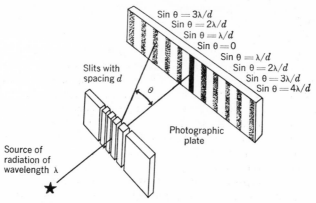

Fig. 10-19. Illustration that by measurement of the angles for constructive interference the spacing d of the slit system can be deduced.   (If $\lambda \cong d$, then a number of diffraction lines will be observed on the photographic plate for reasonable values of $\sin \theta = n\lambda/d$.)

An electron beam is produced by drawing electrons out of a cathode plate by means of an applied voltage and directing them to the anode in a manner discussed with regard to Thomson's studies of e/m for the electron. If such a beam passes across a potential difference of $\mathcal{U}$ volts, each electron acquires kinetic energy as a result of the acceleration in this electric field. The potential difference, or voltage drop, is defined as the energy given to a unit charge when it falls through the potential difference. To obtain the energy, which becomes the kinetic energy of such an accelerated particle, in cgs units it is necessary to divide the ordinarily used practical voltage unit by 300 and to multiply by the electron charge e. Thus

$$\tfrac{1}{2}mv^2 = \frac{e\mathcal{U}}{300} \tag{40}$$

This relation leads to the momentum expression

$$mv = \sqrt{\frac{2me\mathcal{U}}{300}} \tag{41}$$

which, for an electron, gives the De Broglie wavelength as

$$\lambda = h\sqrt{\frac{150}{me\mathcal{U}}} = \frac{12.24}{\sqrt{\mathcal{U}}} \quad \text{angstroms} \tag{42}$$

An accelerating potential of 40,000 volts, therefore, corresponds to an electron-beam wavelength of 0.06 Å. Such a wavelength leads one to expect that interference effects will be observed when a beam so accelerated passes through a sample containing scattering centers separated by the distances between atoms of a molecule.

When a beam of electrons passes through a chamber containing gas molecules, the charges of the nuclei and the electrons of the molecules will interact with the incoming beam and each of the atoms of the molecules of the gas will act as a radiation-scattering center in much the same way as each of the slits of Fig. 10-19 acts as a center of radiation.

Since the particles of the electron beam carry a charge, the amount of scattering resulting from the interaction of the electron beam and the gas molecules is relatively large and few molecules are needed to produce a detectable amount of scattered beam. With an X-ray beam, on the other hand, the amount of scattering produced by each molecule would be much less, and crystals, with their higher concentration of scattering centers, are generally studied. The electrons are affected by the atoms of a molecule as a result of the change in the potential energy that the beam experiences when it passes near an atom. The scattering power of atoms can, in fact, be taken as approximately proportional to the atomic number Z. It follows that hydrogen atoms are "seen" very poorly by an electron beam, and for many molecules their presence can be ignored in electron-diffraction studies. While this introduces a considerable simplification, it implies that the positions of hydrogen atoms cannot be determined. Such has in fact been the case. Recent results for simple molecules do, however, manage to determine hydrogen-atom positions.

The detailed mechanism by which the incoming electron beam, in an apparatus such as that shown schematically in Fig. 10-20, interacts with the atoms of the sample molecules cannot be dealt with here and need not be understood for an appreciation of many features of electron diffraction studies. It can be mentioned, however, that the scattering of the beam can be attributed to coherent scattering, which implies no exchange of energy between the beam and the scattering centers, and incoherent scattering, in which there is energy exchange and a resulting change in the wavelength of the scattered electron beam. Both types of scattering lead to more forward than lateral scattering, and a detailed analysis shows that the intensity of such scattered beams falls off from the incident direction according to $1/\sin^4 \theta$, where θ is the scattering angle such as that in Fig. 10-19.

It is in the coherent, or elastic, scattering that the interference effects show up. These effects are, therefore, superimposed on a background of scattering that is not dependent on the structure of the molecule. The interference or diffraction effects can, however, be sorted out from the background on the photographic plate.

To an electron beam passing through a gas, as in Fig. 10-20, each molecule appears to be made up of a number of scattering centers at some fixed distance from one another. It is now necessary to see whether or not the interference effects between the scattered beams from the different atoms lead to a diffraction pattern from which the distances between the atoms can be deduced.

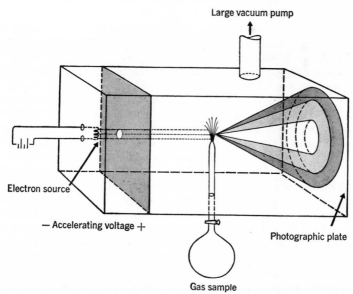

Fig. 10-20. Arrangement for the study of gases by electron diffraction.

The relation between the molecular geometry and the diffraction pattern is given by the Wierl equation, which will now be derived.

10-5. The Wierl Equation.   The essential features of electron diffraction can be studied and the basic relation, the Wierl equation, can be obtained by considering the scattering pattern produced by a homonuclear diatomic molecule. The structure, i.e., the length of the bond between the atoms, will be deduced from the observed diffraction pattern.

A beam of electrons with wavelength λ, as Fig. 10-20 illustrates, is passed through a sample, actually a jet, of gas.   Much of the beam will be unaffected by the gas and will form a strong central spot on the photographic plate. Some of the beam will, however, be scattered by the molecules of the gas jet. Because of interference between the beams scattered from the different atoms of each molecule, a set of darkened rings will appear on the photographic plate.

For the scattering interference effects produced by the simple slit assembly of Fig. 10-19 it was easy to deduce how much scattering would occur at some scattering angle θ.   It is now necessary to obtain this relation when the atoms of a molecule, which can have all orientations in space, take the place of the set of slits.   Figure 10-21 shows a molecule in the electron beam.   We shall deduce an expression for the amount of scattering that comes off at an angle θ to the original direction for the molecule with the orientation of that in Fig. 10-21.   It will then be necessary to integrate this expression over all the orientations of the molecule in space.   Since only the orientations of the molecules are important in producing different diffraction effects and not their position in the well-defined electron beam, it is sufficient to keep atom A at the origin and to carry B through all positions that it could adopt and remain a distance r from atom A.

The beam scattered by an angle θ from the original beam arrives at the photographic plate and forms a ring on the plate.   The intensity of the beam arriving at a point on the photographic plate at an angle θ will be considered.

The interference between waves coming off in the direction defined by θ from A and B depends on the phase difference that is imparted to the two beams as a result of their different origins.   Three shafts of the incoming beam that go through D, E and B, and A are represented.   At a cross section perpendicular to such a beam of electromagnetic radiation all the waves must be in phase; otherwise destructive interference would occur, and the wave would vanish.   Point E is drawn, on the beam that reaches B, on the perpendicular from D to this beam.   Thus A, D, and E are on a plane perpendicular to the incoming beam, and at these points the waves must be in phase, as indicated. In a similar manner the directions of the shafts of the scattered beam in the direction θ to the incident beam are shown leaving A and B.   Since F is drawn on the perpendicular from C to the beam leaving A, the points B and F are on a line perpendicular to the direction of the scattered beam.   The net intensity of the scattered beam depends, therefore, on whether the beams leaving B and F are in phase or not.   The waves have been added to Fig. 10-21 in such a way that constructive interference would result.

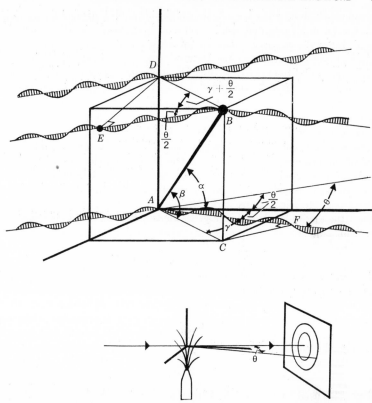

Fig. 10-21. Diffraction from a diatomic molecule AB. The amount of scattered radiation that comes off at an angle θ to the direction of the incident beam depends on the phase difference imposed by the different path lengths EB and AF.

The difference in path length δ of the beams that must combine at B and F is seen from Fig. 10-21 to be given by the difference in the path lengths EB and AF; that is,

$$\delta = EB - AF \qquad (43)$$

The phase difference at B and F depends on the relation of δ to the wavelength of the electron beam. If, for example, δ is an integral multiple of λ, the two scattered beams will arrive in phase and will constructively interfere, as drawn in Fig. 10-21, whereas if δ is a half integral multiple of λ, the beams will be exactly out of phase and will destructively interfere. Since the amplitude of the scattered wave from each atom is approximately proportional to the atomic number Z, the net amplitude of the combined waves at P can be written as

$$\text{Amplitude} \propto Z \cos \frac{\pi \delta}{\lambda} \qquad (44)$$

One can check that, when $\delta = n\lambda$, the amplitude is proportional to Z, whereas when $\delta = (n + \frac{1}{2})\lambda$, the amplitude is zero. Intermediate situations, i.e., when n is not integral, are also handled by this expression.

The intensity, or energy, of any classical wave motion is proportional to the square of the amplitude of the wave. The intensity $I(\theta)$ of the beam scattered at an angle θ by the molecule oriented as in Fig. 10-21 is given, therefore, by

$$I(\theta) \propto Z^2 \cos^2 \frac{\pi\delta}{\lambda} \tag{45}$$

It now remains to relate δ to the geometry of the system.

A considerable amount of geometric manipulation is necessary in order to obtain a convenient expression for δ. One may wish, therefore, to omit this material and proceed directly to Eq. (60), which gives the intensity at a point on the photographic plate that would result from diffraction from molecules AB with all possible orientations.

With the angles labeled as in Fig. 10-21, the distances that contribute to δ can be obtained as

$$DB = AC = r \cos \beta \tag{46}$$

and
$$EB = (r \cos \beta) \cos (\gamma + \theta) \tag{47}$$
and
$$AF = (r \cos \beta) \cos \gamma \tag{48}$$

With these values one obtains δ as

$$\begin{aligned} \delta &= EB - AF \\ &= r \cos \beta [\cos (\gamma + \theta) - \cos \gamma] \end{aligned} \tag{49}$$

The general expression for the difference in two cosines

$$\cos x - \cos y = 2 \cos \frac{x + y}{2} \sin \frac{x - y}{2} \tag{50}$$

can now be used to convert the expression for δ to the result

$$\delta = 2r \cos \beta \cos \left(\gamma + \frac{\theta}{2}\right) \sin \frac{\theta}{2} \tag{51}$$

A further manipulation of this result is necessary if the integration of Eq. (45) over all positions of B is to be performed. One needs to recognize that $r \cos \beta$ is the projection of AB on the plane to give AC and that multiplication by $\cos (\gamma + \theta/2)$ further projects this onto the coordinate axis that lies between the incident and scattered directions. These two projections are equivalent to a direct projection of AB onto this axis. We can, therefore, make the replacement

$$r \cos \beta \cos \left(\gamma + \frac{\theta}{2}\right) = r \cos \alpha \tag{52}$$

With this simplification, Eq. (51) becomes

$$\delta = 2r \cos \alpha \sin \frac{\theta}{2} \tag{53}$$

The scattered intensity produced by the molecule of Fig. 10-21 is thus given by

$$I(\theta) \propto Z^2 \cos^2 \frac{2\pi r \cos \alpha \sin (\theta/2)}{\lambda} \tag{54}$$

It is customary to make the substitution

$$s = \frac{4\pi}{\lambda} \sin \frac{\theta}{2} \tag{55}$$

where it should be recognized that, for a given electron-beam voltage, a position on the photographic plate could be specified either by θ or, through Eq. (55), by s.   With this notation Eq. (54) becomes

$$I(s) \propto Z^2 \cos^2 \frac{sr \cos \alpha}{2} \tag{56}$$

The integration over all positions of atom B is performed with the spherical-coordinate angular element of $\sin \alpha \, d\alpha \, d\phi$ of Fig. 10-22.   Since ϕ does not enter into Eq. (56), the integration of this variable introduces only the constant term 2π and the total intensity scattered at an angle θ is given by the proportionality equation

$$I(s) \propto Z^2 \int_0^\pi \cos^2 \frac{sr \cos \alpha}{2} \sin \alpha \, d\alpha \tag{57}$$

This troublesome-looking integral turns out to be easily handled.   One first writes

$$\sin \alpha \, d\alpha = -d(\cos \alpha)$$

and

$$-d(\cos \alpha) = -\frac{2}{sr} d\left(\frac{sr}{2} \cos \alpha\right) \tag{58}$$

Introduction of y for $(sr/2) \cos \alpha$ puts Eq. (57) in the form

$$I(s) \propto Z^2 \left(-\frac{2}{sr}\right) \int_{(sr/2)}^{-(sr/2)} \cos^2 y \, dy \tag{59}$$

Integration and substitution of the limits gives

$$I(s) \propto Z^2 \left(-\frac{2}{sr}\right) \frac{1}{2} [y + \sin y \cos y]_{(sr/2)}^{(-sr/2)}$$

$$\propto Z^2 \left[1 + \frac{2 \sin (sr/2) \cos (sr/2)}{sr}\right]$$

and finally

$$I(s) \propto Z^2 \left(1 + \frac{\sin sr}{sr}\right) \tag{60}$$

Fig. 10-22. The angular coordinates that move atom B of Fig. 10-21 through all positions about atom A as β goes from 0 to 2π and α from 0 to π.

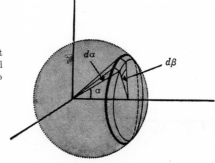

This expression is the Wierl equation for a diatomic, homonuclear molecule and is the desired result of our derivation. It relates the intensity, at a ring at angle θ, of the scattered beam that is involved in the interference effect to the quantity $s = (4\pi/\lambda) \sin (\theta/2)$ and the internuclear distance r.

The Wierl equation for a polyatomic molecule is obtained by recognizing that the net interference of the scattered beams can be deduced by taking the atoms two at a time in a manner like that for the diatomic case. When this is done, the equation applicable to polyatomic molecules is obtained as

$$I(s) \propto \sum_j \sum_k Z_j Z_k \frac{\sin sr_{jk}}{sr_{jk}} \tag{61}$$

where the summation is over all atoms j and k of the molecule. It can be easily verified that Eq. (61) reduces to Eq. (60) when a diatomic molecule is treated.

The Wierl equation does not, unfortunately, allow the direct calculation of the internuclear distances r_{jk} from measurements of $I(s)$ at various values of s. An indirect method for obtaining these quantities must be resorted to.

In the simplest and earliest of the methods that have been used, the photographic plate is observed visually from the origin outward along any direction. The positions of the darkened rings on the photographic plate are estimated visually and a plot is sketched for the plate darkening as a function of $s = (4\pi/\lambda) \sin (\theta/2)$. This plot is reported as the *experimental scattering curve*. An example is shown for the CHF_3 molecule in Fig. 10-23. The procedure now requires one to assume a structure for the molecule being studied; for a diatomic molecule this amounts to choosing a value of r. With this assumed structure, Eqs. (60) and (61) can be used to calculate $I(s)$ as a function of s. Such calculations can be made for various assumed structures, and plots of $I(s)$ versus s, called *theoretical scattering curves*, can be made. The theoretical

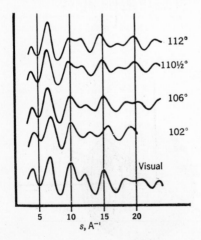

Fig. 10-23. Comparison of the visual scattering curve for CHF_3 with curves calculated for various F-C-F angles. It is concluded that the angle is between 106° and 110°. (Spectroscopic data give the angle as 108°48′.) (*From L. O. Brockway, in Weissberger, "Physical Methods of Organic Chemistry," Part II, 2d ed., page 1123.*)

curves are then compared, as shown in Fig. 10-23, with the experimental curve, and that most like the experimental curve is taken as being based on the best structure.

For a diatomic molecule it is a relatively simple matter to calculate theoretical curves for various bond lengths and to decide on the bond length that gives the best agreement between the curves.

For a polyatomic molecule, on the other hand, a number of parameters r_{jk} must be varied to obtain the best structure. One does not now come so directly onto the correct structure. Furthermore, very incorrect structures may happen to lead to a theoretical pattern little different from the experimental one. It is clear, therefore, that a number of difficulties lie in the path of structure determinations by this method. In spite of these difficulties, very many structures have been determined, and Table 10-5 lists a few of these.

10-6. The Radial-distribution Method. A very great aid to the use of electron-diffraction techniques is the suggestion made by Pauling and Brockway that the data on the photographic plate could be used directly to obtain some information on the structure of the sample molecules. This method, known as the *radial-distribution method*, in effect forms a relation that is the inverse of Eqs. (60) and (61) and gives the distances between scattering centers of the molecule in terms of the data of the photographic plate.

The procedure requires the molecule to be represented by a continuous distribution in space of regions with varying scattering power. In place of the atom B of Fig. 10-20, for example, one would recognize that, as far as the electron-diffraction experiment is concerned, there is merely a region of large scattering power a distance r from the origin. A function $D(r)$, called the *radial-distribution function*, can be introduced such that $D(r)$ represents the product of the scattering powers of unit volumes a distance r apart, and

Table 10-5. Some Molecular-structure Results from Recent Electron-diffraction Studies

	Bond angles		Bond lengths (A)	
$P(CH_3)_3$	C—P—C	$98.6 \pm 3°$	C—P	1.846 ± 0.003
	P—C—H	$110.7 \pm 5°$	C—H	1.091 ± 0.006
CH_3Cl	H—C—H	$110 \pm 2°$	C—Cl	1.784 ± 0.003
			C—H	1.11 ± 0.01
CF_3Cl	F—C—F	$108.6 \pm 0.4°$	C—F	1.328 ± 0.002
			C—Cl	1.751 ± 0.004
CCl_4	Tetrahedral		C—Cl	1.769 ± 0.005
C_2H_4	H—C—H	$115.5 \pm 0.6°$	C=C	1.333 ± 0.002
			C—H	1.084 ± 0.003
CH_3OH	C—O—H	$108 \pm 3°$	C—O	1.427 ± 0.004
	H—C—H	$109°28'$ (assumed)	C—H	1.095 ± 0.010
			O—H	0.960 ± 0.020
$(CH_3)_2O$	C—O—C	$111.5 \pm 1.5°$	C—O	1.416 ± 0.003
			C—H	1.094 ± 0.006
C_6H_6	C—C—C	$120 \pm 4°$	C—C	1.39 ± 0.03
			C—H	1.08 ± 0.02

$4\pi r^2 D(r) \, dr$ represents the product of the total scattering powers a distance r apart. For a diatomic molecule, therefore, $D(r)$ would have a large value for r equal to the bond length and would be zero elsewhere. With this description of the scattering effects in a molecule the Wierl equation becomes the integral equation

$$I(s) \propto \int_0^\infty 4\pi r^2 D(r) \, \frac{\sin sr}{sr} \, dr \qquad (62)$$

or

$$I(s) = k \int_0^\infty \frac{rD(r) \sin sr}{s} \, dr \qquad (63)$$

where k is a proportionality constant. The factor s in the denominator leads to nothing more than a continuous decrease in scattering from the origin outward, and in the simple visual treatment of the photographic plate this factor cannot be adequately handled and was generally ignored. We can write therefore

$$I(s) = k' \int_0^\infty rD(r) \sin sr \, dr \qquad (64)$$

In this form, the integral can be considered to be a Fourier-integral representation of the function $I(s)$. The coefficients of the Fourier terms are $rD(r)$, and these are given by the inverted form as

$$rD(r) = k'' \int_0^\infty I(s) \sin sr \, ds \qquad (65)$$

or

$$D(r) = k'' \int_0^\infty I(s) \, \frac{\sin sr}{r} \, ds \qquad (66)$$

This important result can be put in a summation form, as was customary in earlier work, and for visual estimates is usually given as

$$D(r) = \sum_i I(i) \, \frac{\sin s_i r}{s_i r} \qquad (67)$$

where i numbers off the diffraction rings occurring at successively larger values of s on the photographic plate.

To obtain the function $D(r)$, therefore, it is necessary only to choose various values of r and for each value to make the summation of Eq. (67). In this way one is led to a curve which shows the spacing between scattering centers in the molecule without any assumption as to the molecular structure. The radial distribution function for $CClF_3$ is shown in Fig. 10-24. It should be mentioned that the radial-distribution method does not identify the atoms that are to be associated with the large values of $D(r)$. All that is learned is that there are scattering centers separated by the amounts for which peaks on the $D(r)$ curve occur.

Modern electron-diffraction techniques make use of microphotometer traces of the diffraction photograph and, furthermore, use a sector disk in front of the plate so that the rapid fall-off in intensity of the beam from the center of the plate outward is properly compensated for. With these techniques a very detailed radial-distribution curve can be obtained even for quite complex molecules.

One of the chief remaining limitations of the electron-diffraction method is that there are a small number of "wiggles" in the experimental curve. These wiggles are really the data provided by the experiment, and with a small number of data only a few molecular parameters can be determined. A very large molecule cannot be satisfactorily treated unless, like carbon tetrachloride or benzene, there is some geometric relation which makes several interatomic distances dependent on each other. A second limitation is that

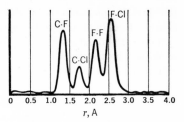

Fig. 10-24. Radial distribution function for CF_3Cl. [*From L. S. Bartell and L. O. Brockway, J. Chem. Phys.,* **23**: 1860 (1955).]

the electron beam is not scattered very effectively by hydrogen atoms. It follows that the position of such atoms in a molecule cannot easily be determined by this method. The method of X-ray diffraction studies of crystals, as we shall see, overcomes the first difficulty by yielding very many scattered beams and therefore very much information. The method of neutron diffraction overcomes the second difficulty since protons have a reasonably large scattering cross section for neutrons.

ELECTRICAL PROPERTIES: MOLECULAR DIPOLE MOMENTS

Since molecules are made up of charged units, electrons and the atomic nuclei, much of the behavior of molecules is understandable in terms of electrical interactions. A detailed theoretical treatment of a molecule by the methods of quantum mechanics would reveal the electron distribution of the molecule and would lead to deductions as to how a particular assembly of charges that make up a molecule would interact with other molecules, with a surrounding medium, or with an electric field. Such applications of quantum mechanics cannot be made except for the very simplest systems. It is possible, however, to learn much about the electric nature of molecules by an experimental approach. In this section the procedure which produces results for the dipole moment of a molecule will be dealt with. The goal, however, is not only to obtain such results but also to show how some electrical phenomena in chemical systems are treated.

The principal characteristic of the charge distribution in a molecule that can be measured is the extent to which the center of the electron distribution of a molecule fails to coincide with the center of the positive nuclear charge distribution. The charge asymmetry is obtained as the dipole moment of the molecule. This charge asymmetry, as we shall see, may result from an unequal sharing of the bonding electrons, the extreme case of which leads to a molecule with positively and negatively charged ions such as a molecule of NaCl vapor. More subtle electron distributions such as the apparent slight asymmetry of the bonding electrons, as in a CH bond, or the projection of the nonbonding electrons of, for example, the nitrogen atom in ammonia, also lead to molecular dipole moments. Dipole-moment results allow such aspects of the electronic configuration of molecules to be discussed.

As Fig. 10-25 indicates, the dipole moment of two equal and opposite charges is defined as the product of the charges and the distance separating them. Thus the dipole moment is given by

$$\mu = qr \qquad (68)$$

The dipole moment has, furthermore, a direction as well as a magnitude; i.e., it is a *vector* quantity. It is frequently convenient diagrammatically to represent a dipole moment by an arrow showing the direction from the positive to the negative charge and the magnitude by the length of the arrow, as is done in Fig. 10-25. In molecular systems, of course, the dipole moment of the molecule represents the net asymmetry of the charge distributions. The dipole moment is the quantity that is experimentally determined; the individual charges and distances that make up the dipole moment are usually understood and determined only with great difficulty. We shall see, furthermore, that the dipole moment is the quantity that determines many of the electrical interactions between molecules.

The order of magnitude of molecular dipole moments can be deduced by recognizing that these moments result from charges like that of an electron, that is, 4.80×10^{-10} esu, separated by angstrom distances. For one electron separated from an equally charged positive center by a distance of 1 A the dipole moment would be

$$\mu = 4.80 \times 10^{-10}(1 \times 10^{-8}) = 4.80 \times 10^{-18} \text{ esu-cm} \qquad (69)$$

It proves convenient in discussing molecular dipole moments to introduce the unit called the *debye*. This unit is defined such that

$$10^{-18} \text{ esu-cm} = 1 \text{ debye} \qquad (70)$$

In addition to a dipole moment that a molecule can have as a result of its asymmetric charge distribution there is, for all molecules, the possibility of distorting the electronic distribution in a molecule by applying an electric field. In this way an *induced dipole moment* can be produced. The effectiveness of an applied field in making a molecule polar is determined by the *polarizability* of the molecule. The polarizability, defined as the dipole moment induced by an electric field of unit strength, is the second important electrical property of molecules with which we shall deal. The units and values of this quantity are best left until its determination from measurable quantities is considered. It should be immediately clear, however, that all molecules, symmetric or not, are polarizable and can have an induced dipole moment. There will, on the other hand, be many symmetric molecules, like H_2, CO_2, and CCl_4, that necessarily have a zero "permanent" dipole moment.

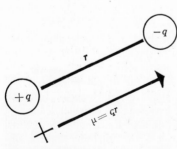

Fig. 10-25. The dipole moment as the vector quantity qr.

10-7. Some Basic Electrostatic Ideas. Some basic ideas that enter into the treatment of charged particles in a vacuum (or, approximately, in air) must be reviewed. This and the following section, where media other than vacuum are considered, provide the necessary background to the theory of the measurement of molecular dipole moments.

The basic relation in treating the interaction of stationary charges is Coulomb's law, which states that two point charges q_1 and q_2 separated by a distance r in vacuum (or, approximately, air) will repel each other with a force f given by

$$f = q_1 q_2 / r^2 \tag{71}$$

If q_1 and q_2 are of the same sign, the force will be positive and will be that of repulsion since it acts in the same direction as increasing r. If q_1 and q_2 have opposite signs, the force will be one of attraction. For q_1 and q_2 in esu and r in centimeters, the force f is given in dynes. In fact, the esu unit of charge is defined as that which repels an equal charge placed 1 cm away with a force of 1 dyne. The unit of charge in ordinary use, the coulomb, is related to the esu by the relation 1 coulomb = 3×10^9 esu.

The interaction of charges at a distance suggests that an electric field exists around each charge. The intensity of the electric field $\mathcal{E}$ at a point is defined as the force which would be exerted on a positive charge placed at that point. Thus the electric-field strength is the force on a unit charge, or

$$\mathcal{E} = f / q \tag{72}$$

The field strength is measured in dynes per esu. The force on the unit test charge has a direction as well as a magnitude. The electric field $\mathcal{E}$ is therefore a vector quantity and has the direction as well as the magnitude of the force on a unit positive test charge. It is frequently helpful to draw *lines of force* to represent the intensity and the direction of an electric field. The intensity is denoted by drawing, or mentally picturing, one line of force per square centimeter for each dyne per esu of field strength. The field direction is represented by the direction of the lines of force.

Consider, for example, the electric field about a point charge $+q$, as in Fig. 10-26. At a distance r from this charge a unit positive charge would be repelled by a force of q/r^2. The electric-field intensity is therefore given by

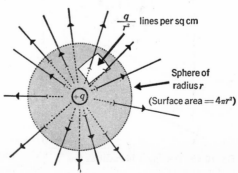

Fig. 10-26. The electric field of a charge $+q$ represented by lines of force. A total of $q/r^2(4\pi r^2) = 4\pi q$ lines emanate from a charge of $+q$.

$\dfrac{q}{r^2}$ lines per sq cm

Sphere of radius r

(Surface area $= 4\pi r^2$)

q/r^2 at a distance r from the $+q$ charge. This electric field can be depicted by drawing q/r^2 lines of force per square centimeter at a distance r from the charge q. The total of such lines at a distance r is the line density times the total cross-section area at a distance r, or

$$\frac{q}{r^2}\,(4\pi r^2) \,=\, 4\pi q \tag{73}$$

Thus $4\pi q$ lines of force emanate from a charge $+q$. Or *the electric field of a unit positive charge can be represented by 4π lines of force*. This example will be made use of in a later development.

Another important aspect of an electric field is described by the electrical potential $\mathcal{U}$. This quantity represents the potential energy of a unit positive charge in the electric field. A unit positive charge in an electric field of intensity $\mathcal{E}$ experiences a force equal to $\mathcal{E}$, and for a given displacement of the unit charge the work involved is the force, or the field strength, times the distance that the charge is moved. Since the potential energy increases as the unit positive test charge is brought closer to the positive charge q which generates the electric field, the change $d\mathcal{U}$ for an infinitesimal change dr is

$$d\mathcal{U} \,=\, -\mathcal{E}\,dr \tag{74}$$

Rearrangement of Eq. (74) gives a relation that is useful when electric fields are deduced from applied or known potentials. This expression is

$$\mathcal{E} \,=\, -\,\frac{d\mathcal{U}}{dr} \tag{75}$$

The unit of potential difference, the volt, is related to the esu unit of dynes per cm by the relation 300 volts = 1 esu.

The example of a plane-parallel condenser with air (or, more properly, vacuum) between the plates can now be considered. If, as in Fig. 10-27, the condenser

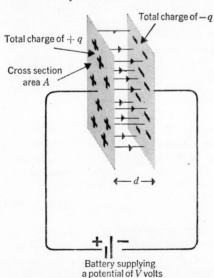

Total charge of $-q$

Total charge of $+q$

Cross section area A

$\leftarrow d \rightarrow$

Battery supplying a potential of V volts

Fig. 10-27. A plane-parallel condenser with no dielectric material between the condenser plates.

is connected to a battery that produces a potential difference of υ volts, there will be a potential drop of υ volts across the condenser. According to Eq. (75) the field between the plates of the condenser will be υ/d, where d is the distance between the plates.

The electric field in the condenser can also be understood in terms of the charges that the condenser plates acquire when the condenser is charged by the battery. If q is the charge, positive on one plate and negative on the other, and if the area of each condenser plate is A, there will be a charge density of $\sigma = q/A$ charges per square centimeter. The previous result that each charge has associated with it 4π lines of force can now be carried over to imply $4\pi\sigma$ lines of force per square centimeter between the plates. The field strength is therefore $\mathcal{E} = 4\pi\sigma$ dynes/esu since one line of force per square centimeter corresponds to a unit field.

A condenser is most readily characterized experimentally by the ratio of the charge q acquired by the plates to the voltage υ applied across the condenser. The *capacitance* of a condenser is defined by this ratio, and if there is air or a vacuum between the plates, the capacitance is C_0, given by

$$C_0 = \frac{q}{\upsilon} \tag{76}$$

The capacitance is seen to be the charge held by the condenser plates per unit potential.

The capacitance can be related to the geometry of the condenser by substituting the results $q = \sigma A$ and ignoring the direction and sign of $\mathcal{E}$,

$$\upsilon = \mathcal{E}d = 4\pi\sigma d$$

to give

$$C_0 = \frac{\sigma A}{4\pi\sigma d} = \frac{A}{4\pi d} \tag{77}$$

The capacitance is thus a property of the geometry of the condenser and for a plane-parallel condenser is large for large A and small d.

10-8. Electrostatics for Dielectric Media. The presence of a nonconducting, or *dielectric*, material around the charges that have been dealt with alters the relations which have been obtained. The understanding of this dielectric effect will be the basis from which the electrical properties of molecules are deduced.

The starting point is again Coulomb's law. When the charges q_1 and q_2 are immersed in a dielectric material, it is found that the force between them is less at any given value of r than when such a dielectric medium is absent. Coulomb's law can be written to apply to both vacuum and dielectric media by writing it in the form

$$f = \frac{q_1 q_2}{\epsilon r} \tag{78}$$

where ϵ is a constant, at a given temperature, for any medium. It is known as the *dielectric constant* and represents the effect of the dielectric material in decreasing the force between the charges.

The definition [Eq. (72)] of the electric field as the force exerted on a unit positive charge can now be applied to determine the field of the charge $+q$ when it is immersed in a dielectric material. The force on the unit positive charge at a distance r would be $q/\epsilon r^2$, and the total lines of force emanating for such a surrounded charge would be

$$\frac{q}{\epsilon r^2}(4\pi r^2) = \frac{4\pi q}{\epsilon} \tag{79}$$

The electric field is therefore lowered by the presence of the nonconducting materials by a factor equal to the dielectric constant ϵ.

Now we can consider the properties of the condenser of Fig. 10-27 that can be measured and that will allow an understanding of the role of the dielectric material. Suppose the condenser is charged until the same charge q as for vacuum accumulates on the plates. The charge per square centimeter is again $\sigma = q/A$, but the lines of force per square centimeter, and therefore the electric field $\mathcal{E}$, are reduced to $4\pi\sigma/\epsilon$. Again, ignoring the direction and sign of $\mathcal{E}$, we have $\mathcal{E} = \upsilon/d$. This implies that the applied voltage is

$$\upsilon = \frac{4\pi\sigma}{\epsilon d} \tag{80}$$

and the capacitance is

$$C = \frac{q}{\upsilon} = \frac{\sigma A}{4\pi\sigma/\epsilon d} = \epsilon\frac{A}{4\pi d} \tag{81}$$

By comparison with Eq. (77), we see that measured capacitances with and without dielectric material give ϵ from

$$\frac{C}{C_0} = \epsilon \tag{82}$$

where C_0 is the capacitance of the condenser in vacuum. The dielectric material has therefore increased the capacitance of the condenser. It is this relationship, Eq. (82), that is often used as a more directly operational definition of the dielectric constant. It is a quite straightforward matter to measure the capacitance of a condenser.

Now it is necessary to investigate the mechanism by which the dielectric material decreases the electric field between the condenser plates when a given charge is placed on the plates. Again consider the condenser to be charged to a suitable potential so that charges $+q$ and $-q$ reside on the two plates. The effect of the dielectric can be understood, without going into the molecular behavior, by supposing that the dielectric material is *polarizable* and that the charges on the plates distort the electric balance within the dielectric material so that it develops an opposing charge arrangement, as shown in Fig. 10-28. This opposing effect is conveniently described by introducing the term *polarization* and symbol p to represent the dipole moment induced in one cubic centimeter of the dielectric material. Considering 1 cc of the dielectric, one sees that its dipole moment p can be described as being due to charges of $+p$ on one end and $-p$ on the other. In the interior of the dielectric material between the condenser plates, such charges cancel out and one is left with only the charges on the surfaces of the dielectric next to the condenser plates. This situation is represented in Fig. 10-28.

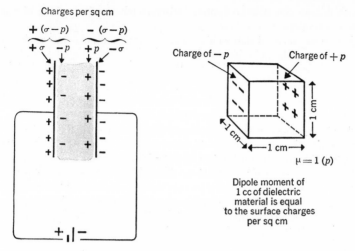

Charges per sq cm

$+ (\sigma - p) \qquad - (\sigma - p)$

$+\sigma \quad -p \quad +p \quad -\sigma$

Charge of $-p$ Charge of $+p$

1 cm

1 cm

1 cm

$\mu = 1\ (p)$

Dipole moment of
1 cc of dielectric
material is equal
to the surface charges
per sq cm

Fig. 10-28. The electrical behavior of the dielectric material of a condenser.

The manner in which the dielectric reduces the field between the condenser plates can now be understood. The field $\mathcal{E}_0$ with vacuum between the condenser plates is related to the plate charge density by

$$\mathcal{E}_0 = 4\pi\sigma \tag{83}$$

When a dielectric material is present, the charge q on the plates is partially balanced by the charge p on the surface of the dielectric. This interpretation of the factors affecting $\mathcal{E}$ gives

$$\mathcal{E} = 4\pi(\sigma - p)$$

or
$$\mathcal{E} = \mathcal{E}_0 - 4\pi p \tag{84}$$

Combination of this mechanistic interpretation of the reduction of $\mathcal{E}$ with the expression $\mathcal{E} = 4\pi\sigma/\epsilon$ leads to the desired result

$$\mathcal{E} = \frac{4\pi p}{\epsilon - 1} \tag{85}$$

for the electric field in a dielectric medium in terms of the polarization of the dielectric and the dielectric constant.

10-9. The Molecular Basis for Dielectric Behavior. A molecular explanation of the role of dielectric material in affecting electrical phenomena will now be given. Our attention will at first be restricted to the effect of the induced dipole moment that all molecules possess as a result of the electrical distortions of the electron distribution in a molecule by an applied electric field. All molecules are polarizable and, therefore, will have contributions from this factor.

Let the dipole moment induced in a molecule be denoted by μ_{ind}. If there are n molecules per cubic centimeter of the dielectric material which has a polarization, or dipole moment per cubic centimeter, of p, then

$$p = n\mu_{\text{ind}} \tag{86}$$

The nature of the dielectric can be understood, therefore, in terms of the molecular property μ_{ind}.

The simplest relation that would account for the consequences of the induced dipole moment in a molecule is one in which the induced dipole is proportional to the field acting on the molecule. If this field is $\mathcal{E}_{internal}$ and the proportionality constant is α, the relations

$$\mu_{ind} = \alpha\mathcal{E}_{internal} \tag{87}$$

and

$$p = n\alpha\mathcal{E}_{internal} \tag{88}$$

are obtained. The polarizability α is one of the molecular properties that will be deduced. It represents the ease with which the electron configuration of the molecule can be distorted by an acting electric field.

The field acting on the molecule results from several contributions. With reference to Fig. 20-29 it can be seen that the charges on the plates, the charges at boundaries of the dielectric adjacent to the plates, and the charges on the surface of a small cavity that is supposed to surround the molecule all generate lines of force that contribute to the field on the molecule. The net result of these terms is

$$\mathcal{E}_{internal} = 4\pi\sigma - 4\pi p + \frac{4\pi p}{3} \tag{89}$$

where the last term is the cavity-charge contribution. It is obtained by integrating, over the surface of the sphere, the effects of the surface charge in generating a field in the direction perpendicular to the condenser plates. Finally with the help of Eq. (84) one eliminates σ and obtains

$$\mathcal{E}_{internal} = \mathcal{E} + \tfrac{4}{3}\pi p \tag{90}$$

The relation of Eq. (88) eliminates the not directly measurable quantity $\mathcal{E}_{internal}$ and gives

$$p = n\alpha(\mathcal{E} + \tfrac{4}{3}\pi p) \tag{91}$$

Substitution for $\mathcal{E}$ by the relation of Eq. (85)

$$\mathcal{E} = \frac{4\pi p}{\epsilon - 1}$$

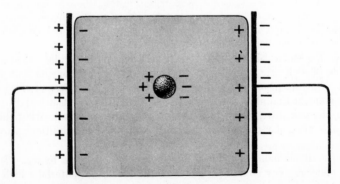

Fig. 10-29. The charges that contribute to the field $\mathcal{E}$ acting on a molecule which is treated as being in a cavity within the dielectric material.

allows the elimination of ε and p to give, on rearrangement,

$$\tfrac{4}{3}\pi n\alpha = \frac{\epsilon - 1}{\epsilon + 2} \tag{92}$$

The more frequently used form of this result is obtained by writing

$$n = \frac{\rho}{M}\,N$$

where ρ is the density, ρ/M is the number of moles per cubic centimeter, and $(\rho/M)N$ the molecules per cubic centimeter to get

$$\mathcal{P} = \tfrac{4}{3}\pi N\alpha = \frac{\epsilon - 1}{\epsilon + 2}\frac{M}{\rho} \tag{93}$$

where $\mathcal{P}$, called the *molar polarization*, has been introduced for the set of quantities $\tfrac{4}{3}\pi N\alpha$. The derivation has now led to an expression, known as the Clausius-Mosotti equation, that allows the calculation of either the polarizability of a molecule α or the molar distortion polarization $\mathcal{P}$ from measurements of the dielectric constant of the dielectric material. Something of the nature and importance of these molecular properties will be mentioned after the more general case, where a molecule has a permanent dipole moment, as well as being polarizable, is considered.

Consider now, as was done by Debye in 1912, the contribution to the dielectric material of the permanent dipole moment μ of the molecules of the material if they have such a moment. With no applied field the dipoles will be lined up in all directions and will be ineffective in contributing to the polarizability $\mathcal{P}$ of the dielectric. In the presence of a field, however, as Fig. 10-30 illustrates, the molecules will tend to line up with the field so that their dipole moments add to the polarizability $\mathcal{P}$. The energy u of the dipole varies with the angle with which it is oriented to the acting field direction according to

$$u = -\mu\mathcal{E}_{\text{internal}}\cos\theta \tag{94}$$

The tendency of the molecules to go to the lowest energy position by lining up with the field is opposed, however, by the thermal motions of the molecules. The distribution expression of Boltzmann gives the way in which these two factors operate. According to this distribution law, the fraction dn/n of the molecules that are lined up at an angle θ to the field is given by an expression of the type

$$\frac{dn}{n} = Ae^{-u/kT}\,d\theta$$
$$= Ae^{\mathcal{E}_{\text{internal}}\cos\theta/kT}\,d\theta \tag{95}$$

where A is a proportionality constant. This expression gives the number of molecules whose dipoles are lined up at given angles, and from an integration, which need not be included, one obtains the net dipole effect in the direction of the field. This net or average dipole in the direction of the field is found approximately to be

$$\mu_{\text{av}} = \frac{\mu^2}{3kT}\mathcal{E}_{\text{internal}} \tag{96}$$

Comparison of this result with Eq. (51) shows that the factor $\mu^2/3kT$ enters in just the way that the term α did. If the previous derivation were now

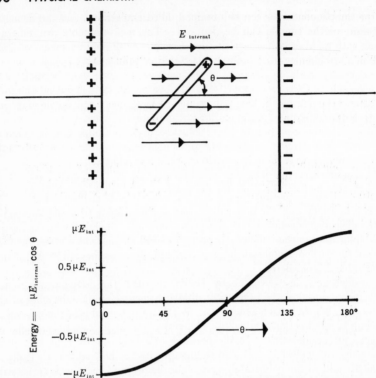

Fig. 10-30. The energy of a dipole as a function of its orientation in an electric field ε internal.

carried out with the dipole-moment term as well as the polarizability term, it follows that the result, comparable with Eq. (57), would be obtained as

$$\mathcal{P} = \frac{\epsilon - 1}{\epsilon + 2}\frac{M}{\rho} = \tfrac{4}{3}\pi N\left(\alpha + \frac{\mu^2}{3kT}\right) \tag{97}$$

This result is known as the Debye equation. It shows how the molecular polarizability α and the molecular dipole moment μ contribute to produce a dielectric constant greater than unity in any nonconducting material. Conversely it suggests that these molecular properties might be deduced from measurement of the dielectric constant.

10-10. Determination of the Dipole Moment and the Molecular Polarizability. The dielectric constant of a material is measured by placing it between the plates of a condenser or, for liquids, filling a cell in which the plates are inserted. This condenser can then be used as one arm of an electrical bridge, like a Wheatstone bridge for measuring resistances, and the capacitance of the sample condenser can be balanced against a variable-reference condenser which has no dielectric between its plates. In principle the capacitance of the reference condenser can be deduced from its geometry. In this way the capacitance of the sample condenser can be obtained, filled and empty, and the dielectric constant of the sample can be deduced. The measurements are generally made with an alternating current with a frequency of about 1 megacycle/sec.

When the compound of interest is a liquid or solid material, measurements are generally made on solutions of the material in some inert nonpolar substance such as CCl_4 or benzene. The Debye equation is based on the independent behavior of the polar molecules. Molecules with dipole moments exert considerable interaction on one another, and it is necessary therefore to apply the Debye equation to dilute solutions of polar compounds in nonpolar solvents. For gaseous samples the intermolecular distance is usually sufficiently great so that these interactions present no difficulty.

Measurement of the dielectric constant and use of the Debye equation do not directly lead to the separate determination of α and μ. Two principal ways are available for sorting out these two factors.

The first way consists in measuring ϵ and ρ as functions of temperature and using these data to plot $\dfrac{\epsilon - 1}{\epsilon + 2} \dfrac{M}{\rho}$ against $1/T$. The Debye equation leads us to expect such a plot to yield a straight line, and Fig. 10-31 shows that the data for the hydrogen halides do behave in this manner. From such plots the slope of the straight line can be used to obtain the dipole moment μ, while the intercept at $1/T$ can be made to yield the polarizability α. This procedure is quite straightforward and fails only if the molecules are associated to different extents at different temperatures or if the molecular configuration changes with temperature.

The second procedure evaluates the polarizability part of the molar polarization $\mathcal{P}$ by an interesting relation between the dielectric constant and the refractive index given by Clerk Maxwell's theory of electromagnetic radiation. The theory cannot be dealt with here, but the basis of the relation can be sug-

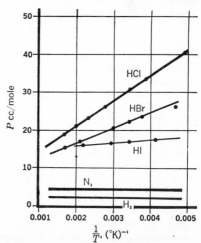

Fig. 10-31. The molar polarization versus the reciprocal of the absolute temperature. [*From the data of C. T. Zahn, Phys. Rev.,* **24**: 400 (1924).]

gested. The refractive index of a material measures the ratio of the velocity of light in the material to the velocity of light in a vacuum. The velocity is always less in dielectric material than it is in vacuum. The slowing down is due to the interaction of the polarizable electrons of the molecules of the medium with the oscillating electric field of the radiation. The permanent dipoles of the molecules would also interfere, but the visible radiation used to measure the refractive index carries such a rapidly alternating electric field, about 10^{15} cycles/sec, that the molecules are unable to orient themselves rapidly enough to keep up with the field. Thus, only the polarizability interferes with the passage of the light.

Maxwell's theory shows that for materials composed of molecules with no permanent dipole moment

$$\epsilon = n_R^2 \tag{98}$$

where n_R is the refractive index of the material. It is apparent therefore that, even when the molecules of the dielectric do have dipole moments, the polarizability term of the total molar polarizability $\mathcal{P}$ can be calculated as

$$\frac{n_R^2 - 1}{n_R^2 + 2} \frac{M}{\rho} = \frac{4\pi N}{3} \alpha \tag{99}$$

Refractive-index data provide, therefore, a value for α that can be used along with the dielectric-constant data to give the molecular dipole moment μ. Some results for a few simpler molecules are shown in Table 10-6. The

Table 10-6. The Dipole Moment and the Polarizability of Some Simple Molecules
(Those molecules for which α is given have zero dipole moment. The polarizabilities along the molecular axis, if present, are given as α_x)

Substance	μ (debye)	Substance	α_x (cc)	α_y (cc)	α_z (cc)
HF	1.9	He	0.20×10^{-24}	0.20×10^{-24}	0.20×10^{-24}
HCl	1.0	N_2	2.43	1.43	1.43
HBr	0.8	O_2	2.43	1.19	1.19
HI	0.4	CO_2	4.10	1.93	1.93
CO	0.1	CS_2	15.19	5.54	5.54
H_2O	1.9	CCl_4	10.5	10.5	10.5
NH_3	1.4	$SnCl_4$	13.8	13.8	13.8
CH_3Cl	1.9				
CH_2Cl_2	1.6				
$CHCl_3$	1.1				
HCN	3.0				
CH_3CN	3.9				
CH_3NO_2	3.5				
$(C_2H_5)_2O$	1.2				
CH_3OH	1.7				
CsF*	7.9				
CsCl*	10.5				
KF*	7.3				
KCl*	10.4				
KBr	10.5				

* Determined by molecular-beam techniques. N. F. Ramsey, "Molecular Beams," Oxford University Press, New York, 1956.

information on molecular polarizabilities provided by these experiments finds rather less molecular-structure application than do the dipole-moment results. The data of Table 10-6 should show, however, a qualitative correlation of molecular polarizability with the number of electrons in the molecule and the "looseness" with which they are bound. The polarizability data obtained here will be of value when molecular interactions are treated in the study of liquids.

10-11. Dipole Moments and Ionic Character. Considering, at first, only diatomic molecules, the measured dipole moment of a molecule gives information on the displacement of the center of negative charge from that of the positive charge. In the past, this asymmetry has been interpreted primarily in terms of an unequal sharing of the bonding electrons. The theoretical treatment of heteronuclear molecules of the previous chapter anticipated such unequal sharing and introduced *per cent ionic character* as a measure of such bonding.

The assumption that a dipole moment results from the location of the bonding electrons leads to a calculation of the ionic character from a dipole moment. The example of HCl, with a dipole moment of 1.03 debye and a bond length of 1.275 A, will illustrate the calculation. If the pair of bonding electrons were completely held by the chlorine atom, the molecule would be represented as positively and negatively charged ions separated by the equilibrium bond length. The dipole moment of such a completely ionic structure would be

$$\mu_{\text{ionic}} = (4.80 \times 10^{-10})(1.275 \times 10^{-8})$$
$$= 6.11 \times 10^{-18} \text{ esu-cm}$$
$$= 6.11 \text{ debye} \tag{100}$$

On the other hand, if the pair of bonding electrons were equally shared, the bonding electrons would be almost symmetrically placed relative to the positive nuclear charges and the dipole moment would be zero. In fact, the dipole moment is in between these two extremes, and the amount of ionic character is calculated as

$$\% \text{ ionic character} = \frac{\mu_{\text{obs}}}{\mu_{\text{ionic}}} \times (100\%)$$
$$= \frac{1.03}{6.11} \times (100) = 17\% \tag{101}$$

The result does not, of course, tell which end of the molecule is positive and which is negative. This aspect must be deduced, or inferred, by other means.

It is necessary to point out, however, that, although this procedure for obtaining ionic characters has led to a considerable body of apparently consistent and chemically reasonable data, the method appears to have some inherent uncertainties. The problem arises because there are other electrons in the molecule besides the pair of bonding electrons on which attention has been focused. The inner-shell electrons present little difficulty since even in molecules they undoubtedly remain nearly symmetrically arranged about the nucleus to which they belong. The nonbonding electrons of chlorine in the HCl example, however, cannot be so easily dismissed. The bonding in such a molecule might result from overlap of the 1s wave function of the hydrogen atom, with anything from a $2p$ orbital of chlorine to a $2(sp^3)$ orbital of the chlorine. These two extremes are represented in Fig. 10-32, and it is there apparent that, if hybridized orbitals are used for bonding, the nonbonding electrons will project away from the bond and will make a large contribution to the molecular dipole. The role of such *nonbonding* electrons is not easy to evaluate, but it appears difficult to justify the procedure of ignoring them. Thus, although apparently reasonable values of ionic character are obtained

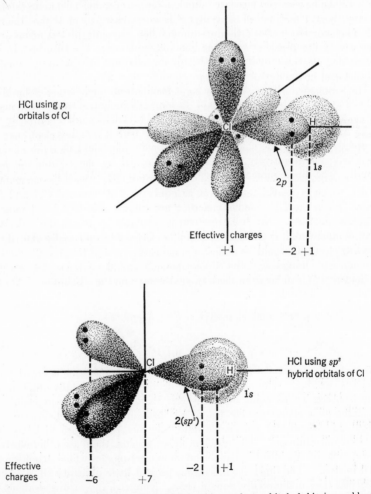

Fig. 10-32. Descriptions of the bonding in HCl by the use of a p orbital of chlorine and by the use of an sp^3 hybrid of chlorine. With hybrid orbitals the center of the nonbonding electron positions cannot be assumed to coincide with the chlorine nucleus.

from dipole-moment data, the reliability of such results is open to serious question.

10-12. Bond Moments. For polyatomic molecules it is customary to try to understand the molecular dipole moment in terms of the contributions of the individual bonds of the molecule in a similar manner in which one tried to understand the energy of a molecule in terms of bond energies. With this approach one obtains *bond moments*. For the water molecule, for example, the measured dipole moment is 1.85 debyes, and, as Fig. 10-33 shows, this quantity can be resolved into two bond moments which are in the directions of the two bonds and which add together, vectorially, to give the observed molecular moment. The procedure implies that the molecular moment arises from within the separate bonds of the molecule. The contribution of any nonbonding electrons to the total dipole moment will, of course, be resolved and included in the derived bond moments.

A real difficulty arises when the bond moments of a carbon compound are sought. Methane, for instance, has a zero dipole moment that results from the symmetry of the molecule rather than the electron distribution in the bonds. If such a molecule is drawn, as in Fig. 10-34, it is apparent that one C—H bond is equivalent to the other three CH bonds projecting out at tetrahedral angles from the first bond. No information on the CH bond moment can be deduced from the zero molecular moment of CH_4. In the same manner, CH_3Cl, which is nearly tetrahedral, is equivalent to opposed CH and CCl bonds. Since the CH bond moment is not known, the CCl bond moment cannot be deduced. No direct method is available by which the individual bond moments of such molecules can be deduced from molecular dipole moments.

Some rather unsatisfactory methods have suggested a CH bond moment of 0.4 debye, with the hydrogen being the positive end of the dipole. On the

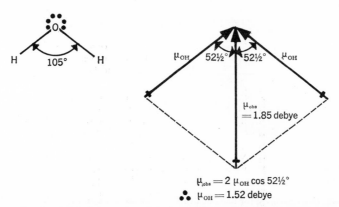

$$\mu_{obs} = 2\ \mu_{OH} \cos 52\tfrac{1}{2}°$$
$$\therefore\ \mu_{OH} = 1.52\ \text{debye}$$

Fig. 10-33. Resolution of the total dipole moment of the water molecule into OH bond moments. (The dipole direction that indicates that H is positive relative to O is assumed.)

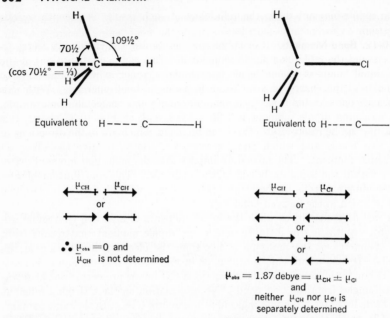

Fig. 10-34. The problem of deducing bond moments for bonds to carbon compounds.

basis of this rather arbitrary value, the bond moments of other atoms joined to a carbon atom can be deduced.   Table 10-7 includes some results.

The principal difficulty with the bond-moment analysis is that the electron distribution that results in the molecular dipole moment cannot always be

Table 10-7. Dipole Moments Deduced for Some Chemical Bonds

Bond	Dipole moment (debye)	Bond	Dipole moment (debye)
H—F	1.9	F—Cl	0.9
H—Cl	1.0	F—Br	1.3
H—Br	0.8	Br—Cl	0.6
H—I	0.4	C—H	(0.4)
H—O	1.5	C—F	1.4
H—N	1.3	C—Cl	1.5
H—P	0.4	C—Br	1.4
P—Cl	0.8	C—I	1.2
P—Br	0.4	C—O	0.7
As—F	2.0	C—N	0.2
As—Cl	1.6	C=O	2.3
As—Br	1.3		

treated in terms of separate, noninteracting components. Thus, it is rather arbitrary to assign any contribution from the nonbonding electrons to the bonds of the molecule. Likewise the presence of one bond in a molecule may alter the contribution of a neighboring bond. This interaction occurs through the dipole moment of one bond inducing an opposing dipole moment in a neighboring polarizable bond. In such cases, the molecular moment is not understandable in terms of the individual bond-moment contributions.

MAGNETIC PROPERTIES

Magnetic measurements are a tool for molecular studies that have not been of such general applicability as have electric measurements. For certain types of compounds, however, magnetic measurements constitute one of the most powerful approaches for the elucidation of the arrangement of the electrons in the compound. The theory of magnetic studies sufficiently parallels that of electric studies so that a detailed treatment will not be given. Following some mention of the parallels between electric and magnetic phenomena, the applications of magnetic studies will be dealt with.

10-13. Determination of Magnetic Molecular Properties. The effect of magnets on one another at a distance suggests the presence of a magnetic field surrounding a magnet, just as electric fields were suggested by the effects between separated electric charges. The intensity of a magnetic field in vacuum is denoted by $\mathcal{3C}$, and the field at a point is defined as the force that would be exerted on a unit magnetic pole placed at that point. The magnetic field strength is expressed in oersteds or gauss. Magnetic fields, like electric fields, are represented in magnitude and direction by lines of force. Figure 10-35 illustrates this description of the magnetic field between two magnetic poles.

When any material is placed between the poles of a magnet, the magnetic field is different in the material from what it was in vacuum. The magnetic field in the material is denoted by B. The difference between B and $\mathcal{3C}$ is dependent on I, the magnetic moment per unit volume of the material or, as it is more frequently called, the *intensity of magnetization*. Unlike the case of electric fields and dielectric materials, the magnetic field may be either increased or decreased by the presence of the material. The quantities $\mathcal{3C}$, B, and I are related by the expression

$$B = \mathcal{3C} + 4\pi I \tag{102}$$

and I may be either positive or negative. Each of these possibilities is illustrated by the lines-of-force diagrams of Fig. 10-35.

In magnetic measurements the quantity that is obtained experimentally is the intensity of magnetization per unit field strength, that is, $I/\mathcal{3C}$. It is convenient, for chemical treatments, to multiply by the molecular volume M/ρ and to deal with the quantity

$$\chi_M = \frac{M}{\rho} \frac{I}{\mathcal{3C}} \tag{103}$$

called the *magnetic susceptibility per mole*, or the *molar magnetic susceptibility*.

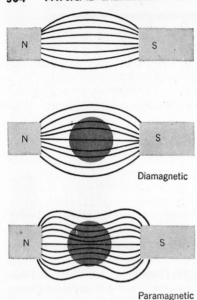

Diamagnetic

Paramagnetic

Fig. 10-35. Magnetic lines of force showing the effect of diamagnetic and paramagnetic materials on the magnetic field.

The molar magnetic susceptibility, being the magnetization per mole induced by unit field strength, can be recognized as the magnetic counterpart, on a molar basis, of the sum of the electrical polarizability α and the molecular-dipole term $\mu^2/3kT$. This parallel does, in fact, exist, and it is convenient to deal therefore with the corresponding terms α_M, the magnetic polarizability, and μ_M, the magnetic moment. Without treating the theory in detail, the relation of these quantities is stated as

$$\chi_M = N\left(\alpha_M + \frac{\mu_M^2}{3kT}\right) \quad (104)$$

Several qualitatively different behaviors are recognized. Most organic compounds have only a magnetic-polarizability contribution, and this term acts to reduce the magnetic field in the material; that is, α_M is negative. It follows, since μ_M is zero for these materials, that χ_M and I are also negative. Materials that behave in this manner are said to be *diamagnetic*.

Other materials, which we shall see are characterized by having unpaired electrons, have, on a microscopic scale, permanent magnets. The magnetic-moment term, when it exists, is almost always much larger than the polarizability term. The magnetic-moment contribution to χ_M is necessarily positive, and this is illustrated by a diagram such as that of Fig. 10-36, in which the microscopic magnets tend to line up to draw the magnetic field into the sample. Materials that behave in this manner are said to be *paramagnetic*.

There are, finally, the important classes of ferromagnetic and antiferromagnetic materials in which the magnetic properties depend on cooperative phenomena among many atoms of the sample. These materials will not be dealt with here.

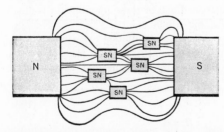

Fig. 10-36. The microscopic explanation of paramagnetism. The magnetic moments of the sample molecules or ions tend to draw the magnetic field through the sample.

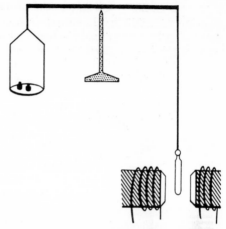

Fig. 10-37. The Gouy balance for the measurement of magnetic susceptibilities.

Experimentally, one frequently obtains magnetic-susceptibility data from measurements with a Gouy balance. In this method, as illustrated in Fig. 10-37, a sample is suspended from one arm of a balance in such a way that it is partly in the magnetic field. An electromagnet is ordinarily used, and when the magnet is turned on, the sample is generally repelled by or attracted into the magnetic field. The force required to maintain the position of the sample is measured by the weight that must be added or removed from the balance pan to maintain equilibrium. If the sample is paramagnetic, the magnetic moments will tend to line up with the field and the sample will have lower energy in the magnetic field and will therefore be drawn into the field. If the sample is diamagnetic, the reverse will be the case and the sample will be repelled by the field.

The relation between the force exerted on a sample by a nonhomogeneous magnetic field and the magnetic susceptibility of the sample can be determined with reference to Fig. 10-38. It is supposed that the sample is paramagnetic

Fig. 10-38. The effect of an inhomogeneous magnetic field on a sample.

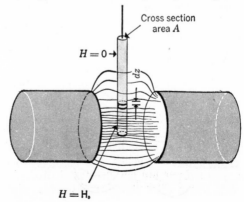

Cross section
area A

$H = 0$

dz

$H = H_0$

so that the magnetic field lines up the microscopic magnets of the sample. The magnetic susceptibility χ_M corresponds, as comparison of Eqs. (97) and (104) shows, to the electrical polarization $\mathcal{P}$ in that it gives the effective magnetic moment per mole of sample in the magnetic field. The magnetic moment per cubic centimeter is then $(\rho/M)(\chi_M)$, that is, χ_M divided by the molecular volume, and this quantity is the counterpart of the electric polarization ρ of Sec. 10-8.

The magnetic moment of the section of thickness dz and volume $A\,dz$ in Fig. 10-38 which experiences a magnetic field $\mathcal{3C}$ is therefore

$$\frac{\rho}{M}(\chi_M)\mathcal{3C}A\,dz \tag{105}$$

This induced magnetic moment is in the direction of the applied magnetic field if the material is paramagnetic. If the magnetic field increases along the sample toward the center of the magnetic field, the lowering of the potential energy of successive segments will be greater as a result of the lining up of the magnetic moments of expression (105) with the greater magnetic fields. The force corresponding to this varying potential energy is the rate of change of the potential with z. If the magnetic-field gradient is $d\mathcal{3C}/dz$, the force on a sample segment is

$$\frac{\rho}{M}\chi_M\mathcal{3C}A\,dz\left(\frac{d\mathcal{3C}}{dz}\right) = \frac{\rho}{M}\chi_M A\mathcal{3C}\,d\mathcal{3C} \tag{106}$$

If the segments of the sample extend from the center of the magnetic field, where the magnetic-field value is $\mathcal{3C}_0$, to outside the magnetic field, where the value is zero, the total force on the sample is

$$f = \int_0^{\mathcal{3C}_0} \frac{\rho}{M}\chi_M A\mathcal{3C}\,d\mathcal{3C}$$

$$= \frac{1}{2}\left(\frac{\rho}{M}\chi_M\right)A\mathcal{3C}_0^2 \tag{107}$$

This result is the basis of the Gouy-balance method and shows that, for an experimental arrangement such as that of Fig. 10-37, the measurement of the force exerted on the sample by a known maximum field strength $\mathcal{3C}_0$ can be used to deduce the magnetic susceptibility of the sample. In practice, however, one frequently compares the force on a standard sample with that on an unknown sample instead of evaluating the cross-section sample area and the magnetic field directly.

A typical experiment with a paramagnetic substance or solution might make use of a sample tube of 1 sq cm cross section and a magnet with $\mathcal{3C}_0$ of 10,000 gauss. For such an arrangement the force exerted by the magnetic field might be equivalent to a few tenths of a gram, i.e., perhaps 100 dynes, and for such a value Eq. (107) indicates a susceptibility of about 10^{-4} or, as susceptibilities are usually reported, 100×10^{-6}. Diamagnetic susceptibilities are negative and typically are smaller than this value by a factor of about 100.

10-14. Molecular Interpretation of Diamagnetism. All materials affect a magnetic field in which they are inserted as a result of an induced magnetic moment, which produces a diamagnetic effect, just as all compounds show an induced dipole moment in an electric field.   This induced magnetic effect is generally of secondary importance and is almost always greatly overshadowed by the more interesting permanent-magnetic-moment contribution, when one exists. It is necessary, however, to be able to subtract the induced-moment contribution from the total magnetic susceptibility.

The diamagnetic effect is produced by the orbital motion of the electrons of the atoms, ions, or molecules of the sample.   It can be understood qualitatively on the basis of Lenz's law, which, for an ordinary-sized system of a current flowing in a coil of wire in a magnetic field, states that the field will induce a current in the coil in such a way as to oppose the applied field.   In a similar way, the orbital motion of the electrons is disturbed by the applied field, and the disturbance is such that a magnetic-field contribution in opposition to the applied field is produced.   The diamagnetic effect is, in fact, temperature-independent and is a function of the quantum numbers of the electrons; i.e., it depends on the nature of the electron orbitals, as these ideas would suggest.

The diamagnetic effect of a given molecule can be estimated from tables that give the contribution of the various atoms within the molecule.   Such terms, some of which are shown in Table 10-8, are known as *Pascal's constants*.   It is necessary, for good agreement with the observed diamagnetic susceptibilities, to include also terms for any multiple or unusual bonding situation in which the atoms are involved.   Some of these terms are also included in Table 10-8.

Table 10-8. Pascal's Constants for the Determination of the Diamagnetic Susceptibility*

Atomic contributions			
H	-2.93×10^{-6}	Cl	-20.1×10^{-6}
C	-6.00	Br	-30.6
N (open chain)	-5.55	I	-44.6
N (ring)	-4.61	S	-15
N (monomide)	-1.54	Se	-23
O (alcohol, ether)	-4.61	B	-7
O (carbonyl)	1.72	Si	-13
O (carboxyl group)	-3.36	P	-10
F	-6.3	As	-21

Group corrections	
C=C	5.5×10^{-6}
C=C—C=C	10.6
N=N	1.85
C=N	8.15
—C≡N	0.8
Benzene	-1.4
Cyclohexane	-3.0

* From P. W. Selwood, "Magnetochemistry," 2d ed., Interscience Publishers, Inc., New York, 1956.

For most purposes, the diamagnetic term can be satisfactorily estimated from such a table of Pascal's constants.

10-15. Molecular Interpretation of Paramagnetism. The paramagnetic effect can be most easily introduced by considering the introductory problem of the magnetic behavior of an electron in the lowest-energy Bohr orbit of a hydrogen atom. A classical treatment is easily made and, as it happens, yields the correct result. The motion of an electron in an orbit corresponds, in this connection, to the passage of a current through a coil of wire. It is known that a current in a coil of wire of ordinary dimensions produces a magnetic field perpendicular to the coil. The magnetic field so produced is, according to Ampère's law, equal to that of a magnet with magnetic moment μ_M equal to the product of the current and the cross-section area of the loop of wire. The magnetic moment of a magnet is defined in a manner similar to that for a dipole moment of a dipole. For the magnetic moment produced by a current of i amp circulating in a coil of enclosed area A to have the proper electromagnetic units, it is necessary to divide the Ampère's-law terms by the factor c, the velocity of light, to obtain

$$\mu_M = \frac{iA}{c} \tag{108}$$

The current corresponding to an electron in an orbit is obtained by multiplying the number of times the electron passes any point on the orbit by its electronic charge. Thus,

$$i = \frac{v}{2\pi r} e \tag{109}$$

where the electron velocity is v and the orbit has radius r. The cross-section area is

$$A = \pi r^2 \tag{110}$$

Thus the magnetic moment μ_0 for the lowest Bohr orbit is obtained as

$$\mu_0 = \frac{vre}{2c} \tag{111}$$

which can be written as

$$\mu_0 = \frac{mvre}{2mc} \tag{112}$$

The Bohr relation for the lowest orbit

$$mvr = \frac{h}{2\pi} \tag{113}$$

can now be substituted to give

$$\mu_0 = \frac{eh}{4\pi^2 mc} \tag{114}$$

This important result, although classically obtained and based on a particular orbit of the hydrogen atom, provides a magnetic-moment unit to which magnetic moments of molecules and ions can be conveniently referred. The quantity μ_0, called the *Bohr magneton*, thus becomes a unit in which atomic and molecular magnetic moments are reported. Its value can be obtained by inserting the necessary constants and is found to be

$$1 \text{ Bohr magneton} = \mu_0 = 0.927 \times 10^{-20} \tag{115}$$

with the magnetic units of ergs per gauss.

Our interest will be principally in molecules and ions, and it would seem reasonable to expect, in terms of the above development, that the orbital motions of the electrons would contribute a magnetic moment of the order of magnitude of a Bohr magneton. This expectation is not borne out, and it appears that the orbital motion of the electrons in a polyatomic system are tied into the nuclear configuration of the molecule or the ion so tightly that they are unable to line up with the applied magnetic field and are therefore ineffective. Even for single-atom ions in solution the interaction of the orbitals of the ion with the solvating molecules is apparently sufficient to prevent the orbitals being oriented such that their magnetic moment contributes in the direction of the field. Thus, for most purposes, the orbital magnetic moment can be ignored.

We must look to the spinning of the electron about its own axis to explain the larger part of the magnetic moment of those molecules and ions which have magnetic moments. The results are understandable in terms of a magnetic-moment contribution of 1 Bohr magneton for each *unpaired* electron. While an explanation of why an electron should have a magnetic moment of this value cannot be given, it is not unreasonable, with a picture of an electron as a spinning, negatively charged body, to associate a magnetic moment with the electron. When the magnetic moment of an atom, ion, or molecule is interpreted in this way, a *spin-only* calculation is said to be used. To the extent to which such a calculation is valid, information on the *number of unpaired electrons* in a molecule or ion is obtained. Such results sometimes play a very important role in deductions of electronic structures.

A quantum-mechanical treatment shows that when a molecule or ion has several unpaired electrons and a total electron-spin angular momentum of $S(h/2\pi)$ and spin quantum number S, the electron-spin magnetic moment is not simply the arithmetic sum of the magnetic-moment contributions of the separate spinning electrons but rather is given by the expression

$$\mu_M = 2 \sqrt{S(S + 1)} \, \mu_0 \tag{116}$$

where for one, two, three, . . . unpaired electrons the spin-angular-momentum quantum number S is $\frac{1}{2}, \frac{2}{2}, \frac{3}{2}, \ldots$. With Eq. (116) and the assumption that the α_M contribution has been taken care of, the magnetic susceptibility of Eq. (104) is related to the total electron spin by the relation

$$\chi_M = \frac{4\mu_0^2 N}{3kT} \, S(S + 1) \tag{117}$$

Thus, a measurement of χ_M leads to a value of S, and this value can be interpreted in terms of a number of unpaired electrons. Table 10-9 shows the results to be expected for χ_M for various numbers of unpaired electrons at 25°C.

Equation (117) implies that, if the magnetic-polarizability term is not too

Table 10-9. Contributions of Unpaired Electrons to the Magnetic Susceptibility

No. of unpaired electrons	Total electron-spin quantum number S	Spin magnetic moment $2\sqrt{S(S+1)}\,\mu_0$	Magnetic susceptibility at 25°C $\chi_M = \dfrac{4\mu_0^2 N}{3kT} S(S+1)$
1	$\frac{1}{2}$	$1.73\mu_0$	$1,260 \times 10^{-6}$
2	$\frac{2}{2}$	$2.83\mu_0$	$3,360 \times 10^{-6}$
3	$\frac{3}{2}$	$3.87\mu_0$	$6,290 \times 10^{-6}$
4	$\frac{4}{2}$	$4.90\mu_0$	$10,100 \times 10^{-6}$
5	$\frac{5}{2}$	$5.92\mu_0$	$14,700 \times 10^{-6}$

large, the magnetic susceptibility will vary inversely as the absolute temperature; i.e.,

$$\chi_M = \frac{\text{const}}{T} \tag{118}$$

This relation, known as *Curie's law*, is, in fact, found to be valid over not too large a temperature range.

10-16. Magnetic Results for Molecules.   The best example of a simple molecule for which the magnetic data bear on the electronic structure is provided by oxygen.   Over a considerable temperature range the molar magnetic susceptibility is found to be represented by

$$\chi_M = \frac{1.00}{T} \tag{119}$$

giving, at 25°C, the value

$$\chi_M = 3,360 \times 10^{-6} \tag{120}$$

The values of Table 10-9 show that this susceptibility is to be interpreted as arising from two unpaired electrons.   The bonding in O_2 is therefore unusual.   The reason for this molecule assuming such a structure, rather than a completely paired double-bonded arrangement, cannot be given here.

A class of compounds, consisting mostly of highly aromatic substituted systems, shows a tendency to dissociate into fragments, called *free radicals*, that have unpaired electrons.   Thus, hexaphenyl ethane dissociates according to

Such dissociation is understandable as a result of the number of resonance structures that can be drawn for the free radical.   Measurement of the susceptibility for such substances in solution allows the effective number of unpaired electrons and the degree of dissociation to the free radicals to be deduced.

10-17. Magnetic Results for Coordination Compounds.   The principal application of magnetic susceptibility in chemistry at present is to the study of coordination complexes of the transition elements.   In the previous chapter it was shown that different reasonable bonding arrangements could sometimes be drawn for different ligands on a given metal ion.   These bonding descriptions, moreover, were such that different numbers of unpaired electrons could sometimes be expected in the partially filled d orbitals.   Magnetic results are of value in assigning an electronic structure to such complexes and, in some cases, in deciding the geometry of the ligand attachment.

The complexes $Fe(CN)_6^{3-}$ and FeF_6^{3-} were used previously to illustrate different bonding descriptions.   Magnetic studies of the salts $K_3Fe(CN)_6$ and K_3FeF_6 in aqueous solution assign a magnetic moment of 2.3 Bohr magnetons to the former and 6.0 to the latter.   Reference to Table 10-9 then shows that each FeF_6^{3-} ion can best be ascribed one unpaired electron and each $Fe(CN)_6^{3-}$ ion five unpaired electrons.   It was these data which were primarily responsible for the different bonding descriptions that were given in Sec. 9-8 to the two ions.

ELECTRON AND NUCLEAR MAGNETIC SPECTROSCOPY

The spectroscopic methods treated earlier in the chapter dealt with the study of transitions between energy levels of free, or nearly free, molecules. The spacing between such molecular energy levels is a characteristic of the electronic structure and atomic make-up of the molecule.   The spectroscopic methods now to be studied treat transitions between energy levels whose spacing is dependent on the magnetic field that is applied to the sample. Present-day studies make use of energy levels that arise in two different ways. The first type of energy level, and the transitions between such energy levels, to be discussed arises because the nuclei of some atoms have a magnetic moment, and different orientations of such nuclear magnets relative to the applied field have different energies.   The second type of energy level to be dealt with arises from the magnetic moment of the electron.   An electron that does not have a counterpart with opposite spin direction can also line up with a magnetic field in different directions, and, because the electron has a magnetic moment associated with it, these different orientations will correspond to different energies.

The transitions between both the energy levels due to nuclear orientation and those due to electron orientation are studied by means of a resonance method, which will be briefly described later, and one identifies these types of spectroscopic studies as nuclear magnetic resonance, or *nmr*, spectroscopy, and electron-spin resonance, or *esr*, spectroscopy.

10-18. The Energy Levels of Nuclei in Magnetic Fields.   Many nuclei have spin angular momentum, and this can be pictured as resulting from the spinning of the nucleus about an axis in much the same way as an electron has a spin angular momentum of $s(h/2\pi)$, where s for the electron must be $\frac{1}{2}$. The angular momentum of atomic nuclei is also quantized and comes in units of $h/2\pi$. The nuclear spin quantum number I can therefore be introduced and allows the spin angular momentum to be written as $I(h/2\pi)$. The spin quantum number is a characteristic of the nucleus and can be zero or can have various integral or half-integral values. These values can to some extent be correlated to the neutron and proton make-up of the nucleus. Most *nmr* studies have been concerned with the hydrogen nucleus, which has $I = \frac{1}{2}$, and the method of *nmr* spectroscopy can be satisfactorily illustrated by restricting our attention to this nucleus.

Along any defined direction in space, and now the applied magnetic field will specify this direction, the angular momentum of the spinning nucleus must present quantized components. A nucleus with an angular momentum $\frac{1}{2}(h/2\pi)$ must therefore line itself up, as indicated in Fig. 10-39, in such a way that the angular momentum in the direction of the magnetic field is $+\frac{1}{2}(h/2\pi)$

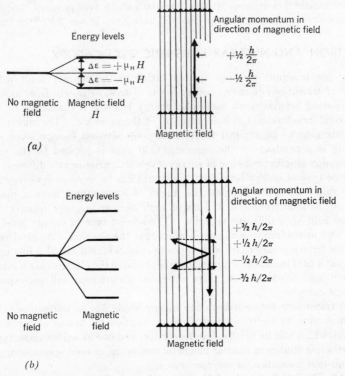

Fig. 10-39. The allowed orientations of the angular-momentum vector in a magnetic field and the corresponding energy levels. (*a*) The hydrogen-atom nucleus with $I = \frac{1}{2}$ and magnetic moment μ_H. (*b*) A nucleus with $I = \frac{3}{2}$.

or $-\frac{1}{2}(h/2\pi)$. The allowed orientations of a nucleus with spin quantum number $\frac{3}{2}$ is also shown to illustrate the more general case. (A rigorous quantum-mechanical treatment shows, in fact, that the spin vectors of Fig. 10-39 should not be drawn exactly in these directions relative to the field for the component to have the required value. This feature need not, however, concern us.)

The number of different allowed orientations of the nuclear spin direction is seen from Fig. 10-39 to be determined by the nuclear spin-quantum number. The difference in the energies of these different orientations is dependent on the interaction of the nuclear magnetic moment with the magnetic field. A spinning nucleus, which is a charged particle, can be expected to have a magnetic moment in a manner analogous to that in which a coil of wire carrying a current has, according to Ampère's law, a magnetic moment. Our lack of understanding of the details of the charge distribution in a nucleus prevents us, however, from obtaining a theoretical value for the nuclear magnetic moment by this approach.

If, however, the magnetic moment of the nucleus of the hydrogen atom is denoted by μ_H and the magnetic field acting on the proton by $\mathcal{3C}$, the lining up of the nuclear magnets with and against the magnetic field will produce the energy levels indicated in Fig. 10-39. These values are calculated from the energy of a magnet lined up at various directions to the magnetic field [the expression is like that for a dipole in an electric field as given by Eq. (94)] and the quantum stipulation that the spin be lined up with or opposed to the field. Before proceeding to a more detailed treatment of the method used to study transitions between these energy levels and the complications that arise when the nuclei being studied are part of a molecule, a few general features will be reported.

Magnetic fields used in *nmr* spectroscopy usually have values of about 10,000 gauss. With this field strength it is found that radiation with a frequency of about 40×10^6 cycles/sec has quanta with energies of the order of magnitude of the separation of the levels shown in Fig. 10-39. The nuclei will, therefore, absorb such radiation, which is in the radio-frequency range, and jump from the lower to the higher energy state. They will, that is, flip their orientation from a direction with the field to one against the field.

It is of interest to notice that the energy-level separation is extremely small. The quanta of radiation of frequency 40×10^6 cycles/sec have energies of 0.00003×10^{-14} erg, or 0.004 cal/mole compared with a room-temperature value of kT of 4.1×10^{-14} erg, or 600 cal/mole. The magnitude of this separation is spectroscopically important in that it implies a population in the lower of the two states that is little greater than that of the upper state. According to the Boltzmann distribution the excess population in the lower state is calculated as

$$\frac{N(\text{lower})}{N(\text{upper})} = e^{\Delta\epsilon/kT}$$

$$= e^{\frac{0.00003 \times 10^{-14}}{4.1 \times 10^{-14}}} = 1.000007$$

It has not been necessary to point out in previous spectroscopic work that incident radiation induces not only transition to higher energy levels, for which radiation is absorbed, but also transitions from higher to lower levels, for which radiation is emitted. In *nmr* experiments the two levels are nearly equally populated, and the absorption of radiation is only slightly the more important effect. It follows that only weak absorption of radiation will occur and, therefore, that a very sensitive experimental arrangement will be necessary.

10-19. *nmr* **Spectroscopy.** The frequency of the radiation that corresponds to the nuclear magnetic-energy-level spacings and the weakness of the radiation absorption that must be expected lead to a spectrometer of a radically different k̇nd to those prism instruments which are used for electronic and vibrational spectral analyses. The arrangement that is most frequently used is shown in Fig. 10-40. The principal magnetic field acts on the nuclei of the sample to produce energy levels such as those indicated in Fig. 10-39. Transitions between these levels are stimulated by radiation from the radio-frequency transmitter, which sends out electromagnetic radiation from the transmitter coil. Radiation will be absorbed by the sample if the frequency of the radiation is such that the quanta of radiation have an energy matching the nuclear energy-level spacing. When such radiation is absorbed, it can be thought of as producing nuclei in the excited state, which will then tend to reemit the radiation in order to approach the Boltzmann-distribution ratio. It is this

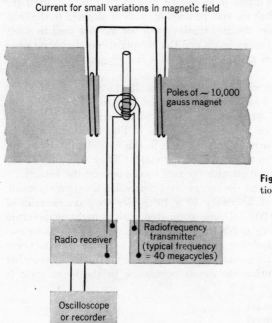

Fig. **10-40.** Schematic representation of an *nmr* spectrometer.

emitted radiation which is detected by the receiver coil, which, being oriented at right angles to the transmitter, receives no signal unless the sample provides this coupling with the transmitter.   The signal from the receiver coil can be displayed on an oscilloscope or a recorder.

This indication of the operation of an *nmr* spectrometer implies that a fixed magnetic field is imposed on the sample and that the frequency of the radiation is varied.   Thus, if the energy spacing is, as indicated in Fig. 10-39, $2\mu_H\mathfrak{IC}$ and the radiation has frequency ν and quanta with energy $h\nu$, absorption of radiation can occur when

$$2\mu_H\mathfrak{IC} = h\nu \tag{121}$$

Since it is here possible to control the energy-level spacing by manipulating $\mathfrak{IC}$, the equality of Eq. (121) can be brought about either by adjusting ν after some fixed value of $\mathfrak{IC}$ is chosen or by adjusting $\mathfrak{IC}$ after some fixed value of ν has been selected.   The latter procedure turns out to be experimentally more satisfactory.   A fixed frequency, usually 40 or 60 megacycles, is supplied by the transmitter, and the magnetic field is varied through a small range until Eq. (121) is satisfied.   At this point the sample absorbs radiation, the transmitter and receiver are coupled, or the circuit can be said to be in resonance, and a signal is produced from the receiver circuit.

The signal that is obtained as a function of magnetic field for a fixed frequency of 40 megacycles is shown in Fig. 10-41a and b for several simple compounds.   The identification of the hydrogen atom, or groups of hydrogen atoms that produce a given signal, can be made by a simple comparison of these spectra or can be more definitely established by the use of deuterium substituted derivatives.

If spectra are obtained at higher resolution, a considerable complexity appears as is shown by the solid curves of (a) and the lower curve of (b).

The theory of Sec. 10-17 suggested that the nuclear energy-level splitting is dependent on the nuclear magnetic moment and the magnetic-field strength. The experimental results indicate that even if the absorptions of only hydrogen atoms is studied a number of closely spaced absorptions are observed.   It is now necessary to see whether or not these finer details of *nmr* spectroscopy, which contain the information of principal interest to the chemist, can be understood.

10-20. Chemical Shifts and Nuclear Magnetic Interactions.   The factors which lead to the different absorptions of Fig. 10-41 can often be treated separately from the factors that lead to the finer splittings indicated there.

The separation in the positions of the spectral lines associated with hydrogen atoms in different chemical environments is called the *chemical shift*.   These shifts can be conveniently reported by means of the difference in magnetic field necessary for absorption compared with that necessary for absorption by some reference.   This difference is usually reported as the chemical shift δ, defined as

$$\delta = \frac{\mathfrak{IC}_{\text{sample}} - \mathfrak{IC}_{\text{reference}}}{\mathfrak{IC}_{\text{reference}}} \times 10^6 \tag{122}$$

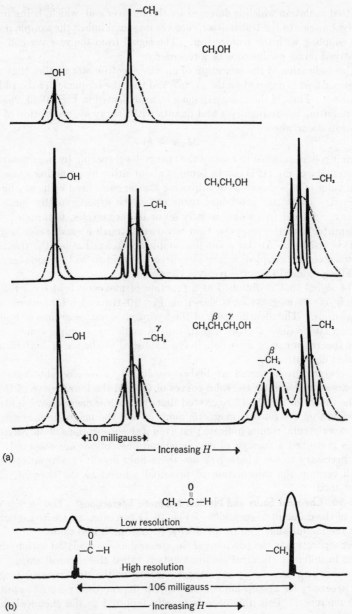

(a)

←10 milligauss→

—— Increasing H ——→

(b)

CH_3—$\overset{\overset{\text{O}}{\|}}{C}$—H

Low resolution

$\overset{\overset{\text{O}}{\|}}{C}$—H

High resolution

←———— 106 milligauss ————→

—— Increasing H ——→

Fig. 10-41. The *nmr* spectra of several simple compounds at a frequency of 40 megacycles/sec and a magnetic field of 10,000 gauss. In (*a*) the solid lines give the high-resolution spectra and the dashed lines show the appearance of the spectra at low resolution where the splitting arising from the interactions of the nuclei would not be observed.

where the reference chosen may be water, benzene, cyclohexane, and so forth. Since hydrogen atoms in different samples show absorption, or resonance, at fields that differ by the order of milligauss when the magnetic field is 10,000 gauss, the values of δ are made of convenient size by the inclusion of the factor 10^6 in Eq. (122).

The existence of the chemical shift can be attributed to the screening effect that the electrons about a nucleus exert. Thus, although the external magnetic field is the same for all hydrogen atoms of a sample of CH_3OH, for example, the electron distribution in the C—H and O—H bonds screens the nuclei from the applied field to different extents. Some correlations have succeeded in showing that the more the electrons of the bond to hydrogen are drawn to the bonding atom the more exposed is the nucleus of the hydrogen atom. Such exposed nuclei generally absorb at lower magnetic fields than do well-shielded nuclei.

The *nmr* spectrum is, as a result of chemical shifts, a portrayal of the chemical environment of the various hydrogen atoms of the material. It follows that an analysis of a spectrum of an unknown material can lead to information on the types of bonding to hydrogen atoms and often to the molecular structure of the sample. In this respect *nmr* complements infrared and ultraviolet spectroscopy in the elucidation of the structures of large molecules. Some of the characteristic chemical shifts that are used in such analyses are shown in Table 10-10.

The high-resolution detail, such as that shown in Fig. 10-41, is also characteristic of the hydrogen-atom arrangement of the molecule and is therefore also

Table 10-10. Characteristic Values for the Chemical Shift δ for Protons with Water as the Reference Substance*

Group	δ
—SO₃H	-6.7 ± 0.3
—CO₂H	-6.4 ± 0.8
RCHO	-4.7 ± 0.3
RCONH₂	-2.9
ArOH	-2.3 ± 0.3
ArH	-1.9 ± 1.0
=CH₂	-0.6 ± 0.7
ROH	-0.1 ± 0.7
H₂O	(0.00)
—OCH₃	1.6 ± 0.3
—CH₂X	1.7 ± 1.2
≡C—H	2.4 ± 0.4
=C—CH₃	3.3 ± 0.5
—CH₂—	3.5 ± 0.5
RNH₂	3.6 ± 0.7
—C—CH₃	4.1 ± 0.6

* From J. D. Roberts, "Nuclear Magnetic Resonance," McGraw-Hill Book Company, Inc., New York, 1959.

helpful in structural determinations. Only some features of the source of these additional splittings can be given.

The magnetic field at a nucleus in a molecule is determined not only by the external magnetic field as modified by the shielding electrons but also by the presence and orientation of the other nuclei in the molecule that behave as magnets, i.e., have magnetic moments. Since both O^{16} and C^{12} have zero spin and zero magnetic moment, the magnetic nuclei of many organic compounds consist only of the hydrogen atoms. It is the interaction between the nuclei of these atoms that leads to the additional splitting beyond that of the chemical shifts.

The nature and effect of these interactions can be illustrated by reference to

$$O$$

the spectrum of acetaldehyde, CH_3—$\overset{\|}{C}$—H. The hydrogen atoms of the methyl group experience a magnetic field that depends on the applied field, on the chemical-shift effect of the shielding electrons, and on the influence of the magnetic field of the nucleus of the hydrogen atom adjacent to the carbonyl group. This nucleus, as Fig. 10-42 indicates, can line up with or against the principal magnetic field. The methyl hydrogen atoms will experience, therefore, a slightly greater or lesser magnetic field depending on the orientation of the lone hydrogen atom. The methyl absorption will therefore be split into a doublet.

The single hydrogen atom also experiences a magnetic field that depends on the applied field, on the shielding provided by its bonding electrons, and on the influence of the three magnetic nuclei in the methyl group. There are four different ways in which the three magnets can arrange themselves relative to the applied field. These are shown in Fig. 10-42, where it is indicated that two of the ways are three times as probable as the other two. The lone hydrogen atom can experience therefore four slightly different magnetic fields, depending on the orientation of the spins of the methyl hydrogen nuclei. Four different resonance frequencies would be expected for the lone hydrogen nucleus, or, in view of the experimental arrangement, four slightly different applied fields at a fixed radiation frequency. The spectrum of Fig. 10-42 bears out these analyses.

This simple example should illustrate that the magnetic nuclear interactions give information on the type of neighbors of any hydrogen atom or group of atoms in the molecule. Such intimate details can be obtained even for quite large molecules, and it is this aspect which makes the fine splittings of *nmr* spectra of great value in molecular-structure studies.

A number of important features of *nmr* spectroscopy have not been dealt with in this brief introduction. It is frequently of interest, for example, to examine the mechanism by which the radiation is able to interact with the magnetic nuclei to turn them to a different orientation. This has not been treated here. Likewise no mention has been made of the fact that if atoms, such as the hydrogen atoms of a water–sodium hydroxide solution, move their position from one molecule to another, so that they occupy a given position for less than about 10^{-2} sec, the *nmr* spectrum shows a single absorption at a position characteristic of the average of the environments of the nuclei.   If the nuclei change position less rapidly, the *nmr* spectrum will indicate two absorptions, one characteristic of the one environment and the other characteristic of the other.

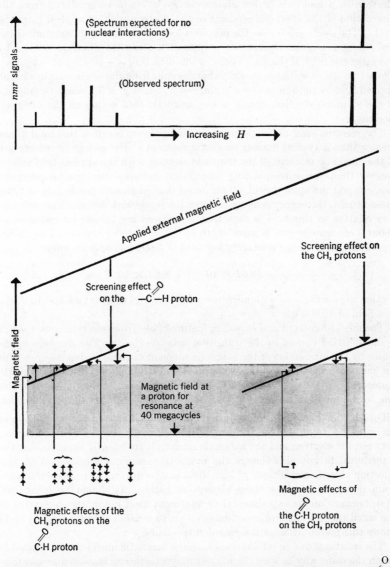

Fig. 10-42. A schematic representation of the *nmr* spectrum of acetaldehyde, $CH_3\!-\!\overset{\displaystyle O}{\overset{\|}{C}}\!-\!H$, and its interpretation in terms of the screening effects and nuclear interactions.

It follows that *nmr* techniques can be used to study the rate of very fast reactions, and this, in fact, is one of the most interesting aspects of *nmr* spectroscopy.

10-21. Electron-spin Resonance Spectroscopy. The presence of an unpaired electron in a molecule or ion allows energy levels to be produced from the interaction of the magnetic moment of the electron with an applied magnetic field. The electron has, like the proton, a half unit of spin angular momentum, and the spin angular momentum is quantized along the direction defined by the magnetic field, if the component in this direction is $+\frac{1}{2}(h/2\pi)$ or $-\frac{1}{2}(h/2\pi)$. These two states will have energies that are split from the original state with no applied field by the amounts $+\mu_e\mathcal{3C}$ and $-\mu_e\mathcal{3C}$, where μ_e is the magnetic moment of the spinning electron and $\mathcal{3C}$ is the magnetic field acting on the unpaired electron.

The electron-spin magnetic moment is, however, about a thousand times greater than a typical nuclear magnetic moment. The energy of interaction of the magnetic moment of the unpaired electron with the applied field will be greater than the corresponding interaction between the nuclear-magnetic moment and the applied field. It is found that when a magnetic field of 3,000 gauss is used, the energy spacing between the levels with different spin orientation relative to this field is such that transitions are caused by radiation of about 3 cm wavelength, a wavelength of the microwave region. The energy separation, even in the relatively low field of 3,000 gauss, is therefore

$$\frac{3 \times 10^{10}}{3} (6.62 \times 10^{-27}) = 6.62 \times 10^{-17} \text{ erg}$$

a value to be compared with nuclear-energy spacings of about 0.03×10^{-17} erg in a field of 10,000 gauss.

The most prominent and revealing feature of electron-spin resonance spectra is the splitting caused in the transition between the two electron-orientation states by the interaction of the magnetic moment of the spinning electron with the magnetic moments of those nuclei in the molecule which have magnetic moments. The electron-spin energies and the splitting of these energies due to the nitrogen nucleus, which has one unit of spin, are shown for the ion $(SO_3)_2\dot{N}O^=$ in Fig. 10-43. Transitions occur which change the orientation of the electron spin relative to the applied magnetic field. The interaction between the electron and the magnetic nucleus is sufficiently small so that the transitions do not also change the magnetic-moment direction. With this selection rule the transitions of Fig. 10-43 can be drawn. The observed spectrum does in fact show three absorption bands. It should be mentioned that, because of the experimental arrangement used in *esr*, the derivative of the usual spectral absorption or emission curve is often shown. Figure 10-44 shows this presentation of the recorded spectrum.

The splittings due to interactions with the magnetic nuclei can be treated in much the same way as were the nuclear magnetic interactions in *nmr* spectros-

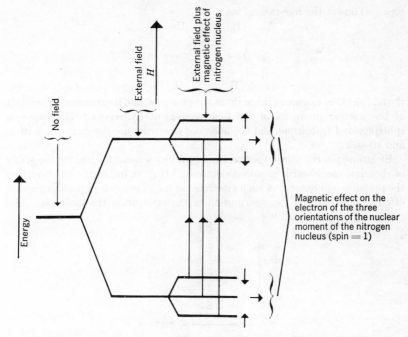

Fig. 10-43. The energy-level diagram for the unpaired electron of the radical ion $(SO_3)_2\dot{N}O^-$, showing the splitting of the two electron-spin states by the magnetic moment of the nitrogen nucleus.

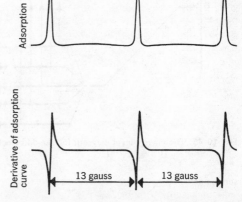

Fig. 10-44. The *esr* spectrum of the radical ion $[O\dot{N}(SO_3)_2]^-$ at a frequency of 9,500 megacycles/sec and a magnetic field of about 3,400 gauss.

copy.   Thus in the free-radical ion

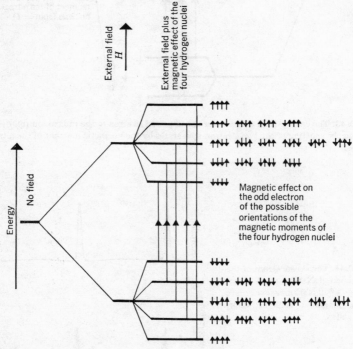

the odd electron can move throughout the molecule, and it experiences the effect of the nuclear moments of the four equivalent hydrogens.   The expected splittings and transitions and the observed spectrum are shown in Figs. 10-45 and 10-46.

Electron-spin resonance spectroscopy provides a powerful tool for the study of chemical species with unpaired electrons.   It gives information not only on the presence and number of such electrons, as measurements of paramagnetism often do, but also on the distribution of the electron in the molecule.   The

Fig. 10-45. The energy-level diagram for the odd electron of the free-radical ion 1,4-benzo-semiquinone, $\dot{O}$—O⁻.

splitting due to interactions with a nuclear magnetic moment depends on the odd electron being distributed throughout the molecule so that it is to some extent near that nucleus. Such details of electronic configuration in free-radical-type molecules are one of the important features treated by *esr*.

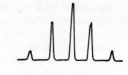

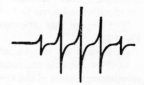

Problems

1. The molecule CO has absorptions in the microwave region at frequencies of 1.15×10^{11} and 2.30×10^{11} cycles/sec. These absorptions can be associated with the $J = 0$ to $J = 1$ and $J = 1$ to $J = 2$ transitions. Calculate the moment of inertia and the internuclear distance for the CO molecule.

Fig. 10-46. The *esr* spectrum of 1,4-benzosemiquinone,

$$\overset{H}{\underset{H}{\diagdown}} \quad \overset{H}{\underset{H}{\diagup}}$$
$$\dot{O}- \quad -O^-, \text{ at a fre-}$$

quency of 9,500 megacycles/ sec and a magnetic field of about 3,400 gauss.

Ans. $I = 14.6 \times 10^{-40}$ g/sq cm, $r = 1.13$ A.

2. Plot, side by side, the energies of some of the lower rotational states of a molecule like CO (for which the moment of inertia can be obtained from Prob. 1), which has a rather low moment of inertia, and the energies of some of the rotational states of CO_2, which has $I = 71.1 \times 10^{-40}$ g/sq cm and represents molecules with larger moments of inertia.

Calculate the populations, relative to the number n_0 in the lowest state, of some of the energy levels of both CO and CO_2, and represent them as has been done for HCl in Fig. 10-5.

3. The bond length of the gas-phase NaCl molecule is 2.36 A. Show by vertical lines on a frequency abscissa the positions of the three lowest-frequency rotational transitions that will occur. Indicate the rotational quantum numbers involved in each transition.

4. Obtain a general expression for the energies of the $\Delta J = +1$ transitions which start from the J level and end in the $J + 1$ level. Base the derivation on a linear molecule for which the rotational energy levels are given by Eq. (11).

5. For a chemical bond with a typical force constant k of 5×10^5 dynes/cm and equilibrium bond length of 1.5 A, plot the potential energy as a function of bond length for bond-length changes of up to 10 per cent of the equilibrium bond length.

Draw a line indicating the value of the energy kT at 25°C. What per cent distortion of the bond could be produced by this amount of energy if the bond behaved as a classical spring?

6. Calculate the energies of the three lowest-energy vibrational states for HF, for which the force constant is 9.7×10^5 dynes/cm. What is the energy spacing between these levels, and what would be the wave number of the radiation that would cause the transition from the $v = 0$ to the $v = 1$ level?

Ans. $\Delta\epsilon = 8.27 \times 10^{-13}$ ergs, $\bar{\nu} = 4,160$ cm^{-1}.

7. The infrared spectrum, at low resolution, of CO shows an absorption band centered at 2,170 cm^{-1}. What is the force constant of CO in dynes per centimeter?

8. The vibrational-energy-level spacings of H_2, HD, and D_2 can be deduced from Raman spectra to be 4,395, 3,817, and 3,118 cm^{-1}, respectively. Calculate the force constant of each isotopic species, and verify that isotopic substitution, which would not

be expected to alter the electronic behavior in a molecule, does not change the bond force constant. (The small variation can be attributed to a deviation of the bond from a Hooke's law force.)

9. Since HCl consists of 75 per cent HCl^{35} and 25 per cent HCl^{37}, a spectrum of HCl should show absorption bands due to the two isotopic types.

(a) Calculate the difference in frequency expected for the $v = 0$ to $v = 1$ vibrational transition of HCl^{35} and HCl^{37}, assuming that the force constants of the two molecules are identical and equal to 4.84×10^5 dynes/cm.

(b) Compare this difference with the splitting of the vibration-rotation lines of Fig. 10-8.

(c) Identify the components due to HCl^{35} and those due to HCl^{37}.

10. Plot, showing the rotational-energy-level spacings to scale, some of the rotational-energy-levels of the $v = 0$ and $v = 1$ states of the CO molecule. The moment of inertia of CO is 14.5×10^{-40} g/sq cm, and the force constant is 19×10^5 dynes/cm.

Indicate the transitions that are responsible for the rotational-vibrational spectrum.

11. Explain, according to Fig. 10-15, what process would lead to the appearance of the relatively weak Raman lines on the short-wavelength side of the exciting 4,358-A line.

What relative intensities of the Raman lines on the short- and long-wavelength side of 4,358 A would be expected for the Raman lines at 25°C of $SOCl_2$ that correspond to the vibrational transitions of 283 and 489 cm^{-1}? Compare these results with Fig. 10-14.

$$Ans. \left\{ \frac{I \text{ (antistokes)}}{I \text{ (stokes)}} \right\}_{283 \text{cm}^{-1}} = 0.25.$$

12. A frequently used empirical expression that generates a potential-energy curve like that expected for a diatomic molecule has been given by Morse as $U(r) = D_e(1 - e^{-\beta(r-r_e)})^2$, where D_e is the dissociation energy measured from the minimum of the potential curve, r_e is the equilibrium bond length, and β is a constant that is related to the molecular properties by $\beta = \sqrt{k/2D_e}$.

(a) Draw the potential curve for HCl according to the Morse function.

(b) Obtain the relation $\beta = \sqrt{k/2D_e}$ by forming $d^2U(r)/dr^2$ and comparing this expression with the expression for the region around the potential minimum $[d^2U(r)/dr^2]_{r=r_e} = k$.

13. An electronic transition in CO is responsible for an absorption band around 1,400 A in the ultraviolet. A photograph of this band shows that it consists, in part, of a series of lines, expressed in wave numbers, at 64,703, 66,231, 67,675, 69,088, 70,470 cm^{-1}, and so forth. From the fact that these are absorption lines and are observed at fairly low temperatures they can be assumed to arise from CO molecules in the lowest vibrational state. The abrupt beginning of the series at 64,703 cm^{-1} suggests that this transition leads to the $v = 0$ level of the excited electronic state.

(a) Draw a diagram like Fig. 10-16 to illustrate these transitions.

(b) The assumption of Hooke's law for chemical bonds leads to Eq. (34), which states that vibrational levels have a constant spacing. Recognize that electronic spectra allow this expression to be checked.

Calculate a force constant from the $v = 0$, $v = 1$ spacing of the excited electronic state of the CO molecule. Compare this with the force constant for the normal, or ground, electronic state obtained in Prob. 7.

$$Ans. \ 9.4 \times 10^5 \text{ dynes/cm.}$$

14. Plot, underneath one another, the theoretical scattering curves that would be obtained for a CO molecule with assumed bond lengths of 1.00, 1.20, and 1.40 A. Carry each plot out to a value of s, equal to $(4\pi/\lambda) \sin (\theta/2)$, of about 20.

15. Plot, underneath one another, the theoretical scattering curves for CCl_4 that would be obtained with an assumed tetrahedral structure and carbon-chlorine bond lengths of 1.7 and 1.8. Carry the curves out to $s = 15$. Compare with the reported results of Karle and Karle [*J. Chem. Phys.*, **17**: 1052 (1949)] and Bartell, Brockway, and Schwendeman [*J. Chem. Phys.*, **23**: 1854 (1955)].

16. The visual appearance of the photograph of the diffracted electron beam, of 40,000 volts, from CO_2 shows maxima at $s = 6.7, 12.2, 17.8$, and 23; shoulders on these maxima at about 8.5, 14, and 19; and minima at 4.4, 10.0, 15.4, and 21.

By plotting theoretical scattering curves for assumed values of the bond lengths (assuming a linear symmetric structure) deduce the $C{=}O$ bond length in CO_2 [see Karle and Karle, *J. Chem. Phys.*, **17**: 1052 (1949)].

17. A potential of 100 volts is placed across the plates of a condenser. The area of each plate is 2.4 sq cm, and the distance between the plates is 1 cm.

(a) Calculate the electric field between the plates of the condenser and the force that would be exerted on an electron in this region. What would be the charge density on the condenser plates?

(b) If the condenser is filled with CCl_4, which has $\epsilon = 2.238$, and the charge density on the plates is that in (a), what would be the charge density on the carbon tetrachloride adjacent to the plates? What would be the electric field in a cavity in the CCl_4?

(c) What would be the force exerted on an electron in a cavity in the CCl_4?

Ans. (a) $E_0 = 0.333$ esu/sq cm, $f = 1.6 \times 10^{-10}$ dynes, $\sigma = 0.027$ esu/sq cm;
(c) 0.42×10^{-10} dynes.

18. The maximum voltage that can be applied to dielectric materials, with dielectric constants of about 2.4, is about 10^6 volts/cm. Calculate the energy difference between most favorable and most unfavorable orientations of a molecule with a dipole moment of 1 debye in the dielectric subjected to this applied potential. At 25°C what would be the relative population of the two states? Recognize from this the relative unimportance of applied electric fields in the molecular world.

19. The dielectric constant of liquid CCl_4, whose molecules are tetrahedral and have no permanent dipole moment, is 2.238 at 20°C.

The density of CCl_4 is 1.595 g/cc.

Calculate the molar polarizability P and the polarizability α.

20. The following values have been reported for the dielectric constant of BrF_5 vapor at 1 atm pressure [Rogers, Pruett, Thompson, and Speirs, *J. Am. Chem. Soc.*, **78**: 44 (1956)]:

$T(°K)$	345.6	362.6	374.9	388.9	402.4	417.2	430.8
ϵ	1.006320	1.005824	1.005525	1.005180	1.004910	1.004603	1.004378

(a) Assuming ideal-gas behavior, calculate the molar polarization at each temperature.

(b) Deduce α and μ for BrF_5 from the plot of these data suggested by Eq. (97).

Ans. $\alpha = 8.6 \times 10^{-24}$, $\mu = 1.51$ debyes.

21. The dipole moment of CH_3Cl is 1.86 debyes and of $CHCl_3$ is 1.15 debyes. Both molecules are nearly tetrahedral. Assuming that C—H has a bond moment of 0.4 debye with H positive, calculate the C—Cl bond moment for each compound. The disagreement can be understood in terms of the induced dipoles in the three very polarizable chlorine atoms of $CHCl_3$.

22. The dipole moment of NH_3 is found to be 1.46 debyes, and the angles between two N—H bonds is 107°.

Calculate the NH bond moment.

23. Calculate the per cent ionic character of HF, HCl, HBr, and HI. With these results and the electronegativities of Fig. 9-3, plot per cent ionic character against electronegativity difference of the atoms of the bond. This graph has found much use in supplying per cent ionic-character values.

24. Calculate the ionic character of the five metal halides of Table 10-6 on the basis of point electronic charges separated by the equilibrium bond length. The bond lengths for CsF, CsCl, KF, KCl, and KBr are 2.34, 2.90, 2.55, 2.67, and 2.82, respectively.

25. Compare the frequency of rotation of a representative gas-phase molecule with the frequency of visible light of about 10^{15} cycles/sec. Recognize the implications of this comparison on the ability of a molecule to rotate so as to affect an index-of-refraction measurement.

26. Show that the units ergs per gauss for μ_0 lead to units for χ_M that give force of Eq. (107) in dynes.

27. The ion Co $(NH_3)_6^{3+}$ has been shown from magnetic measurements to have no unpaired electrons, while the ion CoF_6^{3-} has four unpaired electrons. Considering only the effect of unpaired electrons, calculate the change in apparent weight of a 0.1 M solution of salts of these ions in 1-cm-diameter test tubes suspended in a Gouy balance when a magnetic field of 5,000 gauss is turned on.

Ans. For CoF_6^{3-}, 0.0102 g.

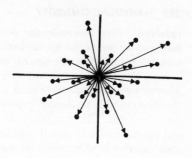

11

The Rates and Mechanisms
of Chemical Reactions

Our study of the molecular world has so far been concerned with only one of the two broad aspects which interest chemists. So far, chemical systems at equilibrium have been treated, and the nature of chemical compounds, which may be reactants or products in a chemical reaction, have been studied. Now the actual process of chemical reactions is investigated, and our attention is focused not only on the reactants and the products, but also on the details of the transformation from one set of chemical species to another. That this aspect has previously been neglected, or avoided, is emphasized by recognizing that the time variable has so far been absent and that it will now play a major role.

The principal experimental approach to the study of the reaction process is through the measurement of the rate with which a reaction proceeds and the dependence of this reaction rate on the concentrations of the reacting species and on the temperature. These factors are grouped together in the term *reaction kinetics*. These results are summarized, for a given reaction, by a *rate equation* which is of the general form

$$\text{Rate} = k(T) \times \text{function of concentration of reagents} \qquad (1)$$

The quantity $k(T)$ is called, as will be made reasonable later, the *rate constant* and, if the term involving the reagent concentrations correctly expresses the rate dependence on concentration, will be a function only of the temperature. Thus the experimental information on the reaction process is summarized in the rate equation by the nature of the concentration function and by the value and temperature dependence of the rate constant.

Previously our knowledge of molecular behavior has been used to give us an understanding of the equilibrium state of a chemical system either directly or through an understanding of the thermodynamic properties of the species involved. Now the molecular details of reactions themselves can be looked into and attempts can be made to deduce detailed pictures of the nature of molecules that are in the process of reacting.

Since any theory of the way in which a reaction proceeds, i.e., of the *mechanism* of a reaction, involves ideas as to how events occur as a function of time, thermodynamics no longer provides commandments to which the theories must conform. Thermodynamics applies directly only to the reactants and the products of a chemical reaction and, as indicated by the absence of the time variable in all previous thermodynamic discussions, is not concerned with the reaction process itself. The prime factor that influences theories of reaction mechanisms are the experimental results summarized by the concentration dependence shown in the rate equation. The present subject, therefore, consists primarily of the experimental study of reaction kinetics and the molecular theories of reaction mechanisms. To this principal study must be added a section dealing with the theories that have been developed to explain the numerical value and temperature dependence found for the rate constant.

It may seem presumptuous, and it is indeed a bold and exciting endeavor, to attempt to learn how, for example, two molecules come together, how the atoms change their positions, and how the electrons shift so that one or two new molecules emerge. Much certainly remains to be learned about such intimate details of molecular life, and the unraveling of the details of the reactions of the molecular world is as fascinating a story as is that already introduced of the molecular world in its equilibrium state.

Just as the previous study of the molecular nature of matter let us more easily understand many of the properties of chemical systems, so also does the study of the molecular details of reactions lead us to a better understanding of chemical reactions. Ideas arising from reaction-mechanism studies are contributing to our classification and understanding of the immense number of individual reactions that occur in organic and inorganic chemistry. It is, in fact, an understanding of reaction mechanisms, rather than of thermodynamics, that leads to most of the qualitative ideas as to what reactions might occur in both organic and inorganic systems of much complexity.

The emphasis on the relation of reaction kinetics to reaction mechanisms should not, however, completely obscure the fact that data on the rate of reactions are often of immediate practical value. It is frequently important to know, for example, under what conditions a particular reaction will proceed rapidly to give a high yield of a product while at the same time the conditions are such that a side reaction that gives an undesirable product is slowed down. Of particular importance, in this regard, is the role of catalysts. The action of catalysts in homogeneous systems will be treated here, but the very important subject of heterogeneous catalysis will be postponed until the phenomenon of adsorption is studied.

It is convenient to divide the present subject into two principal divisions. The first deals with the effect of the concentrations of the reagents on the rate of the reaction and the mechanisms that are suggested to describe the molecular course of the reaction. The second division treats the theories that attempt to explain the data for the absolute rate with which a chemical reaction proceeds for given reagent concentrations and a given temperature; i.e., the theories attempt to derive the numerical value of the rate constants for individual reactions.

RATE EQUATIONS AND REACTION MECHANISMS

11-1. Experimental Approaches. The experimental results for the dependence of the rate of a reaction on the concentrations of the components in the reaction system are summarized in the rate equation. To deduce the form of the function of the concentrations and the species involved, it is necessary to have data for the rate of the reaction, at some fixed temperature, as a function of the concentrations of the reagents. It is usually necessary only to determine the concentration of a reagent, or of a product, at various times, and, as specific examples will later show, these data lead to values for the reaction rate and to the deduction of the rate equation.

For a reaction that is slow relative to the time it takes to remove a sample from the reaction mixture and to perform an analysis, the data from which the rate equation can be deduced can be obtained by any analytical method, physical or chemical, that is applicable to the particular system. When the reaction is a relatively rapid one, the time of sampling and analysis is appreciable and the analytical results are not then easily related to any well-defined reaction time. The two principal types of procedures that are then resorted to consist in "freezing" the reaction system, or a sample from it, or in using some rapid physical measurement that can be made on the reacting system.

The freezing of a reaction implies doing anything that abruptly slows or stops the reaction so that an analytical method that would otherwise be too slow can be used. One procedure is rapidly to cool a sample and thereby slow the reaction. In other cases one can quickly dilute a sample of the reaction system. Reactions which proceed rapidly only in the presence of a catalyst can be slowed down by the removal of the catalyst. An often-encountered example is an acid catalyzed reaction that is frozen by dilution or neutralization of the acid.

Frequently more convenient than the withdrawal and analysis of samples is the use of some physical measurement which can be made on the reaction mixture and from which the concentrations of a reactant or a product can be deduced. Any physical property can be made use of as long as the property changes as the reaction mixture changes from reactants to products. Thus one might use the pressure change in a gaseous reaction proceeding in a constant-volume system, or the volume change in a constant-pressure system, or the refractive-index change that accompanies many solution reactions, or the optical rotation when the reactants or products are optically active, and so forth.

More satisfactory physical properties, however, are those that are more definitely related to a reactant or a product. One species in the reaction system, for example, may absorb radiation at a particular wavelength in the infrared, visible, or ultraviolet regions, and the amount of absorption at that wavelength can be used as a measure of the concentration of that species. Measurements of such quantities are less susceptible to interference from side reactions than are the physical properties previously listed.

The study of very fast reactions has become one of the most interesting aspects of reaction kinetics. The procedure of mixing the reagents and then measuring some physical property is limited, if a suitably rapid physical method is used, by the time required for the mixing process itself. Much progress has been made by using a flow system in which the two reagents flow together in a T arrangement and a physical property, such as electrical conductivity or ultraviolet absorption, is measured at various positions along the united stream. In this way reactions that proceed appreciably in times as short as $\frac{1}{100}$ sec can be studied.

Even more rapid reactions, however, interest the chemist. The reaction of an acid and a base, for example, the combination of H^+ and OH^-, is often said to be instantaneous. A number of methods are being developed for studying such fast reactions. Some of these, known as *relaxation methods*, depend upon the procedure of disturbing a reaction system from equilibrium, as by the sudden imposition of an electric field or a high pressure, and determining the time required for the system to relax, i.e., return to its original state. It appears that reactions that occur almost as rapidly as molecules vibrate, i.e., in times down to 10^{-13} sec, are not beyond the realm in which the modern kineticist can work.

The way in which the data obtained from chemical or physical measurements on a reacting system at various time intervals are used to deduce the rate of the reaction and rate equation for the reaction will be illustrated by specific examples in Secs. 11-5 to 11-8.

The information provided by a rate equation for a reaction is seldom sufficient to lead to the postulation of a single mechanism and the ruling out of other possible mechanisms. Frequently additional experimental results can be brought to bear. For example, the course of a reaction might be clarified if one of the hydrogen atoms that is suspected of being involved in the reaction of an organic molecule is replaced by a deuterium atom. Analysis of the product molecule will then show whether the reaction does, in fact, proceed by a mechanism that changes the position of that particular hydrogen atom.

Another technique that has proved helpful in both organic and inorganic reactions depends on the use of an optically active reagent and the determination of the optical activity of the product. The information that can be gained is illustrated by the three mechanisms that might be considered for the displacement of a group b from an optically active carbon atom by an incoming group a. These three paths can be depicted as

$$(a) \qquad a + \underset{R_2}{\overset{R_1}{\underset{|}{C}}} - b \rightarrow \left[a \cdots \underset{R_2}{\overset{R_1}{\underset{|}{C}}} \cdots b \right] + a - \underset{R_2}{\overset{R_1}{C}} + b$$

Inversion of configuration

(b)

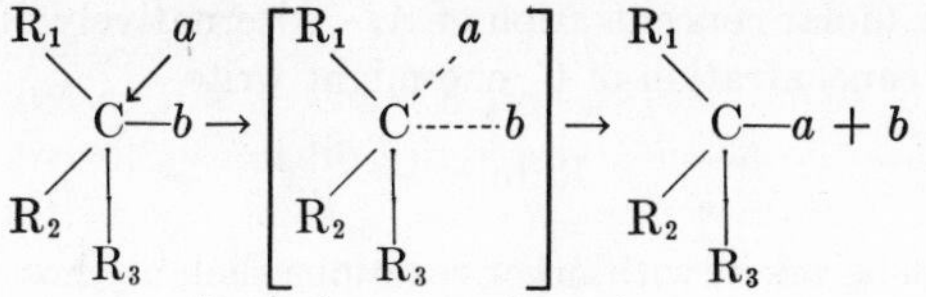

Retention of configuration

(c)

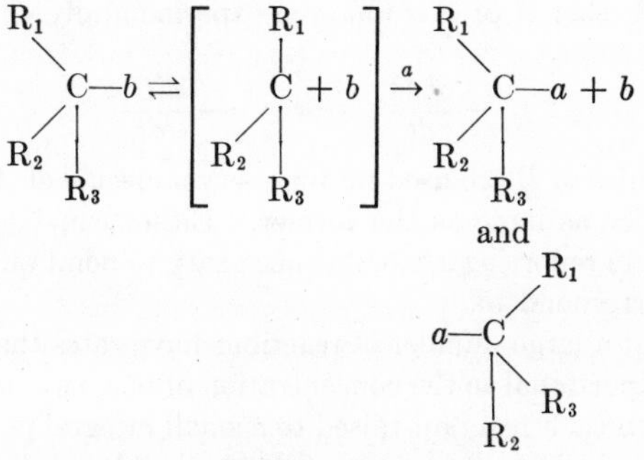

and

Racemization

Thus the optical nature of the product would allow the nature of the displacement step to be deduced.

It is necessary to make use of all such information, as well as the data on the rate of the reaction, in order to deduce, as we shall see, the details of the reaction process.

11-2. Introduction to Rate Equations and Reaction Orders. The rate of a reaction is usually expressed in terms of the decrease in the amount of one of the reagents that occurs in some time interval. Alternatively, the increase in the amount of a product can be used. If the reaction system is one of constant, or near-constant, volume, the change in the amount of reagent will correspond to a change in the concentration of that reagent. For liquid systems one usually states the rate of a reaction in terms of the rate of change of the molar concentration of a reagent. For constant-volume gaseous systems it is generally more convenient to use the partial pressure of the reagent which, for ideal gases, is seen from $P = (n/V)RT$ to be proportional to a concentration term. The time units that enter into the statement of the rate of a reaction may be seconds, minutes, hours, and so forth.

The rate of a reaction is always considered to be a positive quantity. Thus, for the reaction

$$A + B \rightarrow C + D \tag{2}$$

the rate, which will be a function of the concentrations and temperature, can be given in terms of the decrease in A by writing

$$\text{Rate} = -\frac{d[A]}{dt} \tag{3}$$

where $[A]$ is the molar concentration of A. Alternatively, if one measures the increase in the concentration of C, one might write

$$\text{Rate} = +\frac{d[C]}{dt} \qquad (4)$$

Some care must be taken with other reactions such as those of the type

$$A + 2B \rightarrow \text{products} \qquad (5)$$

Depending on whether A or B is followed experimentally, one might write the rate as

$$-\frac{d[A]}{dt} \quad \text{or} \quad -\frac{d[B]}{dt} \qquad (6)$$

Since two molecules of B are used up for every molecule of A, the latter derivative will be twice as large as the former. Either can be called the rate of the reaction, but in reporting a rate it is necessary to point out which derivative the rate data correspond to.

It is found that a large number of reactions have rates that, at a given temperature, are proportional to the concentration of one, two, or possibly three of the reactants with each reactant raised to a small integral power. If reactions are considered in which A, B, and C represent possible reactants, the rate equations for reactions with such concentration dependence would be of the form

$$\text{Rate} = k[A] \qquad \qquad \text{1st order} \qquad (7)$$
$$\text{Rate} = k[A]^2 \text{ or } k[A][B] \qquad \text{2d order} \qquad (8)$$
$$\text{Rate} = k[A]^3 \text{ or } k[A]^2[B] \text{ or } k[A][B][C] \qquad \text{3d order} \qquad (9)$$

Reactions that proceed according to such simple rate equations are said to be reactions of the first, second, or third order as indicated. As we shall see, not all reactions have such simple rate laws. Some involve concentrations raised to nonintegral powers, while others consist of more elaborate algebraic expressions. There are, however, enough reactions that, at least under certain conditions, are simple first, second, or third order to make the idea of the order of a reaction useful.

It should be pointed out immediately that the rate law has no necessary relation to the form of the equation for the over-all reaction. The frequently given, simplified derivation for the form of the equilibrium-constant expression that depends on equating the rate of the forward reaction to the rate of the reverse reaction, each written in terms of the over-all equation, is a formalism that should not be taken as implying anything about the form of the actual rate equations.

The units of the rate constants for first-, second-, and third-order reactions can be deduced from the form of Eqs. (7) to (9) and the fact that the rate is expressed in the form $-d[A]/dt$. For a first-order reaction, therefore, the rate constant has the units of the reciprocal of time, i.e., reciprocal seconds, reciprocal minutes, and so forth, and is independent of the concentration units. The second-order rate constant, on the other hand, has units such as (moles per liter)$^{-1}$ second^{-1}, or liters per mole second. The units of the rate constants for more complicated rate equations must be determined by inspection of the experimentally deduced rate equation.

Since rate constants always involve reciprocal seconds, reciprocal minutes, and so forth, a quick and approximate idea of how fast a reaction proceeds can be obtained from a reported rate constant by taking the reciprocal of the rate constant. As the units indicate, this gives a quantity that can be interpreted as the time required for the reaction to proceed appreciably when the reagents have about unit concentrations. A more quantitative interpretation will be given when individual reactions are taken up.

It is very important to realize that the order of a reaction and the rate equation are summaries of experimental results. Later, when attempts are made to devise mechanisms that are consistent with the rate equations, it will be necessary to keep in mind the fact that mechanisms are theoretical but that the rate equation is an experimental result.

To this general introduction of the treatment that is applied to the experimental data of reaction kinetics is now added a similar introductory discussion of the new features that appear when mechanisms are devised to explain the molecular transformations that correspond to a chemical reaction.

11-3. Introduction to Reaction Mechanisms. The physical chemist's role in reaction kinetics has often been considered to end when the experimental measurements of the rate of reaction have been obtained and a rate equation has been formulated. For such efforts to be rewarding, however, it is necessary to continue to the exciting phase of theorizing on the molecular behavior that leads to the observed results. In this way one is led to consider reaction mechanisms. Since the study of the details of reaction processes could lead to an investigation of all organic and inorganic chemistry, it is necessary that only a few representative reactions be considered and that the approach to an understanding of chemical reactions that comes from reaction kinetics be indicated. The qualitative and chemical considerations of this section will later be combined with the experimental rate data for specific reactions to show the power of the kinetic approach for the understanding of chemical reactions.

All the features of some reactions can be accounted for by a mechanism that consists of the single step of a coming together of all the reactant molecules, a rearrangement of the atoms and electrons in the moment of impact, and the flying apart of product molecules. Such a mechanism is said to involve a *concerted* process.

In most reactions, however, such a concerted process would require a complicated and improbable combination of changes to get from reagents to products. It is then more satisfactory to attempt to explain the reaction as proceeding by means of a sequence of steps, each step consisting of simple atomic or electronic moves. It will be seen that such sequences of steps are often needed to explain the observed rate equation.

The idea of a stepwise reaction leads one to consider the *chemical intermediates* which are formed from the reactants in the first step and which finally react in some way to give the products of the reaction. On the basis of the type of intermediate that is postulated, or, in a few cases, demonstrated, reactions can be classified as *free-radical reactions* or as *ionic, or polar, reactions*.

Gas reactions appear generally to involve free-radical intermediates. In addition, a few important solution reactions in nonpolar solvents proceed by such a mechanism, as do most of those reactions which are initiated by light, i.e., photochemical reactions. These reactions are characterized by the fact that the postulated intermediate species, as well as the reactants and the products, are electrically neutral and that some of the intermediates have an odd, or unpaired, electron; i.e., they are free radicals.

Ionic reactions, on the other hand, include the bulk of reactions, both organic and inorganic, that occur in solution. They are characterized by charged, or ionic, intermediates. Some of these charged species may be the familiar ions such as are encountered in aqueous solutions, but many of the postulated species are never observed directly. The mechanisms postulated for most organic reactions, for example, will involve ionic species that are never observed as reactants or products.

A brief introduction to some of the suggestions as to the ways in which these two types of intermediates arise and to the ways in which they appear to react to give product molecules will provide a background against which specific reaction mechanisms can later be studied.

The Formation of Free Radicals. A number of methods are available that demonstrate the presence of free radicals as intermediates in gas-phase reactions. The first such demonstration was performed by Paneth in 1929, using an apparatus shown schematically in Fig. 11-1. The original experiment consisted in passing a stream of the inert carrier gas, nitrogen, saturated with lead tetramethyl vapor, through a tube, a section of which was kept at about 450°C by means of an external furnace. About 20 cm farther along the tube a lead film, or mirror, had been previously deposited on the inside of the tube. As the experiment proceeded, it was found that metallic lead was deposited in the form of a mirror in the 450°C section of the tube and that at the same time the previously deposited mirror was gradually removed. The exit gas stream had

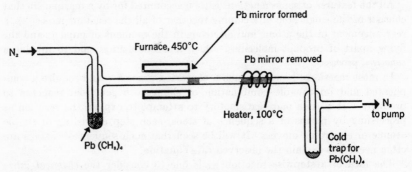

Fig. 11-1. Paneth experiment on the pyrolysis of $Pb(CH_3)_4$ to demonstrate the formation of methyl free radicals.

the same composition as did the entering stream.   The explanation given by
Paneth was that in the high-temperature section a decomposition proceeded
according to the equation

$$Pb(CH_3)_4 \rightarrow Pb + 4(\cdot CH_3)$$

and that the methyl free radicals survived without further reaction long enough
to be swept down the tube to the second mirror, where, at the lower temperature, they could react with the metallic lead to give the final, volatile product
$Pb(CH_3)_4$.   The experiment is not understandable on the basis of an initial
decomposition that leads to the formation of ionic species.

Later experiments of a similar type showed that many organic vapors could
be passed through a heated tube and that the exit vapor was capable of removing a previously deposited lead mirror.   Such experiments lead to the general
conclusion that heating a vapor to decomposition, i.e., gas-phase *pyrolysis*,
leads initially to the formation of free radicals which react further to give the
final products.

Another chemical method that uses a flow technique to demonstrate the
formation of free radicals was developed by Polanyi.   The apparatus is
sketched in Fig. 11-2.   In chamber A, in which sodium vapor and an alkyl
halide, such as methyl chloride, are mixed, NaCl is deposited in amounts that
account for all the incoming chlorine atoms.   It follows that the $\cdot CH_3$ free
radicals, which remain from the reaction of Na and CH_3Cl, must emerge from
the nozzle of compartment A.   This is confirmed by the formation of CH_3I in
chamber B when iodine vapor is present.   The reactions are

$$CH_3Cl + Na\cdot \rightarrow NaCl + \cdot CH_3 \qquad \text{in } A$$
$$\cdot CH_3 + I_2 \rightarrow CH_3I + I\cdot \qquad \text{in } B$$
$$2I\cdot \xrightarrow{\text{at surface}} I_2$$

The iodine molecules, having a low dissociation energy, are easily broken by
the active methyl free radicals.   They are said to act as *free-radical traps*.   It
should be pointed out that in both the experiments of Paneth and Polanyi the
partial pressure of the reagents and the inert carrier gas must be controlled to
prevent the free radicals from entering into reactions other than those mentioned here.

One should be reminded that not all free radicals are as reactive and elusive
as these gas-phase intermediates.   Thus, as mentioned in our earlier magnetic
studies, hexaphenyl ethane dissociates in solution even at room temperature
to give a large concentration of free radicals.

It is clear therefore that the ease of formation of free radicals varies greatly

Fig. 11-2. Schematic arrangement
of the Polanyi apparatus for the
demonstration of free radicals.

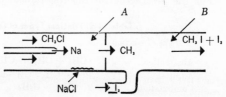

Table 11-1. Energies for Homolytic Bond Cleavage
(Kcal/mole)

C_6H_5—CH_3	89	C_6H_5—H	102
H_3C—CH_3	84	$C_6H_5CH_2$—H	77
$C_6H_5CH_2$—CH_3	63	$H_3\overset{.}{C}$—H	102
$C_6H_5CH_2$—$CH_2C_6H_5$	47	$H_2\overset{..}{C}$—H	(92)
$(C_6H_5)_3C$—$C(C_6H_5)_3$	11 (in soln)	$H\overset{..}{C}$—H	88
		$\cdot\overset{..}{\underset{.}{C}}$—H	80

with the chemical nature of the reagent. Some quantitative data which bear this out are the dissociation energies for homolytic bond cleavage, i.e., for the breaking of bonds so that the bonding pair of electrons is divided equally between the two fragments, listed in Table 11-1.

The study of photochemistry will be dealt with later in the chapter, but included in our discussion of the formation of free radicals should be mention of the fact that the absorption of radiant energy by a molecule leads, for sufficiently high-energy quanta, to the homolytic cleavage of a bond of the absorbing molecule. It follows that *photolysis*, like pyrolysis, leads to free-radical-type intermediates.

Reactions of Free Radicals. The final products that emerge from a free-radical reaction depend on the way in which the free-radical intermediates react and produce stable molecules. Several of the types of reactions most frequently attributed to free radicals are listed in Table 11-2. The first two are steps that do not eliminate the free-radical center and do not therefore give directly the final products but constitute only steps in that direction. The abstraction step can lead to *chain reactions*, as in the system of H_2 and Cl_2, that is,

$$H\cdot + Cl_2 \rightarrow HCl + Cl\cdot$$
$$Cl\cdot + H_2 \rightarrow HCl + H\cdot$$
$$H\cdot + Cl_2 \rightarrow \text{etc.}$$

The addition step can lead to *polymerization* reactions, as in the formation of polyethylene,

$$R\cdot + CH_2{=}CH_2 \rightarrow R{-}CH_2{-}\overset{.}{C}H_2$$
$$R{-}CH_2{-}\overset{.}{C}H_2 + CH_2{=}CH_2 \rightarrow R{-}CH_2CH_2{-}CH_2{-}\overset{.}{C}H_2$$
$$R{-}CH_2CH_2CH_2\overset{.}{C}H_2 + CH_2{=}CH_2 \rightarrow \text{etc.}$$

For the destruction of the free-radical centers, which must occur to give

Table 11-2. Principal Types of Free-radical Reactions

Type of reaction	*Example*
Abstraction..........	$\cdot CH_3 + CH_3CH_2CH_2CH_3 \rightarrow CH_4 + CH_3\overset{.}{C}HCH_2CH_3$
Addition............	$Br\cdot + CH_2{=}CH{-}R \rightarrow BrCH_2{-}\overset{.}{C}H{-}R$
Combination........	$2(\cdot CH_3) \rightarrow C_2H_6$

the final product, there must be a radical recombination.   While a reaction between two highly active species might be expected to proceed easily and rapidly, one must recognize that, for example, two hydrogen atoms coming together will produce something more than 103 kcal of energy per mole and that, unless this energy is removed, it will be enough to redissociate the molecule.   For radical recombination to occur, it is necessary therefore to have either a *third body*, usually the wall of the container, present or to be dealing with large molecules so that the many degrees of freedom can spread out the energy evolved in the bond formation.

Table 11-3. Some Reactions in Which Carbonium Ions and Carbanions Are Postulated as Intermediates

Substitution reactions

Nucleophilic.. Reaction $HO^- + (CH_3)_3CCl \rightarrow HOC(CH_3)_3 + Cl^-$
Mechanism $(CH_3)_3CCl \rightleftharpoons (CH_3)_3C^+ + Cl^-$
$(CH_3)_3C^+ + OH^- \rightarrow (CH_3)_3COH$

Electrophilic.. Reaction

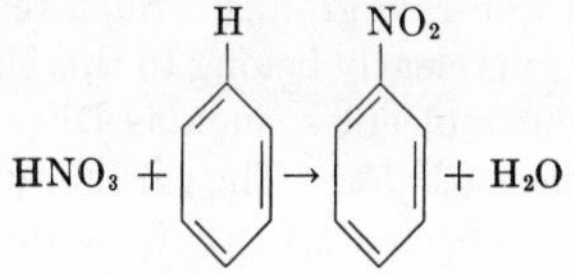

Mechanism step

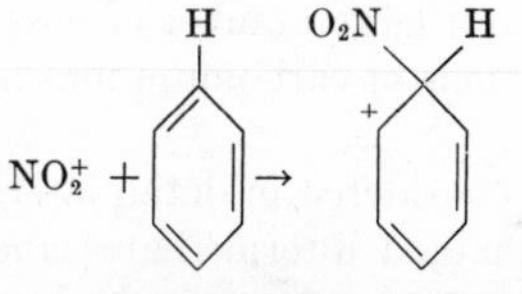

Addition reactions

Nucleophilic.. Reaction $H_3N: + CH_2{=}CH{-}\overset{\overset{O}{\|}}{C}{-}OR \rightarrow H_2NCH_2CH_2COOR$

Mechanism $H_3N: + CH_2{=}CH{-}\overset{\overset{O}{\|}}{C}{-}OR \rightarrow H_3\overset{+}{N}{-}CH_2{-}\overset{\cdot\cdot}{\underset{-}{C}H}{-}\overset{\overset{O}{\|}}{C}{-}OR$

Electrophilic . Reaction $HCl + CH_2{=}CH_2 \rightarrow CH_3{-}CH_2Cl$

Mechanism $H^+ + CH_2{=}CH_2 \rightarrow CH_3{-}\overset{+}{C}H_2$

$CH_3\overset{+}{C}H_2 + Cl^- \rightarrow CH_3{-}CH_2Cl$

Elimination reactions

Reaction $CH_3\overset{\overset{Br}{|}}{C}H{-}CH_3 + HO^- \rightarrow CH_3{-}CH{=}CH_2 + H_2O + Br^-$

Mechanism step $CH_3\overset{\overset{Br}{|}}{C}H{-}CH_3 + HO^- \rightarrow CH_3{-}\overset{\overset{Br}{|}}{C}H{-}\overset{\cdot\cdot}{\underset{-}{C}}H_2 + H_2O$

Formation of Ionic Intermediates. Only those ionic species, both inorganic and organic, that occur as intermediates need be dealt with here; the more general subject of behavior of ionic systems is treated in later chapters. In organic systems the most important new species that are postulated are those in which a positive or negative charge resides on a carbon atom. Positive ions of this type are called *carbonium ions,* and negative ions are called *carbanions.* A knowledge of the conditions of the formation and of the reactions of these intermediates is of great value, not only in understanding reaction kinetics, but also in understanding much of organic chemistry itself.

A few of the more common types of reactions in which carbonium ions and carbanions are postulated to occur as intermediates are listed in Table 11-3.

In discussing reactions which form these intermediates, or reactions of these intermediates, it is convenient to distinguish two classes of reagents. One class consists of those reagents which have a free pair of electrons that can be used to bind another group or nucleus. These reagents are said to be *nucleophilic.* All carbanions fall in this class, as do stable molecules such as amines. The second class consists of reagents that are lacking electrons and that react by combining with electron-rich groups. Such reagents are said to be *electrophilic.* All carbonium ions clearly belong to this class, as also do the hydrogen-ion and electron-deficient molecules, such as BF_3.

Reactions of Ionic Intermediates. The carbonium ions and carbanions, being unstable intermediates, must react further, in any complete reaction, to give the final products. Again a large number of possibilities exist, but a few representative types of reactions of carbonium ions and carbanions are shown in Table 11-4.

Some reactions will be considered in detail later and these will further illustrate the formation of charged intermediates and their further reactions to final products.

Concerted Reactions. Some reactions, as has been mentioned, do not occur by the stepwise formation and further reaction of intermediates but appear to proceed by a single concerted process. These reactions do not involve either free-radical or ionic intermediates. Some concerted reactions, however, can be classified along with ionic, or polar, reactions. Two important reactions of this type are *displacement reactions* and *elimination reactions.*

The first can be illustrated by the example of the displacement of the bromide of an alkyl bromide by an amine.

$$R_3N: + CH_3Br \rightarrow \left[R_3\overset{\delta+}{N}\mathrel{-\!-\!-\!-\!-}\underset{\underset{H}{\overset{\displaystyle H}{|}}}{\overset{\displaystyle H}{\underset{|}{C}}}\mathrel{-\!-\!-\!-\!-}\overset{\delta-}{Br} \right]$$

$$\rightarrow R_3N^+\!\!-\!\!\overset{\displaystyle H}{\underset{\displaystyle H}{C}}\!\!-\!\!H + Br^-$$

Table 11-4. Some Reactions of Carbonium and Carbanion Intermediates

---

Rearrangements (to lead to a different intermediate)

$$CH_3CH_2\overset{+}{C}HCH_3 \rightarrow \left[\begin{array}{c} CH_3 \\ C\overset{/}{H}_2-\overset{+}{C}H-CH_3 \end{array}\right] \rightarrow \begin{array}{c} CH_3 \\ \overset{|}{\overset{+}{C}H_2-CH-CH_3} \end{array}$$

$$CH_3CH_2\overset{+}{C}HCH_3 \rightarrow CH_3CH_2CH_2\overset{+}{C}H_2$$

Reactions to give stable products

Addition of an ionic species:

$$(CH_3)_3C^+ + OH^- \rightarrow (CH_3)_3COH$$

$$H_3\overset{+}{N}CH_2\overset{..}{\overset{-}{C}}H-COOR \rightarrow \left[\begin{array}{c} H\frown \\ H_2N\overset{|}{\overset{+}{—}}CH_2-\overset{..}{\overset{-}{C}}H-COOR \end{array}\right] \rightarrow H_2N-CH_2CH_2COOR$$

Elimination of an ionic species:

$$\overset{Br}{\underset{|}{CH_3-}}\overset{..}{\overset{|}{C}}H-\overset{..}{\overset{-}{C}}H_2 \rightarrow \left[CH_3-\overset{Br}{\overset{|}{C}}H-\overset{..}{\overset{-}{C}}H_2\right] \rightarrow CH_3-CH{=}CH_2 + Br^-$$

The postulated mechanism consists of the formation of the N—C bond and the simultaneous breaking of the C—Br bond. The intermediate is depicted as the reaction species when this concerted process is partly complete. Since such displacement reactions can be said to result from the nucleophilic character of the attacking amine group and since two species must collide or come together for the reaction to occur in this single step, the reaction can be said to be a substitution, that is nucleophilic and second-order, abbreviated as S_N2.

A representative concerted elimination reaction is the removal of HBr when an alkyl halide is placed in alkali media. The postulated mechanism is

$$HO^- + H-\overset{|}{C}-\overset{|}{C}-Br \rightarrow \left[H-\overset{\delta^-}{O}---H---\overset{|}{C}---\overset{|}{C}---\overset{\delta^-}{Br} \right]$$

$$\rightarrow HOH + \overset{\diagdown}{\underset{\diagup}{C}}{=}\overset{\diagup}{\underset{\diagdown}{C}} + Br^-$$

in which the net effect is the removal of HBr. Since this type of reaction is an elimination reaction and it is again expected to be second-order, it is sometimes designated as an $E2$ reaction.

Concerted reactions also are postulated for nonpolar systems and belong with the previous classification of free-radical reactions. It will later be seen that the reaction of H_2 and I_2 in the gas phase to form 2HI appears to go by the path

$$H_2 + I_2 \rightarrow \begin{bmatrix} H\!\!-\!\!H & H\cdots H \\ \vdots & \vdots & \rightarrow & | & | \\ I\!\!-\!\!I & I\cdots I \end{bmatrix} \rightarrow 2HI$$

Such a reaction is an example of the class known, for obvious reasons, as *four-center reactions*.

11-4. The Relation between the Rate Equation and the Reaction Mechanism.
While it is apparent that both experimental determinations of reaction rates
and theoretical ideas about the mechanism of a reaction treat aspects of the
reaction process, it has not yet been made clear how the reaction rate and the
reaction mechanism are related. The basic idea can be reached by considering
a simple gas-phase reaction in which the mechanism is, by some means, known
to depend on the coming together of two molecules of A to give directly
the final product B. The kinetic-theory treatment of Chap. 2 showed that
for ideal gases the number of binary collisions in a unit volume per unit time is
proportional to the square of the pressure of the gas. The rate equation for
the reaction with the simple mechanism $2A \rightarrow B$ would, therefore, be expected
to show that the rate was proportional to P_A^2 or to $[A]^2$; that is, the reaction
would be second-order in A.

A development to be given in Sec. 11-13 will show that for a gas mixture of
components A and B the number of collisions per unit volume per unit time
between a molecule of A and one of B is proportional to the product $P_A P_B$ or to
$[A][B]$. A rate law involving such a concentration term could, therefore, be
explained by a mechanism in which one molecule of A came together with one
of B to give immediately the final product.

Ideas such as these are carried over to liquid systems. For dilute solutions
of noninteracting components this extension *seems* reasonable. One assumes
that the concentration terms of the rate law can be used, just as can the pressure terms in the simple gas-phase example, to deduce the molecule species that
must collide, or come together, for the reaction to occur.

The basis for the use of kinetic studies in the deduction of mechanisms can
be stated as follows: *The rate of a single reaction step is proportional to the
product of the concentrations of the species that occur as reactants in that step.*

It is necessary to emphasize that this idea is directly applicable only to a
single reaction step. One can appreciate, even before a detailed treatment is
encountered, that, if a reaction proceeds by a series of individual steps and if
some or all of these steps control the rate, the rate of the over-all reaction will
not necessarily be simply related to any concentration terms. A simplification occurs in many stepwise reactions. If the initial step that forms intermediates is slow relative to all the succeeding steps, this first step is said to be
rate-determining. If the initial step, for example, is the relatively slow reaction

$$A + B \rightarrow [AB]$$

where $[AB]$ is an intermediate that, as soon as it is formed, quickly passes
through a series of steps to give the final product, the rate of the over-all reaction will be just that of the initial rate-determining step. This mechanism

therefore would be consistent with a rate equation involving the concentration product $[A][B]$.

For stepwise reactions in which the simplification of one slow step followed by fast steps cannot be expected, the relation of the mechanism to the rate equation is more complicated, as specific examples will show.

With these background sections we are now in a position to investigate, for specific reactions, the observed rate data and the postulated mechanisms.

11-5. First-order Reactions. A first-order reaction is defined as one for which, at a given temperature, the rate of the reaction depends only on the first power of the concentration of a single reacting species. If the concentration of this species is represented by c (for solutions the units of moles per liter are ordinarily used) and if the volume of the system remains essentially constant during the course of the reaction, the first-order rate law can be written as

$$- \frac{dc}{dt} = kc \tag{10}$$

The rate constant k is then a positive quantity and has the units of the reciprocal of time.

The experimental results obtained in a study of the rate of a reaction are usually values of c, or some quantity related to c, at various times. Such data can best be compared with the integrated form of the first-order rate law. If the initial concentration, at time $t = 0$, is c_0 and if at some later time t the concentration has fallen to c, the integration gives

$$- \int_{c_0}^{c} \frac{dc}{c} = k \int_{0}^{t} dt$$

and

$$- \ln \frac{c}{c_0} = \ln \frac{c_0}{c} = kt$$

or

$$\log \frac{c_0}{c} = \frac{k}{2.303} t \tag{11}$$

A sometimes more convenient form is

$$\log c = - \frac{k}{2.303} t + \log c_0 \tag{12}$$

A reaction can, therefore, be said to be a first-order reaction if a plot of $\log (c_0/c)$, or of $\log c$, against t gives a straight line. If a straight line is obtained, the slope of the line can be used to give the value of the rate constant k. An alternative to this graphical procedure is the calculation of a value of k from the individual measurements of c at the various times t, from Eq. (11), for example. The reaction is classified as first-order if all the data lead to essentially the same values for k, that is, if Eq. (11) is satisfied with k a constant.

These equations can be illustrated by a reaction which is found to be first-order, under certain conditions, and whose mechanism is of some interest. The conversion of *tert*-butyl bromide to *tert*-butyl alcohol in a solvent containing 90 per cent acetone and 10 per cent, that is, 5 M, water has been studied by Bateman, Hughes, and Ingold. The over-all reaction is

$$(CH_3)_3CBr + H_2O \rightarrow (CH_3)_3COH + HBr$$

and is slow enough so that its progress can be followed by the titration of samples for their HBr content. Some of the data that were obtained are shown in Table 11-5. Figure 11-3 shows the concentration of the *tert*-butyl bromide plotted against time and also the plot of the logarithm of these concentrations versus time. The linearity of this second plot shows that, in this water-acetone system, the reaction follows first order kinetics. The rate equation for the reaction is, therefore,

$$- \frac{d[(CH_3)_3CBr]}{dt} = k[(CH_3)_3CBr]$$

and the slope of the line of Fig. 11-3 leads to a value for k of 1.4×10^{-5} sec^{-1}.

As is frequently the case, the rate equation is informative but, by itself, does not rule out all but one of the reasonable mechanisms. In this example, the concentration of water is large and almost constant throughout the course of the reaction. Even if water molecules were involved in the rate-determining step, the water concentration would not show up in the rate equation but would be one of the constant factors that are contained in the rate-constant term. If, in fact, the water of the solvent should enter into the *tert*-butyl bromide displacement reaction, the reaction would be said to be *pseudo-first-order*.

Two reasonable mechanisms can be written for this reaction. If the solvent

Table 11-5. The Concentration of *tert*-Butyl Bromide as a Function of Time for the Reaction $(CH_3)_3CBr + H_2O \rightarrow (CH_3)_3COH + HBr$ in a 10 Per Cent Water–90 Per Cent Acetone Solvent*

At 25°C		At 50°C	
Time (hr)	Conc. of $(CH_3)_3CBr$ (moles/liter)	Time (min)	Conc. of $(CH_3)_3CBr$ (moles/liter)
0	0.1039	0	0.1056
3.15	0.0896	9	0.0961
4.10	0.0859	18	0.0856
6.20	0.0776	27	0.0767
8.20	0.0701	40	0.0645
10.0	0.0639	54	0.0536
13.5	0.0529	72	0.0432
18.3	0.0353	105	0.0270
26.0	0.0270	135	0.0174
30.8	0.0207	180	0.0089
37.3	0.0142		
43.8	0.0101		

* From the data of L. C. Bateman, E. D. Hughes, and C. K. Ingold, *J. Chem. Soc.*, p. 960 (1940).

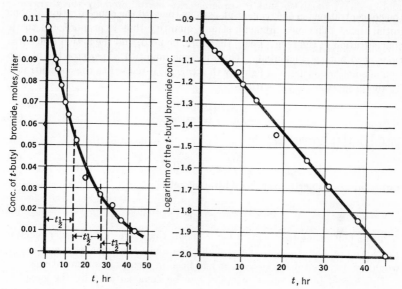

Fig. 11-3. Graphical representation of the 25°C rate data of Table 11-5, showing that, for the conditions used, the reaction $(CH_3)_3CBr + H_2O \rightarrow (CH_3)_3COH + HBr$ is first-order with respect to $(CH_3)_3CBr$. The rate constant is found to be 1.4×10^{-5} sec^{-1} and the half-live 0.42×10^5 sec, or 12 hr.

does not play a role, one might postulate the steps

$$(CH_3)_3CBr \rightarrow (CH_3)_3C^+ + Br^- \qquad \text{slow and rate-determining}$$
$$(CH_3)_3C^+ + :OH_2 \rightarrow (CH_3)_3C-O^+H_2 \qquad \text{fast}$$

$$(CH_3)_3C-\overset{+}{O}H_2 \rightarrow (CH_3)_3COH + H^+ \qquad \text{fast}$$

On the other hand, a concerted S_N2 displacement can be written if the reaction is pseudo-first-order.   Thus

$$H_2O: + \underset{CH_3}{\overset{CH_3}{C}}-Br \rightarrow \left[H_2O^{\delta+} \cdots \cdots \underset{CH_3}{\overset{CH_3}{C}} \cdots \cdots Br^{\delta-} \right] \rightarrow H_2\overset{+}{O}-C(CH_3)_3 + Br^-$$

slow and rate-determining

$$(CH_3)_3C-\overset{+}{O}H_2 \rightarrow (CH_3)_3COH + H^+ \qquad \text{fast}$$

Additional evidence must be brought to bear to decide between these two mechanisms—and any others that are proposed.   The original workers were, in fact, led to the first, or carbonium-ion, mechanism.

It is characteristic of first-order reactions that, as Eq. (11) shows, all that need be measured to see whether or not a reaction is first-order is the ratio of the concentrations of the reagent at various times to the concentration at some initial time. The measurement of any quantity that is proportional to the concentration of the reagent can, therefore, be used, and the actual concentrations need not be calculated. Thus, if some quantity α, perhaps the absorption of some wavelength of light by the reagent, is related to the concentration by the proportionality equations

$$c = (\text{const})\alpha$$

and
$$c_0 = (\text{const})\alpha_0 \tag{13}$$

then Eq. (11) becomes

$$\log \frac{\alpha_0}{\alpha} = \frac{k}{2.303} t \tag{14}$$

From this, or directly from Eq. (12), one gets

$$\log \alpha = -\frac{k}{2.303} t + \log \alpha_0 \tag{15}$$

A linear plot of $\log (\alpha_0/\alpha)$ or of $\log \alpha$ versus t indicates a first-order reaction. Furthermore, the slope of the straight line gives the same rate constant as would be obtained if the treatment had been in terms of concentrations.

This aspect of first-order reactions can be demonstrated by the gas-phase thermal decomposition of di-*tert*-butyl peroxide, which, in a reaction vessel packed with glass wool, proceeds predominantly according to the over-all

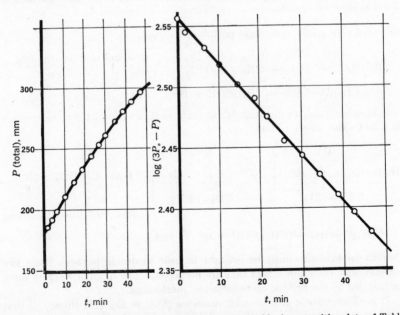

Fig. 11-4. Graphical representation of the *tert*-butyl peroxide decomposition data of Table 11-6 at 147.2°C. The first-order rate constant is 1.43×10^{-4} sec^{-1}.

reaction

$$(CH_3)_3C-O-O-C(CH_3)_3 \rightarrow 2CH_3-\overset{\overset{\displaystyle O}{\|}}{C}-CH_3 + CH_3CH_3$$

In a constant-volume system the reaction proceeds with a continual increase in pressure due to the occurrence of 3 moles of gaseous products compared with 1 mole of gaseous reactant.   If the initial pressure of the di-*tert*-butyl peroxide in some experiment is P_0, the final pressure, when the reaction is complete, will be $3P_0$.   A net pressure increase of $2P_0$ occurs, therefore, for the complete reaction.   The increase in pressure that occurs from any time t until the end of the reaction is proportional to the amount of di-*tert*-butyl peroxide existing, i.e., that has not yet reacted, at time t.   If the pressure of the system at time t is P, the proportionalities that can be set up are

$$C_0 \propto (P_{\text{final}} - P_0) = 3P_0 - P_0 = 2P_0$$
$$\text{and} \qquad C \propto (P_{\text{final}} - P) = 3P_0 - P \qquad (16)$$

where C_0 and C are the concentrations of di-*tert*-butyl peroxide at time 0 and t. The plot that tests whether or not the reaction is first-order can be based on Eq. (15), which in this case becomes

$$\log (3P_0 - P) = -\frac{k}{2.303} t + \log 2P_0 \qquad (17)$$

and is seen to be a plot of $\log (3P_0 - P)$ versus t.   Figure 11-4 indicates that

Table 11-6. The Total Pressure of the Gas-phase System in Which Di-*tert*-butyl Peroxide Is Decomposing, Predominantly by the Reaction

$$(CH_3)_3C-O-O-C(CH_3)_3 \rightarrow 2(CH_3-\overset{\overset{\displaystyle O}{\|}}{C}-CH_3) + C_2H_6 \dagger$$

147.2°C		154.9°C	
Time (min)	Total pressure (mm)	Time (min)	Total pressure (mm)
0	179.5	0	169.3
2	187.4	2	183.1
6	198.6	3	189.2
10	210.5	5	201.1
14	221.2	6	207.1
18	231.9	8	218.7
22	242.3	9	224.4
26	252.5	11	235.6
30	262.1	12	240.2
34	271.3	14	250.3
38	280.2	15	255.2
42	288.9	17	264.5
46	297.1	18	269.7
		20	277.8
		21	284.6

† Calculated from the results of J. R. Raley, R. F. Rust, and W. E. Vaughan, *J. Am. Chem. Soc.*, **70**: 88 (1948).

the data of Table 11-6, which have been calculated from the work of Raley, Rust, and Vaughan, do yield a linear plot. The decomposition is, under these reaction conditions, first-order, and this conclusion is reached without calculation or measurement of the actual concentration of the reacting species.

The use of a quantity such as the total pressure to follow such a reaction is subject to disturbance by any of the side reactions that might occur. A more direct analysis for the reagents is therefore much to be preferred. The data of Table 11-6 have, in fact, been calculated, merely to illustrate that the total pressure could be used, from the original mass spectroscopic analyses of Raley, Rust, and Vaughan.

A mechanism that explains the rate equation and the observed products consists of the slow, rate-determining homolytic-bond-cleavage step

$$(CH_3)_3C—O—O—C(CH_3)_3 \rightarrow 2(CH_3)_3C—O\cdot$$

followed by the fast disproportionation step

$$CH_3—\underset{\underset{CH_3}{|}}{\overset{\overset{CH_3}{|}}{C}}—O\cdot \rightarrow CH_3—\overset{\overset{O}{\|}}{C}—CH_3 + \cdot CH_3$$

and, probably to an appreciable extent at the surface of the glass wool, the fast radical recombination step

$$2(\cdot CH_3) \rightarrow CH_3CH_3$$

The homolytic cleavage of such peroxides occurs relatively easily, even in solution, and such a free-radical-formation step finds considerable use as an initiating step for polymerization reactions that occur by a free-radical mechanism, such as the one indicated in Sec. 11-3.

For first-order reactions it is customary to use not only the rate constant k for the reaction but also the related quantity, the *half-life* of the reaction. The half-life is defined as the time required for the concentration, or amount, of the reagent to decrease to half its initial value. For a first-order reaction the relation of the half-life, denoted by $t_{\frac{1}{2}}$, to the rate constant can be found from Eq. (13) by inserting the requirement that at $t = t_{\frac{1}{2}}$ the concentration is $c = \frac{1}{2}c_0$. In this way one obtains

$$\log \frac{c_0}{\frac{1}{2}c_0} = \frac{k}{2.303} t_{\frac{1}{2}}$$

or
$$t_{\frac{1}{2}} = \frac{0.693}{k} \tag{18}$$

This result shows that, for a first-order reaction, there is a simple reciprocal relation between k and $t_{\frac{1}{2}}$. Furthermore, since the expression involves no term for the concentration, or amount, of material, the time required for half the reactant to be used up is independent of the initial concentration, or amount, of the reactant. This can be seen graphically in Fig. 11-3, where dashed lines have been drawn to show that the time intervals for the amount of *tert*-butyl bromide to decrease to half its value are all equal. It is the simple relation of

Eq. (18) that makes the half-life a useful quantity for first-order reactions. Higher-order reactions, as we shall see, have a half-life that is a function of the initial concentration as well as of the rate constant, and the concept of half-life is then of little value.

A type of reaction which is in some ways outside the realm of chemistry but which conforms beautifully to first-order kinetics is that of radioactive decay. It is found that the rate with which a radioactive species decays is proportional to the amount of that species.   The decay is therefore first-order, and one can, as is invariably done, use a half-life to characterize the decay rate.

11-6. Theory of First-order Gas-phase Reactions.   Before leaving first-order reactions we might consider, in more detail than has been done so far, the implications of a first-order rate dependence on the molecular nature of the reaction.

The simplest molecular explanation of a first-order reaction is that some fraction of the reactant species has sufficiently high energy so that, depending on how this energy is distributed throughout the different vibrational modes of the molecules, there is a certain chance of these *activated* molecules decomposing. The rate of reaction would then be proportional to the number, or concentration, of such activated molecules, and, at a given temperature, this number is proportional to the number, or concentration, of the reactant molecules.   With these proportionalities the reaction would conform to a first-order rate law.

A difficulty arises when it is asked how the high-energy molecules accumulate their greater-than-average thermal energy.   Since they must do so as a result of collisions with other molecules and these collisions can be assumed to be binary collisions, one could write, if the reactant molecules are designated by A and those with rather large thermal energies by A^*, the reaction

$$A + A \rightarrow A + A^*$$

The rate of this reaction, and the rate of formation of A^*, would then be proportional to $[A]^2$.

The implication that this process should correspond to a second-order reaction can be avoided by saying that in the gas there is an equilibrium reservoir of high-energy molecules, as could be calculated from the Boltzmann distribution, and that the reaction being considered never proceeds fast enough to deplete this reservoir.   In this case the reaction rate is proportional to the number of high-energy molecules and not to the rate with which they are formed.

These ideas were first put forward by Lindemann.   He suggested considering the reaction

$$A + A \underset{k_{-2}}{\overset{k_2}{\rightleftharpoons}} A + A^*$$

where the rate constants for the second-order forward and reverse reactions are indicated by k_2 and k_{-2}.   It is this reaction which builds up the reservoir of activated molecules.   A first-order decomposition might then occur as

$$A^* \overset{k_1}{\rightarrow} B + B$$

A net rate of formation of A^* can be written in terms of its formation and destruction in the second-order step and its destruction in the first-order step. Thus

$$\frac{d[A^*]}{dt} = k_2[A]^2 - k_{-2}[A][A^*] - k_1[A^*] \tag{19}$$

Furthermore, if the formation of the fragments B does not occur rapidly compared with the steps of the second-order activation process, the rate of change of $[A^*]$ will be small and $d[A^*]/dt$ can be set equal to zero. The supposition of

$$k_{-2}[A][A^*] \gg k_1[A^*]$$

i.e., that the deactivation of A^* is a more rapid process than is its decomposition, leads, with a zero value of $d[A^*]/dt$, to

$$k_2[A]^2 = k_{-2}[A][A^*]$$

or

$$\frac{[A^*]}{[A]} = \frac{k_2}{k_{-2}} = \text{a const} \tag{20}$$

Thus these assumptions of relative rates lead to the conclusion that A^* is in equilibrium with A and that the concentration of A^* is proportional to that of A. The first-order decomposition step has therefore the rate

$$-\frac{d[A]}{dt} = k_1[A^*] = \frac{k_1 k_2}{k_{-2}}[A] = k_1'[A] \tag{21}$$

The above explanations of the details of first-order reactions imply that at low pressures, where the rate of collisions is decreased, the rate of the reactions by which the equilibrium concentration of energy-rich molecules is formed might not be very much greater than the rate of decomposition of the activated molecules. Evidence for a falling off of the rate constant at low pressures has in fact been found for a few unimolecular reactions.

It should now be pointed out, and the delay in doing so corresponds to the historical development of unimolecular-reaction theory, that the unsubstantiated assumption that the rate of decomposition is simply proportional to the number of activated species has been made. It is now beginning to appear that a detailed understanding of first-order gas-phase reactions may require a consideration of the details of the energy distribution of the reacting species. The probability of a molecular decomposition occurring in a given time interval must be expected to be very dependent on just how much extra energy the activated molecule has.

11-7. Second-order Reactions. A reaction is classified as second-order if the rate of the reaction is proportional to the square of the concentration of one of the reagents or to the product of the concentrations of two species of the reagents. The second situation leads to the same equations as the first if the two reactants are used up at the same rate and if their initial concentrations are equal. For these situations, the rate law is

$$-\frac{dc}{dt} = kc^2 \tag{22}$$

where c is the concentration of the single reagent or of one of the two reagents. Again the kinetic data are usually compared with the integrated form of the equation. One has

$$-\int_{c_0}^{c} \frac{dc}{c^2} = k \int_{0}^{t} dt \tag{23}$$

and
$$\frac{1}{c} - \frac{1}{c_0} = kt \tag{24}$$

A reaction, of the types considered so far, is second-order therefore if a plot of $1/c$ versus t gives a straight line. The slope of the straight line is equal to the rate constant. As Eq. (24) shows, this constant involves the units of concentration and, in this respect, differs from the first-order rate constant that involves only the units of time. Furthermore, the time for the concentration to drop to half its initial value is deduced from Eq. (24) to be

$$t_{\frac{1}{2}} = \frac{1}{kc_0} \tag{25}$$

The half-life depends, therefore, on the initial concentration and is not a convenient way of expressing the rate constant of second-order reactions.

Sometimes it is more convenient to develop the rate equation by introducing a term for the amount of reaction that has occurred at time t. The over-all reaction might, for example, be of the form

$$A + B \rightarrow \text{products}$$

and it might be inconvenient to arrange to have the initial concentrations of A and B equal. The kinetic data can then be treated in terms of the following quantities

a = initial concentration of A

b = initial concentration of B

x = decrease in A or B at time t. Therefore x is equal to the amount
   of product at time t

$a - x$ = concentration of A at time t

$b - x$ = concentration of B at time t

The differential second-order rate equation might then be

$$\frac{dx}{dt} = k[A][B]$$
$$= k(a - x)(b - x) \tag{26}$$

The integration can be performed by using partial fractions. Thus

$$\frac{dx}{(a - x)(b - x)} = k\, dt$$

and
$$\frac{1}{a - b} \int_{0}^{x} \left(-\frac{dx}{a - x} + \frac{dx}{b - x} \right) = k \int_{0}^{t} dt$$

which, on integration, gives

$$\frac{1}{a - b} \left[\ln (a - x) - \ln (b - x) \right]_{0}^{x} = kt \tag{27}$$

Insertion of the limits and rearrangement gives, finally,

$$\frac{1}{a - b} \ln \frac{b(a - x)}{a(b - x)} = kt \tag{28}$$

The data obtained by Dostrovsky and Hughes for the reaction of isobutyl bromide and sodium ethoxide are shown in Table 11-7. Such data can be compared with the second-order rate equation by calculating the values of k for the various times, to get the values listed in Table 11-7, or by making the appropriate plot, as in Fig. 11-5, and observing the linearity of the data. Either test shows that the reaction under these conditions is second-order and has the rate equation

$$- \frac{d[C_4H_9Br]}{dt} = - \frac{d[NaOEt]}{dt} = 5.5 \times 10^{-3}[C_4H_9Br][NaOEt] \qquad (29)$$

where the concentrations are expressed in moles per liter and the time in seconds. Analysis of the products, which has not been necessary in the deduction of the rate equation, shows that the reaction involves some displacement of the bromide for which the mechanism

$$EtO^- + CH_3{-}\underset{\underset{H}{|}}{\overset{\overset{CH_3}{|}}{C}}{-}CH_2{-}Br \rightarrow \left[CH_3{-}\underset{\underset{H}{|}}{\overset{\overset{CH_3}{|}}{C}}{-}\underset{\underset{\underset{Et}{\overset{\delta^-}{\diagdown}}}{O}}{\overset{H_2}{C}}\cdots\cdots\overset{\delta^-}{Br} \right]$$

$$CH_3{-}\underset{\underset{H}{|}}{\overset{\overset{CH_3}{|}}{C}}{-}CH_2{-}OCH_2CH_3 + Br^-$$

Table 11-7. The Concentrations of Isobutyl Bromide and Sodium Ethoxide in Ethyl Alcohol at 95.15°C*

t (min)	C_4H_9Br (moles/liter) $(b-x)$	NaOH (moles/liter) $(a-x)$	x = decrease in conc. of C_4H_9Br or NaOH	k [from Eq. (28)]
0	0.0505	0.0762		
2.5	0.0475	0.0732	0.0030	5.6
5	0.0446	0.0703	0.0059	5.6
7.5	0.0419	0.0676	0.0086	5.8
10	0.0398	0.0655	0.0107	5.6
13	0.0370	0.0627	0.0135	5.8
17	0.0340	0.0596	0.0166	5.8
20	0.0322	0.0580	0.0182	5.7
30	0.0275	0.0532	0.0230	5.4
40	0.0228	0.0485	0.0277	5.5
50	0.0193	0.0451	0.0311	5.6
60	0.0169	0.0427	0.0335	5.5
70	0.0150	0.0407	0.0355	5.5
90	0.0119	0.0376	0.0386	5.4
120	0.0084	0.0341	0.0421	5.4

* From the data of I. Dostrovsky and E. D. Hughes, *J. Chem. Soc.*, p. 157 (1946).

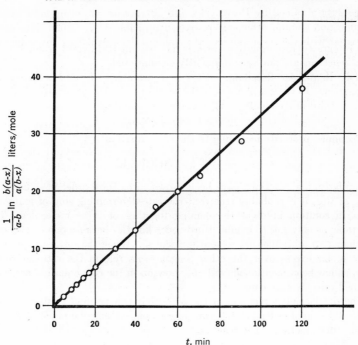

Fig. 11-5. Plot of Eq. (28) for the data of Table 11-7.   The slope of the line gives k as 0.33 liter/mole min or 5.5×10^{-3} liter/mole sec.

can be suggested and some elimination to form the olefin according to the mechanism

$$EtO^- + CH_3-\underset{\underset{H}{|}}{\overset{\overset{CH_3}{|}}{C}}-CH_2-Br \rightarrow \left[CH_3-\underset{\underset{-OEt}{\overset{|}{\underset{H}{|}}}}{\overset{\overset{CH_3}{|}}{C}}\text{---}CH_2\text{---}\overset{\frown}{Br} \right]$$

$$CH_3-\overset{\overset{CH_3}{|}}{C}=CH_2 + HOEt + Br^-$$

Since the two reactions, referred to as an S_N2 reaction and an $E2$ reaction, are second-order, the kinetics of the total reaction, if the reactant concentrations are measured, can be studied without any complication.   If, however, reactions following different rate equations compete with one another, the over-all rate will not be simply related to the reagent concentrations.

A similar treatment involving the amount of reaction that has occurred at time t can be applied if, for example, the over-all reaction follows the equation of the form

$$A + 2B \rightarrow \text{products}$$

The integrated rate equation corresponds to, but is different from, Eq. (28). Such reactions are not very frequently encountered.

11-8. Third-order Reactions. Very few examples of third-order reactions are known. In the gas phase only the reactions of nitric oxide provide illustrations of third-order kinetics. The gas-phase reaction

$$2NO + Cl_2 \rightarrow 2NOCl$$

for example, proceeds according to the rate equation

$$- \frac{d[NO]}{dt} = k[NO]^2[Cl_2] \tag{30}$$

Similarly, few reactions have been shown to be third-order in solution. In spite of this, it is probably true that the rate-determining step of many reactions in solution involves the coming together of three molecules. These reactions usually fail to exhibit third-order kinetics because one or two of the participating molecules are solvent molecules. When the solvent is present in large molar excess over the other reagents, its role in the rate-determining step, as has been mentioned, will not show up in the rate equation but will be lumped into the rate constant.

The displacement reaction of the type that can be used to illustrate both first- and second-order kinetics can, in suitable systems, be made to illustrate third-order kinetics. The reaction

$$\langle \rangle N + CH_3Br \rightarrow \langle \rangle N^+\!\!-CH_3 + Br^-$$

proceeds, in benzene, according to the rate equation

$$- \frac{d[C_5H_5N]}{dt} = - \frac{d[CH_3Br]}{dt} = k[C_5H_5N][CH_3Br] \tag{31}$$

and is apparently a straightforward example of an S_N2 displacement reaction. It has, however, been shown by Swain [*J. Am. Chem. Soc.*, **70**: 2989 (1948)] that, when an alcohol or phenol is added to this reaction system, the rate increases although the added hydroxyl compound does not enter into the equation for the over-all reaction. Since the alcohol or phenol is not used up during the reaction, the rate of the accelerated reaction can easily be shown to be first-order in the bromide, first-order in pyridine, and first-order in the hydroxyl compound; i.e.,

$$- \frac{d[CH_3Br]}{dt} = k[CH_3Br][C_5H_5N][ROH] \tag{32}$$

A mechanism that is in accord with this rate equation is a "push-pull" type of displacement with the rate-determining step leading to the intermediate

$$\langle \rangle \overset{\delta^+}{N}\text{-----}\underset{\underset{H}{\overset{H}{|}}}{C}\text{-----}\overset{\delta^-}{Br}\text{------}H\text{---}\underset{R}{O}$$

Similar solvation of such a displaced group as the bromide ion must be expected in similar reactions that occur in aqueous and alcoholic solutions. Such solvent participation then does not directly show up in rate equation and must be deduced from reactions in other solvents or by some other means.

It should be mentioned, although the subject will be treated more fully in a later section, that the role of the hydroxyl compound in the displacement reaction can be looked upon as being that of a catalyst. It speeds up the reaction without itself being consumed.

11-9. Consecutive and Opposing Reactions: The Method of the Stationary State. Although some of the mechanisms suggested in Sec. 11-3 lead one to expect that many reactions do not proceed by a single step from reactants to products, the treatment so far has assumed that, even with a sequence of steps, the rate of the reaction can depend on one rate-determining step. Now, well worked out, stepwise mechanisms for two reactions will be considered in more detail. The possible influence on the reaction rate of more than one of the mechanism steps and of the reversal of one of the steps will be treated to illustrate the general method that is used when the simplification of a single rate-determining step involving reactants cannot be assumed.

The first example is the reaction of bromine with acetone in a basic aqueous solution. This is known as the *bromoform reaction*, the products being the acetate ion and bromoform. The over-all reaction, which is seen to involve a complicated interchange of atoms, can be written as

$$2CH_3-\overset{\overset{\displaystyle O}{\|}}{C}-CH_3 + 3Br_2 + 2OH^- \rightarrow 2CH_3-\overset{\overset{\displaystyle O}{\|}}{C}-O^- + 2CHBr_3$$

Studies of the rate of this reaction lead to the rate equation

$$-\frac{d\left[CH_3-\overset{\overset{\displaystyle O}{\|}}{C}-CH_3\right]}{dt} = k\left[CH_3-\overset{\overset{\displaystyle O}{\|}}{C}-CH_3\right][OH^-] \qquad (33)$$

A mechanism which is consistent with this rate equation has as its first and rate-determining step the formation of the enolate ion of acetone, according to

$$CH_3-\overset{\overset{\displaystyle O}{\|}}{C}-CH_3 + OH^- \rightarrow CH_3-\overset{\overset{\displaystyle O}{\|}}{C}-CH_2^- + H_2O$$

The ion formed can, of course, be written with the alternative resonance form

$$CH_3-\overset{\overset{\displaystyle O^-}{|}}{C}=CH_2$$

Enough supporting evidence exists for this initial step so that it can be considered to be one of the best-established of all organic mechanisms that have been postulated. After these supporting arguments are indicated, a complete mechanism will be suggested.

First, it has been found that the basic racemization of an optically active ketone, with the asymmetric carbon atom α to the carbonyl, occurs with the same rate equation and with the same rate constant as does the bromination of that compound. It seems very reasonable to suggest that the racemization occurs through the loss of configuration accompanying the formation of the enolate ion. For the ketone that has been studied, one has

At equilibrium only a small amount of the carbanion exists but since a proton can add in the reverse reaction to the charged α-carbon atom to give either the d or l ketone, the optical activity is lost at a rate which corresponds to the rate of formation of the ion. Since this rate is the same as the rate of bromination, it can be expected that the two reactions proceed by the same rate-determining step, the formation of the enolate ion.

Another indication that the removal of an α-hydrogen from a ketone is a valid mechanism step is the finding that for the optically active ketone

the rate observed for the loss of optical activity is the same, in basic media, as the rate of exchange of the α-hydrogen with deuterium in alkaline D_2O. Again the equality of the rate of the two reactions is understandable in terms of the formation of the enolate ion in the rate-determining step.

Finally it is found that the rate of the reaction of acetone with iodine in aqueous alkali is the same as that with bromine. The mechanism of the reaction, therefore, must be one that can be independent of the kind of halogen as well as independent of its concentration. The suggested rate-determining step clearly fits this requirement. It will, however, be shown later that the chlorination of acetone proceeds at a different rate and according to a different rate law. This behavior, we shall see, is understandable in terms of the same mechanism as that proposed for the bromination.

The initial step of the mechanism can, with these supporting arguments, be accepted with some confidence. The remaining steps that are postulated and that can reasonably be assumed to be fast compared with the first step are

$$CH_3-\overset{O}{\overset{\|}{C}}-\overset{..}{\overset{-}{C}H_2} + Br_2 \rightarrow CH_3-\overset{O}{\overset{\|}{C}}-CH_2Br + Br^-$$

$$CH_3-\overset{O}{\overset{\|}{C}}-CH_2Br + OH^- \rightarrow CH_3-\overset{O}{\overset{\|}{C}}-\overset{..}{\overset{-}{C}HBr} + H_2O$$

$$CH_3-\overset{O}{\overset{\|}{C}}-\overset{..}{\overset{-}{C}HBr} + Br_2 \rightarrow CH_3-\overset{O}{\overset{\|}{C}}-CHBr_2 + Br^-$$

$$CH_3\text{---}\overset{\overset{\text{O}}{\|}}{C}\text{---}CHBr_2 + OH^- \rightarrow CH_3\text{---}\overset{\overset{\text{O}}{\|}}{C}\text{---}\overset{..}{C}Br_2^{\;-} + H_2O$$

$$CH_3\text{---}\overset{\overset{\text{O}}{\|}}{C}\text{---}\overset{..}{C}Br_2^{\;-} + Br_2 \rightarrow CH_3\text{---}\overset{\overset{\text{O}}{\|}}{C}\text{---}CBr_3 + Br^-$$

$$CH_3\text{---}\overset{\overset{\text{O}}{\|}}{C}\text{---}CBr_3 + OH^- \rightarrow \left[H\text{---}\overset{\delta^-}{O}\cdots\overset{\overset{\text{O}}{\|}}{\underset{\underset{CH_3}{|}}{C}}\cdots\overset{\delta^-}{C}Br_3 \right] \rightarrow H\text{---}O\text{---}\overset{\overset{\text{O}}{\|}}{C}\text{---}CH_3 + \text{:}\overset{-}{C}Br_3$$

$$\rightarrow CH_3\text{---}\overset{\overset{\text{O}}{\|}}{C}\text{---}O^- + HCBr_3$$

Let us now consider what rate equation this mechanism would lead to if the simple assumption that the first step is slow and rate-determining and all succeeding steps are fast is not made. We shall treat the possibility of the first step being reversible and the second step not necessarily fast compared with the first step, but to keep the analysis reasonably simple all steps after the first two will be assumed to be fast. With the symbols A for acetone and I for the intermediate enolate ion, the reaction steps to be considered are

$$A + OH^- \underset{k_{-1}}{\overset{k_1}{\rightleftharpoons}} I + H_2O$$

$$I + Br_2 \overset{k_2}{\rightarrow} CH_3\text{---}\overset{\overset{\text{O}}{\|}}{C}\text{---}CH_2Br + Br^-$$

where the rate constants for the various reactions are k_1, k_{-1}, and k_2.

The net rate with which acetone is used up, considering its reaction by the first step and its formation by the reverse of the first step, is

$$- \frac{d[A]}{dt} = k_1[A][OH^-] - k_{-1}[I] \tag{34}$$

where the concentration of water is assumed to be essentially constant and can be included in k_{-1}. This expression cannot be used without some knowledge of the concentration of the intermediate species I. To obtain this information, we can write the net rate of formation of I as

$$\frac{d[I]}{dt} = k_1[A][OH^-] - k_{-1}[I] - k_2[I][Br_2] \tag{35}$$

The complications from this immeasurable species I appear to be increasing, but they can be diminished by use of the *method of the stationary state,* or the *method of the unstable intermediate.* In this method one recognizes that the concentration of the intermediate is always very small; it is, for example, not detectable. The rate of the increase of its concentration except, possibly, for times very near $t = 0$ must therefore also be very small. The assumption is made that the net rate of growth $d[I]/dt$ can be neglected for the time interval studied, or can be put equal to zero in Eq. (35). This assumption allows the equation to be rearranged to give

$$[I] = \frac{k_1[A][OH^-]}{k_{-1} + k_2[Br_2]} \tag{36}$$

which is a helpful expression in that it gives the concentration of the intermediate in terms of the concentrations of the reagents. Elimination of the troublesome $[I]$ term from Eq. (34) gives, for the net rate of reaction of acetone, the expression

$$-\frac{d[A]}{dt} = k_1[A][OH^-]\frac{k_2[Br_2]}{k_{-1} + k_2[Br_2]} \tag{37}$$

The recognition that a step may be reversible and that two steps may need to be considered leads, therefore, to a rather more complicated rate equation than that deduced on the basis of a single, initial rate-determining step for the reaction of acetone with bromine in aqueous alkali.

The idea that the first step of a mechanism, such as that being considered, is the rate-determining step amounts to the assumption that when the intermediate is formed in the first step it is used up much more rapidly by the second and all succeeding steps than it can react reversibly to give the initial reagents. The assumption corresponds to the inequality

$$k_2[Br_2][I] \gg k_{-1}[I]$$

or
$$k_2[Br_2] \gg k_{-1} \tag{38}$$

Use of this inequality in the denominator of Eq. (37) allows k_{-1} to be neglected. The $k_2[Br_2]$ terms then cancel, and the deduced rate law

$$-\frac{d[A]}{dt} = k_1[A][OH^-] \tag{39}$$

shows that the mechanism, with the assumed relative rates of the different steps, is consistent with the observed rate law for the bromoform reaction.

The reason why the chlorination of acetone does not, as mentioned previously, obey the same rate equation is that, although the same mechanism can be written, the inequality of Eq. (38) does not apply and the complicated concentration dependence of Eq. (37) cannot be reduced to a simpler expression.

The second reaction that has been extensively studied and that serves as an illustration of the effect of reverse and consecutive mechanism steps is the alkaline hydrolysis of chloroform. The complete reaction yields carbon monoxide, formate ions, and chloride ions. The over-all equation

$$2CHCl_3 + 7OH^- \rightarrow CO + HCOO^- + 6Cl^- + 4H_2O$$

can be written.

The rate of the reaction is found to be expressed by the rate equation

$$-\frac{d[CHCl_3]}{dt} = k[CHCl_3][OH^-] \tag{40}$$

Another datum that is pertinent to mechanistic considerations is that the rate of deuterium exchange of $CHCl_3$ in alkaline D_2O is very much faster than is the hydrolysis reaction.

A mechanism that has been proposed to account for these results has the first two steps

$$HCCl_3 + OH^- \underset{k_{-1}}{\overset{k_1}{\rightleftharpoons}} {:}CCl_3^- + H_2O$$

$${:}CCl_3^- \overset{k_2}{\rightarrow} {:}CCl_2 + Cl^-$$

followed by the rapid reaction of the carbon dichloride with hydroxide to give, after a series of steps, the final products.

An analysis of the first two steps, in a way analogous to that indicated for the bromoform reaction, gives

$$- \frac{d[\text{CHCl}_3]}{dt} = \frac{k_1 k_2}{k_{-1} + k_2} [\text{CHCl}_3][\text{OH}^-] \tag{41}$$

which agrees with the observed rate equation when k is identified with $k_1 k_2/(k_{-1} + k_2)$. In this example, regardless of the relative values of k_1, k_{-1}, and k_2, the mechanism leads to the observed rate expression. The observation that exchange is more rapid than hydrolysis leads us, however, to write

$$k_2[:\text{CCl}_3^-] \ll k_{-1}[:\text{CCl}_3^-]$$

or

$$k_2 \ll k_{-1} \tag{42}$$

and to interpret the rate constant for the reaction simply as $k_1 k_2/k_{-1}$ rather than as $k_1 k_2/(k_{-1} + k_2)$.

It is interesting to notice that the same result can be obtained more directly by assuming, to begin with, that the first step of the mechanism is an equilibrium step and that the further reaction of the small equilibrium amount of $:\text{CCl}_3^-$ is the rate-determining step. For the equilibrium step one writes

$$\frac{[:\text{CCl}_3^-]}{[\text{CHCl}_3][\text{OH}^-]} = K = \frac{k_1}{k_{-1}}$$

or

$$[:\text{CCl}_3^-] = \frac{k_1}{k_{-1}} [\text{CHCl}_3][\text{OH}^-] \tag{43}$$

The net rate depends on the rate of the rate-determining step. Thus

$$- \frac{d[\text{CHCl}_3]}{dt} = - \frac{d[:\text{CCl}_3^-]}{dt}$$
$$= k_2[:\text{CCl}_3^-]$$

Substitution of the equilibrium expression for the concentration of $:\text{CCl}_3^-$ gives, again,

$$- \frac{d[\text{CHCl}_3]}{dt} = \frac{k_2 k_1}{k_{-1}} [\text{CHCl}_3][\text{OH}^-] \tag{44}$$

which is the same result as obtained from the steady-state method with $k_2 \ll k_{-1}$.

These two reactions, which have been treated in some detail, indicate how a rate equation is deduced from a stepwise reaction when the initial step cannot be assumed to be the rate-determining step. It should also now be especially clear that the rate equation for a stepwise reaction may be, but need not be, a simple function of the reagent concentrations and that the rate equation need not be simply related to the equation for the over-all reaction.

11-10. Chain Reactions. All the reactions encountered thus far can be understood in terms of mechanisms that lead after one or, at most, a few steps to the final products. There are some very important reactions, however, that proceed by a long series of self-propagating steps. Representative of such reactions are gas-phase free-radical chain reactions, such as occur in combustion reactions, and liquid-phase free-radical polymerization reactions.

A gas-phase example is the reaction of hydrogen and chlorine to give hydrogen chloride. In the dark and in relatively clean containers no reaction occurs when the reagent gases are mixed. It is characteristic of chain reactions that an initiator is required, and it is found that the hydrogen-chlorine reaction proceeds appreciably when light falls on the system or when a relatively small number of sodium atoms are admitted. These chain-initiation steps produce chlorine atoms by

$$Cl_2 + h\nu \rightarrow 2Cl\cdot$$
or
$$Cl_2 + Na \rightarrow NaCl + Cl\cdot$$

The reaction then proceeds—and it is found that as many as 10^6 HCl molecules result from each initiating chlorine atom—by the steps

$$Cl\cdot + H_2 \rightarrow HCl + H\cdot$$
$$H\cdot + Cl_2 \rightarrow HCl + Cl\cdot \text{ etc.}$$

The chain is energetically self-sustaining because of the greater bond energy of HCl than of either H_2 or Cl_2.

The chain is *terminated* when two atoms come together in the presence of a third body, usually the container wall, that can take away the energy liberated when the atoms combine.

Such a mechanism can be analyzed and a rate law can be deduced by using the steady-state assumption that the chain-carrying atoms are present only in low concentrations. The derivation is not different in principle from the derivations of the previous section. It is necessary, however, to take into account the chain-initiating and the chain-terminating steps. Since the latter generally occur on the surface of the container, one finds that chain reactions have a characteristic surface-area dependence.

The formation of polymer molecules proceeds by a similar chain mechanism.

11-11. Homogeneous Catalysis. One of the most dramatic effects in the field of chemical kinetics is that of catalysis. A catalyst is a material that increases the rate of a chemical reaction without itself being used up. Remarkable accelerations of reactions can occur, and this is often the result of a very small amount of catalysts. Catalysis, moreover, occurs in a great variety of reactions, and the catalysts may be anything from a solid metal to the complicated organic structures that constitute enzymes.

The general mode of operation of all catalysts can be clarified by considering a reaction in solution catalyzed by an added solute. It is, in fact, frequently possible to deduce the exact role of a catalyst in such a homogeneous system. The details of the important phenomenon of heterogeneous catalyses, where the catalyst is usually a solid and the reaction system is a liquid or vapor, remain, however, quite obscure. Since heterogeneous catalysis is closely tied up with the process by which reagents are adsorbed onto solids, detailed discussion of this subject will be postponed until adsorption is studied in Chap. 19.

One of the most frequently encountered types of catalysis in solution is that in which a reaction is accelerated by the presence of an acid or a base. The molecular nature of catalysis is perhaps best illustrated by the example of the hydrolysis of an ester.   The reaction is catalyzed by both acids and bases. The designation of a base as a catalyst is, admittedly, a little upset by the reaction of the base with the acidic product.   In spite of this, the reaction will nicely illustrate the role of the catalyst.

In neutral aqueous systems an ester such as methyl acetate hydrolyzes very slowly according to the over-all reaction

$$CH_3-\overset{\overset{\textstyle O}{\|}}{C}-O-CH_3 + H_2O \rightarrow CH_3-\overset{\overset{\textstyle O}{\|}}{C}-OH + CH_3OH$$

A reasonable mechanism suggests that the reaction proceeds through the attack of the water molecule on the carbonyl (recall the resonance form

$$CH_3-\overset{\overset{\textstyle O^-}{|}}{C^+}-O-CH_3)\ as$$

$$CH_3-\overset{\overset{\textstyle O}{\|}}{\underset{\overset{\textstyle \uparrow}{\underset{\textstyle \ddot{O}}{}}}{C}}-O-CH_3 \rightarrow CH_3-\overset{\overset{\textstyle O^-}{|}}{\underset{\overset{\textstyle |}{O^+}}{C}}-O-CH_3$$

$$\underset{\overset{\textstyle H \quad\quad H}{}}{}\qquad\qquad \overset{}{H \quad\quad H}$$

Redistribution of the electrons gives

$$CH_3-\overset{\overset{\textstyle O^-}{|}}{\underset{\overset{\textstyle |}{O^+}}{C}}-O-CH_3 \rightarrow CH_3-\overset{\overset{\textstyle O}{\|}}{C}-\overset{+}{O}H_2 + \bar{O}CH_3$$

$$\overset{}{H \quad\quad H}$$

which, with proton transfer, yields the observed final products.   The rate-determining step is the initial attack of water on the carbonyl, and it is to the difficulty of this step that the slowness of the reaction is attributed.

The addition of acid to the aqueous methyl acetate system results in a greatly accelerated reaction, and the added acid does not enter into the equation for the over-all reaction.   It is, therefore, a catalyst.   For this reaction it is possible to suggest a mechanism that explains this catalytic process.

In the presence of acid a small amount of acid-base reaction will occur to give the rapid equilibrium

$$CH_3-\overset{\overset{\textstyle O}{\|}}{C}-O-CH_3 + H^+ \rightleftharpoons CH_3-\overset{\overset{\textstyle O}{\overset{\textstyle /}{\underset{\textstyle H}{}}}}{\underset{}{C^+}}-O-CH_3$$

The ion that is formed will be much more susceptible to nucleophilic attack by a water molecule, and the rate-determining step will now be the easier reaction

$$CH_3-\overset{\overset{\displaystyle O-H}{|}}{\underset{\underset{\displaystyle H_2\overset{..}{O}}{\uparrow}}{C^+}}-O-CH_3 \rightarrow CH_3-\overset{\overset{\displaystyle O-H}{|}}{\underset{\underset{\displaystyle \overset{H\quad H}{}}{\overset{O^+}{|}}}{C}}-O-CH_3$$

which can be expected to proceed rapidly. Rearrangement of the electrons and protons again yields the final products. The presence of acid in the solution and its participation in the rate-determining step have provided an easier, i.e., lower-energy, path for the rate-determining step. This is the role that all catalysts can be assumed to play. For reactions that a mechanism cannot be suggested for it is of course impossible to understand the action of the catalyst. In heterogeneous catalysis the surface reactions are little understood, and the role of the surface, which is the catalyst, is therefore also obscure.

Before leaving the methyl acetate example a mechanism should be suggested to show how the hydrolysis is base-catalyzed as well as acid-catalyzed. The attack of negative hydroxide ions on the partially positively charged carbon atom of the carbonyl can be expected to proceed much more rapidly than the corresponding attack by water. The suggested rate-determining step for the base-catalyzed reaction is, therefore, the hydroxyl-ion attack

$$CH_3-\overset{\overset{\displaystyle O}{\|}}{\underset{\underset{\displaystyle H\overset{..}{O}{}^-}{\uparrow}}{C}}-O-CH_3 \rightarrow CH_3-\overset{\overset{\displaystyle O^-}{|}}{\underset{\underset{\displaystyle O-H}{|}}{C}}-O-CH_3$$

the product of which can again be easily converted to the final reaction products.

The rate equation for such a reaction can be written to include these catalytic effects if the rate constant is given the form

$$k = k_0 + k_{H^+}[H^+] + k_{OH^-}[OH^-] \tag{45}$$

where k_0 is the rate constant of the noncatalyzed reaction, such as occurs in neutral solution where $[H^+]$ and $[OH^-]$ are both small, and k_{H^+} and k_{OH^-} are the *catalytic constants* for H^+ and OH^-. It should be mentioned that some reactions need not, of course, be catalyzed by both acid *and* base. Also it can be pointed out that, if only H^+ or OH^- is an effective catalyst, the reaction is said to be *specific acid- or base-catalyzed*, whereas, if any acid, such as CH_3COOH molecules, or any base, such as NEt_3, is effective, the reaction is said to be subject to *general acid or base catalysis*.

Many other types of catalysts are known, but they need not be mentioned here. It appears that, no matter how the systems vary, the catalyst will enter into the rate-determining step to provide an easier path in some way such as that illustrated for catalytic hydrolysis of methyl acetate.

THEORIES OF THE RATE CONSTANT

The previous sections have shown that the form of the concentration terms of the rate equation is of great value in influencing theories of reaction mechanisms. It is this aspect of kinetics which leads to much of our present understanding of the reactions of organic and inorganic chemistry. So far almost no attention has been paid to the numerical values of the rate constants appearing in the rate equations. A considerable extension of our understanding of molecular phenomena results from attempts to explain the actual values of the rate constants and therefore the actual rates of reactions for given reagent concentrations.

When this problem is approached, the first striking feature that is noticed is the large variation of all rate constants with temperature. This dependence proves not to be merely a troublesome factor but rather furnishes the most important clue to the approach that must be used to understand the molecular basis of rate constants.

11-12. Temperature Dependence of the Reaction Rate. The rate equation and the rate constant for a reaction are determined from kinetic data at a fixed temperature. If experiments are performed at several different temperatures, it is generally found that the concentration dependence exhibited in the rate equation is unchanged but the value of the rate constant is much greater at the higher temperatures.

In 1889 Arrhenius showed that the rate constant increases in an exponential manner with the temperature. It is perhaps best to recognize that by an entirely empirical procedure he could have found that a plot of log k versus $1/T$ gives a linear relation. The data on the rate constant of a second-order reaction as a function of temperature given in Table 11-8 are shown in such a plot in Fig. 11-6.

Such linear plots imply the relation

$$\ln k \propto \frac{1}{T} \tag{46}$$

or
$$k \propto e^{\text{const}/T} \tag{47}$$

Table 11-8. The Rate Constant as a Function of Temperature for the Reaction
$CH_3I + C_2H_5ONa \rightarrow CH_3OC_2H_5 + NaI$ in Ethyl Alcohol*

$t°C$	k_2 (liters/mole sec)
0	5.60×10^{-5}
6	11.8
12	24.5
18	48.8
24	100
30	208

* From W. Hecht and M. Conrad, *Z. physik. Chem.*, **3**: 450 (1889).

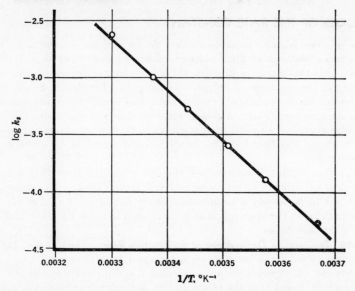

Fig. 11-6. The Arrhenius plot [Eq. (49)] for the data of Table 11-8.   The straight line is represented by log $k = -4{,}250/T + 11.38$ or ln $k = -19{,}490/RT + 26.21$, giving $E_a = 19{,}490$ cal and $A = 26.21$.

In view of later deductions, and in line with the treatment of Arrhenius, this empirical relation can be conveniently written as

$$k = A e^{-E_a/RT} \qquad (48)$$

where A is called the *pre-exponential factor* and E_a is known as the *activation energy*.   With this notation one writes the logarithmic form of Eq. (48) as

$$\ln k = -\frac{E_a}{RT} + A$$

or
$$\log k = -\frac{E_a}{2.303R}\frac{1}{T} + \frac{\log A}{2.303} \qquad (49)$$

The empirical constants E_a and A can therefore be deduced from the slope and intercept of the appropriate plot of the values of k at different temperatures.

Although these expressions are empirical correlations of rate data and the terms E_a and A are, for the present, to be treated as empirical parameters, the form of the expression for the rate constant might have been anticipated from the previously derived relation for the temperature dependence of the equilibrium constant.   The thermodynamic equation

$$\frac{d(\ln K)}{dT} = \frac{\Delta H}{RT^2} \qquad (50)$$

can be written as

$$K = \text{const } e^{-\Delta H/RT} \qquad (51)$$

and if K is interpreted as k_1/k_{-1}, the simplest temperature dependence that can be assumed for the rate constants that is consistent with Eq. (51) is

$$k_1 = A_1 e^{-(E_a)_1/RT} \qquad \text{and} \qquad k_{-1} = A_{-1} e^{-(E_a)_{-1}/RT}$$

which gives

$$\frac{k_1}{k_{-1}} = \frac{A_{-1}}{A_1} e^{-[(E_a)_{-1}-(E_a)_{-1}]/RT} \tag{52}$$

and agreement with the form of Eq. (51).

Most reactions that proceed at a reasonable rate, i.e., that have half-lives of minutes or hours, have values of E_a of about 20 kcal. For such reactions one can use Eq. (48) to verify the photographer's rule of thumb that reactions go two or three times as fast when the temperature increases by 10°C.

The empirical breakdown of the rate constant according to Eq. (48), for example, introduces the two new quantities A and E_a. Attempts to understand the nature of k become therefore attempts to understand the molecular basis and interpretation of A and E_a. A beginning to this was made by Arrhenius himself.

11-13. The Arrhenius Theory.   Arrhenius developed a simple and primarily qualitative theory for the molecular behavior that leads to the form of the empirically determined expression for the rate constant. Later theories elaborate and make more quantitative these original ideas.

The very simple reversible vapor-phase reaction of hydrogen and iodine to give hydrogen iodide can be used to illustrate the ideas of Arrhenius. The reaction

$$H_2 + I_2 \rightleftharpoons 2HI$$

is second-order in both the forward and the reverse direction and apparently proceeds by a one-step four-center process so that the path of the reaction can be depicted as

$$H_2 + I_2 \rightarrow \begin{bmatrix} H{-}H & H\cdots H \\ | \quad | & | \quad | \\ I{-}I & I\cdots I \end{bmatrix} \rightarrow 2HI$$

For more complicated systems, even when a mechanism has been postulated, it is not so easy to see how the electrons and atoms move around as the reaction proceeds. Even Arrhenius, however, recognized that any reaction process could be considered as proceeding by means, first, of the formation of some high-energy species, which we now call the *activated complex*, and, second, the breakdown of this complex into products.

If the activated complex is assumed to have an energy E_a greater than the reactants, the number of activated-complex molecules compared with the number of reagent molecules can be written in terms of the Boltzmann distribution as

$$\frac{\text{No. activated-complex molecules}}{\text{No. reagent molecules}} = e^{-E_a/RT} \tag{53}$$

Alternatively this type of expression can be written from the thermodynamic result

$$\frac{d(\ln K)}{dT} = \frac{\Delta H}{RT^2}$$

The theory of Arrhenius now says that the rate of the reaction is proportional to the number, or concentration, of the activated complex. If the proportionality factor is denoted by A, one deduces the relation

Rate $= A$(no., or concentration, of activated-complex molecules)
     $= Ae^{-E_a/RT}$(concentration of reagents)   (54)

which, if the reagent-concentration term is treated in more detail, agrees with the observed rate equations since it leads to the relation

$$k = Ae^{-E_a/RT}$$

The theory, moreover, says that the empirical constant E_a is to be interpreted as the energy of the activated-complex compared with the reagent molecules.

The idea of an activated complex can be presented on a plot of the energy of the system as ordinate versus the *reaction coordinate* as abscissa. The reaction coordinate is not any single internuclear distance but rather depends on all the internuclear distances that change as the reactant molecules are converted into product molecules. In general, it is impossible, and for the present purpose unnecessary, to give a quantitative description of the reaction coordinate. It consists merely of a qualitative description of the extent of the transformation from reactants to products. The diagram that can be constructed to represent the hydrogen-iodine reaction is shown in Fig. 11-7.

The Arrhenius theory suggests that the energy of the system which is partially transformed from the reagents H_2 and I_2 to the products $2HI$ is given by the activation-energy term from the empirical expression for the rate con-

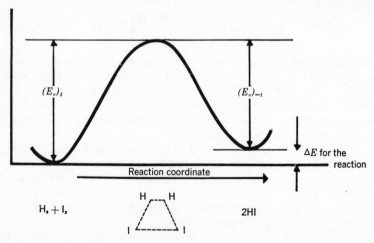

Fig. 11-7. The energy of the reaction $H_2 + I_2 \rightarrow 2HI$ as a function of the reaction coordinate.

stant. This information is added to Fig. 11-7, and a smooth, but otherwise undetermined, curve is drawn to pass through the three known energies. The hydrogen-iodine example is especially nice in that the reverse reaction has also been studied and the energy of activation from the products to the activated complex has been obtained.

The Arrhenius theory leads to a considerable improvement in our understanding of the reaction process. It is, however, still a very qualitative theory in that it does not show how the pre-exponential factor A depends on the molecular properties of the reaction system, nor does it attempt to predict the value of E_a. Two later theories make some progress in the interpretation of the factor A, but the energy of the activated complex remains too subtle a quantity for evaluation, except in the very simplest example.

11-14. The Collision Theory. The collision theory, as its name implies, focuses attention on the idea that the reaction of molecules, considering particularly molecules in the gas phase, can occur only as a result of a coming together, or a collision, of the reactant molecules. Thus, in this view, the rate should be proportional to the number of collisions per unit time between reactant molecules. The idea of an activation energy still enters, however, because it seems reasonable to expect only those collisions to lead to reaction in which there is enough energy available so that in the moment of impact the necessary rearrangements of atoms and electrons can occur.

It is necessary first of all, if the reaction

$$A + B \rightarrow \text{products}$$

is considered, to calculate the number of collisions that occur each second in a volume of 1 cc containing n_A^* molecules of A and n_B^* molecules of B. This calculation can be performed for gases, and the collision theory restricts itself therefore to the interpretation of gas-phase reactions. The basic equation, obtained for a single gas species, has been given in Sec. 2-5 as

$$Z_{11} = \frac{1}{\sqrt{2}} \pi \sigma^2 \bar{c} (n^*)^2 \tag{55}$$

where n^* is the number of molecules per cubic centimeter, $\bar{c}$ the average speed, and σ the molecular diameter. If for simplicity it is assumed that the molecules A and B are similar in molecular weight and diameter, the total number of collisions in 1 cc containing a total of $n_A^* + n_B^*$ molecules is

$$Z_{11} = \frac{1}{\sqrt{2}} \pi \sigma^2 \bar{c} (n_A^* + n_B^*)^2 \tag{56}$$

We are interested, however, only in collisions involving one molecule of A and one of B. Subtraction of the number of collisions involving just A molecules and just B molecules gives

$$Z_{AB} = \frac{1}{\sqrt{2}} \pi \sigma^2 \bar{c} (n_A^* + n_B^*)^2 - \frac{1}{\sqrt{2}} \pi \sigma^2 \bar{c} (n_A^*)^2 - \frac{1}{\sqrt{2}} \pi \sigma^2 \bar{c} (n_B^*)^2$$

$$= \sqrt{2} \, \pi \sigma^2 \bar{c} n_A^* n_B^* \tag{57}$$

Substitution of the relation obtained in Sec. 2-9 for the average speed gives

$$Z_{AB} = \sqrt{2}\,\pi\sigma^2\,\sqrt{\frac{8RT}{\pi M}}\,n_A^* n_B^* \tag{58}$$

where M and σ are the molecular weight and collision diameter, which have been assumed to be the same for A and B.

Recognition that A and B can have different molecular weights and diameters leads to the relation

$$Z_{AB} = \sqrt{2\pi}\left(\frac{\sigma_A + \sigma_B}{2}\right)^2 \sqrt{\frac{8RT}{2\mu_M}}\,n_A^* n_B^*$$

$$= (\sigma_A + \sigma_B)^2 \sqrt{\frac{\pi RT}{2\mu_M}}\,n_A^* n_B^* \tag{59}$$

where $\mu_M = M_A M_B/(M_A + M_B)$ and is the molar reduced mass.

It is now necessary to calculate the fraction of these collisions that will have enough energy to permit the necessary rearrangement to produce product molecules to occur. Let the necessary energy again be designated by E_a. If for simplicity a head-on collision is pictured, one sees that the 1 degree of freedom of translational energy of each molecule is converted by the collision into other forms of energy within the collision system, and at least the energy of these translational degrees of freedom is available to surmount the energy hump blocking the reaction. The number of molecules having various velocities in two dimensions is given by distribution expressions like those for one and three dimensions in Sec. 2-9 as

$$\frac{dn}{n} = \frac{m}{kT}\,e^{-\frac{1}{2}mc^2/kT}c\,dc \tag{60}$$

The expression is usually applied to one molecule with 2 degrees of freedom, but the problem is the same as that of two molecules each with 1 degree of freedom. The expression can be put in terms of molar energies, i.e., the energies of an Avogadro's number of particles, by the relations

$$E = \tfrac{1}{2}Nmc^2$$
and
$$dE = Nmc\,dc \tag{61}$$
which give

$$\frac{dn}{n} = \frac{1}{RT}\,e^{-E/RT}\,dE \tag{62}$$

Finally the fraction of the head-on collisions that have more energy than E_a is obtained by the integration

$$\frac{\Delta n}{n} = \frac{1}{RT}\int_{E_a}^{\infty} e^{-E/RT}\,dE = -e^{-E/RT}\Big]_{E_a}^{\infty}$$

$$= e^{-E_a/RT} \tag{63}$$

A similar exponential type of expression would have been obtained even if the simplifying assumption of head-on collisions had not been made. The rate of a reaction according to the collision theory is, therefore,

Rate = (no. collisions/sec)(fraction that are effective collisions)

or
$$- \frac{dn_A^*}{dt} = - \frac{dn_B^*}{dt} = (Z_{AB})e^{-E_a/RT}$$

$$= (\sigma_A + \sigma_B)^2 \sqrt{\frac{\pi RT}{2\mu_M}} \, e^{-E_a/RT} n_A^* n_B^* \tag{64}$$

Comparison can be made with the equation for an observed rate if this relation is expressed in terms of molar concentrations, denoted by c_A and c_B, rather than in terms of molecules per cubic centimeter.   Since

$$c = \frac{10^3 n^*}{N}$$

or
$$n^* = \frac{N}{10^3} c \quad \text{and} \quad dn^* = \frac{N}{10^3} dc \tag{65}$$

one obtains

$$- \frac{dc_A}{dt} = - \frac{dc_B}{dt} = \frac{\sqrt{\pi} (\sigma_A + \sigma_B)^2}{\sqrt{2} \times 10^3} N \sqrt{\frac{RT}{\mu_M}} \, e^{-E_a/RT}(c_A)(c_B) \tag{66}$$

This result corresponds to the rate equation for a bimolecular reaction between A and B if the rate constant is interpreted as

$$k = \frac{\sqrt{\pi} (\sigma_A + \sigma_B)^2}{\sqrt{2} \times 10^3} N \sqrt{\frac{RT}{\mu_M}} \, e^{-E_a/RT} \tag{67}$$

Finally, this derived result for the rate constant can be compared with the empirical Arrhenius expression of Eq. (48).   When it is recognized that the $\sqrt{T}$ term shows a usually negligible temperature dependence compared with the exponential term, one sees that the derivation has led to a result of the form

$$k = Ae^{-E_a/RT}$$

and furthermore that the pre-exponential factor A is predicted and can be calculated from the expression

$$A = \frac{\sqrt{\pi} (\sigma_A + \sigma_B)^2}{\sqrt{2} \times 10^3} N \sqrt{\frac{RT}{\mu_M}} \tag{68}$$

In all but one or two very simple reactions it is too severe a test of the theory to put in actual values of σ_A, σ_B, and μ_M and to compare the calculated and observed values of A.   The principal accomplishment of the collision theory is that it gives a value of A, for reasonable values of σ_A, σ_B, and μ_M, that is typical of that found for a number of second-order gas-phase reactions.   To see this, the simpler equation, with

$$\sigma = \sigma_A = \sigma_B \quad \text{and} \quad M = M_A = M_B$$

is sufficient and gives

$$A = \frac{4\sigma^2 N}{10^3} \sqrt{\frac{\pi RT}{M}} \tag{69}$$

Thus with typical values of $\sigma = 3.5A$ and $M = 50$ one calculates

$$A = 6.6 \times 10^9 \sqrt{T} \qquad \text{moles/liter sec}$$

The pre-exponential factors in Table 11-9, page 371, are seen mostly to fall around this value. The theory has, therefore, been successful to some extent. Closer inspection will show that disagreement can become quite appreciable, amounting often to a factor of 10 and sometimes to several powers of 10.

The details that the collision theory have overlooked are readily recognized but are less easily rectified. It seems likely, for example, that for a reaction to occur as a result of a collision there must not only be enough energy but also a suitable orientation of the colliding molecules. For larger molecules this *steric factor* can be expected to be much less than unity, as many collisions would not bring the reactive parts of the molecules together. There seems, however, to be no satisfactory quantitative way of allowing for this effect, and all that can be done is to expect the observed pre-exponential factor to be less than that calculated when such geometric considerations are important.

An even more serious difficulty arises in the activation energy term. The result that has been obtained is based on the supposition that only 2 degrees of freedom can contribute the energy that goes into surmounting the activated-complex-energy barrier. There is, however, no reason to ignore energy contributions from rotational and vibrational degrees of freedom. If these contribute appreciably, a larger fraction of the collisions will be effective and the rate of the reaction will be greater than that calculated on the basis of 2 degrees of freedom. Although it is easy to see that corrections of several powers of 10 are in this way possible, there is as yet no way of determining what molecular energies should be included in the calculation.

The chief contribution of the collision theory is that it leads to a definite prediction for the rates of gas-phase reactions. Its chief defects are that it is inflexible in that there is no definite way to allow for steric effects and for participation of the energy from various degrees of freedom and that it is applicable only to gas-phase reactions.

The second theory that attempts to explain reaction rates is now given. Judgment of it is, as we shall see, rather the opposite of that applied to the collision theory. It generally makes no quantitative prediction and thereby avoids the test that the collision theory could be put to. Its chief merit is that it is very flexible and that the variations found in the rates of different reactions can be discussed in terms of the quantities introduced by the transition-state theory.

11-15. The Transition-state Theory. The collision theory is from the outset tied to the kinetic-molecular theory and, as a consequence, is removed from the realm of thermodynamics. The transition-state theory, on the other hand, is an approach that allows some use to be made of the important thermodynamic concepts. The transition-state theory, like the collision theory, falls far short of the goal of a completely theoretical prediction of rate constants. Nevertheless, the approach of the transition-state theory helps us to understand not only the molecular features of gas-phase reactions but also some of the molecular features that operate on reactions in solution.

The transition-state theory focuses attention on the species in the reaction process that corresponds to the maximum in the energy curve such as that of Fig. 11-7. This species, called the *activated-complex*, or *transition, state*, is, in this theory, treated formally as a molecule in spite of its ill-defined nature and transitory existence. More specifically, the theory assumes that this species can be treated as a thermodynamic entity.

To illustrate, let us again consider the hydrogen-iodine reaction. At equilibrium, which is a dynamic balancing in this case of the two simple opposing steps, one could recognize explicitly that there must be at all times some small number of molecules that are in the process of reacting. It is customary to label these reacting, or transition-state, molecules by $\neq$, and with this notation a more detailed statement of the equilibrium system can be written as

$$H_2 + I_2 \rightleftharpoons (H_2,I_2)^{\neq} \rightleftharpoons 2HI$$

It will now be indicated that such explicit consideration of the transition state, together with a thermodynamic development, leads to a new and valuable view of the reaction process. The development of this approach has been due mainly to the work of Eyring.

When the molecules A and B react to give products, one now can suggest, in an approach similar to that originated by Arrhenius, that A and B establish an equilibrium concentration of the transition-state species and that this species reacts further to form products. Thus

$$A + B \rightarrow (AB)^{\neq} \rightarrow \text{products}$$

The rate of the reaction depends on two factors: the concentration of the transition-state species and the rate with which it breaks up to give products.

The concentration of the activated complex can, at least formally, be written in terms of the equilibrium expression

$$K^{\neq} = \frac{(AB)^{\neq}}{[A][B]}$$

or
$$[(AB)^{\neq}] = K^{\neq}[A][B] \tag{70}$$

Although no value is given for $K^{\neq}$, it will be seen that its thermodynamic interpretation is profitable and justifies its introduction.

The rate with which the complex breaks up can be estimated by recognizing that it can fly apart into product molecules when a suitable vibration happens to have a large enough amplitude to break open the complex. The frequency of such a vibration will therefore be something like the rate with which the complex breaks up. An activated complex is an unstable species and is held together by loose bonds. The vibrations of such a species will have therefore rather low frequencies, and the average energy of such a vibrational degree of freedom will have approximately the classical energy kT. (Boltzmann's constant will be written as k, and the rate constant will, in what follows, be written with a subscript as k_2.) Planck's expression $\epsilon = h\nu$ can therefore be applied to the vibrational mode that breaks the complex, and its frequency can be estimated from

$$h\nu = kT$$

or
$$\nu = \frac{kT}{h} \tag{71}$$

It should be noticed that this argument leads to a value of ν of

$$\nu = \frac{1.38 \times 10^{-16} \times 300}{6.62 \times 10^{-27}} = 6.3 \times 10^{13} \text{ cycle/sec}$$

or

$$\bar{\nu} = \frac{6.3 \times 10^{13}}{3 \times 10^{10}} = 210 \text{ cm}^{-1}$$

and that this values is, according to the data of Table 10-3, reasonable for weak chemical bonds.

The rate of the reaction is, therefore, given by the transition-state theory as

$$\text{Rate} = -\frac{d[A]}{dt} = -\frac{d[B]}{dt} = K^{\ddagger} \frac{kT}{h} [A][B] \tag{72}$$

Comparison with empirical rate equations for second-order reactions shows that the second-order rate constant k_2 is to be identified according to

$$k_2 = K^{\ddagger} \frac{kT}{h} \tag{73}$$

This result becomes of value when the equilibrium constant is interpreted thermodynamically. To do this, one introduces the *free energy of activation*, the *entropy of activation*, and the *enthalpy of activation*. The equilibrium constant can be related to the free energy of formation of the activated complex by the expression obtained in Sec. 7-5. Thus

$$(\Delta F^\circ)^{\ddagger} = -RT \ln K^{\ddagger}$$

and

$$K^{\ddagger} = e^{-(\Delta F^\circ)^{\ddagger}/RT} \tag{74}$$

For the reaction at a given temperature the free energy of activation can be interpreted in terms of an entropy and an enthalpy contribution according to

$$(\Delta F^\circ)^{\ddagger} = (\Delta H^\circ)^{\ddagger} - T(\Delta S^\circ)^{\ddagger} \tag{75}$$

Substitution of this relation in Eq. (74) yields

$$K^{\ddagger} = e^{+(\Delta S^\circ)^{\ddagger}/R} e^{-(\Delta H^\circ)^{\ddagger}/RT} \tag{76}$$

With this expression for $K^{\ddagger}$, the derived rate constant becomes

$$k_2 = \frac{kT}{h} e^{+(\Delta S^\circ)^{\ddagger}/R} e^{-(\Delta H^\circ)^{\ddagger}/RT} \tag{77}$$

which, with the recognition that the variation of T is small compared with that in the exponential term, agrees in form with the empirical Arrhenius expression.

The exponential term now involves an enthalpy rather than an energy of activation. For liquid systems the difference, as discussed in Sec. 5-3, will be completely negligible and for gaseous systems will be small and, if necessary, can be calculated from $RT \, \Delta n$.

It is again the theoretical interpretation of the pre-exponential A factor that is of particular interest.

11-16. The Entropy of Activation. The transition-state theory interprets the pre-exponential A factor of the Arrhenius equation as

$$A = \frac{kT}{h} e^{+(\Delta S^\circ)^{\ddagger}/R} \tag{78}$$

and, therefore, requires an evaluation of the entropy of activation before a quantitative prediction of A can be made. Since $(\Delta S^\circ)^{\ddagger}$ is the entropy change in going from the reagents to the activated complex and since little can be easily said about the properties of the activated complex, the transition-state theory tends to avoid any definite quantitative predictions. In spite of the ill-defined nature of the transition state, a number of conclusions can be drawn concerning $(\Delta S°)^{\ddagger}$, and these can be compared with the kinetic results.

In gas-phase reactions, such as the formation of hydrogen iodide from hydrogen and iodine, one can recognize that, when the two reagent molecules come together to form the transition state, the total number of translational degrees of freedom decreases from 6 to 3 and the total rotational number from 4 to 3 (or from 6 to 3 if each of the reagents is nonlinear). These degrees of freedom which are lost become 4 (or 6) vibrational degrees of freedom of the activated complex. No matter how weak the bonds are in the transition state, there will be a net loss in freedom of motion when translation and rotation become vibrations. The energy levels of the complex will, according to the discussions of Secs. 6-7 and 7-10, be more widely spaced, and the entropy of the complex will be less than that of the two reagent molecules. These ideas can be carried through more quantitatively if expressions are available for the entropy of the various degrees of freedom. Here we shall be content with the qualitative argument. The experimental pre-exponential factors for quite a number of reactions, like the hydrogen iodide reaction, all lead, with Eq. (78), to negative values for $(\Delta S°)^{\ddagger}$ as the above argument requires. Such a result is not surprising since a reaction which decreases the number of gas-phase molecules proceeds with a negative ΔS. The same effect is expected when two molecules form an activated complex. If, however, the rigidity imposed by the complex is quite small, the entropy change will be correspondingly small. The variation in the pre-exponential factors, as shown in Table 11-9, are therefore readily allowed by, if not calculated from, the detailed nature of the transition-state complex.

An alternative to the interpretation of $K^{\ddagger}$ in terms of $\Delta S^{\ddagger}$ and $\Delta H^{\ddagger}$, as was done to obtain Eq. (76), is to recall the understanding achieved in Secs. 7-7 and 7-8 of an equilibrium constant in terms of the allowed energy levels of the molecular species involved in the reaction. The expression of Eq. (64) of Chap. 7, for example, would allow the equilibrium constant $K^{\ddagger}$ of the reaction

$$A + B \rightarrow (AB)^{\ddagger}$$

to be written as

$$K^{\ddagger} = \frac{Q_{(AB)^{\ddagger}}}{Q_A Q_B} e^{-\Delta E_0^{\ddagger}/RT} \tag{79}$$

Table 11-9. Rate Constants for Second-order Gas-phase Reactions

Reaction	Rate constant (liter/mole sec)
$H_2 + I_2 \rightarrow 2HI$	$2.0 \times 10^9 \sqrt{T}\, e^{-42,500/RT}$
$2HI \rightarrow H_2 + I_2$	$3.3 \times 10^9 \sqrt{T}\, e^{-38,900/RT}$
$2NO_2 \rightarrow 2NO + O_2$	$2.6 \times 10^8 \sqrt{T}\, e^{-26,600/RT}$
$2NOCl \rightarrow 2NO + Cl_2$	$3.3 \times 10^9 \sqrt{T}\, e^{-25,800/RT}$
$NO + Cl_2 \rightarrow NOCl + Cl$	$1 \times 10^8 \sqrt{T}\, e^{-19,600/RT}$
$NO + O_3 \rightarrow NO_2 + O_2$	$6.3 \times 10^7 \sqrt{T}\, e^{-2,300/RT}$
$CH_3I + HI \rightarrow CH_4 + I_2$	$5.2 \times 10^{10} \sqrt{T}\, e^{-33,100/RT}$
$2C_2F_4 \rightarrow \text{cyclo-}C_4F_8$	$3.8 \times 10^6 \sqrt{T}\, e^{-25,600/RT}$

With this interpretation of $K^{\ddagger}$ the transition-state theory, which views the rate of reaction in terms of a frequency times the concentration of the activated complex, leads to a rate constant of

$$k_2 = \nu \frac{Q_{(AB)^{\ddagger}}}{Q_A Q_B} e^{-E_0^{\ddagger}/RT} \qquad (80)$$

This expression shows, even more explicitly than does Eq. (78), that it is necessary to know the details of the energy-level patterns of the transition-state complex in order to calculate the pre-exponential factor in the rate constant.

Some progress can be made, but the uncertainties in rigidity of the complex and the consequent lack of information on the vibrational contributions to the partition function for the complex impose severe limitations on this approach.

For a simple bimolecular reaction involving monatomic species the partition functions of Eq. (80) can, however, be written down. It is necessary only to recall, from Chap. 7, the results that for 3 translational degrees of freedom

$$Q_{\text{trans}} = \left(\frac{2\pi m k T}{h^2}\right)^{\frac{3}{2}}$$

and for 2 rotational degrees of freedom, such as the activated complex AB will have,

$$Q_{\text{rot}} = \frac{8\pi^2 I k T}{h^2}$$

Finally the activated complex will have 1 vibrational degree of freedom. The vibrational partition function $Q_{\text{vib}} = 1/(e^{h\nu/kT} - 1)$ can be simplified with the assumption that the complex is not very tightly bound, ν is low, and $h\nu$ is small compared with kT. The exponential can then be expanded in a series and only the first two terms retained to give

$$Q_{\text{vib}} = \frac{1}{1 + h\nu/kT - 1} = \frac{kT}{h\nu} \qquad (81)$$

Substitution of the partition-function terms in Eq. (80) gives

$$k_2 = \nu \frac{\left[\dfrac{2\pi(m_A + m_B)kT}{h^2}\right]^{\frac{3}{2}} \left[\dfrac{8\pi^2 I k T}{h^2}\right] \dfrac{kT}{h\nu}}{(2\pi m_A kT/h^2)^{\frac{3}{2}}(2\pi m_B kT/h^2)^{\frac{3}{2}}} e^{-\Delta E_0^{\ddagger}/RT} \qquad (82)$$

If the frequency factor for the breakup of the activated complex is identified with the vibrational frequency of the activated complex and the moment-of-inertia expression $I = \mu r^2 = [m_A m_B/(m_A + m_B)](\sigma_A + \sigma_B)^2$ is introduced, Eq. (82) reduces to

$$k_2 = 2(\sigma_A + \sigma_B)^2 \sqrt{\frac{2\pi kT(m_A + m_B)}{m_A m_B}} e^{-\Delta E_0^{\ddagger}/RT}$$

$$= 4(\sigma_A + \sigma_B)^2 \sqrt{\frac{\pi RT}{2\mu_M}} e^{-\Delta E_0^{\ddagger}/RT} \qquad (83)$$

where μ_M, the molar reduced mass, has been introduced.

Equation (83), derived from the transition-state theory, is remarkably similar to the rate constant implied by Eq. (64), obtained from the collision theory. It should be noticed, however, that one expression has the energy difference for the lowest allowed energy levels, while the other has an energy corresponding to an activation energy.

The differences between the two theories of reaction rates is well brought out by the partition-function calculation of the transition-state theory. It is clear that the degrees of freedom of the activated complex must be considered and that these are ignored in the collision theory. On the other hand the activated complex is often too little understood to proceed with the necessary detailed treatment.

Solution reactions present a rather different situation. All solutes, and particularly ions, in solvents other than very inert ones, interact with solvent molecules. The solvent molecules are to some extent oriented about the solute, and this orientation imposes a restriction on the motion of some of the solvent molecules. This solvation is an appreciable factor in determining the entropy of the system. Changes in this solvation entropy must, therefore, be considered in the formation of the activated complex. The uniformly negative value of $\Delta S^{\ddagger}$ for gas-phase reactions, corresponding to a loss of freedom of motion, does not therefore hold for reactions of solvated species in solution.

When oppositely charged ions, for example, react to form a neutral molecule, the extent of solvation is greatly reduced. Even the activated complex, in which the opposite charges will, at least, be close together, can be expected to be formed with a decrease in solvation and a corresponding positive entropy of activation. An example of such a situation is provided by the displacement of water molecules in the reaction

$$Cr(OH_2)_6^{3+} + CNS^- \rightarrow [Cr(OH)_5CNS]^{++}$$

which has a value of $\Delta S^{\ddagger}$ of $+29$ cal/mole deg.

On the other hand, the formation of an activated complex that carries charges when the reagents do not will lead to a large negative value for $\Delta S^{\ddagger}$ corresponding to the additional loss of freedom of motion by the solvating molecules. The displacement of bromide in the reaction step

is an example of such a situation. The entropy of activation for this reaction has been reported as -50 cal/deg mole, a very large negative value.

While not all entropies of activation-of-solution reactions can be so easily rationalized, this type of argument shows how the transition-state theory gives a valuable framework within which observed rate constants can be understood.

RADIATION CHEMISTRY

A number of methods exist for stimulating chemical reactions or decompositions by the interaction of the molecules with high-energy radiation. Of particular importance is the method of photochemistry, in which electromagnetic radiation in the visible or ultraviolet region initiates a reaction. Much of the remainder of the chapter will be devoted to photochemistry. It seems appropriate, however, to mention also the recent and more specialized process in which molecules are bombarded with high-energy electrons. The molecular ions that are produced are generally detected with a mass spectrometer. Finally some chemical results due to the interaction of very high-energy radiation with matter will be pointed out. This subject tends now to preempt the title *radiation chemistry*.

11-17. Light Absorption. In ordinary chemical reactions the energy of activation is supplied by the chance collection in a molecule or a pair of molecules of a large amount of thermal energy. An alternative way in which the necessary activation energy can be acquired is through the absorption of quanta of visible or ultraviolet radiation. Reactions which follow as a result of energy so acquired are classified as *photochemical* reactions. With this description, photochemistry appears as a special branch of kinetics. In practice the theory and the experimental arrangements used in photochemistry set it off as a rather special subject. The goal of these reaction studies is, however, still the elucidation of the mechanism of the reaction.

Basic to the understanding of photochemical processes is an appreciation of the energy acquired by a molecule as a result of the absorption of light. It will be recalled that the energy of a light quantum is related to the frequency of the light by Planck's law, $\epsilon = h\nu$. The energy of an Avogadro's number of light quanta is called an *einstein*. The einstein is, therefore, the energy acquired when each of an Avogadro's number of molecules absorbs one quantum of radiation. The name of the einstein unit of radiation stems from Einstein's photochemical law, which states that each molecule is activated by the absorption of one light quantum.

The amount of energy in an einstein of radiation can be appreciated from a calculation of this quantity for visible light, say of 6,000 A wavelength. The frequency of such light is given by c/λ and the energy in ergs per quantum by $h\nu = hc/\lambda$. Multiplication by Avogadro's number gives the value of the einstein in ergs. Conversion to calories is then obtained by division by 4.18×10^7. In this way it is found that 1 einstein of yellow light has an energy of 45 kcal. Light of shorter wavelength will have a correspondingly higher energy. In the ultraviolet, for example, at a wavelength of 2,000 A, the energy of 1 einstein is $3 \times 45 = 135$ kcal.

From these energy values and the bond energies deduced in the thermodynamic study of Chap. 5, it is seen that the absorption of light in the visible or ultraviolet can be expected to be sufficient to break a chemical bond or at least to produce a high-energy reactive molecule.

The amount of the chemical reaction that occurs in a photochemical experiment is related to the amount of light that is absorbed. The decrease in the intensity of a given wavelength of light as the light traverses a length dl of a cell containing a light-absorbing compound of concentration c is found to be proportional to I, c, and dl, that is,

$$dI = -\alpha c I \, dl \tag{84}$$

where α is a proportionality constant, the *absorption coefficient*. This coefficient is generally very dependent on the wavelength and is large for wavelengths at which absorption occurs. If the incident-light intensity on the cell is I_0 and the intensity after traversal of the cell of length l is I, the Beer's-law expression is obtained from an integration of Eq. (84) as

$$\ln \frac{I_0}{I} = \alpha c l \tag{85}$$

The experimental arrangement for a photochemical experiment is indicated in Fig. 11-8. The source of radiation may be either one that emits a continuum, i.e., radiation of all wavelengths, as does a common tungsten lamp, or one that emits only certain wavelengths, i.e., is a line source, such as a mercury arc. With either type of source an optical filter system is generally used so that only a certain wavelength or range of wavelengths of radiation enters the reaction cell. The reaction cell consists of a tube with flat ends and is made either of Pyrex glass or, if ultraviolet radiation, about 3,000 to 2,000 A, is being studied, of quartz. The detector measures the light intensity with and without the absorbing, reacting material in the reaction cell. The most convenient detectors are a large-area thermopile, a photocell, or a photomultiplier cell. Each of these must, however, be calibrated, usually against a standard lamp placed a specified distance from the detector, so that an absolute value of the amount of light corresponding to the observed electrical output of the detector can be calculated. The data that are obtained in an experiment with the apparatus of Fig. 11-8, using a setup that has been suitably calibrated, allow the determination of the number of light quanta that are absorbed in a particular experiment.

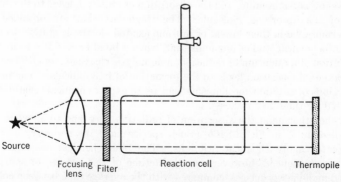

Fig. 11-8. Apparatus for photochemical studies.

A characteristic, and often limiting, feature of photochemical studies is the fact that only a small fraction of an einstein of radiation can be absorbed in a reasonable time with typical monochromatic light sources and experimental systems. In a typical photolysis of methyl cyclopropyl ketone using 2,537 A radiation, for example, experiments lasting about 6 hr resulted in the absorption of about 10^{19} quanta or 1.6×10^{-5} einstein of radiation. We shall see that one frequently gets something like one product molecule for each quantum absorbed and therefore a number of moles of product that is equal to the number of einsteins of radiation absorbed. The analyses of such small fractions of a mole of products, as in this methyl cyclopropyl ketone example, can present considerable experimental difficulties. The use of the mass spectrometer, and more recently of gas chromatography, has been an invaluable aid in the analysis of these small quantities.

11-18. The Primary Process. A photochemical reaction follows from the absorption of a quantum of radiation by a species in the reaction mixture. This absorption of radiation is known as the *primary process* in the photochemical reaction.

In a system involving atoms, those most commonly studied being mercury atoms, this primary process consists in the formation of an excited atom or, if short-wavelength high-energy radiation is used, of the ionized atom.

In molecular systems the equivalent of these two types of primary processes can be recognized, but a great variety of detail can occur. Some of the possible results of the absorption of a quantum of visible or ultraviolet light were mentioned in Sec. 10-3. Again it is convenient to consider the excitation in terms of potential-energy curves which represent the potential energy of the molecule as a function of the internuclear distance of some bond in the molecule.

It is sufficient, for our purposes, to consider again the two excited-state potential-energy curves shown in Fig. 10-16.

The excited electronic state may, as in Fig. 10-16a, correspond to an electronic form in which the electrons of the bond of the absorbing molecule no longer maintain a chemical bond. In such cases the upper-state potential curve shows no minimum, and the absorption of radiation leads to the dissociation of the absorbing molecule. The fragments that are obtained may, furthermore, be in their lowest or in some excited electronic state. In almost all photochemical studies one finds that, when a bond breaks as a result of the absorption of a quantum of radiation, a homolytic cleavage of a chemical bond occurs; i.e., dissociation leads to the formation of free radicals. The previous discussions of reaction mechanisms lead us to expect chemical reactions to be initiated by these free radicals.

On the other hand the absorption of radiation may lead to an excited, but bound, state as in Fig. 10-16b. Such species have the necessary activation energy for many chemical reactions. The photochemical consequences of such species depend, however, on the lifetime of this species, or some other related high-energy species, compared with the average time between collisions of this species and a molecule with which it can react. The fate of an excited molecule, or of the directly formed molecular fragments, is treated under the following heading of Secondary Processes.

11-19. Secondary Processes. A detailed story of the fate of an excited molecule can seldom be given. A number of courses are generally open to a molecule in a high-energy electronic state; some of these lead to the return of the molecule to the ground state by the emission or dissipation of its excess energy, while other paths produce chemical decomposition or reaction.

The most direct path that returns the system to the ground state is, as indicated in Fig. 11-9, the rapid loss of vibrational energy to form the excited state with its lowest vibrational energy and the subsequent emission, which the Franck-Condon principle requires to be vertical, to the ground electronic state. Such a process, known as *fluorescence*, occurs after a relatively short lifetime of about 10^{-9} sec of the upper state. The process allows the excited molecule little chance to participate in a photochemical reaction.

A second process that involves the emission of radiation is *phosphorescence*. Phosphorescence is characterized by an emission of radiation at times longer than about 10^{-5} sec, and up to minutes or hours. It is now quite well established that such long excited-state lifetimes depend on the molecule getting into an excited triplet state, as by the crossing over from one potential-energy curve to another as shown in Fig. 11-10. Such triplet states cannot readily emit radiation and form the ground singlet state because of the selection rule that transitions can occur only between states of like multiplicity. This rule is particularly effective if the molecule under study is embedded in a rigid glass, which minimizes the intermolecular electric-field fluctuations and increases the lifetime of the excited triplet state to times even up to hours.

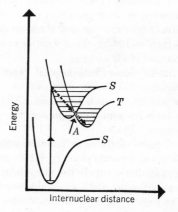

Fig. 11-10. The formation of an excited triplet state by internal conversion from an excited singlet state. (At point A the molecule has the same potential energy, the same internuclear distances, and zero kinetic energy regardless of whether it has the S or T electronic configuration. Crossing from one to the other is therefore relatively easy.)

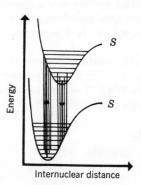

Fig. 11-9. Electronic excitation and fluorescence in a molecule. (Both electronic states are singlets.)

It follows that, if the molecule attains the excited triplet state, it is susceptible to photochemical reaction during its relatively long lifetime.

It may not, however, be necessary for the molecule to emit radiation for the ground state to be reached by the initially excited molecule. For a molecule of any complexity there will be a large number of different excited electronic-energy states, and, furthermore, one or more of these may have a potential-energy curve that crosses that of the ground state. Just as the triplet state was reached from the excited singlet state of Fig. 11-10, so also can the ground state be reached by the crossing over from the potential-energy curves of excited states. Such a process, which appears to be very important in poly-atomic molecules, is known as *internal conversion*. Since this process can be rapid, the molecule with such potential-energy curves will probably be returned to the ground state before a photochemical reaction occurs.

A photochemical reaction can, therefore, be expected to occur if the excited state is a repulsive one and free radicals are formed and do not immediately recombine. Furthermore, if the lifetime of a bound excited state is long enough, i.e., if the energy is not lost too rapidly by fluorescence, or internal conversion to the ground state, a collision can occur which forms intermediate or product species. Experimentally one determines the number of quanta absorbed and the number of molecules of reactant used or of product produced in a given experiment. From these data the *quantum yield*, or *quantum efficiency*, defined as the ratio of the number of molecules reacting to the number of quanta absorbed, is determined. The quantum yield is usually denoted by Φ. A number of reactions have quantum yields close to unity. The extremes, however, go from quantum yields of zero for molecules that absorb visible or ultraviolet radiation and show no photochemical reactions to quantum yields as high as 10^6 for chain reactions such as that which will be discussed for the reaction of H_2 and Cl_2.

11-20. Some Photochemical Reactions. A few representative photochemical reactions will now be discussed to show that detailed reaction mechanisms can be written for such reactions. Although photochemical reactions are studied in both gas and liquid phases, the present examples will be drawn from gas-phase studies.

A particularly clean reaction which can be nicely understood is the photochemical decomposition of HI to give hydrogen and iodine. The absorption of radiation occurs in the ultraviolet at around 2,500 A. The absorption band is a continuum and corresponds to a transition of the type shown in Fig. 10-16a. The primary process can be written as

$$HI + h\nu \rightarrow H\cdot + I\cdot$$

Quantum-yield measurements show that two molecules of HI are decomposed for each quantum absorbed. Secondary reactions that lead to this yield and are energetically reasonable are

$$H\cdot + HI \rightarrow H_2 + I\cdot$$

and
$$M + I\cdot + I\cdot \rightarrow I_2 + M$$

where M is some third body, perhaps the container wall, that takes up the energy liberated by the bond formation.   The sum of the three reaction steps is

$$2HI + h\nu \rightarrow H_2 + I_2$$

which agrees with the quantum-yield data.

A number of other steps can be written, but arguments can be given for assuming them to be unimportant contributors.   As bond energies indicate, for example, the reaction

$$I\cdot + HI \rightarrow I_2 + H\cdot$$

is endothermic to the extent of 35 kcal and would not be expected to be as important as a reaction of H atoms with HI, which is exothermic to the extent of 32 kcal.

It should also be pointed out that, while it is expected that there is very little activation-energy requirement for the reaction between free radicals, the reaction between two monatomic radicals can occur only if a third body, usually the container wall, is present to remove the energy that would be released by bond formation.   The combination of two iodine atoms can occur, therefore, only in the presence of an energy-accepting third body.

The photochemical reaction of H_2 and Cl_2 to form hydrogen chloride is the example par excellence of a photochemical chain reaction.   In this reaction, unlike the first reaction of this section, the possible atomic attacks on the molecular species are all energetically allowed and long reaction chains result.

The primary process is again a molecular dissociation, now resulting from the absorption of radiation by Cl_2; that is,

$$Cl_2 + h\nu \rightarrow 2Cl\cdot$$

The reactions that follow are

$$Cl\cdot + H_2 \rightarrow HCl + H\cdot$$

and

$$H\cdot + Cl_2 \rightarrow HCl + Cl\cdot$$

Again the bond energies of Table 5-5 can be used to show that these reactions are energetically feasible.   The pair of reactions proceed with an energy output of

$$2D_{HCl} - D_{H_2} - D_{Cl_2} = (2)(102) - 103 - 57 = 44 \text{ kcal/mole}$$

Repetition of the two steps will not, therefore, be limited by energy requirements.   The chain-terminating steps that will occur are the three body processes

$$M + 2Cl\cdot \rightarrow Cl_2 + M$$

or

$$M + 2H\cdot \rightarrow H_2 + M$$

or

$$M + H\cdot + Cl\cdot \rightarrow HCl + M$$

At low free-radical concentrations these three body collisions, or wall reactions, will be highly unlikely, and it appears that as many as 1 million chain steps can occur before such a chain-terminating step destroys the free radicals.   The quantum yield in such chain reactions is dependent on the size of the reaction vessel, and this dependence can be attributed to the chain-terminating surface reactions.

More typical of the photochemical reactions that are now being studied is the photolysis of acetone. The presence of the carbonyl group results in the absorption of radiation of about 3,000 A. Such quanta have energy of 95 kcal/mole and are insufficient therefore to cause rupture of the carbonyl double bond. Dissociation does occur, however, and it appears that the weaker adjacent C—C bond breaks to give the primary process

$$CH_3-\overset{\overset{\displaystyle O}{\|}}{C}-CH_3 + h\nu \rightarrow CH_3-\overset{\overset{\displaystyle O}{\|}}{C}\cdot + \cdot CH_3$$

Secondary reactions that explain the principal reaction products of some experiments are the further radical breakup

$$CH_3-\overset{\overset{\displaystyle O}{\|}}{C}\cdot \rightarrow CO + \cdot CH_3$$

and the radical combination

$$\cdot CH_3 + \cdot CH_3 \rightarrow C_2H_6$$

Small amounts of the other products that are observed can also be accounted for by the reactions of the species postulated here.

In one of the early studies on the photolysis of acetone the quantum yield, based on the number of acetone molecules that were decomposed, was measured by Daniels and Damon to be 0.17. Furthermore, a green fluorescence was observed from the reaction cell, and measurements of the quantum output of this radiation showed that it comprised about 3 per cent of the quanta lost by the radiation beam in passing through the reaction cell. It follows, therefore, that about 80 per cent of the absorbed radiation is in this case degraded without emission or reaction.

The primary bond-breaking process in acetone appears typical of such processes in that the bond cleavage occurs near the group in the molecule which is responsible for the absorption of the radiation. It appears to be generally true that either the absorbing bond, or group, or an immediately adjacent bond breaks when the primary process leads to bond cleavage.

11-21. Flash Photolysis. The deduction of a mechanism to explain the products of a photolysis experiment postulates various intermediates and reaction steps. The use of radiation to generate the reaction intermediates gives us a better idea of some of the high-energy species than can be obtained in ordinary thermally controlled chemical reactions. In both thermal and photochemical reactions these high-energy intermediates, or transition states, are present at any time at only a vanishingly low concentration. It is possible, however, to generate these interesting and elusive species in appreciable amounts by the photochemical method known as *flash photolysis*. The apparatus is indicated schematically in Fig. 11-11.

A flash of light, of duration of about 10^{-5} sec, can be generated with as much as 500 cal of light energy. In the visible region this means that about 10^{-3} einstein of radiation is emitted, and therefore if this flash is allowed to fall on a small sample, of millimole size, most of the sample molecules can be brought to an excited state. The opportunity is thereby given for directly studying the initial excited state or those states which follow quickly from it.   The opportunity, however, must be quickly grasped since within a matter of milliseconds all intermediates will have been converted to final products.   It is possible, however, to synchronize a spectroscopic flash of light to follow the principal flash by some fraction of a millisecond.   This spectroscopic flash can be used, in the setup of Fig. 11-11, to obtain an absorption spectrum of the species present at the time of the spectroscopic flash.   In this way one can obtain not only indications of what species are generated by the principal flash but also data as to how these species vary, or give rise to others, in the milliseconds that follow the formation of the primary process products.   A very direct picture of the kinetic behavior of reaction intermediates can thus be obtained.

Many interesting results are being produced by this difficult but powerful technique.

11-22. Mass-spectroscopic Results.   Mass spectroscopy provides a rather special, but very promising, method for studying molecular species that do not exist under ordinary conditions but may be important as reaction intermediates.   The mass spectrometer has already established itself as an analytical tool of great value, and although the data that are obtained are used primarily for analyses, it is being recognized that interesting chemical features are exhibited by these data.

Mass spectra are obtained in an apparatus shown schematically in Fig. 11-12.   Positive ions of the gas sample are produced as a result of the bombarding electron beam which knocks electrons, or negative groups, from the molecule and thereby produces excited and reactive species.   Of the ions that are produced, only the singly positively charged ions are usually detected.   They are

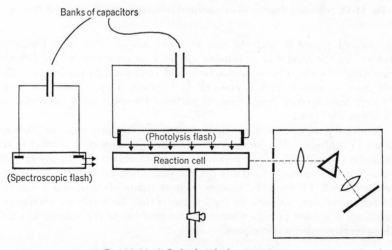

Fig. 11-11. A flash photolysis apparatus.

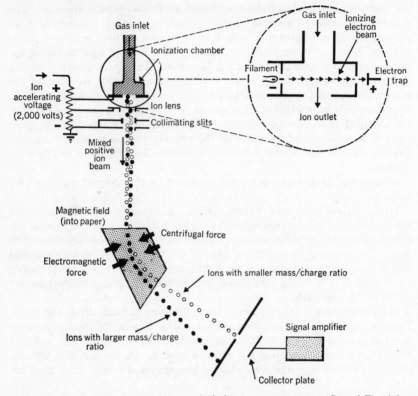

Fig. 11-12. Schematic diagram of an analytical mass spectrometer. (*General Electric.*)

accelerated, passed through the magnetic field, and detected by an ionization gauge. In the same way as isotopic species were separated by the different curvatures of their paths in the magnetic field, so also are the particles of different mass separated when a molecule is fragmented by an electron beam. Typical mass-spectral fragmentation patterns for some small molecules are shown in Fig. 11-13.

It is such patterns, which are characteristic of the sample molecule, that are of use in analyses. The *parent peak*, which has the same mass number as the molecule under study, may or may not show up prominently. In any case the over-all pattern is characteristic of the molecule, and such patterns can be used to distinguish, for example, isomers such as normal butane and isobutane. Clearly, moreover, the data on the fragments that are produced when a gas-phase ion is formed provide a wealth of information on the manner in which these reactive species decompose.

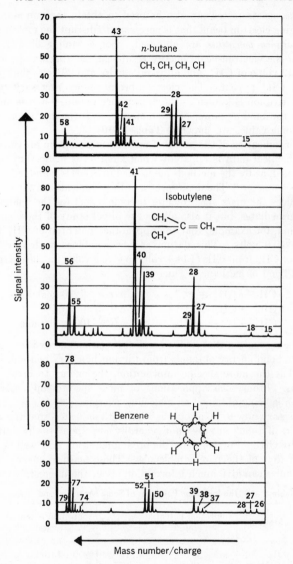

Fig. 11-13. The mass spectra of several hydrocarbons. Most fragments that are detected have a single positive charge. The abscissa numbers then show the mass numbers of the fragments formed by the electron impact. (*Spectra courtesy of G. Barenholz, Case Institute of Technology.*)

The mass spectrometer can also be used to obtain the minimum energy of the impinging electron beam that is necessary to disrupt the molecule. In this way *appearance potentials* are obtained. For a sample of CH_4 a gradual increase in the electron-beam energy results in the appearance, at about an energy of 12 volts, of CH_4^+, and at about 14, 15, and 22 volts the species CH_3^+, CH_2^+, and CH^+ appear. The electron-beam energy necessary to form the parent positive ion is known as the appearance potential and is an indication of the electron-binding power of the molecule, as is the ionization potential of atoms. Some values are shown in Table 11-10.

A further indication of the power of mass spectroscopy in providing valuable physical chemical data is apparent when mention is made that free radicals can be formed, as by the methods mentioned in Sec. 11-3, and led directly into a mass spectrometer. The mass spectra of these radicals can then be obtained. Not only does the mass spectrometer become a tool for the analysis of these active intermediates, but it also allows the direct study of these species.

It is found, for example, that the appearance potential of CH_3^+ from $\cdot CH_3$ radicals is 10.0 volts. This datum can be combined with the appearance potential for CH_3^+ from CH_4 of 14.4 volts to give a value for the energy required to break a bond of methane. Thus

(1) $\quad \cdot CH_3 \rightarrow CH_3^+ + e^- \qquad \Delta H = +230 \text{ kcal/mole}$
(2) $\quad CH_4 \rightarrow CH_3^+ + H\cdot + e^- \qquad \Delta H = +330$
(2 − 1) $\quad CH_4 \rightarrow H\cdot + \cdot CH_3 \qquad \Delta H = 100 \text{ kcal/mole}$

It should be recognized that such a bond-dissociation energy is not the same as the average bond energy obtained from thermochemistry methods in Sec. 5-9. Here one has the more specific information, the energy to break one of the CH_4 bonds. From such applications of mass spectroscopy much detailed information is being obtained on molecular energies.

It is necessary now to point out, as Fig. 11-13 indicates, that the appearance of fragments of a molecule does not generally correspond to the simple pattern exhibited by CH_4. Furthermore, the predominant ion may well be something other than that of the parent molecule. These features suggest that mass-spectral studies can give much information about the interesting chemistry of

Table 11-10. The Ionization Potentials of Some Molecules and Radicals*

Molecule	Ionization potential (volts)	Radical	Ionization potential (volts)
H_2	15.44	H	13.62
CH_4	13.12	CH_2	11.9
C_2H_2	11.42	CH_3	9.96
C_2H_4	10.56	C_2H_3	8.69
C_2H_6	11.62	C_2H_5	8.72
C_3H_8	11.21		
$n\text{-}C_4H_{10}$	10.80		

* From F. H. Field and J. L. Franklin, "Electron Impact Phenomena," Academic Press Inc., New York, 1957.

these gas-phase high-energy carbonium ions. The *cracking* patterns shown in Fig. 11-13 for a number of hydrocarbon molecules indicate that there is, for each molecule, a characteristic pattern of fragments. While little progress has been made in understanding the basis for these patterns, it is clear that a wealth of information on the disintegrations of gas-phase molecules is given by these mass spectra.

Results such as these suggest some of the many interesting structures that occur in these ion fragments. Their importance as possible reaction intermediates is the purpose for which mass-spectral results were introduced here. However, it should be mentioned that the occurrence of species such as CH_5^+, which are formed, presents interesting challenges to our theories of chemical binding.

11-23. High-energy Radiation. The photons used in photochemical studies have energies up to about 150 kcal/einstein or about 6.5 ev. The electron beam of a mass spectrometer consists of electrons accelerated to voltages of about 100 volts. Radiation with much higher energy is, however, available. Electromagnetic radiation with energies up to about 500 ev is usually classified as X rays and beyond this and up into the million-electron-volt (Mev) range the electromagnetic radiation, such as is given off by radioactive CO^{60}, is known as γ *rays*. Also of interest in radiation chemistry are the high-energy electron beams, typically with million-electron-volt energies, produced in a linear accelerator.

The study of the consequences of the passage of such radiation, with energies enormously greater than that required to excite a molecule or break a chemical bond, is relatively recent. It is already evident, however, that this branch of radiation chemistry is exceedingly complex. The selectivity of photochemistry, which allows a particular high-energy electronic state to be populated, is entirely lost. At present few general results can be recognized in the chemical decompositions that follow the passage of high-energy radiation through a material.

Cloud-chamber experiments, in which, for example, cosmic rays are detected as they pass through a supersaturated methyl alcohol vapor by the track of condensed vapor that they leave, are early experiments that can suggest the mechanism of many high-energy radiation reactions. These cloud-chamber tracks apparently consist of groups of condensed droplets along the path of the high-energy particle. It appears that the high-energy particle knocks out an electron from a molecule and that this electron has sufficient energy, say 100 ev, to in turn ionize many molecules. The clusters of condensation correspond therefore to the positions where the primary electron was generated and reacted further to form many more charged centers. It appears, from ionization-chamber experiments, that, quite independently of the nature of the material, it takes about 30 to 35 ev to form an ion pair. A 1-Mev particle penetrating a material will, therefore, form many clusters of ions.

It is generally accepted that, with very high-energy radiation, the molecular disruption is such that ionized species are formed, as they certainly are when such radiation passes through a gas-filled ionization chamber.

Thus in the radiolysis of water the initial step has been postulated to be

$$H_2O \xrightarrow{h\nu} H_2O^+ + e^-$$

The high-energy H_2O^+ species can be expected to decompose readily according to

$$H_2O^+ \rightarrow H^+ + \cdot OH$$

Likewise the ejected electron will probably travel away from the site at which it was generated and will be captured by a molecule to give the reaction

$$H_2O + e^- \rightarrow H \cdot + OH^-$$

Thus the expectation is that along the track of the high-energy radiation particle H^+ and $\cdot OH$ will be formed, while in the body of the solution there will occur the species $H \cdot$ and OH^-. The small amounts of H_2 and H_2O_2 that are formed can be accounted for by combinations of $H \cdot$ and $\cdot OH$ radicals.

The most actively investigated area in radiolysis is, perhaps, that of polymer irradiation. Modification of polymeric materials on irradiation is the chief goal of such studies. The chemical consequences in these rather rigid systems provide, however, problems of considerable chemical interest. Irradiation of polyethylene is, apparently, typical in that a chief result is the formation of cross links between the polyethylene chains and the evolution of hydrogen. The cross-linked material that is formed has a greater rigidity and higher melting point than the original material, and such modifications are often very desirable in polymer technology. The mechanism consists, apparently, of the formation of free-radical centers in the polyethylene chains. These free radicals cannot, particularly at low temperatures, readily react since they are held in the more or less rigid polymer molecule. At ordinary temperatures the centers can apparently migrate along the molecular chain until radical sites on neighboring chains are in a position to combine to form a cross-linking chemical bond.

Problems

1. What are the units of the rate constants of first-, second-, and third-order reactions if the concentrations are expressed in moles per liter and the time in seconds? If the rate of a reaction obeyed the rate law $k[A][B]^{\frac{1}{2}}$, what would be the units of k?

2. Using the data of Table 11-5, prepare graphs like those of Fig. 11-3 for the hydrolysis of *tert*-butyl bromide at 50°C.

(a) Is the reaction first-order at this temperature?

(b) What are the rate constant and the half-life at 50°C?

(c) Show the half-lives on the plot of c versus t. See that the concentration does fall to half its value in time $t_{\frac{1}{2}}$ regardless of the concentration considered.

Ans. (b) $k = 0.013$ min^{-1}.

3. The reaction by which a tertiary chlorine, as in *tert*-butyl chloride, is replaced by a hydroxyl group appears to result from the formation of a carbonium ion which subsequently adds water or hydroxide. The reaction with $(CH_3)_3CCl$ is quite rapid,

$$\begin{array}{c} CH_2{-}CH_2 \\ \diagup \qquad \diagdown \end{array}$$

while that with $HC{-}CH_2{-}CH_2{-}C{-}Cl$ is imperceptibly slow. What do these rela-

$$\begin{array}{c} \diagdown \qquad \diagup \\ CH_2{-}CH_2 \end{array}$$

tive rates imply about the preferred geometry of the carbonium ion?

4. The hydration of ethylene oxide in aqueous solution proceeds according to the over-all equation

$$CH_2\!\!-\!\!CH_2 + H_2O \rightarrow CH_2OHCH_2OH$$
$$\diagdown O \diagup$$

The rate of the reaction has been followed by Bronsted, Kilpatrick, and Kilpatrick [*J. Am. Chem. Soc.*, **51**: 428 (1929)] by measuring the change in volume of the liquid system. (This is done by observing the height of the liquid in the capillary tube of a dilatometer, a large, thermometer-like reaction cell.) They obtained the following results, at 20°C, using 0.12 M ethylene oxide and 0.007574 M HClO$_4$.

t (min)	0	30	60	90	120	240	300	360	390	∞
h (arbitrary units)	18.48	18.05	17.62	17.25	16.89	15.70	15.22	14.80	14.62	12.30

Confirm that the reaction is first-order with respect to ethylene oxide. What is the rate constant? Suggest a mechanism for the reaction that is consistent with the rate data.

Ans. $k = 0.00247$ min^{-1}.

5. Deduce the pressure of unreacted *tert*-butyl peroxide as a function of time, at 147.2°C, from the total pressure data of Table 11-6. By a suitable graphical treatment, show that these pressure data also indicate a first-order reaction and that the same rate constant as that reported in Fig. 11-4 is obtained.

6. Show that the pressure data for the *tert*-butyl peroxide decomposition at 154.9°C given in Table 11-6 are consistent with a first-order rate equation. What are the rate constant and the half-life of the reaction at this temperature?

7. According to the Lindemann description of the process of a first-order gas-phase reaction, could the addition of an inert gas ever alter the rate of such a reaction? Under what conditions and in what way?

8. Calculate a first-order rate constant for each concentration datum at 25°C for the reaction of *tert*-butyl bromide given in Table 11-5. Do these results indicate a first-order reaction?

Assume that the reaction is second-order in *tert*-butyl bromide. Calculate values for the second-order rate constant at each of the reported times. Does the reaction follow a second-order rate law?

9. The gaseous dimerization of butadiene has been followed by measurement of the total gas pressure by Vaughan [*J. Am. Chem. Soc.*, **54**: 3863 (1932)]. The following data were obtained at 326°C.

t (min)	0	3.25	8.02	12.18	17.30	24.55	33.00	42.50
P (mm)	(632.0)	618.5	599.4	584.2	567.3	546.8	527.8	509.3

t (min)	55.08	68.05	90.05	119.00	176.67	259.50	373
P (mm)	490.2	474.6	453.3	432.8	405.3	381.0	357.1

What is the order of the reaction, and what is the rate constant? Suggest a mechanism.

Ans. $k = 2.4 \times 10^{-5}$ mm^{-1} min^{-1}.

10. The displacement of bromide by thiosulfate ion has been studied at 37.50°C, in the reaction

$$n\text{-}C_3H_7Br + S_2O_3^= \rightarrow C_3H_7S_2O_3^- + Br^-$$

by Crowell and Hammett [*J. Am. Chem. Soc.*, **70**: 3444 (1948)]. The thiosulfate-ion concentration remaining at various times was determined by titration with iodine. From these data and the known initial concentrations the following data were obtained:

t (sec)	0	1,110	2,010	3,192	5,052	7,380	11,232	78,840
Conc. $S_2O_3^-$ (moles/liter)	0.0966	0.0904	0.0863	0.0819	0.0766	0.0720	0.0668	0.0571
Conc. C_3H_7Br (moles/liter)	0.0395	0.0333	0.0292	0.0248	0.0196	0.0149	0.0097	0.0000

Derive the rate equation, including a numerical value for the rate constant, for this reaction.

Ans. $k = 1.6 \times 10^{-3}$ liter mole^{-1} sec^{-1}

11. Benzene diazonium chloride in aqueous solution decomposes according to the equation

$$\langle\!\!\!\!\!\bigcirc\!\!\!\!\!\rangle\!\!-\!\!\overset{+}{N}\!\!\equiv\!\!N,\ Cl^- \rightarrow \langle\!\!\!\!\!\bigcirc\!\!\!\!\!\rangle\!\!-\!\!Cl + N_2$$

and the reaction can be conveniently followed by the amount of N_2 evolved. Cain and Nicoll [*J. Chem. Soc.*, **81**: 1412 (1902)] report the following results, for 20°C and 35 cc of a solution containing 10 g of diazobenzene chloride per liter:

t (min)	116	192	355	481	1,282	1,429	∞
Cc of N_2 evolved (measured at 13°C and 750 mm)	9.7	16.2	26.3	33.7	51.4	54.3	60.0

What is the order of the reaction, and what is the rate constant?

12. Using the dissociation energies of Table 5-5, show that, in terms of energy requirements, the reaction $H_2 + Cl_2 \rightarrow 2HCl$ can sustain a chain process, whereas the reaction $H_2 + I_2 \rightarrow 2HI$ cannot.

13. The radioactive decay of radium, with half-life 1,590 years, leads to the formation of the inert gas radon, which, with a half-life of 3.82 days, decays further. If a sample of radium is kept in a sealed vial, the radon gas collects.

(*a*) Derive an expression for the number of radon atoms present as a function of time if a 1-g sample of radium is considered. The expression need be valid only for a time interval of less than about 1 year.

(*b*) Plot the number of atoms of radon as a function of time in the time interval 0 to 2 weeks.

(*c*) The amount of radon is seen to reach a constant value, and radon is said to be in *secular equilibrium* with radium. Why does this differ from ordinary equilibrium?

14. Consider the schematic hypothetical reaction mechanism

$$A \underset{k_{-1}}{\overset{k_1}{\rightleftharpoons}} B$$

$$B + A \underset{k_2}{\rightarrow} C$$

(*a*) Write down expressions for the net rate of change of each of the species A, B, and C.

(*b*) If B is a species that is present in only undetectably small amounts at all times, obtain an expression for the concentration of B in terms of the concentrations of the major reagents A and C.

(c) Obtain, with the result of part b, rate equations for the disappearance of A and for the formation of C.

(d) What relative values of the rate constants would result in the reaction being first-order with respect to A? What values would make it second-order?

15. By what factor would the rate of a reaction, for which the activation energy is 35 kcal, be increased by a temperature rise of 10°C, from 25°C to 35°C?

Ans. 6.7.

16. Calculate the entropies of activation at 25°C for the reactions of Table 11-9. Recognize that low pre-exponential factors can be explained by either a steric difficulty, as the collision theory would suggest, or a very unfavorable entropy of activation, as the transition-state theory would express it.

Ans. $\Delta S^{\pm} = -20.6$ cal/deg for H_2, I_2.

17. According to Table 7-2 the entropy of a fairly simple gas-phase molecule is in the range 40 to 50 cal/deg mole at room temperature. Recognize that the entropies of activation obtained in Prob. 14 do not correspond to the formation of one firmly bound transition-state complex from two reagent molecules. How can the difference between 40 to 50 and the values of Prob. 14 be explained?

18. What is the absorption coefficient of a solute which absorbs 90 per cent of a certain wavelength of light when the light beam is passed through a 1-cm cell containing a 0.25 M solution?

Ans. $\alpha = 0.41$ liters/mole cm.

19. How many kilocalories of energy would 1 mole of acetone acquire if 1 mole absorbed 1 einstein of ultraviolet radiation of wavelength 2,537 A? How does this compare with the C=O bond energy?

20. Irradiation of HI vapor with ultraviolet radiation of wavelength 2,070 A leads to the formation of H_2 and I_2. It has been observed that for every calorie of radiant energy that is absorbed, 0.00184 g of HI is decomposed. How many HI molecules were decomposed per quantum of absorbed radiation?

Ans. 2.

21. A reaction vessel of volume 1 liter contained, at the beginning of a photochemical study, an amount of Cl_2 to give a partial pressure of half an atm at 25°C and an equal pressure of H_2. Irradiation with radiation of 4,000 A wavelength results in the absorption of 1.50 cal of radiant energy and the decrease in the partial pressure of Cl_2 from 0.5 atm to 10 mm Hg, the temperature being held at 25°C.

How many molecules of HCl are formed for each quantum absorbed?

22. A 100-watt sodium-vapor lamp radiates most of its energy in the yellow D line at 5,890 A. How long would such a lamp take to excite more than half the molecules of an absorbing species in a 1-millimole sample if all the radiant energy were absorbed by the sample?

Ans. 1.0 sec.

23. The bond energy of H_2 is 103 kcal/mole, the ionization potential of a hydrogen atom is 13.60 volts, and its electron affinity is 0.74 volts. What appearance potential might be calculated for H^+ in a mass-spectroscopic analysis of H_2?

The bond energy of H_2^+ can be calculated quantum mechanically to be 61 kcal/mole. What would be the appearance potential of H_2^+ in the mass spectrum of H_2?

24. How can the observation that high-energy radiation produces a number of ion pairs that is approximately equal to the energy of the radiation, expressed in electron volts, divided by 30 or 35, be understood when it is known that ionization potentials are much less than 30 volts?

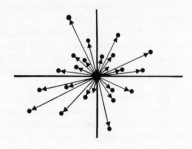

12

Liquids

Our study of those physical chemical phenomena that depend primarily on the mutual effects of a large number of molecules begins with an investigation into the nature of the liquid state. As with most of the succeeding subjects, our knowledge of the properties of individual molecules will be of frequent help. Of prime importance, however, in the behavior of condensed states are the interactions among the individual molecules. Since the nature of these interactions is not easily understood and since it is the mutual interactions of many molecules, or atoms, or ions, the theoretical treatment of condensed states is less satisfactory than the corresponding treatment of individual molecules. A greater dependence on experimental results will therefore be evident.

12-1. The Vapor Pressure of Liquids. A suitable property with which to introduce the study of liquids is the equilibrium vapor pressure, or, simply, the vapor pressure. The vapor pressure i.e., the pressure of the vapor that produces equilibrium between the vapor and the liquid, is readily susceptible to thermodynamic treatment, and such treatment, moreover, leads to values for the heat and entropy of vaporization of the liquid. Molecular-type models of the nature of liquids can then be set up in attempts to interpret these thermodynamic results.

A number of different techniques and devices are available for the measurement of vapor pressures. The apparatus of two methods that are frequently encountered are shown in Fig. 12-1. These methods are applicable to the pressure range from millimeters of mercury to about 1 atm. The high vapor pressures encountered near the critical temperature and the low vapor pressures, of high-molecular-weight compounds, for example, call for special procedures. Table 12-1 and Fig. 12-2 show some of the results that have been obtained for the temperature dependence of the vapor pressure of some simple liquids.

Table 12-1. Vapor Pressure of Liquids as a Function of Temperature

$t°C$	Vapor pressure (mm Hg)					
	H_2O	CCl_4	Acetone, $CH_3-\overset{\overset{O}{\|\|}}{C}-CH_3$	Ethyl ether, $(C_2H_5)_2O$	Ethyl alcohol, C_2H_5OH	n-octane, $CH_3(CH_2)_6CH_3$
0	4.58	33	. . . . .	185	12	3
10	9.21	56	116	292	24	6
20	17.54	91	185	442	44	10
30	31.82	143	283	647	79	18
40	55.32	216	421	921	135	31
50	92.51	317	613	1,277	222	49
60	149.38	451	866	. . . . .	353	78
70	233.7	622	1,200	. . . . .	542	118
80	355.1	843	. . . . .	. . . . .	813	175
90	525.8	1,122	. . . . .	. . . . .	1,187	253
100	760.0	1,463	. . . . .	. . . . .	. . . . .	354

The temperature dependence of the equilibrium between liquid and vapor can now be related, through thermodynamic relations previously obtained, to other thermodynamic properties. The treatment here assumes a liquid-vapor equilibrium, but it should be recognized that the derivation is equally applicable to solid-vapor and liquid-solid equilibria.

The free energy of 1 mole of liquid is equal to the free energy of 1 mole of the vapor that is in equilibrium with the liquid. We can write therefore

$$G_{liq} = G_{vap} \tag{1}$$

and, for an infinitesimal change in the system for which equilibrium is maintained, the differential equation

$$dG_{liq} = dG_{vap} \tag{2}$$

can be written.

In Sec. 7-4 it was shown that such free-energy changes could be related to the pressure and temperature changes that are imposed on each phase of the system. The equation

$$dG = V \, dP - S \, dT \tag{3}$$

was derived.

Application of this equation to the liquid and to the equilibrium vapor, it being recognized that both phases are at the same temperature and pressure, gives

$$V_{liq} \, dP - S_{liq} \, dT = V_{vap} \, dP - S_{vap} \, dT \tag{4}$$

or

$$\frac{dP}{dT} = \frac{S_{vap} - S_{liq}}{V_{vap} - V_{liq}} \tag{5}$$

The entropy difference between 1 mole of liquid and 1 mole of vapor can be calculated directly from the definition of entropy changes [Eq. (22) of Chap. 6] and the fact that the heat absorbed in the equilibrium transformation, at

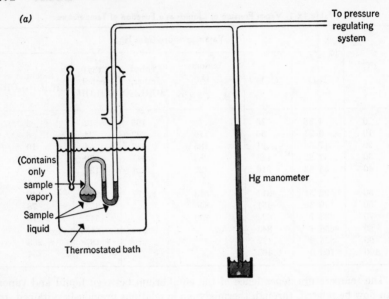

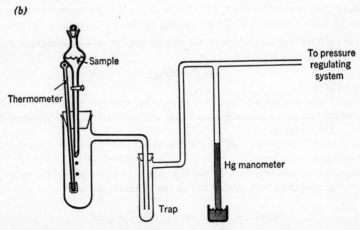

Fig. 12-1. Methods of vapor-pressure determination. (a) The isoteniscope. When the external pressure is equal to the vapor pressure, the sample manometer will show equal heights in the two arms. (b) The Ramsey Young apparatus. The bulb of the thermometer is at the temperature of the liquid, which is in equilibrium with the pressure in the system.

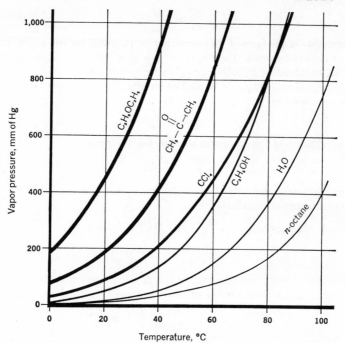

Fig. 12-2. The dependence of the vapor pressure of some liquids on the temperature.

a fixed temperature, of liquid to vapor is the heat of vaporization at that temperature.

Thus, the conversion of 1 mole of liquid to 1 mole of vapor is accompanied by the entropy change

$$S_{vap} - S_{liq} = \int_{n=0}^{n=1} \frac{\Delta H_{vap}\, dn}{T} = \frac{\Delta H_{vap}}{T} \int_{n=0}^{n=1} dn$$
$$= \frac{\Delta H_{vap}}{T}$$

Substitution of this relation into Eq. (5) gives the Clapeyron expression for the liquid-vapor equilibrium,

$$\frac{dP}{dT} = \frac{\Delta H_{vap}}{T(V_{vap} - V_{liq})} \qquad (6)$$

This expression should be recognized, however, as being exactly applicable to any phase transitions if the appropriate ΔH and ΔV terms are entered.

For liquid-vapor equilibria at temperatures well below the critical temperature, as is often the condition of interest, the liquid volume V_{liq} can be neglected compared with the vapor volume V_{vap} in Eq. (5). With this approximation and Eq. (6) we obtain

$$\frac{dP}{dT} = \frac{\Delta H_{vap}}{V_{vap}T} \tag{7}$$

This equation is one form of the expression for the temperature–vapor-pressure relation that is known as the *Clausius-Clapeyron equation*. It is convenient, however, to introduce a further, simplifying approximation.

If the equilibrium vapor is treated as an ideal gas, the molar vapor volume can be expressed as

$$V_{vap} = \frac{RT}{P} \tag{8}$$

and substitution of this approximation in Eq. (7) gives

$$\frac{dP}{dT} = \frac{\Delta H_{vap}P}{RT^2} \tag{9}$$

This result rearranges to the most generally used differential forms of the Clausius-Clapeyron equation,

$$\frac{d(\ln p)}{dT} = \frac{\Delta H_{vap}}{RT^2} \tag{10}$$

and

$$\frac{d(\ln P)}{d(1/T)} = -\frac{\Delta H_{vap}}{R} \tag{11}$$

The integrated form, with the assumption of a constant value of ΔH_{vap} over the temperature range considered, written in terms of logarithms to the base 10, is

$$\log P = -\frac{\Delta H_{vap}}{2.303R}\frac{1}{T} + \text{const} \tag{12}$$

The preceding derivation indicates that a plot of $\log P$ versus $1/T$ should give a straight line and that the slope of such a line is to be identified with $-(\Delta H_{vap}/2.303R)$. As the curves of Fig. 12-3 show, essentially linear plots are obtained. A more careful look at such results, however, reveals deviations from linearity, and these deviations can be attributed to the approximations that have been introduced in obtaining Eqs. (10) to (12).

An interesting kinetic-molecular description of the way in which the equilibrium vapor pressure is established can be given. In this view the equilibrium is described in terms of the balancing of the rate of evaporation with the rate of condensation.

At any temperature, as a result of the thermal jostling of the liquid molecules, some molecules will acquire sufficient energy to overcome the forces of the neighboring molecules and to break away from the liquid. At any temperature there will therefore be a rate of escape of molecules from the liquid. There will furthermore be continual collisions of the vapor molecules with the liquid surface. Again, at a given temperature, a fraction of the colliding molecules will have so little kinetic energy, or will so dissipate their energy on collision with the surface, that they will add to the liquid phase rather than bounce back into the vapor. These opposing processes of evaporation and condensation reach, at a given temperature, an equilibrium state that is characterized by the equilibrium vapor pressure.

On the basis of this picture an interpretation of the temperature dependence of the vapor pressure can be given. Only those liquid molecules can escape

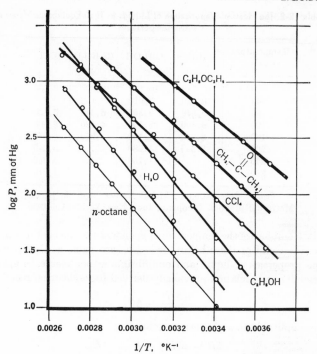

Fig. 12-3. log P versus $1/T$ for the vapor pressures of the liquids of Table 12-1.

which acquire some amount of energy which is enough to overcome the attractive forces of the neighboring molecules. The fraction of liquid molecules that have energy greater than this amount will be proportional to a Boltzmann-type expression $e^{-(\text{energy}/RT)}$. Thus we can expect the vapor pressure to be given by a relation

$$P \propto e^{-(\text{energy}/RT)} \tag{13}$$

and

$$\ln P = -\frac{\text{energy}}{RT} + \text{const} \tag{14}$$

In this way a molecular interpretation is given to the form of the Clausius-Clapeyron equation.

A more profitable molecular interpretation of the free energies of the liquid and the vapor will be considered in Sec. 12-3.

12-2. The Heat and Entropy of Vaporization. Heats of vaporization can be obtained either from the vapor-pressure relations of the previous section or by direct measurement. Direct measurement usually depends on the collection and measurement of the amount of liquid converted to vapor by a measured electrical heat input. Table 12-2 shows some heats of vaporization, i.e., the heat required for the conversion of liquid to the equilibrium vapor, for a number of compounds at various temperatures.

Table 12-2. The Heats of Vaporization of Liquids to Their Equilibrium Vapor at Various Temperatures*

Temperature (°C)	H_2O	C_2H_5OH	$(C_2H_5)_2O$	CCl_4
0	10,710	10,130	ʻ6,890	8,000
40	10,320	9,910	6,150	
80	9,940	9,360	5,340	7,120
120	9,490	8,400	4,520	6,500
160	8,940	7,160	3,260	5,870
200	8,330	5,280	.....	5,040
240	......	1,760	.....	3,950
280	......	......	.....	1,610

* From "International Critical Tables," vol. 5, p. 138, McGraw-Hill Book Company, Inc., New York, 1926–1930.

Such data emphasize the temperature dependence of the heat of vaporization and show the trend of these heats toward a zero value as the critical point, where the properties of liquid and equilibrium vapor merge, is approached. The thermodynamic relation previously derived for a chemical reaction

$$\frac{d(\Delta H)}{dT} = \Delta C_p \qquad (15)$$

is equally applicable to a physical reaction if

$$\Delta H = \Delta H_{vap} = H_{vap} - H_{liq} \qquad (16)$$

and
$$\Delta C_p = (C_p)_{vap} - (C_p)_{liq} \qquad (17)$$

The nonzero value for $d(\Delta H_{vap})/dT$ implies, therefore, that the heat capacity of a liquid is, as would be expected, different from that of the equilibrium vapor.

An interesting empirical generalization involving heats of vaporization at the normal boiling point was made by F. Trouton in 1884. *Trouton's rule* states that the heat of vaporization in calories per mole divided by the normal boiling point, on the absolute scale, is approximately 21 for most liquids, i.e.,

$$\frac{\Delta H_{vap}}{T_{bp}} \cong 21 \text{ cal/deg} \qquad (18)$$

Tests of Trouton's rule are shown for a number of compounds in Table 12-3, and, as these data indicate, a very large number of compounds with very different boiling points and heats of vaporization give values of the Trouton-rule ratio close to 21. Two classes of compounds, however, show serious disagreements, and for both classes these deviations from the rule can be given explanations.

It is important, first of all, to notice that Trouton's rule states that the entropy of vaporization at the normal boiling point is approximately the same for many liquids and that it has the value of 21, that is,

$$\Delta S_{vap} = 21 \text{ cal/deg} \qquad (19)$$

This statement suggests that a theoretical approach which would explain this uniformity in ΔS_{vap} might be possible and that for this purpose it would not be

Table 12-3. Heats and Entropies of Vaporization of Liquids at Their Normal Boiling Points

Liquid	Normal bp (°C)	ΔH_{vap} (cal/mole)	$\Delta S_{vap} = \Delta H_{vap}/T$ (cal/deg mole)
Helium, He...................	−268.9	24	5.7
Hydrogen, H_2................	−252.7	216	10.6
Acetic acid, CH_3COOH........	118.2	5,830	14.9
Formic acid, HCOOH.........	100.8	5,760	15.4
Nitrogen, N_2.................	−195.5	1,330	17.1
n-butane, C_4H_{10}..............	−1.5	5,320	19.6
Naphthalene, $C_{10}H_8$...........	218	9,670	19.7
Methane, CH_4.................	−161.4	2,216	19.8
Ethyl ether, $(C_2H_5)_2O$.........	34.6	6,210	20.2
Cyclohexane, C_6H_{12}...........	80.7	7,190	20.3
Carbon tetrachloride, CCl_4......	76.7	7,170	20.5
Stannic chloride, $SnCl_4$........	112	7,900	20.5
Benzene, C_6H_6................	80.1	7,353	20.8
Chloroform, $CHCl_3$...........	61.5	7,050	21.0
Hydrogen sulfide, H_2S.........	−59.6	4,500	21.1
Mercury, Hg................	356.6	14,166	22.5
Ammonia, NH_3...............	−33.4	5,560	23.2
Methyl alcohol, CH_3OH.......	64.7	8,430	24.9
Water, H_2O..................	100.0	9,717	26.0
Ethyl alcohol, C_2H_5OH........	78.5	9,220	26.2

necessary to become involved with the details of the individual liquids. The next section indicates some of the progress that can be made in this direction.

Those liquids which have entropies of vaporization appreciably higher than the average value of 21 are all of the type that are associated through hydrogen bonding in the liquid state. Water is the best example. The hydrogen bonding in the liquid results in a considerable restriction to the freedom of the molecules of the liquid and, as discussed in Secs. 6-7 and 7-10, in a decrease in the entropy of such liquids compared to normal liquids. Since association of such molecules is of minor importance in the vapor, the unusually large entropy of vaporization can be understood.

The carboxylic acids in Table 12-3 illustrate the opposite deviation, showing small values of the entropy of vaporization. These molecules also form hydrogen bonds, but here the bonds result in the formation of dimers, which persist to an appreciable extent in the vapor state. One mole of liquid in which association is complete in both the liquid and the vapor state would effectively consist of $\frac{1}{2}$ mole of dimers and would have half the expected molar entropy, since, according to Trouton's rule, the entropy of vaporization is independent of molecular weight. The observed carboxylic vaporization entropies show some of this effect.

It has been shown by Hildebrand that a more consistent set of entropies of **vaporization** are obtained if they are calculated not at the normal boiling point but rather at temperatures at which the vapors of the different compounds have the same molar concentrations. This variation of Trouton's rule improves the over-all constancy of the calculated entropies of vaporization, but the abnormalities of the hydrogen-bonded liquids still show up.

12-3. A Theory of Liquids and of the Entropy of Vaporization. One of the prime goals of a theory of the liquid state is the calculation of the free energy of the liquid. A calculation of this quantity would lead to a theoretical value for the pressure at which a vapor is in equilibrium with the liquid, i.e., to the vapor pressure, and, according to Eq. (9) would provide a value for ΔH_{vap} and therefore for ΔS_{vap}. A calculation of the free energy of a liquid, or its vapor pressure, and of the heat of vaporization can be expected to be rather difficult since the calculation would necessarily become involved with the individual characteristics of different liquids. It is therefore more profitable to treat the free energy of vaporization in terms of its components, the entropy and the heat of vaporization. As Trouton's rule suggests, the former factor is the more easily handled.

The entropy of the process

$$\text{Liquid} \rightarrow \text{vapor}$$

can be treated, as were the chemical reactions of Sec. 7-7, in terms of the energy-level spacing of the product molecules as compared with that of the reactants. The energy difference for a molecule in the two states is not involved. It is not, it must be admitted, a straightforward matter to think of molecules in the liquid state. A clear illustration of the difficulty is presented by a liquid metal. The vapor that comes off the liquid is clearly composed of metal atoms, but the properties of the liquid indicate that it is better thought of as metal ions in a sea of electrons. In a similar way any liquid can be thought of as composed of interacting molecules, but if the interactions are very important, the molecular description becomes less satisfactory. For the present entropy calculation it will be assumed that the liquid consists of rather closely packed molecules which compare with similar but less closely packed molecules in the gas phase.

It will be assumed, furthermore, that the rotational- and vibrational-entropy contributions are nearly the same for the molecules of the liquid and the vapor. The empirical justification for this is the obedience to Trouton's rule of both monatomic and polyatomic molecules, the former type having only translational contributions, the latter also having rotational and vibrational contributions. Furthermore, the rotational and vibrational degrees of freedom contribute relatively little to the entropy of a molecule, and it is necessary therefore to look to changes in the translational entropy to account for the principal part of the Trouton's-rule entropy value.

The translational entropy of vapor molecules is well understood and has been treated in Sec. 7-12. A set of closely spaced translational-energy levels exist, and the spacing of these levels can be calculated by treating each gas molecule as a particle in a box. An actual value for this translational entropy can be calculated, as has been done in Sec. 7-12, but for the present purpose it is enough to recognize that the energy-level spacing decreases with increasing size of the container and that the translational entropy includes the term $R \ln V$.

The counterpart of translation for the molecules in the liquid is less easily defined. A simple assumption that can be made is that a given liquid molecule is free to move around in some small volume, or cell, and that it is generally confined to this *cell* by the neighboring molecules. These molecules are also moving about, and the cell is therefore not of fixed geometry, nor is it escape-proof. The potential energy experienced by a liquid molecule will be a very complicated function of the nature and positions of the neighboring molecules. The effect of these neighbors can, however, be approximated by a simple square-well-type potential which has some low potential-energy value throughout the cell volume but is infinite outside this volume.

The assumption of a simple square-well potential for the molecules of the liquid has, as far as the energy-level pattern is concerned, made the liquid-to-vapor transformation similar to an expansion of a gas from a very small volume to a large volume. The energy-level patterns that are involved are illustrated schematically in Fig. 12-4.

If the volume in which the liquid molecules are free to move, called the *free volume*, is denoted by V_f, the entropy of transformation to the vapor state is given by

$$\Delta S_{\text{vap}} = S_{\text{vap}} - S_{\text{liq}} = R \ln \frac{V_{\text{vap}}}{V_f} \qquad (20)$$

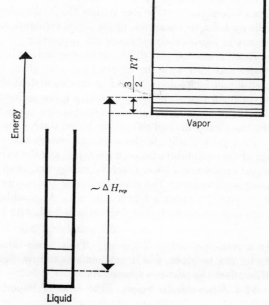

Fig. 12-4. The liquid-vapor system represented by square-well potentials.

Energy

RT

$\frac{3}{2}$

Vapor

$\sim \Delta H_{vap}$

Liquid

Instead of attempting to determine V_f and to obtain thereby a calculated value of ΔS_{vap}, it is more satisfactory to insert the Trouton's-rule result and write

$$21 = R \ln \frac{V_{vap}}{V_f} \tag{21}$$

which requires

$$\frac{V_{vap}}{V_f} \cong 10{,}000 \tag{22}$$

Support is given to our explanation of the entropy of vaporization if all normal liquids can be expected to have the ratio of Eq. (22).

First it must be recognized that the entropy of vaporization is very insensitive to the value of V_{vap}/V_f and that it is necessary only that this ratio can be expected to be within a factor of about 2 of the value in Eq. (22) for a reasonable value of the entropy of vaporization to be obtained.

The volume of 1 mole of vapor will be about 20,000 or 30,000 cc, depending on the normal boiling point, and such values correspond, according to Eq. (22), to a free volume of 2 or 3 cc. Since a typical molar volume of a liquid is 100 cc, this implies that 2 or 3 per cent of the liquid volume is free volume in which the liquid molecules can move. Such a result seems not unreasonable.

A number of other liquid properties can be made to yield values for the free volume of a liquid. There is general, rough agreement with the idea of a free volume of about 1 per cent of the liquid volume. Reference should be made to the articles by Eyring et al. [*J. Chem. Phys.*, **4**: 283 (1936); **5**: 896 (1937); and **6**: 620 (1938)].

There are a number of other approaches to the nature of the liquid state. One of these replaces the free volume that is distributed throughout the liquid cells by *holes*, or vacancies, in the liquid structure that can move around and impart to liquids their characteristic properties.

There are some real difficulties connected with improvements of the cell model and also with the simple treatment given here. The assignment of each liquid molecule to a cell is a treatment that differs from that which we adopt for a gas. The restriction of a given molecule to a given cell raises a number of complications which were pointed out in Sec. 7-12 but which, with the less clearly defined cells of the liquid state, cannot easily be taken care of.

We return, finally, to the schematic energy diagram of Fig. 12-4 to understand the equilibrium between the liquid and the vapor. The molecules in the liquid experience a lower potential energy and have a lower enthalpy than do the gas molecules. The close spacing of the energy levels of the vapor, however, give the vapor a higher entropy. At equilibrium the vapor volume is such that these two factors balance and lead, with the equation

$$\Delta G = \Delta H - T \Delta S$$

to a zero free-energy difference. Thus, some interpretation of the entropy factor can be given, and it now remains to investigate the molecular features that affect the heat of vaporization.

12-4. Intermolecular Forces. The heat of vaporization is a function, primarily, of the forces or the energies that act to bind the molecules together into the liquid state and thereby form the liquid in opposition to the entropy effect. This intermolecular energy determines the individual behavior of different liquids and leads to the potential-energy difference between the two wells of Fig. 12-4.

Either the intermolecular forces of attraction and repulsion or the potential energy can be dealt with as a function of the distance between the molecules. The balancing of the attractive and repulsive forces at some intermolecular distance corresponds to a minimum in the potential energy at that distance. For a liquid the intermolecular distance that must be considered is some average value between a molecule and its nearest neighbors. This poorly defined distance is adequate for the representation of the potential energy shown in Fig. 12-5.

The repulsive contributions to the potential energy form the curve that falls off very steeply with the average molecular separation. This contribution results principally from the interaction, or bumping together, of the outer electrons of one molecule with those of the adjacent molecules. The calculation of the form of this repulsive energy with intermolecular distance is difficult. Often-used expressions represent this term either by an exponential of the type

$$U_{rep} = be^{-ar} \tag{23}$$

with b and a being empirical constants, as was mentioned in connection with intramolecular forces in Sec. 8-7, or by a high inverse power of the internuclear distance such as

$$U_{rep} = \frac{B}{r^9} \tag{24}$$

where the B and 9 are empirical constants.

To understand the contributions to the attractive forces, it is convenient to consider the interactions that occur between a pair of molecules. The liquid-state forces will depend on the operation of these forces over many molecules rather than between a pair of molecules. Four types of contributions to intermolecular attractions can be recognized in ordinary liquids. The forces involved in molten salts and molten metals are best treated in connection with the solid state.

Dipole-Dipole Attraction. Molecules with permanent dipole moments exert a net attraction on each other as a result of the interaction of their dipoles. If the position of one polar molecule is considered to be fixed and if a neighboring molecule is rotated through all possible orientations, the net attraction between the molecules would be zero because of the equal number of repulsive- and attractive-charge orientations. All orientations of the second molecule relative to the first do not, however, occur to the same extent since the attractive, low-potential arrangements are favored over the repulsive, high-energy orientations. A net attraction between two polar molecules therefore results. The average attraction can be worked out, although this will not be done here, by allowing a Boltzmann distribution to yield a higher probability for the attractive orientations. For two polar molecules, with dipole moments μ,

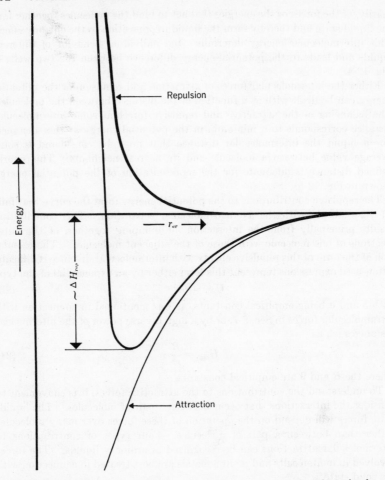

Fig. 12-5. The net attraction, repulsion, and total energy effects among the molecules of a liquid. The coordinate r_{av} can be considered to be an average distance from a molecule to its nearest neighbors.

separated by a distance r, the dipole-dipole energy of attraction, for values of r large compared with the charge separation in the dipole, can be calculated to be

$$U_{D-D} = -\frac{2}{3} \frac{\mu^4}{r^6} \frac{1}{kT} \tag{25}$$

Table 12-4 shows the contribution to the total energy of attraction between a pair of molecules to be expected from this dipole-dipole effect for a few of the simpler molecules. At higher temperatures, as the reciprocal of the temperature in Eq. (25) indicates, the thermal motion of the molecules competes with the tendency toward favorable orientations, and the dipole-dipole attraction becomes less important.

The Induction Effect. The presence of a permanent dipole in a molecule always results in an additional contribution which is not included in the previous dipole-dipole term. The dipole of one molecule can interact with and polarize the electrons of the neighboring molecule. The electrons of the second molecule are thereby distorted in such a way that their interaction with the dipole of the first molecule is an attractive one. The induced dipole moments of two nearby polar molecules are sketched in Fig. 12-6, and qualitatively it can be seen that an attraction results. In 1920 P. Debye showed that for a pair of molecules with dipole moments μ and polarizabilities α the attractive potential resulting from the dipole–induced-dipole, or induction, effect is

$$U_{\text{ind}} = -\frac{2\alpha\mu^2}{r^6} \tag{26}$$

The polarizability α, introduced in Chap. 10, is defined as the dipole moment induced in a molecule by an electric field of 1 volt/cm, and a few results for this quantity were given in Table 10-7. More correctly one should recognize that the polarizability is different in different directions in the molecule and that again one must be concerned with the relative molecular orientations. Here, however, it is a very good approximation to assume all orientations, the induction effect being operative at least to some extent with all molecular orientations.

London Dispersion Forces. All molecules, including those without a permanent dipole, attract each other. The liquid state, for example, is exhibited by all compounds and even by the inert gases. The source of the forces that act independently of the molecular dipole, which is necessary for the attractions discussed under Dipole-Dipole Attraction and The Induction Effect above, was first recognized by F. London in 1930. The effect can only be treated quantum mechanically, being dependent on the detailed motion of the electrons in the neighboring molecules.

The basis for the attraction, known now as *London,* or *dispersion,* forces, can be indicated by reference to a pair of H atoms at a separation great enough so that the exchange of electrons between the atoms can be ignored. Although a time average would indicate that each atom has a zero-dipole moment, instantaneous-dipole moments can be recognized. The two instantaneous dipoles

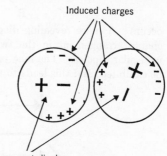

Fig. 12-6. Mutual attraction of randomly oriented polar molecules through induction. Note that the induced charges are favorably arranged relative to the permanent dipole for attraction to occur.

of two neighboring atoms cannot effectively orient themselves favorably with respect to each other as can the permanent dipoles of molecules. An induction effect analogous to that which has been treated on page 403 can, however, act between the instantaneous dipole of one atom and the polarizable adjacent atom. Similar effects, which can be calculated only approximately and only with considerable difficulty, operate in all molecules regardless, of course, of whether they have a permanent dipole or not.

Detailed treatments of the quantitative aspects of this force yield results that can be variously expressed, but all agree that the force is proportional to the square of the polarizability of the molecules and inversely as about the sixth power of the separation; i.e.,

$$V_{\text{London}} \propto \frac{\alpha^2}{r^6} \tag{27}$$

The proportionality constant turns out to be approximately the same for many molecules and has the value 1.8×10^{-10} erg.

Some values that have been calculated for this contribution to the attraction exhibited by a pair of molecules are shown in Table 12-4.

Hydrogen Bonding. One further, and rather special, interaction must be included. The long-range dipole-dipole interaction calculated from the molecular-dipole moments is not always an adequate treatment of the electrostatic interactions between polar molecules. A more localized effect, called a *hydrogen bond*, can occur. When a somewhat acidic hydrogen atom carrying a partial positive charge, as in the bonds O—H, F—H, N—H, and so forth, can approach an electron-rich basic-type atom, such as the oxygen in water, alcohols, or ethers or the nitrogen in amines, an association that can be represented by

$$
\begin{array}{ccc}
& & H \\
& & | \\
O\!-\!\!\!-\!\!\!\underset{\delta^+}{H}\cdots\cdots\underset{\delta^-}{O} & \\
\diagup & & \diagdown \\
R & & R
\end{array}
$$

occurs. A more revealing diagram emphasizes that it is the details of the charge arrangement in the two molecules that is responsible and not the molecular dipoles. The lone pair of nonbinding electrons on the oxygen can be exhibited, and this leads to the diagram

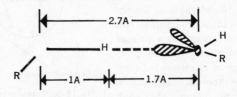

Typical hydrogen-bond distances have been included to emphasize that the hydrogen bond is too long for much covalent character to be expected and is best interpreted as the result of a localized electrostatic attraction.

When hydrogen bonding occurs, it plays a prominent role in determining the intermolecular properties. The high boiling points of H_2O compared with H_2S and of alcohols compared with ethers of the same molecular weight and atomic constitution are primarily the consequence of hydrogen bonding.

A general expression for the potential energy of a hydrogen-bonded pair of molecules as a function of intermolecular distance cannot be given. It can be mentioned, however, that a pair of alcohol molecules that have approached their equilibrium intermolecular distance are held by a potential-energy contribution of about 6 kcal/mole or 4.2×10^{-13} erg per molecular pair.

The relative importance of the contributions listed in Table 12-4 should be noted. One cannot, however, go easily from the interactions between pairs of molecules to the net effect of a given type of force when the molecules of a liquid are considered. The dipole-dipole forces, for example, require certain favorable orientations, and in a liquid all the neighbors of a molecule must compete for this orientation. London forces, on the other hand, can act as effectively in large collections of molecules as in molecular pairs. Only qualitative relations can therefore be seen in a comparison of the molecular-pair intermolecular forces with the boiling points and heats of vaporization.

12-5. Liquid Structure. That there is some organization, or structure, in the liquid state has been assumed in the introduction of the cell theory of the liquid state. In fact, even the concept of nearest neighbors assumes that about any one molecule in a liquid certain nearby positions can be distinguished. Thus one is drawn to the supposition that a certain amount of *short-range order* exists in a liquid and that it is the long-range disorder that gives to a liquid its characteristic properties of fluidity.

This supposition is nicely supported by diffraction studies of simple monatomic liquids. The diffraction principle is essentially that which was used

Table 12-4. Intermolecular-attraction Terms for Some Simple Molecules
(An arbitrary intermolecular distance of 5 A has been used for the comparison)

Molecule	Dipole moment (debye)	Polarizability (A^3)	Interaction energy (ergs/molecule) at $r = 5$ A and $T = 298°K$				ΔH_{vap} (kcal/mole)
			$U_{D-D} \times 10^{15}$	$U_{ind} \times 10^{15}$	$U_{London} \times 10^{15}$	Total $\times 10^{15}$	
He	0	0.2	0	0	0.05	0.05	0.022
A	0	1.6	0	0	2.9	2.9	1.59
Xe	0	4.0	0	0	18	18	3.11
CO	0.12	2.0	0.00021	0.0037	4.6	4.6	1.44
HCl*	1.03	2.6	1.2	0.36	7.8	9.4	3.86
HBr*	0.78	3.6	0.39	0.28	15	16	4.21
HI*	0.38	5.4	0.021	0.10	33	33	4.34
H_2O*	1.84	1.5	11.9	0.65	2.6	15	9.42
NH_3*	1.5	2.2	5.2	0.63	5.6	11	5.58
CCl_4	0	10.5	0	0	116	126	7.14

* Possibility of hydrogen bonding in addition to listed attractions.

to study molecular structure by electron diffraction in Chap. 10. For the study of liquids, as with that of solids, which will be treated in the following chapter, a more penetrating radiation is necessary so that the interior rather than surface structure can be studied. For this reason liquid structures are investigated by the diffraction of X rays rather than by electron diffraction. It is found that a diffraction pattern is in fact obtained, as shown in Fig. 12-7, when a beam of X rays passes through a monatomic-liquid sample, and this observation is by itself sufficient for the statement that liquids do exhibit some structure. It will be recalled from the discussion of electron diffraction that the close-in small-angle diffraction depends on small spacings, while the wider-angle diffraction is dependent on longer internuclear distances. Liquid diffraction patterns characteristically show one or two nicely formed small-angle diffraction maxima that correspond to the short-range order but show rather diffuse diffraction rings corresponding to the farther removed molecules.

The radial-distribution method introduced in Sec. 10-6 can be used here very effectively. It is only the distance of neighboring molecules from a given central one and not the angular arrangement that is of interest. The radial-distribution curve that is calculated from the scattering curve of Fig. 12-7 is also included in that figure. In this way the layer of nearest neighbors clearly shows up, as does the diffuseness of the longer-range structure.

Structures of liquids consisting of molecules of some complexity have been studied, and again a liquid structure, now dependent somewhat on the geometry and intermolecular forces of the molecules, shows up.

All such structure investigations emphasize the similarities between liquids

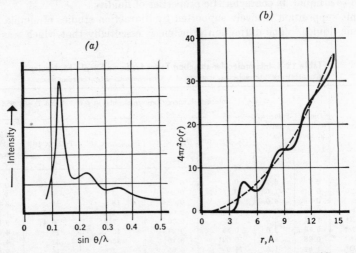

Fig. 12-7. X-ray-diffraction study of the structure of liquid potassium at 70°C. (a) The diffraction intensity with 30-kv-X rays. (b) The radial-distribution curve calculated from the data of (a); the dashed line indicates the distribution curve that would be expected for no structure in the liquid. [*From C. D. Thomas and N. S. Gingrich, J. Chem. Phys.*, **8**: 411 (1938).]

and crystals. We now proceed to another property of liquids that tends to emphasize their likeness to gases.

12-6. The Viscosity of Liquids. The viscosity, or the coefficient of viscosity, has been defined, in connection with our study of gases, by the equation

$$f = \eta A \frac{dv}{dr} \qquad (28)$$

where f is the force necessary to impart, to a fluid with a coefficient of viscosity η, a velocity gradient dv/dr over an area A parallel to the flow direction. Measurements of viscosity are almost always made with a fluid flowing in a tube of circular cross section, and the derivation of the Poiseuille equation [Eq. (25) of Chap. 1], which applies to this case, is now pertinent.

Consider a tube of length l, as in Fig. 12-8. Flow with a uniform velocity results when the pressure drop P along the length l balances the viscous drag of the fluid along this length. The viscous drag stems from the thin film of fluid that, for most liquids, is tightly held to the surface of the tube. This film is effectively stationary, and the fluid must be pushed through the tube against the frictional drag of this layer. The frictional drag on the cylindrical differential layer of Fig. 12-8 is, according to the definition of Eq. (28),

$$\text{Frictional drag} = \eta(2\pi rL)\left(-\frac{dv}{dr}\right) \qquad (29)$$

where the negative sign has been inserted to make the drag a positive quantity, the velocity gradient being negative.

The pressure acts to drive the central cylinder of fluid down the tube in opposition to the viscous drag at the surface of the cylinder, and for steady flow this driving force of $P(\pi r^2)$ can be equated to the frictional drag to give

$$-\eta(2\pi rL)\frac{dv}{dr} = P(\pi r^2)$$

or

$$dv = -\frac{P}{2\eta L} r \, dr \qquad (30)$$

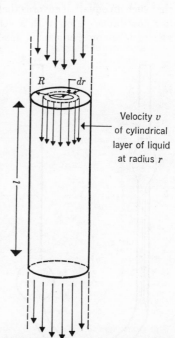

Velocity v of cylindrical layer of liquid at radius r

The velocity gradient across the cylinder is obtained by integration of Eq. (30). Since the flow velocity is zero along the wall of the tube, i.e., at $r = R$, and since the other integration limit is the velocity v at a radial position r, the integration

$$\int_{v=0}^{v=v} dv = -\frac{P}{2\eta L} \int_{r=R}^{r=r} r \, dr$$

gives

$$v = \frac{P}{4\eta L} (R^2 - r^2) \qquad (31)$$

The velocity contour implied by this equation is shown in Fig. 12-8.

Fig. 12-8. Flow in a segment of tube of length l for which the pressure drop is P.

(a)

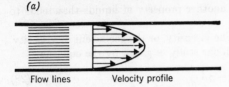

Flow lines   Velocity profile

(b)

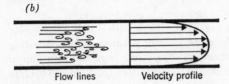

Flow lines   Velocity profile

Fig. 12-9. Nature of laminar flow, to which Eq. (31) applies, and turbulent flow, which occurs at high flow rates and for which Eq. (31) does not apply. (a) Laminar, or viscous, flow. (b) Turbulent flow.

It is at this point that it must be mentioned that fluid flow in a tube does not always conform to the velocity gradient of Eq. (31). It is found empirically that such an equation governs the flow only for rather small-diameter tubes and low flow rates. Flow with a velocity distribution like that of Fig. 12-9a is known as *laminar*, or *viscous*, *flow*, and all measurements of viscosity must deal with flow of this type for the derived equations to be valid.

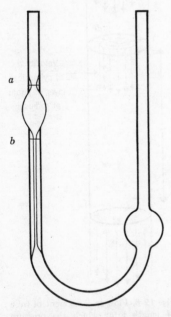

Fig. 12-10. An Ostwald viscometer.

At higher flow rates or for larger-diameter tubing the flow type changes to what is known as *turbulent flow*, which can be described qualitatively in terms of the eddies of Fig. 12-9b. The velocity gradient implied by Eq. (31) is not valid, and it is a matter of considerable difficulty, and considerable practical importance, to treat this flow type. The decision as to which flow type is likely to operate for any set of conditions is usually made in an empirical way on the basis of the dimensionless quantity known as the Reynolds number, which is defined as

$$\text{Reynolds number} = \frac{d\bar{v}\rho}{\eta} \qquad (32)$$

where d is the tube diameter, $\bar{v}$ the average velocity of the fluid along the tube, ρ the density, and η the coefficient of viscosity. Empirically it has been found that for Reynolds numbers less than about 2,100 the flow is laminar, for values greater than 4,000 it is turbulent, and for intermediate values of the Reynolds number the type of flow cannot easily be anticipated.

Measurements of viscosity are made therefore under conditions of low Reynolds numbers. A suitable and often-used apparatus for many ordinary liquids is the Ostwald viscometer shown in Fig. 12-10. Its use depends on the measurement of the time required for the amount of liquid held between a and b, of Fig. 12-10, to flow through the capillary tube. This measurement can be used to obtain a volume rate of flow through the capillary tube.

The volume rate of flow along a cylindrical tube is obtained by integrating the product of the cross-section areas of cylindrical segments and the velocity of flow of the segment. Thus, the Poiseuille equation is obtained as

$$\text{Volume rate of flow} = \int_0^R (2\pi r)v \, dr = \frac{\pi P R^4}{8\eta l} \tag{33}$$

It is this equation which can be used to obtain an absolute value for η, all other quantities being measurable.

In practice one almost invariably determines the viscosity by a comparison of the sample with some standard reference sample, using an apparatus like that of Fig. 12-10. For the Ostwald viscometer the Poiseuille equation [Eq. (33)] can be turned around to give

$$\eta = \frac{\pi P R^4}{8l} \times (\text{time/unit volume of flow}) \tag{34}$$

Measurement of the time for the same volume of flow of the sample and reference and recognition that the driving force P is proportional to the liquid density ρ allows one to write

$$\frac{\eta_1}{\eta_2} = \frac{\rho_1 t_1}{\rho_2 t_2} \tag{35}$$

Viscosities can be determined therefore by measuring, in one way or another, the rate of flow through a cylindrical tube.

Such measurements can be made over a range of temperatures, and as the plots in Fig. 12-11 of the data of Table 12-5 show, the temperature dependence of viscosity conforms to the equation

$$\log \eta = \frac{A}{T} + B \tag{36}$$

Table 12-5. Coefficient of Viscosity of Liquid
(Centipoise)

Liquid	0°C	20°C	40°C	60°C	80°C	100°C
H_2O	1.792	1.005	0.656	0.469	0.356	0.284
C_2H_5OH	1.773	1.200	0.834	0.592		
$n\text{-}C_4H_9OH$	5.186	2.948	1.782	.....	.....	0.540
C_6H_6	0.912	0.652	0.503	0.392	0.329	
$CHCl_3$	0.700	0.563	0.464	0.389		
CCl_4	1.329	0.969	0.739	0.585	0.468	0.384
Hg	1.685	1.554	1.450	1.367	1.298	1.240
$(C_2H_5)_2O$	0.284	0.233	0.197	0.166	0.140	0.118

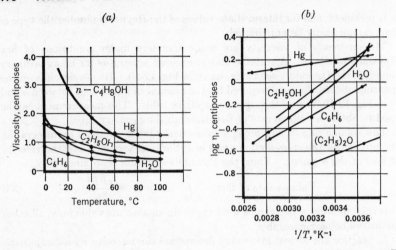

Fig. 12-11. The dependence of viscosity on temperature for some liquids. (a) η versus T. (b) Log η versus $1/T$.

It is of interest to try to obtain a theory of liquid viscosities that leads to an expression of the form of this empirical equation. This goal can be reached, as the following section indicates. The theoretical deduction of the viscosities of liquids is, however, an exceedingly difficult theoretical problem.

12-7. Theory of Viscosity. Now an attempt will be made to understand something of the source of viscosity in liquids. Success such as is achieved by the kinetic-molecular theory in its treatment of gas viscosities cannot, however, be attained.

For theoretical purposes it is more satisfactory to think in terms of *fluidity*, i.e., the tendency to flow, rather than viscosity, the resistance to flow. The fluidity is usually represented by ϕ and defined as

$$\phi = \frac{1}{\eta} \tag{37}$$

The flow of a liquid is a rate process, and we can inquire about the mechanism by which molecules move along a tube in a manner similar to that in which we inquired about the way in which molecules react to form products. Both the chemical rate theories of Chap. 11 led to the prediction of a rate expression with an exponential term involving an activation energy. A similar form for the rate expression for flow can be anticipated, and the counterpart of the activation energy will be the energy maximum encountered by a molecule as it squeezes past its nearest neighbors to a position farther along the tube. The flow process can be likened to that of passengers pushing down the aisle of a crowded bus, and the activated states correspond to those moments and positions when a person crowds past another to get to a better position farther along the aisle. If the activation energy is designated by ΔE_{visc}, the fraction

Table 12-6. The Comparison of the Activation Energy for Viscous Flow with the Internal-energy Change for Vaporization at the Normal Boiling Point*

Liquid	ΔE_{visc} (cal/mole)	ΔE_{vap} (cal/mole)	$\Delta E_{visc}/\Delta E_{vap}$
CCl_4	2500	6,600	0.38
C_6H_6	2540	6,660	0.38
CH_4	719	1,820	0.39
N_2	449	1,210	0.37
O_2	398	1,470	0.27
$CHCl_3$	1760	6,630	0.27
$(C_2H_5)_2O$	1610	5,700	0.28
Acetone	1655	6,400	0.26
Hg	600	13,000	0.05
Na (at 500°C)	1450	23,400	0.06
Pb (at 700°C)	2800	42,600	0.07

* From R. H. Ewell and H. Eyring, *J. Chem. Phys.*, **5**: 726 (1937).

of the molecules that have energy in excess of this amount, and can therefore move past their neighbors, will be given by a Boltzmann-type expression. The fluidity can therefore be written as

$$\phi \propto e^{-\Delta E_{visc}/RT} \tag{38}$$

and the viscosity as

$$\eta = \frac{1}{\phi} \propto e^{\Delta E_{visc}/RT}$$

or

$$\eta = A e^{\Delta E_{visc}/RT} \tag{39}$$

where A is some undetermined constant. The logarithmic form of Eq. (39) is that which was recognized in the plots of Fig. 12-11.

It is of interest to compare the values of ΔE_{visc} listed in Table 12-6 with the heat, or better the internal-energy change, of vaporization. The ΔE_{vap} term gives the energy to remove a molecule completely from its neighbors. The flow process seems to require only about a third of this disruption to move a liquid molecule from its initial equilibrium position through a high-energy intermediate position.

This idea can be extended to rationalize the data for liquid metals. Vaporization removes an atom of the metal from the liquid phase. The flow process, on the other hand, can be thought of as involving the movement of positive ions which exist in a sea of electrons. The much smaller size of the positive metal ions compared with the metal atoms can be given as an explanation for the small value of $\Delta E_{visc}/\Delta E_{vap}$ for liquid metals.

12-8. Surface Tension. One final property of liquids, which in fact is that which distinguishes liquids from gases, can now be treated. The surface tension of a liquid can be looked upon as that property which draws a liquid together and forms a liquid-vapor interface, thereby distinguishing liquids from gases.

The molecular basis for this property is indicated in Fig. 12-12, where the unbalanced attractions experienced by the surface molecules are shown to lead

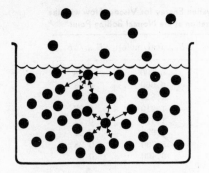

Fig. 12-12. Interaction forces for a surface molecule compared with one in the body of the liquid,

to a net drawing together of the liquid. On this basis it can be expected that a small amount of free liquid will pull itself together to form a more or less spherical drop. It is also clear that the surface layer will have properties, such as free energy, that will be different from those of the bulk of the liquid.

The surface tension of a liquid can be defined with reference to Fig. 12-13. Most easily pictured is a wire frame, arranged like a piston, used to expand a soap film. The definition also applies, however, to the mechanically more difficult systems where the film would be replaced by a layer of liquid of appreciable thickness. The force required to stretch the film, or liquid layer, is found to be proportional to the length l of the piston. Since there are two surfaces to the film, the total length of the film is $2l$ and the proportionality equation

$$f = \gamma(2l) \tag{40}$$

can be written. The proportionality constant γ is known as the *surface tension* and, according to Eq. (40), it can be looked upon as the force exerted by a surface of unit length.

Of more general use is the relation between surface tension and surface energy. The work required to expand the surfaces of Fig. 12-13 by moving the piston a distance dx is $f \cdot dx$ or $2l\gamma\, dx$. Since the area of new surface is $2l\, dx$, the result

$$\frac{\text{Work}}{\text{Change of surface area}} = \frac{2l\gamma\, dx}{2l\, dx} = \gamma \tag{41}$$

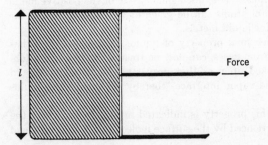

Fig. 12-13. A wire piston supporting a soap film.

Force

can be obtained. This expression shows that the surface tension can be interpreted as the energy per unit surface area. In these terms, the tendency of a surface to reduce its area is just another example of a system tending toward an arrangement of low free energy.

A number of methods are available for the measurement of surface tension, but only the *capillary-rise method* will be dealt with here. The arrangement of Fig. 12-14 showing a capillary glass tube inserted into a container of the liquid to be studied is all that is necessary. All liquids that wet the glass will rise in the tube, and it is this capillary rise which can be used to deduce the surface tension.

The rise of the liquid can be understood if it is assumed that an adsorbed thin film of liquid exists on the wall of the capillary. In order to reduce its

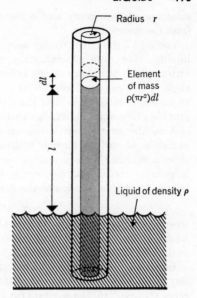

Fig. 12-14. The capillary rise of a liquid which wets the capillary wall.

total surface area, the liquid rises in the tube. Equilibrium is reached when the free energy is a minimum; any further rise would expend more free energy in the work to draw up the liquid column than would be saved by the decrease in surface area.

These ideas can be put in more quantitative form by reference to Fig. 12-13. The decrease in surface area that results from a rise in liquid by an amount dl is $2\pi r\, dl$, and the corresponding decrease in surface energy is

$$dG_{\text{surface energy}} = \gamma\, dA$$
$$= \gamma(2\pi r)\, dl \tag{42}$$

The expenditure of free energy in raising an amount of liquid of volume $\pi r^2\, dl$ and density ρ to a height l is

$$dG_{\text{gravity}} = (\pi r^2\, dl\, \rho)gl \tag{43}$$

When the column of liquid has risen in the capillary to its equilibrium height, these two free energies balance. For this condition

$$2\pi r\gamma\, dl = \pi r^2 \rho gl\, dl$$

and

$$\gamma = \frac{r\rho gl}{2} \tag{44}$$

Measurement of the quantities on the right side of Eq. (44) gives a value of γ.

If the liquid does not adhere to the glass, i.e., does not wet it, a capillary rise does not occur and the phenomenon of a depressed liquid in the tube, as observed with mercury and glass, results. Here the mutual attraction between the mercury atoms is greater than that between mercury and glass, and a minimum glass-mercury area is therefore sought by the mercury withdrawing from the inserted tube.

Table 12-7 shows the results obtained for the surface tension of a number of liquids. The only generalization that can be offered is that liquids, like water, which have very strong cohesive forces tend to have high surface tensions. This can be attributed to a greater tendency for the surface molecules to be pulled into the bulk of the liquid. The molten metals and metal salts provide other examples of high surface tension.

A number of empirical expressions have been suggested to account for the variation of surface tension with temperature. Surface tensions generally show a decrease with increasing temperature, but the effect is not nearly so large as occurs for vapor pressure and viscosity. An expression due to McLeod relates the surface tension to the density of the liquid and the vapor as

$$\gamma = C(\rho - \rho_0)^4 \tag{45}$$

where ρ_0 is the vapor density and C is a constant which is different for each liquid. The fourth power of the density term gives a suitable temperature variation for the surface tension.

In passing, it can be pointed out that this expression is the basis for a quantity, presumably characteristic of the molecular volume, proposed by Sugden. Since C of Eq. (45) is a constant for a given compound, one can construct a new quantity, called the *parachor*, by the relation

$$\text{Parachor} = MC^{\frac{1}{4}} = \frac{M\gamma^{\frac{1}{4}}}{\rho - \rho_0} \tag{46}$$

The parachor presumably measures the molecular volume with a suitable correction for the cohesive forces of the liquid. Many molecular-structure arguments have been made by assigning molecular-volume contributions to the atoms and bonds which make up a molecule. Comparison of a parachor calculated in such a manner with the observed parachor presumably lends support to some assumed structure. This method is now of little value compared with other molecular-structure techniques.

Table 12-7. Surface Tensions of Some Liquids
(Dynes/cm)

Liquid	20°C	60°C	100°C
H_2O	72.75	66.18	58.85
C_2H_5OH	22.3	19.0	
C_6H_6	28.9	23.7	
$(C_2H_5)_2O$	17.0	.....	8.0
Hg	480 at 0°C		
Ag	800 at 970°C		
NaCl	94 at 1080°C		
AgCl	125 at 452°C		

12-9. Surface Tension and the Free Energy of Small Droplets. Although the surface properties of a liquid are different from those of the bulk liquid, this effect can be ignored except in a few situations. One of these is the case in which a liquid is dispersed into fine droplets and the surface then constitutes a large fraction of the total material. A similar situation occurs with finely divided solid material.

Consider the transfer of dn moles of liquid from a plane surface to a droplet of initial radius r. If the normal vapor pressure of the liquid is P_0 and of the droplet is P, the free-energy change for this process can be written, according to Sec. 7-4, as

$$dG = dn\,RT\ln\frac{P}{P_0} \tag{47}$$

The free-energy change can also be calculated from the surface-energy change of the droplet that results from the surface-area increase due to the addition of dn moles, or $M\,dn/\rho$ cc. Addition of this volume adds a spherical shell, whose area is $4\pi r^2$. The thickness dr is given by the relation of this spherical shell

$$\frac{M\,dn}{\rho} = 4\pi r^2\,dr$$

or

$$dr = \frac{M}{4\pi r^2}\,dn \tag{48}$$

The increase in surface energy is γ times the increase in surface area resulting from the increase dr in the droplet radius is

$$\begin{aligned}
dG &= \gamma\,dA \\
&= \gamma[4\pi(r+dr)^2 - 4\pi r^2] \\
&= 8\pi\gamma r\,dr
\end{aligned} \tag{49}$$

Substitution of Eq. (48) now gives

$$\begin{aligned}
dG &= 8\pi\gamma r\,\frac{M}{4\pi r^2}\,dn \\
&= \frac{2\gamma M}{\rho r}\,dn
\end{aligned} \tag{50}$$

Equating the two calculations for the free-energy change [Eqs. (47) and (50)] gives

$$dn\,RT\ln\frac{P}{P_0} = \frac{2\gamma M}{\rho r}\,dn$$

and

$$\ln\frac{P}{P_0} = \frac{2\gamma M}{\rho r RT} \tag{51}$$

This desired result relates the vapor pressure P of a droplet, or really of a liquid element with highly curved surface, to the vapor pressure P_0 of the bulk liquid. The appearance of r in the denominator implies a dependence of vapor pressure on droplet size that is illustrated in Table 12-8.

These data produce something of a dilemma when the condensation of a vapor to a liquid is considered. The formation of an initial small droplet of liquid would lead to a particle with such a high vapor pressure, according to Eq. (51), that it would evaporate even if the pressure of the vapor were greater

Table 12-8. The Vapor Pressure of Water as a Function of the Radius of Curvature of the Surface at 25°C

$(P_0 = 23.76 \text{ mm Hg})$

r (cm)	r (A)	P/P_0
10^{-4}	10^4	1.001
10^{-5}	10^3	1.011
10^{-6}	10^2	1.111
10^{-7}	10^1	2.88

than the vapor pressure of the bulk liquid. It is necessary to imagine the condensation to occur on dust particles or other irregularities so that the equilibrium thermodynamic result can be circumvented by some mechanism that avoids an initial slow equilibrium growth of droplets.

Similar considerations are necessary when the reverse process, the boiling of a liquid, which requires the formation of small vapor nuclei, is treated. Chemically one also encounters this phenomenon in the difficulty with which some precipitates form and in the tendency for liquids to supercool. Likewise the digestion of a precipitate makes use of the high free energy of the smaller crystals to convert them to larger particles.

Problems

1. The vapor pressure of water at 25°C is 23.76 mm Hg. Use this datum and the normal boiling point of water to deduce, according to the Clausius-Clapeyron equation, a value for the heat of vaporization of water.

Ans. 10,210 cal.

2. Normal hexane has a boiling point of 69.0°C. Assuming that Trouton's rule is obeyed, estimate the vapor pressure of *n*-hexane at 25°C.

3. Assuming that benzene obeys Trouton's rule, calculate dP/dT at the normal boiling point 80.1°C and at 25°C.

Ans. At 25°C, $\dfrac{dP}{dT} = 4.5$ mm/deg.

4. Calculate the work of expansion done in the vaporization of water at its normal boiling point of 100°C if the vapor is considered to be ideal. What fraction of ΔH_{vap} is due to this work term?

5. Hildebrand's extension of Trouton's rule suggests that the entropy of vaporization be compared for vaporizations from the liquid to a given vapor volume. Assuming ideal-gas behavior, calculate the entropy of vaporization of H_2, N_2, CCl_4, and Hg for vaporization at their normal boiling points to a vapor of volume 22.4 liters. Compare the agreement of these values with those of Trouton's rule given in Table 12-3.

6. The vapor pressures of neon are reported in the "International Critical Tables" as a function of temperature as follows:

t (°C).........	-228.7	-233.6	-240.2	-243.7	-245.7	-247.3	-248.5
p (mm Hg)....	19,800	10,040	3,170	1,435	816	486	325

Determine the normal boiling point, the heat of vaporization, and Trouton's-rule constant.

7. At what temperature will water boil when the elevation is such that the barometric pressure is 500 mm Hg?

Ans. 89°C.

8. Consider two dipoles each consisting of electronic charges separated by 1 A. These dipoles are placed with their centers 5 A apart and with their axes along a straight line joining their centers. They are allowed to take up the low- or the high-energy orientation.

(a) Using Coulomb's law for the potential energy of separated charges, calculate the energy difference between the two orientations.

(b) With Boltzmann's distribution deduce the fraction of an Avogadro's number of dipoles that would be in the high-energy orientation at 25°C.

(c) Repeat the calculations for the centers of the dipoles separated by 10 A.

(d) Calculate the energy of the Avogadro's number of dipoles separated by 5 A and 10 A in the case in which they are free to adopt either orientation and in the case where both orientations are equally populated. Recognize, as a result of this calculation, the factors that enter into the inverse sixth relation of Eq. (26) that is valid for large distances between the dipoles.

Ans. (a) 76.8×10^{-14} erg; (b) 0; (c) 9.30×10^{-14} erg.

9. The rather viscous material glycerin has the viscosities 1.34×10^5, 12,110, 1,490, and 629 centipoise at the temperatures -20, 0, 20, and 30°C, respectively. What is the activation energy for viscous flow for glycerin?

10. The viscosity of chlorobenzene at 20°C is 0.799 centipoise and its normal boiling point is 132°C. Assuming that it behaves as a typical liquid, estimate its viscosity at 100°C. Compare with the measured value of 0.367 centipoise.

11. Water runs out of a tap connected to a $\frac{1}{2}$-in.-diameter pipe at a rate of about 1 quart in 1 min. Is the flow of water in the pipe likely to be laminar or turbulent?

12. The surface tension of mercury is 520 dynes/cm, and its density is 13.6 g/cc at 25°C. Mercury does not wet glass.

(a) Derive an expression for the lowering of the surface of mercury that will occur when a glass tube of internal radius r is inserted into the liquid.

(b) If r is 1 mm, what will the depression be?

(c) If r is 5 mm, what will the depression be?

13. A particle of mist has a mass of about 10^{-12} g. What is its vapor pressure compared with that of water if the temperature is 20°C?

Ans. $P = 1.002 P_{H_2O}$.

14. In view of Eqs. (44) and (51) consider what will happen as the radius of the capillary tube in which a liquid rises, as treated in Sec. 12-8, is reduced toward the limit of $r = 0$.

15. Suppose that water in a certain container boils when the liquid is at a temperature at which bubbles of 10^{-5} cm diameter can be formed by the equilibrium vapor. Estimate from approximate relations and data previously given:

(a) The vapor pressure that must be reached by the liquid for these vapor bubbles to be formed.

(b) The temperature at which boiling will occur at a pressure of 1 atm.

Ans. (b) 100.4°C.

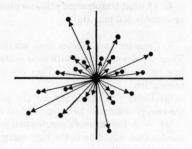

13

Crystals

Of all condensed-phase phenomena those of pure crystalline materials are most easily treated. Again one must, however, deal not only with the properties of individual atoms or molecules but also with interactions between these particles. The ordered array that is characteristic of crystals makes this a less difficult task than with liquids. As a result, some aspects of crystal studies can lead to information on the properties of the separate molecules. Of these, X-ray-diffraction studies of organic crystals, which lead to molecular structures, are the prime example. Other aspects of crystal studies, such as the nature of the bonding in metals, are concerned, however, primarily with communal effects in the crystal.

Crystals are characterized by a highly ordered arrangement of molecules, atoms, or ions. Historically, of course, crystals revealed themselves as such through the smooth planes and symmetry of their external appearance. That crystalline form is dependent on a microscopic order was recognized as early as 1784 by Abbé René Haüy. His suggestion that some microscopic arrangement resulted in the observed faces and the angles between the faces of crystals waited a century and a half for experimental verification.

Some of the interests of physical chemists in crystals stems from the fact that the crystal lattice is a "molecule holder." That the molecules are held in essentially fixed, ordered positions is the basis for the important crystal studies by X-ray diffraction. It is this study which verifies the early guesses as to the reason for the natural external properties of crystals. A considerable part of the chapter will be concerned with X-ray diffraction since it provides the most accurate and dependable method, of all those which we have studied, for determining the dimensions of larger molecules.

A number of other aspects of crystals that are more related to the communal properties of the crystal will also be of interest. Most important of these is the nature of the bonding which acts between the molecules, atoms, or ions to

418

hold these particles in their crystal position. The electronic structures of electrically conducting and semiconducting crystals are of considerable interest. A knowledge of the forces that act in a crystal, furthermore, allows us to understand some of the factors which decide the arrangements adopted by particles in the different crystals. A number of approaches to the general subject of crystal forces will be made. We begin by treating some qualitative aspects of this subject.

13-1. Crystal Forces. The forces that hold crystal particles together can be classified into five main types. In a given crystal, while one of these forces might predominate, there will probably be contributions from forces of some of the other types. In spite of this overlapping, the classification of crystals in terms of the predominant force type is very useful. The forces treated in the previous chapter in connection with liquids operate. A slightly different, but by no means complete or unique, classification is, however, convenient for solids.

Ionic Forces. The forces operating in ionic crystals are very predominantly the electrostatic, or ionic, forces between the charged ions that were discussed in Sec. 8-7 in terms of pairs of ions. A smaller contribution results from the interaction of the charge of a given ion with the polarizability of the neighboring ions. These electrostatic forces result in a completely nondirectional pulling together of the units of the crystal. We find, in fact, that this uncomplicated behavior, together with the well-defined coulombic-force law, makes these crystals in many ways the easiest to understand. The structure, for instance, can in the case of crystals of simple ions be understood in terms of nothing more than the efficient packing together of two sets of spheres of different sizes.

The assumption of coulombic attractions and repulsions, together with some expression for the repulsion when ions of opposite charge come in contact, allows the calculation of the energy required to break apart a simple ionic crystal into separate ions. The calculation is like that performed for a single NaCl molecule in Sec. 8-7. For a crystal, however, it is necessary to take into account all the oppositely and like-charged neighbors that influence a given ion. If the structure of the crystal is known, and later X-ray diffraction studies will show how this is determined, this calculation can be made. It is necessary only to relate all the various interionic distances to one distance parameter, and a curve like that of Fig. 8-5 can then be drawn in terms of this parameter. For NaCl, for example, the energy for the process

$$NaCl(cryst) \rightarrow Na^+(g) + Cl^-(g) \tag{1}$$

which can be called $\Delta E(cryst)$ is calculated, on the assumption of purely coulombic attractions, as 179 kcal/mole.

It is of interest to try to obtain this crystal energy from experimental quantities. An indirect method, known as the *Born-Haber cycle*, accomplishes this. The process of Eq. (1), indicated by a dashed arrow, can be performed by the indirect route, indicated by solid arrows,

$$
\begin{array}{ccc}
\text{NaCl(cryst)} & \dashrightarrow & \text{Na}(g) + \text{Cl}^-(g) \\
{\scriptstyle\downarrow -\Delta H_f^\circ} & I\uparrow & \uparrow \\
\text{Na}(s) & \xrightarrow{H_{\text{sub}}} \text{Na}(g) & -A \\
+ & & \\
\tfrac{1}{2}\text{Cl}_2(g) & \xrightarrow{\frac{1}{2}D} & \text{Cl}(g)
\end{array}
\tag{2}
$$

The terms involved in the indirect route of the cycle are

ΔH_f° = standard heat of formation of NaCl

ΔH_{sub} = heat of sublimation of Na

D = heat of dissociation of Cl_2

I = ionization potential of Na

A = electron affinity of Cl (usually given as a positive number, but since energy is given out in the process $Cl + e \rightarrow Cl^-$, the energy change for the reaction is negative, i.e., is $-A$)

Methods for the determination of all quantities, except the electron affinity, have been discussed in previous sections. The energy $\Delta E(\text{cryst})$ can therefore be written for NaCl as

$$
\begin{aligned}
\Delta E(\text{cryst}) &= -\Delta H_f^\circ + \Delta H_{\text{sub}} + \tfrac{1}{2}D + I - A \\
&= -(-98) + 26.0 + 29 + 118.0 - A
\end{aligned}
\tag{3}
$$

Coupling of this result with the calculated crystal-energy value of 179 kcal leads to a value of 92 kcal/mole, or 4.0 ev, for the electron affinity of chlorine atoms. It is not this quantity that we set out to calculate, but such electron-affinity data are one of the valuable products of such calculations.

The validity of the theoretical crystal-energy calculation cannot be directly checked since few independent electron-affinity results are available. One can, however, use the above procedure to calculate the electron affinity of chlorine atoms from the data for NaCl, KCl, RbCl, and so forth. The fact that one obtains the same electron affinity, within a few per cent, for all these crystals indicates that the procedure is sound. The forces in these crystals can therefore be quite adequately treated in terms of coulombic attractions and repulsions.

Table 13-1 indicates data for the crystal-energy calculation of several metal-halide crystals. Here values of electron affinities have been used that appear, on a somewhat more detailed treatment, to be "best" values. The comparison of the crystal energy from the Born-Haber cycle, using these values, with the calculated value assuming electrostatic interaction between the ions is given in the last two columns. The data are quite consistent, and the differences can be attributed to the neglect of polarization, or van der Waals' terms, in the calculated values.

Since these electrostatic forces are rather strong, ionic crystals are usually quite hard, brittle, and fairly high-melting.

Van der Waals' Forces. Most organic crystals fall into the crystal type in which van der Waals' forces predominate. The forces between the molecules are the same as those which we encountered in dealing with gas imperfections.

Table 13-1. The Born-Haber–Cycle Data and Results
(Kcal/mole or kcal/g atom)

Crystal	ΔH_f	ΔH_{sub} (metal)	I	D	A	E(cryst), Born-Haber	E(cryst), (electrostatic) calculation
NaCl	98	26	118	58	87	184	179
KCl	104	21	100	58	87	168	163
RbCl	103	20	96	58	87	162	158
NaBr	86	26	118	53	81	176	171
KBr	94	21	100	53	81	161	157
RbBr	93	20	96	53	81	156	151
NaF	136	26	118	36	81	218	214
KF	134	21	100	36	81	193	189
RbF	131	20	96	36	81	185	181

They are therefore called van der Waals' forces. The source of these forces can be broken down to dipole-dipole, induction, and London dispersion forces as treated in Sec. 12-4.

These forces are relatively weak, and the typical organic crystal, which is usually held together by such forces, is soft and low-melting.

Again the attractive forces are essentially nondirectional, but the simplifying effect of this on the arrangement of the molecules in the crystal is often obscured by the odd shapes of the molecules. The arrangement taken up by a given organic molecule in a crystal cannot in general be predicted even if the shape of the molecule is known.

Covalent Bonding. A few rather important crystals are made up of atoms joined together throughout the crystal by covalent forces. A number of no less important crystals depend on covalent forces in one or two dimensions and van der Waals' forces in the remaining dimensions.

The example, par excellence, of the first type is that of diamond. Each carbon atom of the lattice is held to its four tetrahedrally arranged neighbors by covalent bonds. These bonds are little different from those found between carbon atoms in organic molecules. The heat of sublimation of diamond, to form gaseous carbon atoms, now appears to be experimentally established as 170 kcal/mole. A diamond crystal with an Avogadro's number N of atoms will have $2N$ carbon-carbon bonds. The conversion of such a crystal to gaseous atoms will require the expenditure of energy equal to twice the bond energy. The bond energy in diamond is therefore calculated as 85 kcal. This value is in line with a covalent-bond energy of about 80 kcal that seems appropriate to hydrocarbon molecules. The tendency of carbon atoms to form four bonds in tetrahedral directions, rather than the close packing of the carbon atoms, is the determining factor in the crystal structure. The hardness of the crystal also stems from the strength of the covalent bond. A few other crystals have three-dimensional arrangements of covalent bonds. Of these the characteristically tough materials silicon carbide, SiC, and silica, SiO_2, can be mentioned.

The most important representatives of the class of crystals which have a two-dimensional array of covalent bonds are graphite and mica. The structure of graphite is shown in Fig. 13-1, and it is apparent that each carbon atom forms bonds in the plane of the infinite molecules, which are similar to those of benzene and the aromatic molecules. All bonds are equivalent and can be looked on as being single bonds with one-third double-bond character. The layers of graphite are held together by the relatively weak van der Waals' forces, and the slippery and flaky nature of graphite is thus readily understood.

The structure of mica is rather more complicated but again consists of two-dimensional covalent or ionic bonds with the layers so formed being held together by relatively weak forces.

A number of very different types of compounds form crystals which illustrate the formation of covalent bonds in only one dimension.

Inorganic examples are provided by SiS_2 and $BeCl_2$, the latter being an example of a number of similar and interesting "electron-deficient" compounds. Figure 13-2 illustrates the form taken by the atoms in these crystals.

Organic examples are provided by crystalline polymer molecules, either natural or synthetic. The simplest example is that of polyethylene, CH_3-$(CH_2)_nCH_3$, with a very long-chain molecule, i.e., a covalently bonded set of atoms. Each molecular chain is more or less oriented to neighboring molecules, and the details of this "more or less" are of sufficient interest to be dealt with in our study of macromolecules in Chap. 20.

The final important type of molecule whose crystal forces can be described in this manner are the biologically important molecules, the proteins. These molecules consist of long, covalently bonded chains of amino acids which are held to each other by relatively weak bonds, mainly hydrogen bonds. The structure of this important class of compounds is again of sufficient interest to merit a more complete treatment, and this detailed study will also be deferred to Chap. 20.

Hydrogen Bonds. The effect of hydrogen bonds on the form and strength of

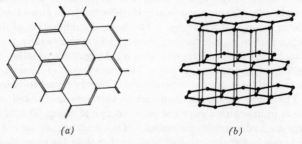

(a)   *(b)*

Fig. 13-1. The structure of the two-dimensionally covalently bonded crystal graphite. In (a) the bonding in a molecular layer is shown and in (b) the arrangement of the layers in the crystal.

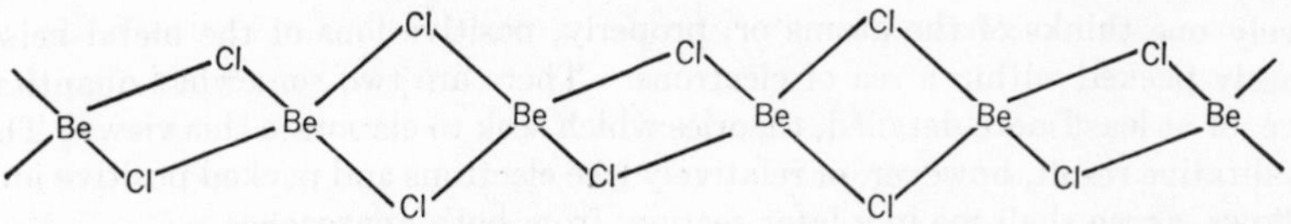

Fig. 13-2. The structure of the one dimensionally covalently bonded crystal BeCl₂. The bonds from each Be atom are approximately tetrahedrally arranged.

crystals is both important and widespread. It has been pointed out that some hydrogen atoms, such as those of —O—H bonds, carry a partial positive charge and can form hydrogen bonds to electronegative atoms, such as oxygen and nitrogen, which carry a partial negative charge. The typical hydrogen-bond energy of 6 kcal puts the strength of this bond between that of the covalent bond and van der Waals' effects. The role of the hydrogen bond in crystals is due not only to its strength but also to the requirement it imposes on the geometry of the molecular arrangement. The maximum strength of the bond is obtained when the hydrogen is located near an electronegative atom and probably positioned near a projecting pair of nonbonding electrons of that atom.

Here again there is a prime example of the effect of this force on the molecular arrangement in a crystal. The crystalline form of ice is unusual in that it is a very open structure, as exhibited, for example, by the fact that ice is less dense than water. The explanation for this fact is that the H₂O molecules arrange themselves in the crystal so that they form good hydrogen bonds to each other rather than so that they are closely packed. The result is a tetrahedral-like arrangement of four hydrogen atoms about each oxygen, two being covalently bonded and the other two hydrogen-bonded. The angle of the water molecule apparently expands from its normal value of 105° to something nearer the tetrahedral angle of $109\frac{1}{2}°$ to accommodate this structure.

Many organic compounds with hydroxyl groups, such as alcohols, phenols, and carboxylic acids, crystallize in a manner at least partly dictated by hydrogen-bond formation. The molecules assume positions in the crystal so that the hydrogen atoms of one molecule can bond to the oxygen or nitrogen atom of a neighboring molecule. Such intermolecular bonds, if they extend throughout the crystal, frequently result in rather high-melting and insoluble materials.

The structure of protein crystals, it should be mentioned, probably constitutes the most important consequence of hydrogen bonding. In Chap. 20 it will be shown how the arrangement of adjacent protein molecules to achieve maximum hydrogen bonding is a determining factor in the configuration of protein molecules in a crystal.

Metallic Bonding. Although one seldom encounters metals in a form in which their crystallinity is obvious from their external appearance, metals show a ready tendency to crystallize. The nature of the forces which operate can be expected to be different from those forces previously mentioned. The electrical conductivity and metallic luster are two properties which indicate that some unique electronic-structure and bonding phenomena operate. Qualitatively one thinks of the atoms or, properly, positive ions of the metal being closely packed within a sea of electrons.   There are two somewhat quantitative, or at least more detailed, theories which seek to elaborate this view.   The qualitative result, however, of relatively free electrons and packed positive ions follows, as we shall see in a later section, from both approaches.

13-2. Crystal Forms.   The attractive forces listed above combine with the size and shape of the particles to produce the ordered arrangement that characterizes the crystal.   The most characteristic external feature of such an order is the constancy of the angle formed between given faces of different crystal specimens of a compound.   These angles depend on the internal arrangement of the crystal.   Study of the angles between crystal planes, either external or internal planes, provides a convenient starting point for our investigation of crystal structure.

The relative direction of crystal planes is most conveniently expressed in terms of the intercepts of the planes on a suitable set of coordinates.   There are, moreover, seven different types of coordinate axes which are useful in this regard.   The crystals which are conveniently described in terms of a given set or system of coordinates are said to form a *crystal system*.   These seven crystal systems can now be described.

Table 13-2 and Fig. 13-3 show the coordinate axes that are used in each system.   The first system, called the *cubic* system, is characterized by three equal axes mutually at right angles.   A crystal belongs to this system, i.e., it can be conveniently described with this set of coordinates, if it has identical properties in three perpendicular directions.   Rock salt, NaCl, is a familiar example.   These external properties reflect an ordering of the particles which make up the crystal such that identical arrangements occur in each of the perpendicular directions.

In a similar manner, one can see that each system of coordinates is convenient for a particular type of crystal.   The axes to which the crystal conveniently fits may not be a right-angled set, and the behavior along one axis may be different from that on the others.   All the possible situations are given by the seven crystal systems.

Something of the dependence of the external crystalline form on the molecular arrangement in the crystal can be recognized from the fact that the faces

Table 13-2. The Crystal Systems

System	Axes	Angles	Example
Cubic....................	$a = b = c$	$\alpha = \beta = \gamma = 90°$	NaCl
Tetragonal................	$a = b; c$	$\alpha = \beta = \gamma = 90°$	White tin
Orthorhombic..............	$a; b; c$	$\alpha = \beta = \gamma = 90°$	Rhombic sulfur
Monoclinic................	$a; b; c$	$\alpha = \gamma = 90°; \beta \neq 90°$	Monoclinic sulfur
Rhombohedral.............	$a = b = c$	$\alpha = \beta = \gamma \neq 90°$	Calcite
Hexagonal................	$a = b; c$	$\alpha = \beta = 90°; \gamma = 120°$	Graphite
Triclinic..................	$a; b; c$	$\alpha \neq \beta \neq \gamma \neq 90°$	$CuSO_4 \cdot 5H_2O$

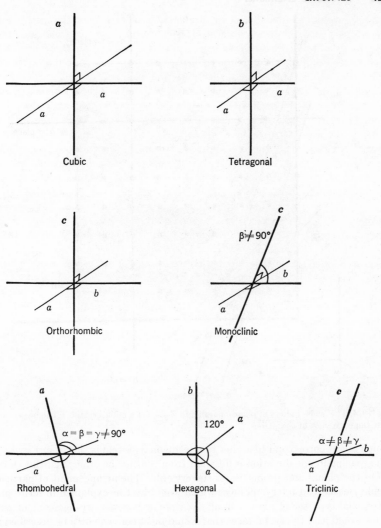

Fig. 13-3. The seven crystal systems.

that a crystal exhibits correspond to the planes that contain a relatively large
number of the particles which make up the crystal.   If these particles are
arranged in some sort of cubic array, as in Fig. 13-4, we might expect to see
crystal planes such as those indicated.   The fact that the particles are arranged
equally in three perpendicular directions results in the crystal exhibiting faces
which would be easily described in terms of the cubic-axis system and which
would place it in the first crystal system.   A two-dimensional array of points

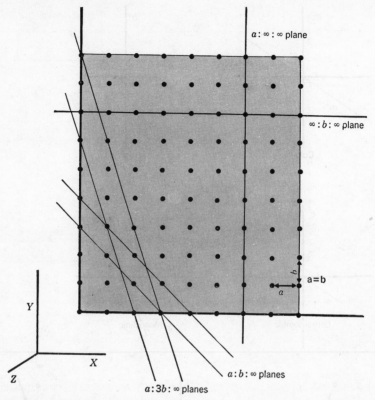

Fig. 13-4. The Weiss indices of planes, parallel to Z axis, of a cubic crystal. The lines represent the edge view of the planes.

which might correspond to a view of a tetragonal system is shown in Fig. 13-5. The spacing in one direction is different from that in the other, and this shows up in the planes and properties of the crystal. The arrangement of particles would clearly lead to crystal faces which would best be explained in terms of a tetragonal-type set of axes. Similarly a nonorthogonal arrangement of particles would lead to crystal faces that would most conveniently be described in terms of a nonorthogonal set of axes, and so forth.

A considerably more detailed classification of crystals can be made. The symmetry of a given crystal can put it in one of 32 crystal classes. The assignment of a crystal to a class is an invaluable aid in the study of the molecular arrangement in all but the simplest molecules. The principles of X-ray diffraction technique can, however, be illustrated without use of such classifications.

Once a suitable set of axes has been decided upon for a given crystal, the **crystal planes** can be described.

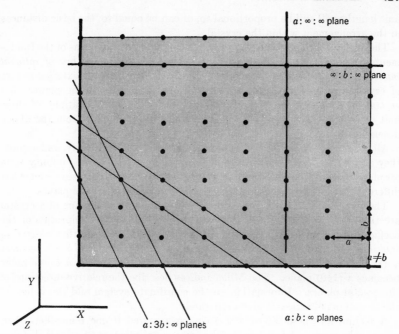

Fig. 13-5. The end view of a tetragonal crystal, showing how planes can be described in terms of intercepts measured in units of a and b.

13-3. Crystal Indices. The characteristic, and as we shall see important, aspect of crystal planes is the relative direction of one to another. The directions of the planes are most conveniently given in terms of their intercepts on the coordinates axes of the system to which the crystal belongs.

Intercepts of all planes that might be drawn through the atoms or ions of a given crystal can be expressed in terms of a set of reference distances, called a, b, and c, along the axes. Figures 13-4 and 13-5 show why this simplification is possible. Suppose that the spacing of the particles that make up the crystal are a, b, and c along the three axes. If only planes, such as are represented, which include a relatively high concentration of particles are important, it can be seen that they will all have intercepts which are simple multiples of a, b, and c on the X, Y, and Z axes, respectively. The direction of any of these planes can, in fact, be recorded by simply writing $a:b:c$, and so forth, to represent the intercepts, as in Figs. 13-4 and 13-5. In such a description of the direction of a plane *Weiss indices* are used. One should recognize, however, that these indices need not be based on the values of a, b, and c that are the particle spacings in the crystal. Any three numbers proportional to these spacings will be as satisfactory. For crystals with a more complicated internal structure, where large molecules must be considered instead of points, the three unit lengths will still be proportional to, or can be equal to, the basic distances in the arrangement within the crystal.

The Weiss indices and the way they can be understood in terms of the fundamental arrangement of the crystal particles lead one to the *law of rational intercepts*. This law was discovered by Haüy in 1784 from the external nature of crystals. The law simply states that the intercepts of the planes of a crystal on a suitable set of axes can be expressed by small multiples of three unit distances. The basis for the law should be quite clear from the above discussion.

Although the Weiss indices appear easily used and are easily understood, they suffer from the disadvantage of introducing a troublesome infinity term for planes parallel to an axis and, primarily for this reason, one uses a somewhat different method for specifying the relative directions of crystal planes.

The indices used in practice to denote the direction of a plane of a crystal are the *Miller indices*. These are obtained by taking the reciprocals of the coefficients of the Weiss indices. These three reciprocals are then cleared of fractions and reduced to the smallest set of integers. The plane $a:b:c$ becomes a (111) plane; the $a:2b:c$ plane becomes a (212) plane; the $a:b:\infty c$ plane becomes a (110) plane. The Miller indices describe the relative directions of the crystal planes. Information on the coordinate system and the values of the three unit distances is given separately.

A feeling for these indices can soon be acquired if one remembers their reciprocal nature. A low first number means an intercept at a large distance on the X axis; a low second number means a large intercept on the Y axis; and so forth. A plane parallel to an axis now has a zero term corresponding to the reciprocal of its intercept on that axis.

The Miller indices provide a convenient way of expressing a particular plane, i.e., a particular direction in a crystal. It should be pointed out that as far as direction is concerned, which is frequently all that is important, the planes (220) and (110) would be the same and the latter notation would be used.

13-4. The Unit Cell. The Miller indices give a convenient system for describing planes of a crystal and, as we shall see, are very helpful in the application of X-ray-diffraction methods to the study of crystal structures. The structure of a crystal is determined by the geometry of each molecule and the arrangement of these molecules in an array which is effectively infinite. Such an infinite array can be conveniently treated in terms of the *unit cell*. The unit cell is the smallest unit of the crystal which, when repeated in three dimensions, will generate the crystal. This unit has within it, therefore, all the essential features of the crystal structure, and a statement of the unit-cell structure is, in fact, a complete statement of the pattern in the crystal. Figure 13-6 illustrates some unit cells. One can verify that, when such units are joined together, a unique crystal structure is generated. It is the dimensions of the unit cell that provide the most convenient set of reference distances within the crystal, and the values given for a, b, and c for a given crystal are usually the unit-cell dimensions. With our knowledge of the Miller index system

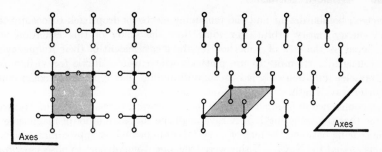

Fig. 13-6. Unit cells in two-dimensional views of a cubic crystal and a monoclinic crystal.

and the concept of the unit cell we are in a position to begin studies of the application of X-ray techniques to crystals.

13-5. X Rays and X-ray Diffraction. As a preliminary to the subject of X rays, a very simple but pertinent calculation can be made on the approximate spacing between the ions of a simple crystal like that of NaCl. For want of other information, we assume that there is a simple cubic arrangement of the ions, ignoring the difference between the Na^+ and Cl^- ions, in the crystal. Such a crystal containing 1 mole of NaCl would have $2N$ ions or $\sqrt[3]{2N} = 1.1 \times 10^8$ ions along an edge. The weight of the crystal is the molecular weight of 58 g. The density of the crystal is 2.15 g/cc, and an NaCl crystal containing 58 g would consist of a cube of 27 cc. The length of a side of the cube is therefore $\sqrt[3]{27} = 3$ cm. The spacing between the ions is thus estimated as $3/(1.1 \times 10^8) = 2.8 \times 10^{-8}$ cm, or 2.8 A. Estimates such as this were common knowledge when the nature of X rays was being investigated in the early 1900s and prompted the early important experiments that brought together studies of X rays and crystal structure.

X ray was the name given to the high-energy radiation emitted from a target when it was bombarded by high-energy electrons as in the apparatus of Fig. 13-7. The radiation was known to be of very high energy and to be very penetrating. We now know that the X rays result when inner and tightly bound electrons, usually K or L electrons, of the target are removed by the

Fig. 13-7. An X-ray tube.

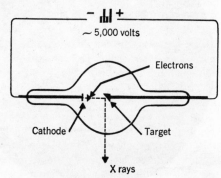

electron bombardment and the remaining electrons drop back to occupy the low-energy empty orbit. For some time the study of this radiation was hindered by the lack of a method for the measurement of their frequency or wavelength. Attempts to use methods which were suitable for visible and ultraviolet radiation only led to the information that X rays had some much shorter wavelength.

A conference in Munich in 1912 brought forward the suggestion of Max von Laue that the wavelength of X rays might be the same order of magnitude as the spacing between the ions of a crystal, as indicated by approximate calculations as that for NaCl. If this were true, one would expect to observe *diffraction effects* when X rays were passed through, or reflected from, crystals. It was known that the available ruled grating had lines which were much too widely spaced to show such effects. Von Laue's suggestion was that the crystals might be, in effect, natural gratings. Experiments were immediately performed by passing a beam of X rays through a crystal of copper sulfate. A more recent and more distinct example of the effect observed is shown in Fig. 13-8. A number of spots on the photographic plate, in addition to that produced by the main X-ray beam, are evident and, as we shall see in the next section, these additional spots are the sought-for diffraction effect.

The immediate goal of the experiments was the use of crystals to study X rays. It soon became apparent, however, that it was to be the other way around and that X rays were to be used to study crystals. Much of the early impetus of this work was due to Sir William Bragg and his son W. L. Bragg at Cambridge. It is the method of the senior Bragg that will be used to explain the diffraction phenomenon.

13-6. The Bragg Method. Diffraction effects occur when radiation is disturbed so that some of the waves of the radiation are shifted out of phase with

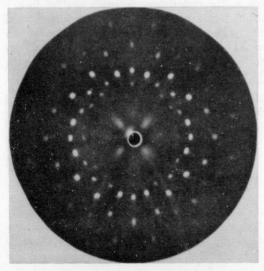

Fig. 13-8. Laue single-crystal X-ray photograph of NH_4Cl. X-ray beam along fourfold axis. (*From C. W. Bunn, "Chemical Crystallography," Oxford University Press, New York*, 1945.)

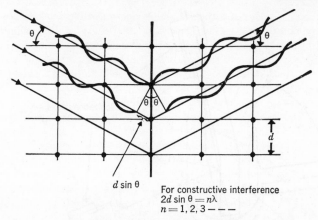

$d \sin \theta$

For constructive interference
$$2d \sin \theta = n\lambda$$
$$n = 1, 2, 3 - - -$$

Fig. 13-9. The Bragg scattering condition.

other waves as described in the electron-diffraction treatment of Chap. 10. In the Bragg method the phenomenon is observed when X rays are reflected from a crystal.

A beam of X rays is passed into a crystal, which in Fig. 13-9 is represented by layers of particles. The X rays are scattered by interaction with the electrons of the atoms or ions of the crystal. Since X rays are known to be quite penetrating, each layer of atoms can be expected to scatter only a small part of the X-ray beam. If the crystal particles did not have a spacing which was of the same order of magnitude as the wavelength of the X rays, a reflection of some of the X rays would occur, like that of light from a mirror. The reflection is, in fact, not simple and is greatly disturbed by the diffraction effect.

The incoming beam of X rays can be represented as in Fig. 13-9 with all the waves in phase. The nature of the reflected beam must be investigated. As Fig. 13-9 shows, the beams scattered from successive layers of crystal particles may show waves that, in a particular direction, are shifted relative to the scattered waves from the other layers. When this happens and the addition of the waves tends to cancel each other out, *destructive interference* is said to occur. Only if all these scattered beams come out in phase will they add up and contribute to a net scattered beam. This *constructive interference* occurs whenever the scattered beams from successive layers are shifted by an integral multiple of wavelengths. Reference to Fig. 13-9 shows that this happens when the relation

$$n\lambda = 2d \sin \theta \qquad \text{with } n = 1, 2, 3, \ldots \tag{4}$$

holds. This important equation is known as *Bragg's reflection law*.

An experimental arrangement for making use of this expression is diagramed in Fig. 13-10. For a given angle θ, which equals the angle of incidence and the angle of reflection, one can measure the intensity of the scattered X-ray beam. A lever arrangement turns the detector through twice the angle through which the crystal is turned. The intensity is measured either with a

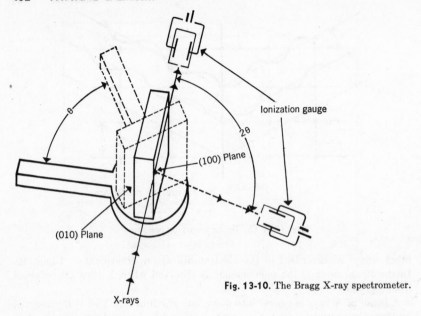

Ionization gauge

(100) Plane

2θ

θ

(010) Plane

X-rays

Fig. 13-10. The Bragg X-ray spectrometer.

photographic plate or an ionization gauge. The latter allows a current to flow across a pair of charged plates in a chamber when X rays enter and produce ions in the gas of the chamber. If a given set of planes of the crystal with a spacing equal to d are considered, it is seen that a scattered beam will be detected when $\sin \theta = \lambda/2d$, $2\lambda/2d$, $3\lambda/2d$, and so forth. These scattered beams with $n = 1, 2, 3, \ldots$ are known as first-order, second-order, and so forth, diffractions. The higher-order scatterings are observed to have a smaller intensity than the lower-order scatterings.

To make use of Bragg's relation [Eq. (4)] to obtain values of d from measured θ's, it is necessary to know the wavelength of the X rays being used. This quantity was originally determined by Bragg from studies of the diffraction from a NaCl crystal. Using an X-ray beam of unknown wavelength, he was able to show that the ions were arranged, not in a simple cubic manner, but in a face-centered cubic lattice as shown in Fig. 13-11. Once this was known, the previous calculation could be accepted. The spacing d of Fig. 13-11, which has the value 2.815 A, could then be used together with the measured values of $\sin \theta$ for which reflections are observed to give a value of λ for the X rays from Bragg's law.

Nowadays one can make use of X-ray tubes which put out a beam of X rays of known wavelength. Most common is the use of a tube with a copper target which gives off X rays of wavelength equal to 1.540 A. With such equipment one can proceed immediately to the determination of the spacings of reflecting planes within the crystal and ultimately to the detailed arrangement of the atoms and molecules in the crystal.

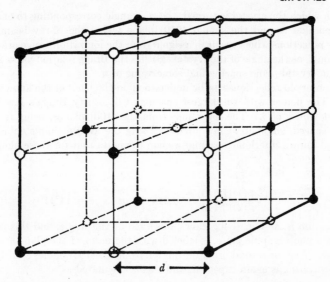

Fig. 13-11. The unit cell of the face-centered cubic NaCl crystal structure.

13-7. Determination of the Unit-cell Dimensions. To illustrate the use of Bragg's law and to show how the fundamental spacings in the crystal, i.e., the dimensions of the unit cell, are obtained, the Bragg reflection pattern from a simple cubic crystal will be considered.   A real example is provided by a KCl crystal which, although face-centered as is NaCl, behaves as if it were simple cubic. Since K+ and Cl− have the same number of electrons, these ions scatter X rays almost equally.   As far as the diffraction pattern is concerned, they are, therefore, indistinguishable.   The distance between rows of these apparently similar ions is 3.146 A.   The diffraction that is obtained with X rays of wavelength 1.540 A will be considered.

Imagine the KCl crystal mounted as in Fig. 13-10 so that one cubic axis, the Z axis, is vertical.   Experimentally the diffracted beam is now measured as the crystal and detector are turned through increasing angles.   Figure 13-12 shows the signal given out from the ionization gauge as a function of the angle

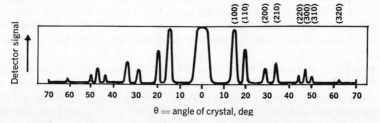

Fig. 13-12. Single crystal signal (schematic) for a KCl crystal mounted as in Fig. 13-10. The indices are based on a KCl crystal with K+ and Cl− assumed to be like particles.

through which the crystal is turned, the zero angle corresponding to one (100) plane parallel to and the similar (010) plane facing the X-ray beam. The various reflections which result in a signal from the ionization gauge are said to "flash out" as the angle of the crystal satisfies the Bragg relation $n\lambda = 2d \sin\theta$ for some crystal-plane spacing and some value of n.

The observed reflections can be understood on the basis of the known structure. The planes with the largest spacings will satisfy Bragg's law for the smallest values of θ. The reflections from the (100) planes, being relatively widely spaced, show up at low angles. Using the known simple cubic structure and known interionic spacing, we can calculate that for these planes

$$\sin\theta = \frac{n\lambda}{2d}$$
$$= \frac{(1)(1.540)}{(2)(3.146)} = 0.245 \quad \text{or} \quad \theta = 14°11'$$

A diffraction is, as Fig. 13-12 shows, observed at this angle, and this peak, or spot on a photographic plate, is labeled with the name of the plane that gives rise to it. For the second-order diffraction from the (100) planes a fairly small angle scattering is again expected, and this is calculated as

$$\sin\theta = \frac{(2)(1.540)}{(2)(3.146)} = \frac{1.540}{(2)(3.146/2)} = 0.499 \quad \text{and} \quad \theta = 29°21'$$

The third-order 100 reflection will, similarly, be at

$$\sin\theta = \frac{(3)(1.540)}{(2)(3.146)} = \frac{1.540}{(2)(3.146/3)} = 0.735 \quad \text{and} \quad \theta = 47°18'$$

These expressions have been written to show that the second- and third-order reflections can be thought of as resulting from planes that have a spacing of one-half and one-third of that of the (100) planes. The above reflections can therefore be conveniently indexed as (200) and (300).

In a similar way the spacings of other planes, such as the (110) plane, can be calculated from the known crystal structure and the angle at which diffraction from these planes can be calculated. Diffraction spots at these angles can be indexed in terms of the plane and the order that gives rise to the spot.

It is seen that all the reflections can be understood and indexed as in Fig. 13-12 when the unit-cell shape and dimensions are known, i.e., in this simple example when it is known that the units are arranged cubically and that the dimensions of the fundamental cube are 3.146 A. The wealth of data that would result if the diffracted beam in directions other than the horizontal plane were measured could be correlated with the known structure in a similar way.

In practice one starts with a crystal of unknown structure. The procedure is then to use the low-angle reflections and Bragg's law to calculate values for plane spacings d. These can be assumed to be some dimension of the unit cell. With such assumed unit-cell distances one then calculates other plane spacings and the angles of reflections expected from these planes. If the original assignment of the unit-cell structure is correct, other reflections will be calculable. If the calculated pattern does not match the observed reflections, one must apply the original wide-spacing data to the unit cell in some other way.   By this procedure one can usually quite easily determine the unit-cell dimensions. In practice the known external symmetry of the crystal is a very great aid.

The procedure described here and illustrated by the very simple example is essentially that of the first step of any X-ray-diffraction study.   It leads to dimensions for the unit cell.   With these data and the density of the solid material one calculates, furthermore, the number of molecules per unit cell.

13-8. The Powder Method.   Before pursuing the structure studies resulting from X-ray-diffraction experiments on single crystals by the Bragg method, it should be pointed out that a usually simpler technique for obtaining some diffraction data is available.   This method was first used by Debye and Scherrer and depends on the use of a powder of the crystalline sample instead of a single crystal.   The sample is usually placed in a fine capillary.   The experimental arrangement, using a photographic plate to detect the diffracted beam, is shown in Fig. 13-13.

The crystals in the sample will present all possible orientations to the X-ray beam.   The diffraction obtained will be just like that which would result from mounting a single crystal and turning it through all possible angles.   For each crystal plane there will be some one angle at which the Bragg law will be satisfied.   Since some of the crystals will have this orientation, a diffracted beam will result at the suitable angle, as is depicted in Fig. 13-13.   Since there are quite a few crystal planes with a fairly high density of particles, there will be reflections from each of these and the pattern will show scattering at a large number of angles.

From the angle at which a given reflection occurs, one can use Bragg's law to get the plane spacing just as for a single crystal.   Again the small-angle scattering corresponds to the widely spaced planes, and one can obtain the unit-cell dimensions from these experiments just as well as from single-crystal studies.

Probably the most widespread application of this powder method is for the analysis of solid samples.   The spacings between crystal planes, and therefore

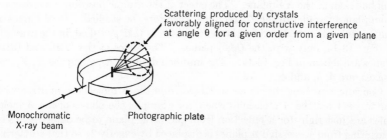

Fig. 13-13. The X-ray powder method.

the position of the line of a powder photograph, are characteristic of a given crystal. The components of a solid mixture can therefore often be rapidly identified from a powder pattern.

Too small a crystal will not, however, give a good diffraction pattern. With any mechanical powdering technique the crystals remain quite large, on a molecular scale, and a good diffraction pattern is obtained. For crystals that are so small that they do not confront the X rays with an apparently infinite array of crystal planes the diffraction pattern becomes poorly defined, and, in fact, one can use this broadening of the diffraction pattern lines to determine the size of the crystals. A sample of a polymer like polyethylene consists of small regions of crystalline material embedded in a general amorphous matrix. The X-ray-diffraction pattern shows the broadening expected for small crystalline regions, and, as Chap. 20 will point out, the size of the crystalline regions can be deduced from these diffraction results.

13-9. The Structure Factor. The symmetry of the crystal and the unit-cell dimensions are usually sufficient information to decide the exact structure of a simple ionic crystal. For a crystal consisting of large molecules and, in particular, for crystals of large organic molecules the problem of determining the arrangement of the atoms within each molecule still remains. Since it is these internal molecular dimensions which are the most important result of X-ray studies, the method, which can become quite elaborate, is illustrated by another very simple model.

Suppose that we have a crystal consisting of diatomic molecules AB, represented by ●—○ in Fig. 13-14, and, furthermore, suppose that atom A is taken as being located at the lattice points of the crystal and that atom B is an unknown bond distance from A, as shown in Fig. 13-14. It will be assumed that the unit-cell dimensions have been determined by the approach indicated for the KCl crystal in Secs. 13-7 and 13-8. The object of the study of the crystal of AB is to locate B relative to A and thus to determine the structure, i.e., the bond length, of the molecule. Actual cases of interest differ only in degree of complexity.

It is helpful to treat the problem as a two-dimensional one, and it will be assumed that the molecules are lined up behind one another as in Fig. 13-14. It is necessary therefore to locate the atoms in the plane of the paper, which will be taken as the XY plane. The effect of the atomic positions on reflection from planes parallel to the Z axis must, therefore, be studied. If all planes of the crystal are represented by the general indices (hkl), we deal, in the example of Fig. 13-14, only with the $(hk0)$ planes. The edges of the (210) and (310) planes are shown in Fig. 13-14. The unit-cell dimensions, along the X, Y, and Z axes, are a, b, and c.

Consider now how the waves scattered from the B molecules interfere with the waves from the A molecules when, for example, the planes of the A molecules are just right for a reflection from the (210) plane to be detected. The scattering from successive A planes is displaced by exactly 2π so that scattering from each A plane reinforces. The planes of B atoms, however, interfere by

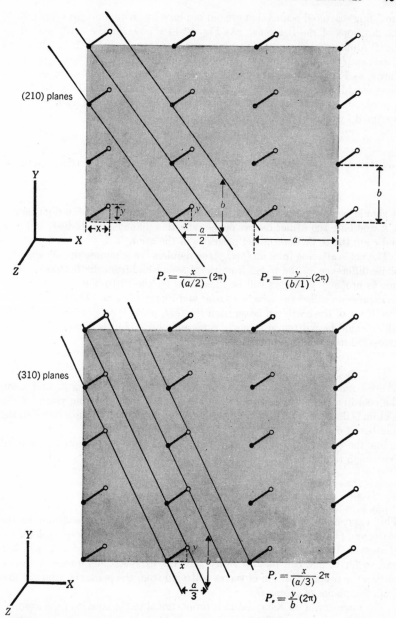

Fig. 13-14. Phase shifts for ○ atoms when ● atoms form planes that are oriented for constructive interference from (210) and (310) planes. (Atom A is here represented by ● and atom B by ○.)

providing scattered beams that are out of phase by an amount that depends on the positions of the B atoms. As Fig. 13-14 shows, for the (210) reflections the B atoms provide waves that are out of phase by $[x/(a/2)]2\pi$ along the X axis and $[y/(b/1)]2\pi$ along the Y axis. Consideration of the (310) reflections shows, as Fig. 13-14 suggests, that for these reflections the B-atom contributions would be out of phase by $[x/(a/3)]2\pi$ and $[y/(b/1)]2\pi$ along the X and Y axes. In general the phase difference of the beam scattered by B from that scattered by A is

$$2\pi \left(h\frac{x}{a} + k\frac{y}{b} \right)$$

and, for a general plane in three dimensions, this phase difference would be

$$2\pi \left(h\frac{x}{a} + k\frac{y}{b} + l\frac{z}{c} \right)$$

It should be remembered that a, b, and c are the known unit-cell dimensions; h, k, and l are the Miller indices of the reflection plane being studied; and x, y, and z are the to be determined positions of the atom B.

The net scattering from an (hkl) plane requires the summing up, allowing for phase difference, of the waves from the A atoms and from the B atoms. This sum is properly given, as will be illustrated by the (210)-plane reflection, by an expression called the *structure factor* and represented by $F(hkl)$. Thus, the amplitude of the scattered beam from the (hkl) plane is proportional to $F(hkl)$, which could be written in terms of sines and cosines but is more conveniently expressed in exponential form as

$$F(hkl) = \sum_\alpha f_\alpha e^{2\pi i(hx_\alpha/a + ky_\alpha/b + lz_\alpha/c)} \tag{5}$$

where α numbers off the different atoms of the molecule and x_α, y_α, and z_α are the coordinates of the α atom of the molecule. The scattering power of the α atom is denoted by f_α and can be taken as approximately proportional to the number of electrons of the atom, i.e., to its atomic number.

For the (210) plane of the AB crystal of Fig. 13-14, one uses this general expression to obtain

$$\begin{aligned}
F(210) &= \text{amplitude from (210) plane} \\
&= f_A e^{2\pi i(0)} + f_B e^{2\pi i(2x/a + 1y/b + 0)} \\
&= f_A + f_B e^{2\pi i(2x/a + 1y/b)} \tag{6}
\end{aligned}$$

This expression shows how a scattered beam depends, in addition to the scattering factors f_A and f_B, on the phase-difference term $2x/a + 1y/b$ for the B atoms. If atom B is placed in various positions, such as $x = a/2$, $y = b/2$, and so forth, one can readily verify that the exponential expression accomplishes the proper addition of waves scattered from the planes of atoms A and from the planes of atoms B.

The intensity of an X-ray beam is proportional to the square of the absolute value of the wave amplitude, as mentioned also for an electron beam, and one has the general expression

$$I(hkl) \propto \left| \sum_\alpha f_\alpha e^{2\pi i(hx_\alpha/a + ky_\alpha/b + lz_\alpha/c)} \right|^2 \tag{7}$$

More easily visualized is the trigonometric form of this expression, which was used in the treatment of electron diffraction and which is obtained by use of the relation

$$e^{i\theta} = \cos \theta + i \sin \theta \qquad (8)$$

In trigonometric form, Eq. (7) becomes

$$I(hkl) \propto \left[\sum_{\alpha} f_{\alpha} \cos 2\pi \left(\frac{hx_{\alpha}}{a} + \frac{ky_{\alpha}}{b} + \frac{lz_{\alpha}}{c} \right) \right]^2$$
$$+ \left[\sum_{\alpha} f_{\alpha} \sin 2\pi \left(\frac{hx_{\alpha}}{a} + \frac{ky_{\alpha}}{b} + \frac{lz_{\alpha}}{c} \right) \right]^2 \qquad (9)$$

For diffraction from the (210) plane of Fig. 13-14, for example, one has

$$I(210) \propto \left[f_A \cos 2\pi(0) + f_B \cos 2\pi \left(\frac{2x}{a} + \frac{y}{b} \right) \right]^2$$
$$+ \left[f_A \sin 2\pi(0) + f_B \sin 2\pi \left(\frac{2x}{a} + \frac{y}{b} \right) \right]^2$$
$$\propto f_A^2 + 2f_A f_B \cos 2\pi \left(\frac{2x}{a} + \frac{y}{b} \right) + f_B^2 \qquad (10)$$

Again the validity of this result can be checked. Complete constructive interference occurs, for example, when $x = y = 0$, for which $I(210)$ becomes proportional, according to Eq. (10), to $(f_A + f_B)^2$. An extreme of maximum interference, on the other hand, can be seen from Fig. 13-14 to occur when $x = a/4$ and $y = 0$, which, according to Eq. (10), gives $I(210)$ proportional to $(f_A - f_B)^2$.

Equation (7) or Eq. (9) is the important result of this treatment. The position of atom B in the example of Fig. 13-14 could be deduced by choosing values for x and y and using Eq. (7) or (9) to calculate the relative intensities of various reflections. The calculated and observed diffraction patterns could then be compared in much the same way as the electron-diffraction trial structure curves were compared with the observed scattering curve. A method has therefore been obtained for going from a crystal structure to a calculated X-ray pattern. One can be content with this result, which shows that, with sufficient trial-and-error steps, a structure for a molecule in a crystal can be obtained. There are, furthermore, very many diffraction spots that can be measured, and a structure which leads to a correct intensity calculation for all the observed spots is unquestionably the correct structure. In this regard X-ray-diffraction results are more satisfactory than those of electron diffraction.

It is of course desirable, and for large organic molecules almost necessary, that a method be available for directly deducing a molecular structure from the observed diffraction pattern without having to resort entirely to this trial-and-error procedure. An indication of the problems that arise when this is attempted and some of the methods that are adopted to overcome these difficulties can now be given.

*13-10. The Fourier Synthesis. One of the most important developments in X-ray-diffraction techniques was the recognition by Sir William Bragg that the approach of the previous section could in fact be, to some extent, turned around. The procedure depends on the suggestion that the crystal can be looked upon, not as a set of discrete scattering points, but as a three-dimensional distribution of varying electron densities. X rays do, in fact, recognize atoms only as regions of high electron density, and therefore high scattering power, compared with that of the surrounding regions. Instead of attempting to deduce the coordinates of the atoms in the crystal one can look for an electron-density function $\rho(xyz)$ that represents the electron-density distribution in the crystal. This function, which is like the radial-distribution function introduced in electron-diffraction studies, will be quite complicated if the molecules of the crystal are at all large. In view of the periodic nature of the crystal, with periodicities a, b, and c, one can formally represent the function by a Fourier-series function with the form

$$\rho(xyz) = \sum_{p=-\infty}^{+\infty} \sum_{q=-\infty}^{+\infty} \sum_{r=-\infty}^{+\infty} A(pqr)e^{2\pi i(px/a+qy/b+rz/c)} \tag{11}$$

where p, q, and r can take on integral values from $-\infty$ to $+\infty$ and $A(pqr)$ are the to be determined coefficients of the many Fourier-series terms. Determination of the coefficients $A(pqr)$ is the goal of the derivation. Knowledge of these coefficients would allow the electron density to be drawn out and the positions of the atoms located.

It is necessary now to recall the amplitude expression of Eq. (5). The *structure factor*, which gives the amplitude of the beam diffracted by the (hkl) plane, was found to be

$$F(hkl) = \sum_{\alpha} f_{\alpha}e^{2\pi i(hx_{\alpha}/a+ky_{\alpha}/b+lz_{\alpha}/c)}$$

In terms of a distribution $\rho(xyz)$ of the electron density throughout the unit cell this amplitude equation can be written in the integral form

$$F(hkl) = (\text{const}) \int_0^a \int_0^b \int_0^c \rho(xyz)e^{2\pi i(hx/a+ky/b+lz/c)} \, dx \, dy \, dz \tag{12}$$

where we need not work out the value of the multiplying constant.

Evaluation of the coefficients $A(pqr)$ of Eq. (11) follows from substitution of the Fourier expression for $\rho(xyz)$ into Eq. (12). This gives

$$F(hkl) = (\text{const}) \int_0^a \int_0^b \int_0^c \sum_p \sum_p \sum_r A(pqr)e^{2\pi i(px/a+qy/b+rz/c)}$$
$$e^{2\pi i(hx/a+ky/b+lz/c)} \, dx \, dy \, dz$$
$$= (\text{const}) \int_0^a \int_0^b \int_0^c \sum_p \sum_p \sum_r A(pqr)e^{2\pi i[(h+p)x/a+(k+q)y/b+(l+r)z/c]} \, dx \, dy \, dz \tag{13}$$

Recognition that all terms of the type $\int_0^a e^{2\pi i\theta/a} \, d\theta$ are zero, as can be easily seen by expressing the exponential term in trigonometric form according to Eq. (8), eliminates all terms of the series except those for which $p = -h$, $q = -k$, and $r = -l$. For these, the exponential is $e^{2\pi i(0)} = 1$, and the net result of all the summations and integrations of Eq. (13) is

$$F(hkl) = (\text{const})(a)(b)(c)A(-h,-k,-l) \tag{14}$$

or
$$A(-h,-k,-l) = \frac{F(hkl)}{(\text{const})(abc)} \tag{15}$$

Recognition that the indices p, q, and r are equivalent to $-h$, $-k$, and $-l$ allows substitution of this result in the Fourier-series expression [Eq. (11)] for the electron density to give, finally,

$$\rho(xyz) = \frac{1}{(\text{const})(abc)} \sum_{h=-\infty}^{+\infty} \sum_{k=-\infty}^{+\infty} \sum_{l=-\infty}^{+\infty} F(hkl)e^{2\pi i(hx/a+ky/b+lz/c)} \tag{16}$$

The power of this elegant result is seen when it is recalled that $F(hkl)$ is the amplitude of the wave scattered by the (hkl) plane. The measured intensity of the beam scattered by the (hkl) plane, furthermore, is proportional to $[F(hkl)]^2$. Thus, measurements lead to relative values of $\pm F(hkl)$. Except for the undetermined sign on the values of $F(hkl)$, the expression of Eq. (16) gives the desired result: a method for using the intensities of the diffraction spots to deduce the crystal structure, as represented by $\rho(xyz)$. If the signs of the amplitudes of the diffracted waves that form the diffraction spots that can be labeled as hkl were known, the electron density at any point xyz in the unit cell could be determined by performing the summation of Eq. (16), for the chosen value of x, y, and z, over all values of hkl, that is, for all the observed diffraction spots. The more intense diffraction spots correspond to the numerically greater diffraction amplitudes so that it is necessary only to extend the summation to all the more important diffraction spots. Such summations could be performed for various points, specified by values of x, y, and z in the unit cell. By determination of the electron density at sufficient points an electron-density map could be drawn which would show the positions of the atoms by regions of high electron density.

The undetermined sign, which results because the intensities and not the amplitudes of the diffraction beams are obtained, turns out to be very troublesome, and a number of techniques have been suggested to make use of Eq. (16) in spite of the sign difficulty.

These approaches depend, usually, on methods for obtaining the approximate shape of the molecule and its approximate position in the unit cell. Some molecules, for instance, contain a heavy metal atom, which has a high scattering probability and can be located, while the complexities of the remainder of the molecule can initially be ignored. The signs of the most important structure factors can then be guessed at. These few diffraction spots can then be used in Eq. (16) to deduce a crude electron-density map. This first approximation map can then lead to the estimate of the position of more of the atoms and thus, with Eq. (12), to the signs of the structure factors of more of the diffraction results. In this way one *refines* a structure by working in the information from more and more of the diffraction spots until a structure of the desired detail is obtained.

Typical electron-distribution maps that are obtained as a result of such a study are shown in Fig. 13-15.

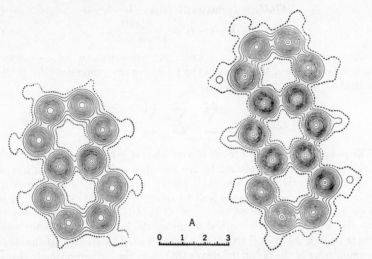

Fig. 13-15. Electron-density maps of naphthalene and anthracene from X-ray diffraction studies by J. M. Robertson and coworkers [*Acta Cryst.*, **2**: 233 (1949) and **3**: 245 (1950)]. Electron-density contour levels are drawn at intervals of $\frac{1}{2}$ electron per A^3. That for a density of $\frac{1}{2}$ electron per A^3 is shown dotted.

The complete deduction of the structure of a complicated molecule by the X-ray-diffraction technique is a major research problem. There is, however, no other method that provides such a wealth of reliable structural information. The number of large molecules whose structure, in the solid state, has been completely worked out continues to grow and to provide valuable basic information for many fields of chemistry.

13-11. The Heat Capacity of Crystals. Our attention is now turned to one aspect of the thermodynamics of crystals. This subject, the heat capacity of crystals, leads to a further understanding of the forces acting between crystal particles.

A very early generalization of the heat capacity of crystals was made by Dulong and Petit in 1819. The data available at that time consisted of heat capacities, measured at atmospheric pressure and room temperature. Dulong and Petit recognized that these data indicated that the heat capacity of solid elements, mostly metals, at room temperature had the same value of about 6.3 cal/(deg)(g atom).

The kinetic theory of gases provides a background that leads to a ready explanation of this observation. Each vibrational degree of freedom would be expected, on the classical, i.e., nonquantum-mechanical, approach, to have an average kinetic energy of $\frac{1}{2}RT$ for an Avogadro's number of particles. The average kinetic energy for the three perpendicular vibration modes of the particles in a crystal lattice would then be $\frac{3}{2}RT$. The swinging of a pendulum or the vibration of a weight on a spring can be analyzed to show that in a simple harmonic motion there is, on the average, an equal amount of kinetic and potential energy.   We expect, therefore,

$$E_{\text{vib}}(\text{classical}) = E_{\text{kinetic}} + E_{\text{potential}}$$
$$= \tfrac{3}{2}RT + \tfrac{3}{2}RT = 3RT \tag{17}$$

The heat capacity is readily calculated by differentiating this result with respect to temperature.   One obtains strictly C_v, but since the work of expansion per degree temperature rise is only a few tenths of a calorie per mole, we can write

$$C_p \cong C_v = \frac{dE}{dT} = 3R \tag{18}$$

This calculation indicates that a heat capacity of about 6 cal/(deg)(g atom) should be expected and that this value should apply to all crystals made up of a lattice of single particles.   The indication of the calculation is, furthermore, that the heat capacity should be independent of temperature.   The nice, if approximate, success of this derivation was soon disrupted by additional experimental results.

Figure 13-16 shows more extensive data for crystals of elements to which the Dulong and Petit rule presumably applies.   One sees that the rule is more or less valid at room temperature if only the heavy metals are considered but that at lower temperatures the heat capacities show no correlation with this rule.   The classical derivation and its prediction of a heat capacity independent of temperature are completely disproved.   In the days of classical treatments, before 1900, these results presented a very perplexing problem.   There seemed no way to avoid the erroneous deductions of the theory.

With the development of the quantum theory it was soon recognized that the classical treatment of the vibrations, i.e., with any vibrational energy allowed, was faulty.   In 1907 Einstein showed that, if a vibrational frequency is assigned to the vibrations of the crystal particles and the motion is treated quantum mechanically, curves of the general shape of Fig. 13-16 can be obtained.   He assumed that he could assign some energy separation $h\nu$ to the energy of the vibration modes of the atoms of the crystal.

The calculation of the heat capacity resulting from vibrational modes has already been treated.   For a gram atom there are N particles each with 3 vibrational degrees of freedom.   The previous formula derived in Sec. 4-16 for molecular vibrations is completely applicable and leads to the heat-capacity prediction for a crystalline solid containing an Avogadro's number of single particles of

$$C_v = 3R \left(\frac{h\nu}{kT}\right)^2 \frac{e^{h\nu/kT}}{(e^{h\nu/kT} - 1)^2} \tag{19}$$

By choosing a value of the vibrational-energy-level spacing $h\nu$ for each crystal,

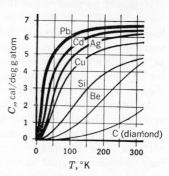

Fig. 13-16. The heat capacities of simple crystalline solids at low temperatures. (*Adapted from E. B. Millard, "Physical Chemistry for Colleges," Mc-Graw-Hill Book Company, Inc., New York, 1953.*)

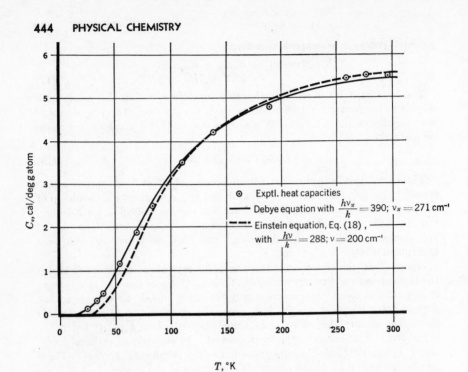

Fig. 13-17. The experimental heat-capacity data at low temperatures for aluminum. The best fits to the data that can be obtained with the Einstein and Debye theories are indicated.

Einstein was able to obtain approximate agreement with each of the curves of Fig. 13-16, as is illustrated by the data for Al in Fig. 13-17.

It should be pointed out that Eq. (19) can be used to form a curve of C_v versus $h\nu/kT$. To the extent that the Einstein theory is satisfactory in handling the heat-capacity data for simple crystalline materials, it follows that for a given material the measured heat capacities when plotted against $h\nu/kT$, with a suitable value of ν for that material, will fall on the general curve for C_v versus $h\nu/kT$. Such a treatment will be illustrated by the Debye theory, which is rather more successful than that of Einstein.

An improvement on Einstein's theory which gives results in even better agreement with the experimental data was soon forthcoming. It was recognized by Debye that the assumption that all the particles of a crystal vibrate with the same frequency was not entirely sound. Although all the particles may be bound by equal forces, the motions of the particles will couple so that vibrations of a wide range of frequencies will result. One finds spectroscopically, for instance, that simple salt crystals show a very broad absorption band in the far-infrared region. On the assumption of a range of vibrational frequencies Debye derived a heat-capacity equation in a manner similar to that used by Einstein. Debye's expression relates the heat capacity to the term $h\nu_M/kT$, where ν_M is the maximum of a whole range of frequencies.   Like the single frequency of the Einstein theory, the value of ν_M must be deduced empirically for each crystal.   Figure 13-17 shows how well this theory fits the data of Al and particularly how the fit at temperatures approaching absolute zero is greatly improved.

Some characteristic frequencies are listed in Table 13-3.   It has, unfortunately, become customary to introduce the *Debye characteristic temperature* θ_D, defined by $\theta_D = h\nu_M/k$, and these numbers are also listed.   The values of $h\nu_M$ indicate the maximum energy spacing for the vibrational energies of the crystal particles.

In a manner similar to that in which the vibrational frequencies of free molecules indicate the force constants of the bonds between the atoms of the molecule, the Debye or Einstein frequencies indicate the rigidity with which the atoms or ions are held at their crystal-lattice sites.   The frequencies depend, however, on both the force constants and the particle masses through a relation of the type $\nu = \dfrac{1}{2\pi}\sqrt{\dfrac{k}{m}}$, where m is the mass of a single vibrating particle, or a reduced mass if more than one particle moves in the vibration. For comparative purposes, it is sufficient to calculate ν_M^2, where M is the molecular weight, for various crystals.   This quantity, exhibited in Table 13-3, is a measure of the stiffness of the crystal bonds uncomplicated by the effect of the mass of the crystal particles.   The gradation from soft, weakly bonded crystals to hard, strongly bonded materials is evident and is given in a quantitative way by the data of Table 13-3.

It should be mentioned, however, that it is the vibrational spacings themselves, ν or ν_M, that determine the heat capacity behavior.   Those crystals with closely spaced levels, as a result of weak bonds or heavy atoms, as in lead, reach the classical heat-capacity value at relatively low temperatures.   Those crystals, on the other hand, with large vibrational spacings, as a result of high

Table 13-3. The Debye Frequencies ν_M, Temperatures $h\nu_M/k$, and Crystal Force Constants

Crystal	ν_M (cm^{-1})	$\theta_D = h\nu_M/k$ (°C)	Force-constant factor $= M\nu_M^2 \times 10^{-5}$
K..................	70	100	2
Na.................	104	150	3
Pb.................	61	88	8
Hg.................	67	96	9
KCl...............	157	227	9
Ca.................	160	230	10
Al.................	271	390	20
Ag.......·........	149	215	24
Au.................	170	118	29
Cu.................	218	315	30
Be.................	695	1000	43
Fe.................	292	420	48
C(diamond)........	1,280	1840	197

force constants or light atoms, reach this limit of $3R$ for C_v only at relatively high temperatures. This latter type, as Fig. 13-16 shows, is illustrated most emphatically by the example of diamond.

It is a matter of considerable practical importance, as was suggested in the discussion of the determination of entropies from the third law of thermodynamics, to be able to predict the way in which the heat capacity of a crystalline solid behaves as the absolute temperature approaches zero. The success of the Debye theory in correlating the measurable heat capacities has led to reliance on its predictions as to the way in which C_v approaches zero. Since the details of the Debye theory have not been given, it is necessary to simply state that the low temperature limit predicts the behavior

$$C_v = aT^3$$

where a is a constant characteristic of each material. With this low-temperature limiting expression it is possible to extrapolate heat-capacity data to absolute zero. The Debye curve for aluminum of Fig. 13-17 shows the form of this predicted behavior. All third-law entropy values depend on this extrapolation of measured heat capacities to absolute zero.

13-12. Theories of Metal Crystals. The special properties of metals make it of interest to consider briefly the current theories for their behavior. The geometry of the arrangement of the atoms in the crystal lattice presents little that is new. These particles are pulled together in the crystal and assume some closely packed structure. It is the nature of the bonding in metallic crystals and molten metals which produces the special metallic properties.

One theory of the nature of the forces in metal crystals, due mainly to Linus Pauling, treats the bonding between the atoms as due to covalent bonds. Each metal atom is said to present projecting orbitals in the direction of the neighboring bonds. These orbitals can be thought of as s, p, d hybrids, or maybe as pure d orbitals, such as were considered for metal atoms in coordination compounds. The atoms of a metal will be held together by the covalent bonds resulting from the overlap of these orbitals. Many different combinations, i.e., resonance forms, of these orbitals are possible, and for metals, the atoms of which are characterized by partially filled outer orbits, there will always be many more available orbitals than there are electrons. As a result, the electrons will be relatively free in the metal, i.e., they are delocalized, and under an external influence can shift around in the available orbitals. An applied electric field can therefore easily make the electrons flow along the metal. The covalently bonded crystal of diamond is different in that none of this freedom is available. There are just enough electrons to fill the available orbits, no resonance-type structures can be drawn, and there are no possibilities of the electrons moving in any combination of free orbitals.

A rather more natural approach to the nature of metal crystals comes about from recognizing at the beginning that the electrons belong to the whole crystal rather than to the individual atoms. This approach leads to the "band" model for metals. One here asks what "molecular" orbitals are available to the electrons where the "molecule" is the whole metal crystal.

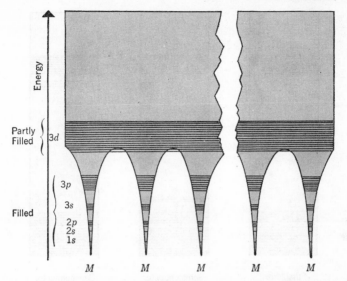

Fig. 13-18. The electron energy bands for a metal, of the transition-metal type.

It is helpful to construct these crystal orbitals from the atomic orbitals as in Fig. 13-18. For the small inner orbitals of the atoms of metal like sodium the 1s, 2s, and 2p orbitals will experience little overlap between adjacent orbitals, and the crystal orbital will be little different from the set of separate atomic orbitals. However, for the larger, outer orbitals, overlap will be appreciable, and an electron will not be localized in the low-potential region of its own nucleus. Each electron, in the 3d level of transition metals, for example, will experience the more or less general low potential of the crystal and will behave not unlike the particles of the previous particle-in-a-box calculation. Figure 13-18 represents this electron energy-level situation and illustrates the energy-level bands that are formed. It is only the upper, partially filled band which contributes to the freedom of the electrons. An applied electric field effectively lowers one end of the potential well, and the electrons can move in the crystal orbitals in a way which corresponds to a drift of electrons in that direction.

Brief mention can be made of the interesting and important class of materials known as *semiconductors*. This type of crystal consists of a normally nonconducting crystal which contains, depending on the nature of the nonconducting crystal, a small number of electron-rich or electron-poor atoms. The effect of these atoms on the energy levels of the nonconductor, looking now at only the highest electron band, or conduction band, is illustrated in Fig. 13-19. In zinc oxide, for example, the presence of a few parts of zinc, each zinc atom contributing the many electrons characteristic of a metal, contributes filled impurity levels that can conduct an electric current by making

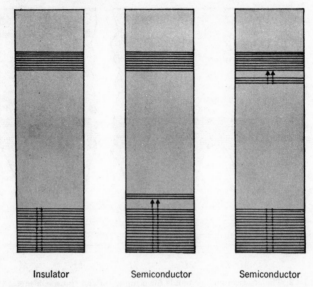

Fig. 13-19. Band models, showing the highest occupied and next higher bands, of an insulator and the two types of semiconductors.

use of the empty orbits of the crystal lattice. On the other hand, the presence of oxygen atoms, with their nonmetallic lack of electrons, in a crystal of cuprous oxide contributes empty impurity levels which the cuprous oxide electrons can make use of. In both cases one finds, contrary to the usual behavior, an increase in conductivity with temperature. The observed temperature dependence, moreover, obeys a Boltzmann-like relation $e^{-E/RT}$, and this dependence is understandable in terms of the excitation energy required to promote electrons to the conduction band, as is illustrated in Fig. 13-19.

Many important details of the behavior of conducting and semiconducting materials are left unmentioned in this brief section. The student must be referred to other texts, most of which are classed as physics rather than chemistry, to pursue this subject.

Problems

1. The heat of sublimation of lithium is 37 kcal, and its ionization potential is 124 kcal/g atom. Calculate the crystal energies of LiF, LiCl, and LiBr, making use of the data of Table 13-1 for the halogens and the standard heats of formation of the crystals of -145, -97, and -84 kcal. Compare these results with the energies, calculated on the basis of simple electrostatic interactions, of 239, 192, and 182 kcal.

2. The heat of sublimation of graphite is 170 kcal/g atom. The energy with which the molecular layers are held to one another can be estimated from heats of sublimation of simpler aromatic systems to be 2 kcal/g atom. Calculate the carbon-carbon bond energy in graphite. If the bonds of graphite have two-thirds single-bond and one-third

double-bond character, what bond energy would be expected from the data of Table 5-5?   Comment on the resonance energy of graphite compared with benzene.

3. A tetragonal crystal has unit-cell dimensions of 12.04, 12.04, and 19.63 A.   The unique axis is taken as the Z axis.

(a) Prepare sketches showing the planes that have Weiss indices $a:b:\infty c$, $a:b:c$, $\infty a:\infty b:c$, and $a:2b:2c$.

(b) What are the Miller indices of these planes?

(c) Prepare sketches showing the planes that have Miller indices (011), (101), (122), and (021).

4. The density of graphite is 2.25 g/cc, and the spacing between the layers is found by X-ray diffraction to be 3.35 A.   What is the carbon-carbon distance in the molecular layers on the assumption of the structure of Fig. 13-1?

Ans. 1.43 A.

5. Cesium chloride forms a cubic crystal in which each Cs^+ ion is surrounded by eight Cl^- ions and likewise each Cl^- ion by eight Cs^+ ions.   The density of CsCl is 3.97 g/cc.   Calculate the distance between two nearest neighbor Cl ions and between Cs and Cl ions.

Ans. 4.13, 3.57 A.

6. A single crystal diffraction pattern is taken of a graphite crystal, X rays of wavelength 1.537 A being used.   The crystal is mounted, as in Fig. 13-10, so that the angle θ is taken as zero when the incoming X-ray beam impinges perpendicularly onto the molecular planes of the crystal.   Consider the carbon-atom planes as presenting only continuous planes of high scattering.   Plot schematically the signal that will be obtained from the detector as a function of θ, the angle through which the crystal is turned, and label the diffraction lines with appropriate Miller indices.   The spacing between the molecular planes of graphite is 3.35 A.

Make a scale drawing showing how the waves from different planes add constructively for the first- and second-order diffractions.

7. Calculate the spacings between (110) planes of KCl if the K^+ and Cl^- ions are taken as identical and the (100) plane spacings are 3.152 A.

At what angles would first- and second-order diffraction from the (100) and the (110) planes be observed if X rays of wavelength 1.537 A are used?

Ans. First order, 14° 7' for (100), 20° 10' for (110).

8. From Fig. 13-14 and Eq. (10), suggest other positions of atom B that would lead to maximum constructive and maximum destructive interference with the (210) reflections from atoms A.

9. Consider the crystal of Fig. 13-14 to have atoms A and B such that the scattering factor f_B is one-half of f_A.   Furthermore suppose that the unit cell has $a = 5$ A and $b = 3$ A and that the position of B relative to A is given by $x = 1.6$ A and $y = 0.9$ A.

(a) Calculate the angles at which first-order constructive interference from the A planes will occur for the planes (100), (010), (110), (210), and (120).

(b) Calculate the effect on the intensities of the diffraction spots corresponding to each of these planes that is produced by the presence of the atom B at the specified positions.   (Take $f_A = 1$ and $f_B = 0.5$.)

(c) Move atom B to a different position, and see that the relative intensities calculated for the different diffractions are changed.   Recognize that in this way various positions of atom B could be assumed until a calculated pattern was obtained that matched an observed pattern.

10. Set up the Fourier series expressions according to Eq. (16) for the electron den-

sity at atom A, with $x = y = z = 0$, and atom B, with $x = 1.6$ A, $y = 0.9$ A, and $z = 0$, as in Prob. 9.   Obtain expressions for $\rho(000)$ and $\rho(1.6, 0.9, 0)$ in terms of the intensities of the reflections calculated in part b of Prob. 9.   Recognize that if the signs of the structure factors, which are the square roots of the intensities, were known, the relative electron densities at the two points could be calculated from data that could be obtained experimentally.

11. Determine a value of the lattice frequency ν for KCl so that the Einstein heat capacity relation fits, as well as possible, the experimental values for C_v.   Compare this value of ν with the value of ν_M required by the Debye theory and shown in Table 13-3. Show graphically the fit obtained to the experimental data by the Einstein relation.

Heat capacity measurements by W. T. Berg and J. A. Morrison [*Proc. Roy. Soc. (London)*, **A242**: 467 (1957)] give:

$T(°K)$	$C_v(cal/deg\ mole)$
10	0.08
20	0.71
30	1.99
40	3.56
60	6.31
80	8.16
100	9.31
140	10.52
180	11.09
220	11.39
260	11.56

14

Phase Equilibria

In previous chapters gases, liquids, and solids have been studied, and some of their properties have been interpreted in terms of molecular behavior. Our attention can now be turned to systems in which a number of phases may exist in equilibrium with one another. For the most part it will be possible only to make qualitative generalizations about such systems and to show how these systems can be conveniently described. Our understanding of the molecular behavior of solids and liquids is far too incomplete at present to allow any molecular explanation to be given to the equilibria in systems of several phases. In the very important type of system involving equilibrium between a liquid phase and a vapor phase, however, we shall see that thermodynamic concepts together with an understanding of molecular behavior give us some insight into the phase equilibrium.

The study of phase equilibria is conveniently divided into three parts. First, a thermodynamic generalization, called the *phase rule*, which governs all phase equilibria is obtained. Second, the way in which the equilibria between phases can be shown diagrammatically is presented, and illustrations are given of some of the more frequently encountered phase-equilibria phenomena. Finally, the important and interesting systems involving liquid-vapor equilibrium are dealt with.

THE PHASE RULE

14-1. The Number of Phases. The statement of the thermodynamic rule regarding the phase equilibria that occur in any system requires the prior precise definition of three quantities. The first of these terms is *phase*. A phase is defined as *that part of a system which is chemically and physically uniform throughout.* The definition is little different from our ordinary use of the word, and only a few points need be made.

A phase may consist of any amount, large or small, of material and may be

451

in one unit or subdivided into a number of smaller units. Thus, ice represents a phase whether it is in a single block or subdivided into fine chips. This subdivision must not, however, be carried to molecular dimensions. A solution in which there are two chemical species, for example, is to be considered as one phase even though subdivision to a molecular scale would reveal that it was not "uniform throughout."

Of particular importance is the *number of phases*, denoted by P, present in a system. Because of the complete mutual solubility of gases, only one gaseous phase can exist in any system. Some liquids are insoluble in one another, and a number of different liquid phases may therefore exist in a system at equilibrium. Different solids, whether they have different chemical composition or the same chemical composition but different crystal structure, constitute different phases.

14-2. The Number of Components. It is necessary now to consider what information must be given to specify the chemical composition of a system. In this connection, the familiar word *components* is used, but a strict definition is attached to it. The *number of components*, denoted by C, is defined as *the least number of independently variable chemical species necessary to describe the composition of each and every phase of the system.*

The composition of a solution of sugar in water, for example, is described by specifying that sugar and water are present. There are two components. If such a solution is cooled, a pure, solid sugar phase may begin to separate out. According to the definition, the *system* still has two components even if the solid phase contains only one chemical species.

Some special care is required when the system involves species which are in chemical equilibrium with one another. The number of species that can be arbitrarily varied in a solution of acetic acid in water is two. A number of equilibria are set up in such a system; in particular,

$$HAc \rightleftharpoons H^+ + Ac^-$$
$$H_2O \rightleftharpoons H^+ + OH^-$$

and various hydrates of these species can also be recognized. Thus there are many chemical species. It should be clear from looking at these equilibria, however, that, if the presence of any two species is specified, then the presence of the other species is determined by the equilibrium relations that could be written. The example should point out that there are no unique components among the species in a system. It is only the *number of components* that is unique.

It should be emphasized that the definition of the number of components assumes that all the physical and chemical equilibria that exist in the system are operative. Thus a system made up from sodium chloride and water has two components. It is true, however, that many chemical species such as H^+, Cl^-, Na^+, OH^-, and various hydrates and complexes of these may occur. Furthermore, any of these species might form a solid phase, and such an accident of solubility will not affect the number of components of the system.

Nevertheless, if any of these many chemical species occur separately or together in any phase, they result from the equilibria that operate. The specification of the systems as consisting of two components, most conveniently NaCl and water, therefore implies all these species.

An overstrict attention to the possible equilibria among the species of a system must, however, be avoided. Consider, for example, the gaseous system of water vapor, hydrogen, and oxygen. In the presence of an electric arc or suitable catalyst, the equilibrium

$$2H_2O \rightleftharpoons 2H_2 + O_2$$

is readily established. Under such conditions the system has two components. Specification of any two of the species implies that, at equilibrium, the third will be present. Alternatively, one can say that the concentration of any two species could be arbitrarily set but that the concentration of the third would then be fixed and could, in fact, be calculated from the equilibrium constant of the reaction.

At room temperature and in the absence of a catalyst, however, this equilibrium is established so slowly that, for all practical purposes, the reaction connecting the three species can be ignored. Under such conditions the concentrations of all three species can be varied arbitrarily, and the system has three components. A system such as this, which appears stable but is not at the thermodynamic equilibrium position with respect to the reaction, is said to be in *metastable equilibrium*. Many systems have thermodynamically feasible reactions, both chemical and physical, which under certain conditions can be conveniently ignored.

14-3. The Number of Degrees of Freedom. Some properties of each phase of a system are independent of the amount of the phase present. Thus, the temperature, pressure, density, and refractive index, for example, of a gas are independent of the amount of gas that one is dealing with. Properties such as these, which are characteristic of the individual phases of the system and are independent of the amounts of the phases, are known as *intensive properties*. Properties such as the weight and volume of a phase, which are dependent on the amount of the phase, are known as *extensive properties*. The latter type of property will not concern us in our study of phase equilibria.

A one-phase system of one component, for example, has a large number of intensive properties. To describe the state of such a simple system exactly, one might measure and report values for many such properties; i.e., one might report the pressure, the temperature, the density, the refractive index, the heat capacity, and so forth. We know *from experience*, however, that it is not necessary to specify all these properties to completely characterize the system. All the intensive properties of a sample of pure, liquid water, for example, are fixed if the temperature and pressure of the sample are stated. Any two intensive properties, instead of temperature and pressure, might have been fixed, and one would again have found that the sample was completely characterized. Our experience tells us that only a few of the many intensive properties of a sample can be arbitrarily fixed, or, as can alternatively be said, need be specified to define the sample.

The number of *degrees of freedom* of a system is defined as *the least number of intensive variables that must be specified to fix the values of all the remaining intensive variables.* The number of degrees of freedom is denoted by Φ. In the previous example of a one-phase system of one component there are 2 degrees of freedom, that is, $\Phi = 2$.

A rearrangement of the statement of the definition, which is sometimes easier to apply, is that the number of degrees of freedom is the number of intensive variables that can be independently varied without changing the number of phases of the system. Examples will bring out the significance of this number and of its definition.

14-4. Systems of One Phase. Before proceeding to a generalization of phase equilibria, the concepts of the preceding sections can be illustrated by consideration of systems of only one phase. It is most convenient to think of a liquid or a gaseous system.

We shall be interested in a relationship between the number of components C of the system and the number of degrees of freedom Φ. Consideration of a few examples will show that for an ordinary chemical system of *one-phase* the quantities C and Φ are related by

$$\Phi = C + 1 \tag{1}$$

The one-phase one-component system considered previously was found to have 2 degrees of freedom, in accordance with Eq. (1).

Consider also the two-component liquid system of water and alcohol. One can arbitrarily assign the pressure, the temperature, and the composition. Our experience now tells us that all other intensive variables are then determined. Mathematically one might write

$$\text{Refractive index} = f_1(T,P,X)$$
$$\text{Density} = f_2(T,P,X)$$
$$\cdots \cdots \cdots \cdots \cdots \cdots \cdots \cdots$$
$$\text{Any intensive property} = f(T,P,X)$$

where X is a term expressing the composition and f, f_1, f_2, . . . are some functions of the three variables. For the present we are concerned not with the nature of the functions f but only with the number of variables involved in the functions. We need not, of course, use T, P, and X as the functions which define this system; any other three would do, though they may not be as convenient. This two-component system has therefore 3 degrees of freedom, in accordance with the suggested equation.

Other examples with one-phase systems with more components will lead to the recognition that $\Phi = C + 1$ is valid for all such systems.

This rule applies, however, only to what have been termed "ordinary" chemical systems. The properties of some systems might be dependent on the electric or magnetic field throughout the system or the intensity of light shining through the system. If any such additional intensive properties are significant—in "ordinary" chemical systems such intensive variables can be ignored—they must be added into the total number of arbitrarily variable properties and one would have $\Phi = C + 2$ or $\Phi = C + 3$, and so forth. In practice, we almost always deal with systems for which such additional variables have no noticeable effect on the system, and they can therefore be left out of all consideration.

14-5. The Phase Rule. Rules, similar to that given in the previous section, might be deduced for systems of more than one phase. It is possible, however, to proceed more generally and to obtain the *phase rule*, which gives the number of degrees of freedom of a system with C components and P phases. This rule was first obtained by J. Willard Gibbs in 1878, but publication in the rather obscure *Transactions of the Connecticut Academy* resulted in its being overlooked for twenty years. The rule which he obtained, and which will be derived, is

$$\Phi = C - P + 2 \tag{2}$$

Consider the C components to be distributed throughout each of the P phases of a system, as schematically indicated in Fig. 14-1. The degrees of freedom of the system can be calculated by first adding up the total number of intensive variables required to describe separately each phase and then subtracting the number of these variables, whose values are fixed by equilibrium relations among the different phases. To begin with, each component is assumed to be present in every phase.

In each phase there are $C - 1$ concentration terms that will be required to define quantitatively the composition of the phase. Thus, if mole fractions are used to measure the concentrations, one needs to specify the mole fraction of all but one of the components, the remaining one being determined since the sum of the mole fractions must be unity. Since there are P phases, there will be a total of $P(C - 1)$ such composition variables. In addition, the pressure and the temperature must be specified, giving a total of $P(C - 1) + 2$ intensive variables if the system is considered phase by phase.

The number of these variables which are fixed by the equilibrium conditions of the system must now be determined. Component C_1, for example, is distributed between phases P_1 and P_2. When equilibrium is established, there

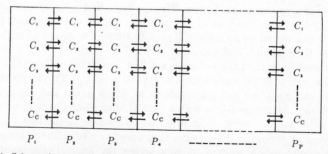

Fig. 14-1. Schematic representation of a system of C components distributed throughout P phases.

will be some distribution relation, which for simplicity can be represented as

$$K = \frac{[C_1]_{P_2}}{[C_1]_{P_1}} \tag{3}$$

Thus, if the concentration of C_1 in phase P_1 is fixed, this relation will determine its concentration in phase P_2. Similar equilibria will be set up for each component between the various pairs of phases. For each component there will be $P - 1$ such relations. Thus, for C components a total of $C(P - 1)$ intensive variables will be fixed by the equilibrium conditions.

The number of degrees of freedom, i.e., the net arbitrarily adjustable intensive variables, is therefore

$$\begin{aligned} \Phi &= P(C - 1) + 2 - C(P - 1) \\ &= C - P + 2 \end{aligned} \tag{4}$$

If a component is not present or, properly, is present to a negligible extent in one of the phases of the system, there will be one fewer intensive variable for that phase since the negligible concentration of the one species is of no interest. There will also be one fewer equilibrium relations. The phase rule applies, therefore, to all systems regardless of whether all phases have the same number of components or not.

The phase rule is an important generalization in that, although it tells us nothing that could not be deduced in any given simple system, it is a valuable check on ideas about the phase equilibrium in more complex systems.

A number of systems will now be considered, and their behavior with regard to the phase rule will be pointed out. It is most convenient to describe phase behavior diagrammatically, and the interpretation of the resulting phase diagrams will now be dealt with.

PHASE DIAGRAMS

A few representative phase diagrams of one, two, and three components will now be discussed. The very important two-component liquid-vapor equilibrium systems will, however, be left for more detailed consideration in a separate section.

14-6. The One-component System, Water. The phase behavior of a one-component system as a function of the pressure and temperature can be conveniently diagrammed on a P versus T plot, as shown for water in Fig. 14-2, for moderate temperatures and pressures.

The meanings of the lines and areas are first considered. Line TC gives the vapor pressure of liquid water up to the critical point C. This line is therefore a plot of the pressures and temperatures at which liquid and vapor exist in equilibrium. At temperatures higher than that of point C condensation does not occur at any pressure. The areas on either side of the line TC can be understood by following the changes that occur as a pressure or temperature change results in the system moving across the line. From point 1, for example, the temperature can be lowered to get to point 2, or the pressure can

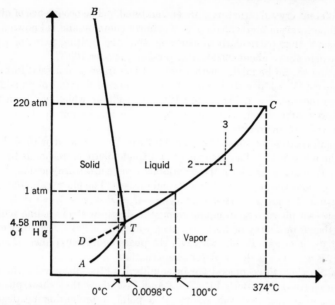

Fig. 14-2. Phase diagram for water at moderate temperatures (not drawn to scale).

be raised to get to point 3. In either process one crosses the liquid-vapor equilibrium line in the direction of condensation from vapor to liquid. The areas below and above line TC can therefore be labeled as vapor and liquid, respectively.

The line TA represents the vapor pressure of solid, i.e., the temperatures and pressures at which the solid and vapor are in equilibrium. Again the areas on either side of the line can be labeled, this time as vapor and solid. Finally, line TB gives the melting point of ice as a function of pressure, i.e., the temperatures and pressures at which ice and liquid water are in equilibrium.

Figure 14-2 is a convenient representation of all the available information about the phases of water that occur at moderate pressures and temperatures. It is interesting also to consider Fig. 14-3, which shows the phase behavior of water at very high pressures. Many new solid phases, corresponding to ice

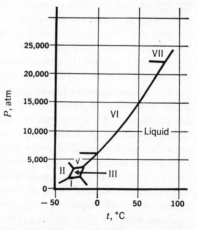

Fig. 14-3. The phase diagram for water at high pressures.

with different crystal structures, are encountered. The occurrence of different crystalline forms of a given compound is fairly common and is known as *polymorphism*. It is particularly remarkable that the melting point of ice VII, which exists above about 20,000 atm pressure, is over 100°C.

Mention should be made, furthermore, of the absence of a solid form designated as ice IV. Early studies had been interpreted in terms of an additional phase to those shown in Fig. 14-3. When this phase, which had been labeled as IV, was later shown to be nonexistent, the numbering of the remaining phases was left unaltered.

The information of Figs. 14-2 and 14-3 can be compared with deductions from the phase rule. The occurrence of a single phase corresponds to an area on a P, T diagram; i.e., both these variables can be arbitrarily assigned, within limits, without the appearance of a second phase. The phase rule confirms the existence of 2 degrees of freedom; i.e., $\Phi = C - P + 2 = 1 - 1 + 2 = 2$.

When two phases are in equilibrium, the diagram shows a line indicating that either P or T may be fixed but that, when one is fixed, the other must be such that the system is somewhere on the phase equilibrium line. The phase rule gives $\Phi = 1 - 2 + 2 = 1$ for this situation.

Finally, when three phases are in equilibrium, the phase rule predicts no degrees of freedom. Both Figs. 14-2 and 14-3 show that three phases can exist together and that this occurs at a point, representing no degrees of freedom, on the diagram. Nowhere on the diagram do four phases coexist. This is to be expected from the phase rule since a negative number for the degrees of freedom would be meaningless.

The most important three-phase equilibrium point, called the *triple point*, is that shown by ordinary ice, liquid, and vapor. This occurs at a pressure of 4.58 mm Hg and a temperature of 0.0098°C. It is completely determined by the system and is therefore sometimes used as a temperature-calibration point.

Finally, it should be mentioned that liquid water can be cooled below its freezing point to give, as indicated by the dotted line TD, *supercooled* water. Supercooled water represents a metastable system since it owes its existence only to the fact that the rate of formation of ice has been interfered with by the use of a very clean sample of water and a smooth container.

14-7. Two-component Liquid Systems. The simplest of the two-component phase diagrams are those for liquid systems which may break up into two liquid phases. Such systems are usually treated at some constant pressure, usually atmospheric, high enough so that no vapor can occur in equilibrium with the liquid phases and over a range of temperatures high enough so that no solid phases appear. If the pressure is fixed, the remaining significant variables are the temperature and composition. Diagrams are therefore made showing the phase behavior in terms of these variables. The composition is usually expressed as weight per cent of one component or as weight fraction.

Three different types of behavior are recognized. Representatives of these are shown in Fig. 14-4a to c. The heavy line on each of these diagram bounds the region in which two liquid phases appear. That the line also gives the composition of the liquid layers can be seen by following, in Fig. 14-4a, the

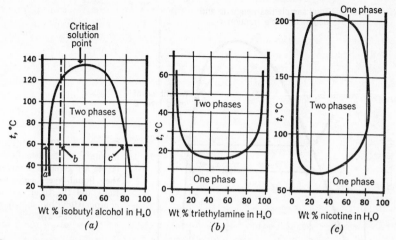

Fig. 14-4. Partially liquid two-component systems at 1 atm pressure.   Measurements made in sealed tube in which the pressure was equal to the vapor pressure of the system.

addition of the second component, isobutyl alcohol, to an initial quantity of pure water at 60°C.   The first additions of butyl alcohol dissolve in the water to form a single phase, and this solubility persists until the total composition of the system corresponds to point a.   At this point the solubility of butyl alcohol in water is reached, and further addition produces a second layer of composition c.   Thus, a total composition of b, at 60°C, results in a two-phase system, the phases having compositions a and c.   As the amount of the second component increases, the total composition approaches c, at which point all the water-rich layer has finally dissolved in the butyl alcohol–rich layer to give again a one-phase system.

The relative amounts of the two phases that a system with given total composition gives rise to can be calculated by the procedure indicated in Fig. 14-5. The system has a total weight w and gross mole fraction, or weight fraction, of component A designated by x.   The weights of the two phases that the system breaks up into are w_1 and w_2, and these phases have mole fractions, or weight fractions, of component A of x_1 and x_2.

The total weight conservation requires

$$w = w_1 + w_2 \tag{5}$$

and the conservation of component A requires

$$xw = x_1w_1 + x_2w_2 \tag{6}$$

Substitution of the expression for w from Eq. (5) in Eq. (6) gives

$$x(w_1 + w_2) = x_1w_1 + x_2w_2 \tag{7}$$

which rearranges to

$$w_1(x - x_1) = w_2(x_2 - x)$$

and

$$\frac{w_1}{w_2} = \frac{x_2 - x}{x - x_1} \tag{8}$$

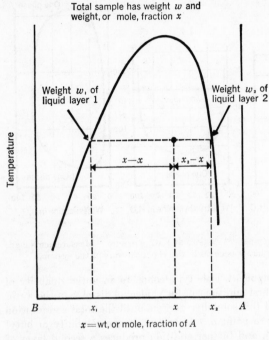

Total sample has weight w and weight, or mole, fraction x

Weight w_1 of liquid layer 1

Weight w_2 of liquid layer 2

Temperature

$x-x$ x_2-x

B x_1 x x_2 A

$x=$ wt, or mole, fraction of A

Fig. 14-5. The relative amounts of the two liquid layers are given in terms of the liquid-layer compositions and the total system composition by $w_2/w_1 = (x_2 - x)/(x - x_1)$.

Thus the weights of the two phases are in the proportion of the two line lengths indicated in Fig. 14-5.

Application of the phase rule to regions of two liquid phases gives

$$\Phi = C - P + 2$$
$$= 2 - 2 + 2 = 2 \tag{9}$$

In the process in which the total composition of the system is changed while both the pressure and temperature are held fixed, there are, according to Eq. (9), no composition degrees of freedom. The compositions of each of the two phases, which is what the phase rule is concerned with, are fixed, and only the relative amounts of the two phases are varied by changes in the total composition.

It is also of interest to investigate the changes that occur when the temperature of a two-phase system, such as that of Fig. 14-4a, is raised. If the temperature is increased for the system of total composition of b, the system moves up along the dotted line. The fraction of the system composed of the water-rich layer gradually increases until, when the two-phase boundary curve is reached, the last of the butyl alcohol–rich layer appears to dissolve in the water-rich layer. By contrast, if a composition equal to that of the curve maximum is picked, the two layers remain in about equal amounts until at the two-phase boundary their composition becomes identical and they form a one-phase system.

The maximum of the curve of Fig. 14-4a is known as the *critical solution temperature*, or the *upper consolute temperature*.

The remaining two diagrams of Fig. 14-4 show that liquid systems can also exhibit a *lower consolute temperature* or, in a few cases, both upper and lower consolute temperatures. This behavior of increased mutual solubility at lower temperatures is certainly not that which is normally expected and must be attributed, very qualitatively, to some interaction between the components that can be effective only at lower temperatures.

14-8. Two-component Solid-Liquid Systems: Formation of a Eutectic Mixture.

Consider now a two-component system, at some fixed pressure, where the temperature range treated is such as to include formation of one or more solid phases. A simple behavior is shown by those systems for which the liquids are completely soluble in one another and in which the only solid phases that occur are the pure crystalline forms of the two components. Such phase behavior is shown in Fig. 14-6 for the system benzene-naphthalene. The curved lines AE and BE show the temperatures at which solutions of various compositions are in equilibrium with pure solid benzene and pure solid naphthalene, respectively. The horizontal straight line is the temperature below which no liquid phase exists.

It is instructive to consider what happens when solutions of various concentrations are cooled. The data that are obtained give the temperature of the system as a function of time. These data are plotted as *cooling curves*, some of which, for concentrations indicated in Fig. 14-6, are shown in Fig. 14-7. It is such cooling curves, in fact, that are used to obtain the data shown in the phase diagram.

The relation between the cooling curves and the information on the phase diagram can be illustrated with one of the cooling curves, b, for example. The liquid system cools until the curve BE is reached, at which point solid naphthalene is in equilibrium with the solution and starts to freeze out. As cooling continues, more naphthalene freezes out, the solution becomes richer in

Fig. 14-6. The freezing-point diagram for the binary-system benzene-naphthalene at 1 atm pressure. (*From Louis P. Hammett, "Introduction to the Study of Physical Chemistry," Mc-Graw-Hill Book Company, Inc., New York, 1952.*)

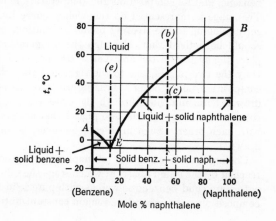

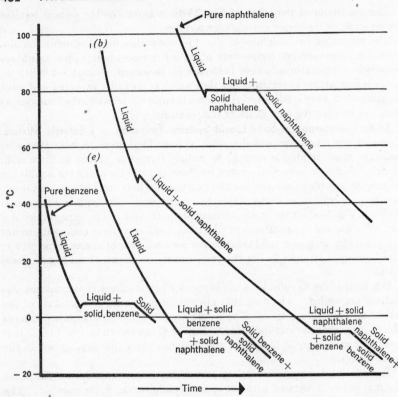

Fig. 14-7. Examples of cooling curves for pure components and solutions e and b of Fig. 14-5.

benzene, and its composition and temperature move down along the line BE. This stage is represented on the cooling curve by the slowly falling portion, corresponding to the freezing points of solutions of varying composition.   It should be noticed that, although the temperature and over-all composition place the system in the area below BE, no phase of such composition exists. Only the two phases, one to the right and the other to the left of the gross-composition point, occur.   It is informative, as is indicated in Fig. 14-6, to draw a horizontal line through the gross composition, at C, for example, to connect or tie together the two phases that are present and are in equilibrium with each other.   Such lines can, however, be understood and need not be drawn.

Cooling and freezing out of naphthalene proceeds until the point E is reached by the liquid phase, at which stage the solution becomes in equilibrium with pure solid benzene as well as with pure solid naphthalene.   The solution composition and temperature remain constant until the system is entirely converted to the two solids. The point E is called the *eutectic,* from the Greek word meaning "easily melted," and the mixture of solids that separates out is called the *eutectic mixture.*

Application of the phase rule to the system at its eutectic point, where there are two solid phases and one liquid phase in equilibrium, gives

$$\Phi = C - P + 2$$
$$= 2 - 3 + 2 = 1 \qquad (10)$$

Since this 1 degree of freedom is used up by the arbitrarily chosen pressure, we learn that, at a given pressure, the properties of the system at the eutectic point are entirely fixed by the system. That the constant freezing point of a eutectic system does not imply the freezing out of a compound is verified by the fact that the eutectic mixture has a different composition at different pressures and that microphotographs show the solid to be a mixture of two crystalline forms.

A variation on the formation of a simple eutectic occurs when the solids that separate out can accommodate some of the second component. The system silver-copper is illustrated in Fig. 14-8. The areas at the extreme right and left along the abscissa scale show regions in which there is a solid solution of silver in copper and copper in silver, respectively. Each region is bordered by a line showing the maximum solubility of the second component in the solid of the first component. Any solution that is cooled will give rise to these solid solutions. The eutectic mixture will, of course, also be a mixture of saturated solid solutions.

14-9. Two-component Solid-Liquid Systems: Compound Formation. Systems in which the components show some attraction for each other sometimes show the formation of a solid-state compound consisting of a simple mole ratio of the

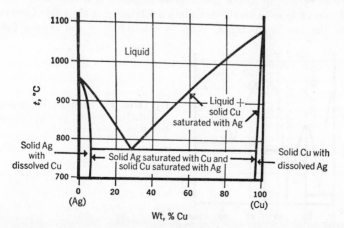

Fig. 14-8. The freezing-point diagram for the system silver-copper at 1 atm pressure.

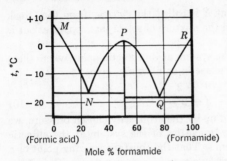

Fig. 14-9. The freezing-point diagram for the system formic acid–formamide at 1 atm pressure. The formation of a one-to-one compound in the solid state. (*From Louis P. Hammett, "Introduction to the Study of Physical Chemistry," McGraw-Hill Book Company, Inc., New York, 1952.*)

two components. Such a system is that of formic acid and formamide, as shown in Fig. 14-9. Diagrams like this are readily understandable on the basis of the discussion of the previous section since each half of Fig. 14-9 corresponds to the simple eutectic diagrams of the previous section.

Solutions which, on cooling, reach line NM or RQ, of Fig. 14-9, give rise to solid formic acid or formamide, respectively. Solutions which, on cooling, reach line PN or PQ give rise to a solid which is a compound containing equimolar amounts of formic acid and formamide. At point N the solution is in equilibrium with this new compound and with formic acid, while at point Q the solution is in equilibrium with the new compound and formamide. Points N and Q represent two eutectics that generally will have different temperatures.

Compound formation in the solid state is frequently encountered with *hydrates*. Figure 14-10 shows the formation of hydrated compounds of sulfuric acid in the solid state. Again such diagrams are easily understood as a series of simple eutectic diagrams side by side.

A complication does occur when a solid compound does not have sufficient stability to persist up to the temperature at which it would melt. In such cases the unstable solid breaks down into a solution and the solid of one or the other of the two components. This is illustrated by the system calcium

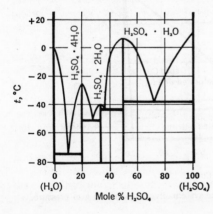

Fig. 14-10. The freezing-point diagram for H_2O-H_2SO_4 showing multiple compound formation in the solid state.

Fig. 14-11. Freezing-point diagram for the system CaF_2-$CaCl_2$, showing the incongruent melting of the solid compound $CaF_2 \cdot CaCl_2$ at 737°C. (*Data from "International Critical Tables," vol. IV, p. 63, McGraw-Hill Book Company, Inc., New York, 1927.*)

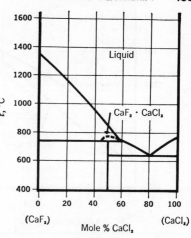

fluoride–calcium chloride, as shown in Fig. 14-11. The decomposition of such a solid is referred to as a *peritectic reaction*, or an *incongruent melting*. Thus the equimolar crystal $CaF_2 \cdot CaCl_2$, of Fig. 14-11, breaks down at 737°C into a solution of composition B and solid CaF_2. The dotted line shows how the diagram might have looked if the compound had survived to a real or congruent melting point. This line is helpful for visualizing the phase behavior but has, of course, no real significance.

14-10. Two-component Solid-Liquid System: Miscible Solids. Brief mention can be made, particularly in view of their importance as alloys, of systems forming only one solid phase which is a solid solution. Such behavior is a result of complete mutual solubility of the two solid components. In Sec. 14-8 it was pointed out how partial solubility of the solid phases in each other affected the phase diagram of a system showing a simple eutectic. Such partial solubility frequently occurs when the atoms of one component are small and can fit into the interstices of the lattice of the major component. In this way an *interstitial* alloy is formed. The carbon atoms in a carbon containing alloy are usually so accommodated.

Complete solubility of two solid phases usually results when the atoms of the two components are about the same size and can substitute for each other in the lattice to form a *substitutional alloy*. The system of copper and nickel, as shown in Fig. 14-12, shows this behavior. The upper of the two curves shows the temperature at which solutions of various compositions start to freeze. The lower curve gives the composition of the solid which separates out at that freezing point. In this system the solid is always richer in the higher-melting component than is the solution from which it separates. The alloy consisting of 60 per cent copper and 40 per cent nickel is known as *constantan*.

14-11. Three-component Systems. To depict the phase behavior of three-component systems on a two-dimensional diagram, it is necessary to consider both

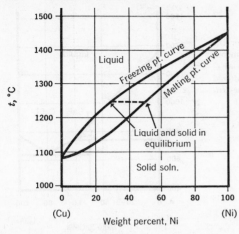

Fig. 14-12. The solid-liquid phase diagram at 1 atm pressure for a system showing complete liquid and solid miscibility. (*Data from "International Critical Tables," vol. II, p. 433, McGraw-Hill Book Company, Inc., New York,* 1927.)

the pressure and the temperature as fixed. The phases of the system as a function of the composition can then be shown. The amounts of the three components, usually presented as per cent by weight, can be shown on a triangular plot, as indicated in Fig. 14-13. The corners of the triangle labeled A, B, and C correspond to the pure components A, B, and C. The side of the triangle opposite the corner labeled A, for example, implies the absence of A. Thus the horizontal lines across the triangle show increasing percentages of A from zero at the base to 100 per cent at the apex. In a similar way the percentages of B and C are given by the distances from the other two sides to the remaining two apices. From the three composition scales of the diagram the composition corresponding to any point can be read off. This procedure for handling the composition of three-component systems is possible, and the total composition is always 100 per cent because of the geometric result that the sum of the three perpendicular distances from any point to the three sides of the triangle is equal to the height of the triangle.

As with two-component systems, the simplest three-component systems are those in which a liquid system breaks down into two phases. The system acetic acid–chloroform–water (Fig. 14-14) is such a system, showing, at 18°C, a two-phase region when the amount of acetic acid is small. A necessary part of the diagram are the *tie lines* through the two-phase region joining the compositions of the two phases that are in equilibrium. (In all previous two-component phase diagrams such lines could have been drawn, but since they would have been horizontal constant-temperature lines, it was unnecessary to exhibit them.) Thus a total composition corresponding to point *a* in the two-phase region gives two phases, one of composition *b* and the other of composition *c*. A unique point on the two-phase boundary is that indicated by *d*. This point, called the *isothermal critical point*, or the *plait point*, is similar to the previously encountered critical-solution temperatures or consolute points in that the compositions of the two phases in equilibrium become equal at this point.

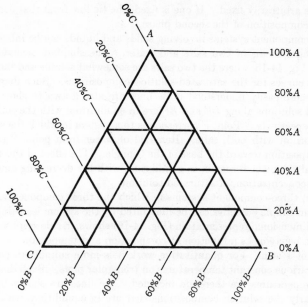

Fig. 14-13. Diagram for plotting the composition of a three-component system.

Application of the phase rule to a system corresponding to a point in the two-phase region gives

$$\Phi = C - P + 2$$
$$= 3 - 2 + 2 = 3 \tag{11}$$

The 3 degrees of freedom can be accounted for by the pressure, the temperature, and one composition variable. Thus the composition of both phases

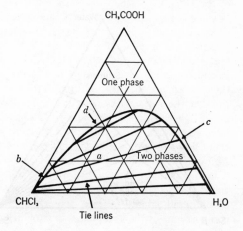

Fig. 14-14. The liquid system acetic acid–chloroform–water at 1 atm pressure and 18°C. (*From "Chemical Engineers' Handbook," 2d ed., McGraw-Hill Book Company, Inc., New York, 1941.*)

cannot be arbitrarily fixed. If one is fixed, the tie line from that composition fixes the composition of the second phase.

Three-component systems involving solids and liquids can be introduced by considering systems of two salts and water. The simplest behavior is that shown in Fig. 14-15, where the two salts are somewhat soluble and the diagram gives the curves for the saturated-solution compositions. Such diagrams are perhaps more easily understood if tie lines are also drawn to show that the saturated solutions along DF and EF are in equilibrium with the solid salts B and C, respectively. Point F corresponds to a system in which the solution is in equilibrium with both salts. Removal of water from point F moves the total composition toward the base of the triangle. The effect of this is to form more solid salts which remain in equilibrium with the decreasing amount, but constant concentration, of saturated solution.

Finally, three-component systems in which the three components, taken in pairs, form simple eutectics can be illustrated by the system lead-tin-bismuth. A three-dimensional representation (Fig. 14-16) shows, in a descriptive manner, the phase behavior as a function of composition and temperature at the fixed pressure of 1 atm. For quantitative work it is more suitable to express the data at various constant temperatures on triangular plots. Such diagrams for a few temperatures are therefore included. Tie lines are shown to indicate more clearly the solution compositions that are in equilibrium with the solid components.

If a solution containing 32 per cent Pb, 15 per cent Sn, and 53 per cent Bi is cooled, it is found that it remains liquid until, at a temperature of 96°C, all three solid components start separating out. The phase rule indicates that at such a point, called a *ternary eutectic*, there is

$$C - P + 2 = 3 - 4 + 2 = 1 \text{ degree of freedom}$$

Since this degree has been used up by the fixed pressure, the system has no remaining variables. It is characteristic of such ternary eutectics that the

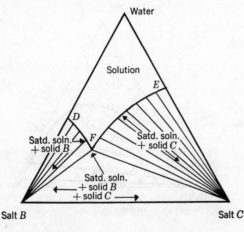

Fig. 14-15. Phase diagram (schematic) for two salts and water at a fixed temperature and pressure.

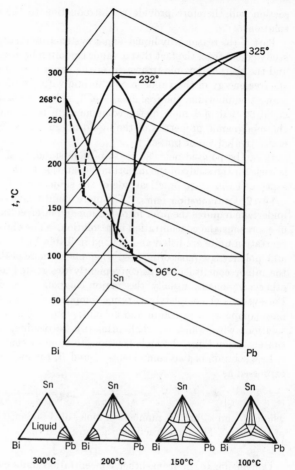

Fig. 14-16. The three-component system bismuth-tin-lead.

eutectic point is at a low temperature compared with the melting points of the pure components. The ternary eutectic of the metal system of the present example will, for instance, melt in boiling water.

LIQUID-VAPOR EQUILIBRIA

The phase equilibria involving the liquid and vapor of a binary system can be treated from both a molecular and a thermodynamic viewpoint. More than the previous, merely descriptive approach to the phase behavior can therefore be taken. The study of the equilibrium between a liquid system and its vapor leads to a further understanding of the behavior of condensed phases. This section will therefore provide an introduction to the study of all types of solutions.

Part of the reason why liquid-vapor systems are susceptible to more detailed study comes from the fact that a vapor can often be assumed to behave ideally and the thermodynamic treatment of the vapor is then easily handled. Thus the free energy of the vapor in equilibrium with a solution can be understood, and, at equilibrium, the free energy of 1 mole of a component of the vapor is equal to that of 1 mole of the component in the liquid phase. As a result, thermodynamic properties of the liquid phase can be deduced from the more easily treated vapor phase.

It can be pointed out also that an understanding of liquid-vapor equilibria is basic for the study of the important separation method of distillation. Some aspects of this more practical side of the subject will be dealt with.

14-12. Concentration Terms. The more quantitative study which we can now undertake requires the prior introduction and interrelation of a number of ways of expressing the concentration of a solution. The three most important concentration units are listed and defined in Table 14-1. The first two, molarity and molality, are most often used when one or more of the components, usually the minor constituents, are conveniently designated as the *solute*, while one other component, usually the major component, is designated the *solvent*. For systems of completely varying composition it is less convenient to designate components as solute and solvent. Since it is such completely variable solutions with which we shall primarily be dealing, we shall find the third concentration term, the mole fraction, to be most convenient.

In a solution of two components A and B, the mole fractions x_A and x_B are expressed as

$$x_A = \frac{n_A}{n_A + n_B} \qquad x_B = \frac{n_B}{n_A + n_B} \tag{12}$$

where n_A and n_B are the numbers of moles of A and of B in some given quantity of solution. The mole fractions then are such that

$$x_A + x_B = 1 \tag{13}$$

Conversion to, or from, other concentration units can usually be made by writing the mole fractions explicitly in terms of the weights of the components in some given amount of solution. Thus, if w_A and w_B are the weights of A and B, then

$$x_A = \frac{w_A/M_A}{w_A/M_A + w_B/M_B} \quad \text{and} \quad x_B = \frac{w_B/M_B}{w_A/M_A + w_B/M_B} \tag{14}$$

where M_A and M_B are the molecular weights of A and B. To obtain mole

Table 14-1. Concentration of Solutions

Name	Symbol	Definition
Molarity..........	M	Moles of solute in 1 liter of solution
Molality..........	m	Moles of solute in 1,000 g of solvent
Mole fraction.....	x	Moles of 1 component divided by the total moles in solution

fractions from molality, one deals with an amount of solution in which there are m moles of one component and 1,000 g of the other component. These data can be used with Eq. (14) to obtain x_A and x_B. Starting with molarity, one considers 1 liter of solution, for which the density must be given. With this, the weight of 1 liter can be obtained, and the weight of solute can be subtracted from the total to obtain the weight of solvent. Again Eq. (14) can be used to deduce mole fractions.

For the conversion from mole fraction to molality or molarity it is convenient to proceed by writing

$$\frac{x_A}{x_B} = \frac{w_A/M_A}{w_B/M_B} = \frac{w_A}{w_B}\frac{M_B}{M_A} \tag{15}$$

The mole fractions and molecular weights allow the calculation of the weight of A for a given weight of B. One can then proceed to the molality and, with the density of the solution, to the molarity.

A sometimes convenient feature of molality and mole fraction, but not of molarity, is the independence of temperature of the former two concentration units.

Other concentration units are also used but will not be encountered in the present study. Some of these, such as volume or weight per cent, often are somewhat ambiguous and seem best suited for stating approximate concentrations.

14-13. The Vapor Pressure of Ideal Solutions.   Mixtures of ideal gases, i.e., gaseous solutions, were treated in the first two chapters and were found to conform to the simple relation expressed by Dalton's law. This result, that the total pressure of a mixture of ideal gases is equal to the sum of the pressures of the components, was easily understandable on the basis of the kinetic-molecular-theory postulate of noninteracting molecules. Since liquids exist only because of molecular interactions, no such "ideal" liquid solutions can be expected in the same sense as an ideal-gas solution. Some solutions, however, behave in a simple and general enough way to warrant use of the term *ideal solution*.

One might anticipate a simplicity of liquid-solution behavior in solutions of components that are molecularly similar in size and intermolecular interactions. The vapor pressures as functions of composition for solutions, such as carbon tetrachloride–silicon tetrachloride, chlorobenzene-bromobenzene, benzene-toluene, do, in fact, show similar and simple behavior. Typical results are shown for benzene-toluene in Fig. 14-17 for the total vapor pressure and for the vapor pressure of each of the components in equilibrium with the solution as a function of the solution composition. The linear relations of Fig. 14-17, which we shall take as being the primary characteristic of an ideal solution, can be expressed as

$$\begin{aligned} P_A &= x_A P_A^\circ \\ P_B &= x_B P_B^\circ \end{aligned} \tag{16}$$

Furthermore, if the vapor behaves ideally, as is being assumed here,

$$P = P_A + P_B$$

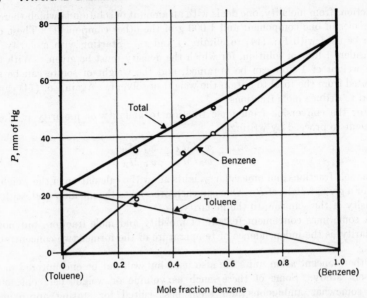

Fig. 14-17. The vapor pressures of the components and the total vapor pressures for the ideal solution benzene-toluene at 20°C. [*Data from R. Bell and T. Wright, J. Phys. Chem.*, **31:** 1884 (1927).]

where P_A and P_B are the vapor pressure of A and B above a solution of mole fraction x_A and x_B and the vapor pressures of the pure components are P_A° and P_B°. Solutions that obey Eq. (16) are said to conform to *Raoult's law*. We shall see that behavior in accordance with Raoult's law merits the designation of the solution as *ideal*. A more careful statement of an ideal solution, however, includes specification that no volume change should occur and that no heat should be evolved or absorbed on mixing of the two components. This lack of volume and heat effects, however, usually occurs in systems obeying Raoult's law.

Just as the ideal-gas laws were a useful basis for understanding the specific deviations shown by real gases, so also will the concept of the ideal solution be helpful in understanding the behavior of nonideal solutions.

It is informative to rearrange the vapor-pressure expression of Eq. (16) to give

$$P_A = x_A P_A^\circ = (1 - x_B)P_A^\circ$$
$$P_A^\circ - P_A = P_A^\circ x_B$$

and

$$\frac{\Delta P_A}{P_A^\circ} = x_B \tag{17}$$

and similarly

$$\frac{\Delta P_B}{P_B^\circ} = x_A$$

where ΔP_A and ΔP_B are the lowerings of the vapor pressures from their values for the pure components.

From these expressions the independence of the vapor pressure of an ideal solution from the individual behavior of the components is more evident.   The relative lowering of the vapor pressure of component A, for example, depends only on the mole fraction of component B and is independent of all other characteristics of the components of the system.   It is such a feature of solutions obeying Raoult's law that merits their description as ideal.

14-14. The Thermodynamic Properties of Ideal Solutions.   In our study of the nature of the free-energy function in Sec. 7-4 it was deduced that for 1 mole of an ideal gas the free energy is simply related to the pressure of the gas by

$$G_2 - G_1 = RT \ln \frac{P_2}{P_1} \tag{18}$$

where G_2 and G_1 are the free energies of 1 mole of the gas at pressures P_2 and P_1. If the vapor in equilibrium with a solution can be treated as an ideal gas, the free-energy changes for 1 mole of component A and 1 mole of component B as they are mixed to form an ideal solution can be written as

$$\begin{aligned} G_A - G_A^\circ &= RT \ln \frac{P_A}{P_A^\circ} \\ G_B - G_B^\circ &= RT \ln \frac{P_B}{P_B^\circ} \end{aligned} \tag{19}$$

These expressions give the free-energy change per mole of each component for the conversion of the equilibrium vapor from that of the pure component to that of the solution and also, therefore, for conversion of 1 mole of each component from the pure liquid to the solution.

If 1 mole of a solution is formed by mixing x_A moles of component A and x_B moles of component B, the net change in free energy from the unmixed components to the mixed components will be

$$\begin{aligned} \Delta G_{\text{mixing}} &= x_A(G_A - G_A^\circ) + x_B(G_B - G_B^\circ) \\ &= RT x_A \ln \frac{P_A}{P_A^\circ} + RT x_B \ln \frac{P_B}{P_B^\circ} \end{aligned} \tag{20}$$

Finally, the Raoult-law relations [Eq. (16)] can be used to express the pressure fractions as mole fractions, to give

$$\Delta G_{\text{mixing}} = RT x_A \ln x_A + RT x_B \ln x_B \tag{21}$$

One should check this important thermodynamic result by verifying that this mixing of two components, which is certainly a spontaneous process, has associated with it a negative free-energy charge.   For the formation of 1 mole of an ideal solution from $\frac{1}{2}$ mole of A and $\frac{1}{2}$ mole of B, for example, one calculates, at 25°C,

$$\begin{aligned} \Delta G_{\text{mixing}} &= (1.987)(298)(0.5)(2.303) \log 0.5 \\ &\quad + (1.987)(298)(0.5)(2.303) \log 0.5 \\ &= -206 - 206 = -412 \text{ cal} \end{aligned}$$

The remaining thermodynamic properties that will interest us are the enthalpy and the entropy. Since an ideal solution is one in which there is no heat effect and no volume change, we can write

$$\Delta H_{\text{mixing}} = 0 \qquad (22)$$

Now the thermodynamic relation, for constant temperature,

$$\Delta G = \Delta H - T\,\Delta S \qquad (23)$$

can be used to give

$$\Delta S_{\text{mixing}} = \frac{\Delta H_{\text{mixing}} - \Delta G_{\text{mixing}}}{T}$$

$$= -Rx_A \ln x_A - Rx_B \ln x_B \qquad (24)$$

The driving force for the spontaneous solution of the two components of an ideal solution is thus seen to be the entropy factor rather than an energy or enthalpy factor. The thermodynamic properties for the formation of 1 mole of solution of any composition can be readily calculated from Eqs. (21), (22), and (24). Table 14-2 shows some calculations, and Fig. 14-18 illustrates these results graphically. It is generally more convenient to show the entropy as $T\,\Delta S_{\text{mixing}}$ rather than simply as ΔS_{mixing}. When this is done, the relative contributions of the enthalpy and entropy to the free energy, according to

$$\Delta G = \Delta H - T\,\Delta S$$

are more immediately apparent.

An understanding of the molecular basis for the increase in entropy, when two components are mixed to form an ideal solution, will form a valuable introduction to the understanding of all solution processes. A molecular explanation of the solution process will now be given.

14-15. The Molecular Interpretation of the Entropy of Mixing. In Secs. 6-7 and 7-10 we saw that entropy is related to the probability of the state of the system or the number of arrangements that correspond to that state of the system. It is necessary now to show that a mixture of components corresponds to a state with a higher probability than do the separate components. If the

Table 14-2. The Free-energy and Entropy Changes for the Formation of 1 Mole of an Ideal Binary Solution

Mole fractions		$x_A R \ln x_A$	$x_B R \ln x_B$	ΔS_{mixing} (cal/deg mole)	$\Delta G_{\text{mixing}} = -T\,\Delta S_{\text{mixing}}$ at 25°C (cal/mole)
x_A	x_B				
1	0	0	0	0	0
0.9	0.1	−0.107	−0.458	0.565	−168
0.8	0.2	−0.355	−0.640	0.995	−297
0.7	0.3	−0.497	−0.718	1.215	−362
0.6	0.4	−0.609	−0.728	1.337	−399
0.5	0.5	−0.689	−0.689	1.378	−411
0.4	0.6	−0.728	−0.609	1.337	−399
0.3	0.7	−0.718	−0.497	1.215	−362
0.2	0.8	−0.640	−0.355	0.995	−297
0.1	0.9	−0.458	−0.107	0.565	−168
0	1	0	0	0	0

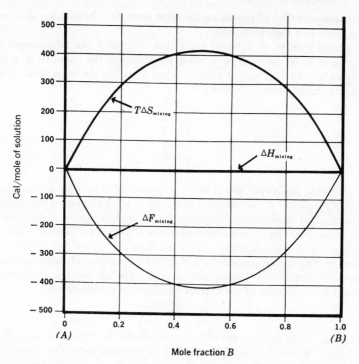

Fig. 14-18. The changes in the thermodynamic functions for the formation of 1 mole of an ideal solution at 25°C.

numbers of arrangements of the molecules that make up the mixed and unmixed states can be deduced, the entropy of mixing can be obtained from the basic relation

$$S = k \ln W \qquad (25)$$

where W is the probability of the state and k is Boltzmann's constant. The qualitative aspects of this relation were discussed in Chaps. 6 and 7. A quantitative result for probability is now obtained so that a quantitative value of the entropy can be deduced.

Consider 1 mole of the two-component liquid system to consist of a lattice with an Avogadro's number N of lattice sites, in which the Avogadro's number of molecules can be placed. One mole of pure component A can be accommodated by placing one molecule of A in each of the sites. Only this one arrangement is possible because the molecules of A must be considered to be indistinguishable, and placing them in the lattice in a different order would not lead to a really different arrangement.

When 1 mole of solution consisting of N_A molecules of A and N_B molecules of B is placed in the lattice, there will be a number of different arrangements of the two different kinds of molecules throughout the lattice. This large number of arrangements that all constitute the same state, i.e., the solution of A and B, corresponds to a high probability.

The total number of different ways that N objects can be arranged in N lattice sites is $N!$, as can be verified by counting the number of ways of arranging several numbers in a line. Thus there are six ways, that is, $3!$, of arranging the numbers 1, 2, and 3:

$$\begin{array}{ccc} 1 & 2 & 3 \\ 1 & 3 & 2 \\ 2 & 1 & 3 \\ 2 & 3 & 1 \\ 3 & 1 & 2 \\ 3 & 2 & 1 \end{array}$$

Considering again the system of N_A molecules of A and N_B molecules of B, where $N_A + N_B = N$, we see that there are a total number of arrangements $N!$ but that, of these, many correspond to the interchange of A particles with other A particles and likewise interchanges of B particles with other B particles. The number of rearrangements of A particles that must not be counted as leading to different arrangements is $N_A!$, and the number of rearrangements of B particles that must not be counted is $N_B!$. The net number of significantly different arrangements of the system which is the probability is

$$W = \frac{N!}{N_A!N_B!} \tag{26}$$

This expression can be verified by considering a few objects labeled A and a few labeled B and deducing the number of different ways that these can be arranged in a line.

The result [Eq. (26)] for the probability of a mixture of A and B allows the calculation of the entropy of mixing as

$$\begin{aligned} \Delta S_{\text{mixing}} &= k \ln \frac{N!}{N_A!N_B!} \\ &= k \ln N! - k \ln N_A! - k \ln N_B! \end{aligned} \tag{27}$$

This expression can be put in a more useful form by recognizing that N, N_A, and N_B are very large numbers, of the order of Avogadro's number, and that Stirling's approximation

$$\ln N! \approx N \ln N - N \tag{28}$$

can be used. Thus

$$\begin{aligned} \Delta S_{\text{mixing}} &= kN \ln N - kN - (kN_A \ln N_A - kN_A) \\ &\quad - (kN_B \ln N_B - kN_B) \\ &= kN \ln N - kN_A \ln N_A - kN_B \ln N_B \end{aligned} \tag{29}$$

where three terms have been canceled because of the relation $N_A + N_B = N$. This relation $N_A + N_B = N$ can furthermore be inserted to give

$$\begin{aligned} \Delta S_{\text{mixing}} &= k(N_A + N_B) \ln N - kN_A \ln N_A - kN_B \ln N_B \\ &= -kN_A \ln \frac{N_A}{N} - kN_B \ln \frac{N_B}{N} \\ &= -(kN) \frac{N_A}{N} \ln \frac{N_A}{N} - (kN) \frac{N_B}{N} \ln \frac{N_B}{N} \end{aligned} \tag{30}$$

Finally, the mole-fraction notation can be used, that is, $x_A = N_A/N$ and $x_B = N_B/N$, and the gas constant R can be inserted in place of kN, to give

$$\Delta S_{mixing} = -Rx_A \ln x_A - Rx_B \ln x_B \qquad (31)$$

We have arrived, by this molecular derivation, at the same result for the entropy of mixing as we obtained from Raoult's law and thermodynamic deductions. The thermodynamics of the formation of an ideal solution can be understood, therefore, simply in terms of the mixing of noninteracting but distinguishable molecules.

14-16. Nonideal Solutions. For solutions other than those carefully chosen ones whose vapor pressure follows Raoult's law, the vapor-pressure–composition curves can take on various shapes. It is convenient to recognize solutions of the type that show vapor pressures lower than those predicted by Raoult's law and those of the type that give higher vapor pressures than predicted by Raoult's law. The system chloroform-acetone belongs to the former class, and its vapor-pressure diagram (Fig. 14-19) is typical of this class. Other systems showing similar vapor-pressure curves are ether–hydrogen chloride, pyridine–acetic acid, and water–nitric acid. An example of a higher than ideal vapor pressure is given by the system pyridine-water, as shown in Fig. 14-20. Other systems of this type are carbon tetrachloride–methyl alcohol, chloro-

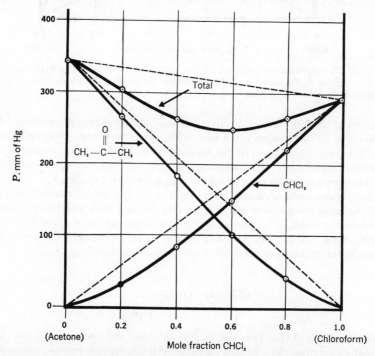

Fig. 14-19. The vapor-pressure diagram for the system chloroform-acetone at 35°C. [*From data of J. von Zawidzki, Z. physik. Chem.,* **35**: 129 (1900).]

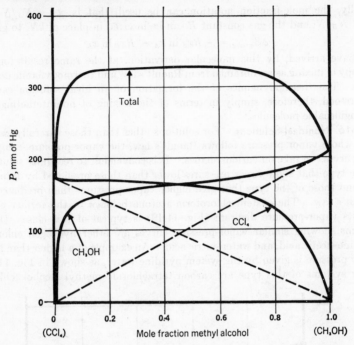

Fig. 14-20. The vapor-pressure diagram for the system carbon tetrachloride–methyl alcohol at 35°C. (*From J. Timmermans, "Physico-chemical Constants of Binary Systems," vol. 2, Interscience Publishers, Inc., New York, 1959.*)

form–ethyl alcohol, carbon disulfide–acetone, and cyclohexane-benzene. In addition to all the systems listed here, which show very large deviations from ideal behavior, there are, of course, many systems which are more nearly ideal. The nonideal behavior of such systems is, however, less easy to explain, and for this reason only the very nonideal solutions will be considered.

The systems listed as showing lower than ideal vapor pressures can be recognized as being composed of components that interact with each other. They consist of mixtures of somewhat acidic and somewhat basic molecules. On mixing, these will interact with one another, and, in the chloroform-acetone example, this interaction takes the form of hydrogen bonding, i.e.,

$$\underset{}{Cl_3C—H\cdots O=C}\overset{CH_3}{\underset{CH_3}{<}}$$

It can be expected that heat will be evolved when the solution is formed; for chloroform-acetone this can easily be noticed if the two components are mixed in a test tube. The nonideal behavior can be accounted for, in part, by a negative enthalpy of mixing in contrast to the zero enthalpy of mixing of an ideal solution.

The association of the components on mixing will also change the entropy from that calculated for an ideal solution. Very qualitatively, one might expect that the association in the solution would tend to restrict the motion of the molecules, and, in view of the general discussion of entropy and freedom in Secs. 6-7 and 7-10, this would be expected to give the system less entropy than in the ideal case.

Thus our expectations are that for a system like chloroform-acetone the enthalpy of mixing should be negative and that the entropy of mixing might be less positive than for an ideal solution. Experimental data can be obtained which verify these hypotheses. The enthalpy of mixing can be obtained by measuring the temperature change for the formation of solutions of various compositions. The free energy of the solution can be calculated from the measured vapor pressures of the two components in the manner indicated for an ideal solution in Sec. 14-14. The entropy of solution is then calculated from the thermodynamic relation

$$\Delta G_{mixing} = \Delta H_{mixing} - T \, \Delta S_{mixing} \tag{32}$$

In this way the curves of Fig. 14-21 are obtained. The lower than ideal total vapor pressure of Fig. 14-18 implies the more negative than ideal free energy of Fig. 14-21. This lower free energy is seen to be primarily due to the negative enthalpy of mixing. The smaller entropy driving force that occurs for ideal solutions is not sufficient to cancel out this heat effect.

In a similar manner the high-vapor-pressure systems like that of Fig. 14-20 can be understood. Systems that show this behavior are frequently those made up of a component that is itself associated, as are water and alcohols, and a more or less inert component. Mixing tends to break up some of the association, and a positive enthalpy term can be expected because of the heat required to break up the associated component. The data for the carbon tetrachloride–methyl alcohol system (Fig. 14-22) indicate that it is primarily this enthalpy effect which produces the free energy effect. The region of negative heat of mixing and the appreciable entropy term should, however, caution against the use of qualitative arguments, such as those used here, when other than very large effects are being considered.

14-17. Dilute-solution Laws. A close look at the vapor-pressure–composition diagrams for all types of solutions, ideal and nonideal, shows that for dilute solutions some generalizations are possible. In discussing dilute solutions it is convenient to use the term *solute* for the minor component and *solvent* for the major component. If, at the left end of the composition scale, A is the solvent and B the solute, at the right end the reverse will be true: A will be the solute and B the solvent.

One of the general features shown by dilute solutions is that the vapor pressure of the *solvent follows the ideal behavior* described by Raoult's law. This behavior is illustrated by Figs. 14-19 and 14-20. Thus, for dilute solutions of both ideal and nonideal systems, if A is the solvent,

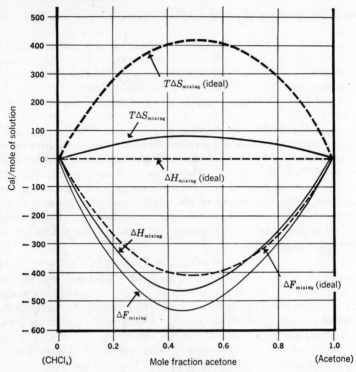

Fig. 14-21. The changes in the thermodynamic functions for the formation of 1 mole of a chloroform-acetone solution at 25°C. (*Sketched from the data of I. Prigogine and R. Defay, "Thermodynamique chimique," Desoer, Liége, 1950.*)

$$P_A = x_A P_A^\circ = (1 - x_B)P_A^\circ$$

or
$$\Delta P_A = x_B P_A^\circ \tag{33}$$

A molecular explanation for the fact that the solvent of a dilute solution follows Raoult's law can be given. This ideal behavior requires that the enthalpy of mixing be zero and the entropy of mixing be given by Eq. (24). If we consider the incremental addition of more solvent to an already dilute solution, we see that, since the solute molecules are already completely surrounded by solvent and the solute molecules are well separated from one another, the added solvent molecules experience interactions only with molecules of their own kind. Thus no, or little, heat should be evolved or absorbed. Likewise, the entropy factor should be that of an ideal system since no change of association or solvation of the solute should result, and the only effect should be the additional number of solvent molecules compared with the solute molecules. Thus, for the solvent of a dilute solution, ideal behavior is to be expected regardless of any special interaction between the solute and the solvent.

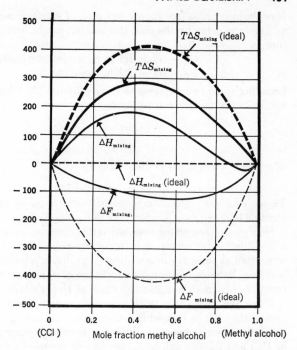

Fig. 14-22. The thermodynamic changes for the formation of a carbon tetrachloride–methyl alcohol solution at 25°C. The dashed lines show ideal behavior. (*Sketched from the data of I. Prigogine and R. Defay,* "*Thermodynamique chimique,*" *Desoer, Liége, 1950.*)

For the solute of dilute solutions a different generalization holds. Again, as Figs. 14-19 and 14-20 indicate, there is a linear relation between the vapor pressure of the solute and the composition for dilute solutions. The linear relation does not, however, coincide with the ideal-solution relation. The vapor pressure of the solute B in any dilute solution is said to follow *Henry's law,*

$$P_B = kx_B \tag{34}$$

where k is a constant, different for each solute and each solution. The Henry's-law constant k is seen to be the slope of the straight-line portion of the solute vapor-pressure curve as the solute concentration approaches zero. For ideal behavior k takes on the value P_B°, whereas for nonideal solution it may be greater or less than P_B°.

The molecular basis for Henry's law can also be given. The solute molecules of a dilute solute will be isolated from one another and surrounded by solvent molecules. The addition of any small amount of solute to a dilute solution will, therefore, produce entropy and enthalpy effects that are dependent on the interaction between solute and solvent as well as on the mixing effect. Thus, one can write the free energy of 1 mole of solute, in terms of its vapor pressure, as

$$G_B - G_B^\circ = RT \ln \frac{P_B}{P_B^\circ} \tag{35}$$

Now, however, this free energy, per mole of solute, is not simply related to the mixing term given by the mole fraction but can be written at a given temperature as

$$G_B - G_B^{\circ} = RT \ln x_B + \text{(interaction term)}$$

or

$$G_B - G_B^{\circ} = RT \ln (\text{const}) x_B \qquad (36)$$

Equating these two expressions [Eqs. (35) and (36)] does not lead to the ideal relation $x_B = P_B/P_B^{\circ}$, but rather to

$$(\text{const}) x_B = \frac{P_B}{P_B^{\circ}}$$

or

$$P_B = (\text{const}) P_B^{\circ} x_B \qquad (37)$$

which can be rewritten as Henry's law,

$$P_B = k x_B$$

Thus a constant molar interaction between the solute and the solvent leads to Henry's law.

Henry's law has so far been written in terms of mole-fraction units. Since it is a dilute-solution law, it is frequently more convenient to express the concentration as molarity or molality. For dilute solutions these units are proportional to mole fractions; so a change of concentration units only has the effect of changing the numerical value of Henry's-law constant.

When the solute of a two-component system is normally a gas, one has a system that can be treated in a manner exactly analogous to that used for two normally liquid components. Thus, the vapor pressure of HCl over solutions of HCl and toluene can be measured and reported as a function of the mole fraction, as shown by the first two columns of Table 14-3. In such systems, however, it is customary to turn around Henry's law, which is obeyed by the HCl, to show the mole fraction, or solubility, of the solute as a function of its vapor pressure. Thus, one would write

$$x_B = k^{-1} P_B \qquad (38)$$

where k^{-1} is just the reciprocal of the k of Eq. (34). Since mole fraction is proportional to molarity and molality for dilute solutions, one can also write

$$M_B = k_M^{-1} P_B \qquad (39)$$

and

$$m_B = k_m^{-1} P_B \qquad (40)$$

Table 14-3 shows the concentrations of a few HCl-in-toluene solutions, expressed in the three ways, and also gives the constants corresponding to each

Table 14-3. Henry's-law Data for HCl in Toluene at 25°C*

$P(\text{HCl})(\text{atm})$	x_B	k^{-1}	m	m_m^{-1}	M	k_M^{-1}
0.0033	0.00141	0.0427	0.0153	0.463	0.0132	0.400
0.0338	0.00154	0.0456	0.0167	0.495	0.0144	0.425
0.0964	0.00431	0.0446	0.0468	0.485	0.0402	0.409
0.158	0.00702	0.0444	0.0762	0.483	0.0655	0.415
0.282	0.0126	0.0446	0.137	0.485	0.117	0.415

* Data from S. J. O'Brien and E. G. Bobalek, *J. Am. Chem. Soc.*, **62**: 3227 (1940).

concentration term. These results can be verified by converting the mole-fraction data to molarity or molality, as indicated in Sec. 14-12.

For systems such as those treated in Table 14-3, one says that Henry's law shows that *the solubility of a sparingly soluble gas is proportional to the partial pressure of the gas over the solution.*

Finally, it should be pointed out that the solubility of a gas in a liquid, and therefore the Henry's-law constant, is a function of the temperature. Some results for the solution of gases in water are shown in Table 14-4. Gases generally become less soluble with increasing temperature, as the table indicates. If one recognizes that Henry's law is an expression for the equilibrium

$$B(g) \rightleftharpoons B(\text{in sol})$$

one expects to relate, according to Sec. 5-7, the equilibrium constant to the heat of the reaction. The formation of a solution from a solid solute may be accompanied by either an increase or a decrease in enthalpy, which implies that some solids are more soluble at higher temperatures and some less soluble. Such is not the case with gases. The entropy of solution of most gases is an appreciably negative quantity. For the gas to be in equilibrium with the dissolved gas, it follows according to $\Delta G = \Delta H - T\,\Delta S$ that, for ΔG to be zero, ΔH must be a negative quantity. It follows that the solubility of most gases will decrease with increasing temperature.

14-18. Vapor-pressure Diagrams Showing Liquid and Vapor Compositions.

Vapor equilibrium data are of use in the study of distillations. In this connection, it is of value to have diagrams showing, not only the vapor pressure of a solution of given composition, but also the composition of the vapor that is in equilibrium with the liquid. This additional information can be put on the vapor-pressure–composition diagrams.

For an ideal solution one can calculate the vapor composition that is in equilibrium with a liquid of mole fraction x_A and x_B. Raoult's law gives

$$P_A = x_A P_A^\circ \qquad \text{and} \qquad P_B = x_B P_B^\circ \qquad (41)$$

Since the partial pressure of a gas is proportional to the number of moles of the gas per unit volume, the mole fractions of the vapor can be written as

$$x_A^{\text{vap}} = \frac{P_A}{P_A + P_B} \qquad \text{and} \qquad x_B^{\text{vap}} = \frac{P_B}{P_A + P_B} \qquad (42)$$

or

$$x_A^{\text{vap}} = \frac{x_A P_A^\circ}{P_A + P_B} \qquad \text{and} \qquad x_B^{\text{vap}} = \frac{x_B P_B^\circ}{P_A + P_B} \qquad (43)$$

Table 14-4. Temperature Dependence of Henry's-law Constant for Gases Dissolved in Water
$(k_m^{-1} = m/p \ [\text{moles}/(1,000 \text{ g solvent})(\text{atm})])$

Gas	0°C	20°C	50°C	80°C
N_2	0.00103	0.00073	0.00051	
H_2	0.00096	0.00081	0.00073	0.00074
O_2	0.0022	0.0014	0.00094	0.00080
He	0.00042	0.00039	0.00040	
Xe	0.0107	0.0057	0.0032	0.0025

484 PHYSICAL CHEMISTRY

The ratio of the mole fractions of the components in the vapor is therefore given as

$$\frac{x_A^{vap}}{x_B^{vap}} = \frac{x_A}{x_B}\frac{P_A^\circ}{P_B^\circ} \tag{44}$$

This expression can be used to calculate the composition of vapor in equilibrium with an ideal solution of any composition. The qualitative result which should be noticed is that the vapor will be relatively richer in A if P_A° is greater than P_B°, that is, if A is the more volatile component.

The vapor-composition information is added to the vapor-pressure–composition diagram by allowing the abscissa to be used to both liquid and vapor compositions, as illustrated for an ideal solution in Fig. 14-23. At a particular vapor pressure one can read, along the horizontal dotted line, for example, the composition of the liquid that gives rise to this vapor pressure and also the composition of the vapor that exists in equilibrium with this liquid. More generally, one uses the diagram by starting with a given liquid composition, a of Fig. 14-23, reading off the vapor pressure of this solution, and also obtaining the composition b of the vapor in equilibrium with the solution.

For nonideal solutions the composition of the vapor in equilibrium with a given solution must be calculated from the experimentally determined vapor pressures of the two components. Typical diagrams for systems showing a minimum and a maximum in their vapor-pressure curves are shown in Figs. 14-24 and 14-25. One finds always that the vapor composition is richer, relative to the liquid, in the more volatile composition. This feature can be appreciated by deducing the vapor in equilibrium with various liquid compositions, as shown by the dashed lines of Figs. 14-24 and 14-25.

It is helpful to notice and remember that on vapor-pressure–composition diagrams the liquid-composition curve always lies above the vapor-composition curve. Where the curve for the vapor pressure of the liquid shows a maximum or minimum, however, the equilibrium vapor has the same composi-

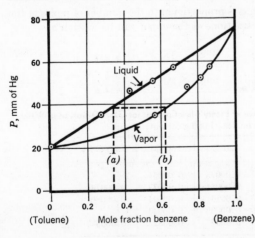

Fig. 14-23. Vapor-pressure diagram showing liquid and vapor compositions for the ideal system benzene-toluene at 20°C. (Data from Fig. 14-17, curves drawn for ideal behavior.)

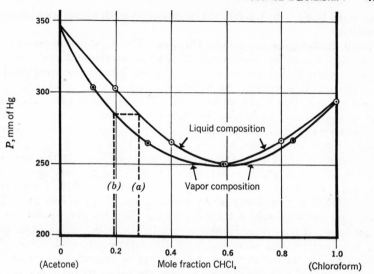

Fig. 14-24. The vapor-pressure diagram for the system chloroform-acetone at 35°C, showing liquid- and vapor-composition curves.

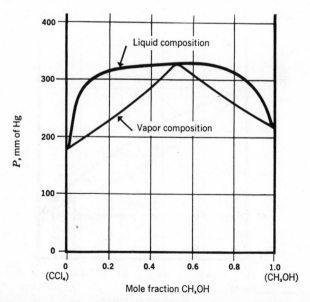

Fig. 14-25. The vapor-pressure diagram for the system carbon tetrachloride–methyl alcohol at 35°C, showing liquid- and vapor-composition curves.

tion as the liquid. Such points will be important when a separation process is considered.

14.19. Boiling-point–Composition Diagrams. The discussion of liquid-vapor equilibrium has, so far, concerned itself with the experimental results that are obtained when the vapor in equilibrium with solutions at some fixed temperature, often 25°C, is studied. Such vapor-pressure data are suited to the theoretical questions that have been discussed. They are not, however, the results that are of primary importance in studies of the more practical aspects of liquid-vapor equilibria. In practice, it is more common to fix the pressure at some constant value, often, but not always, at 1 atm, and to determine the temperature at which liquid and vapor are in equilibrium. In this way, data are obtained from which a *boiling-point–composition diagram* can be constructed. It is again customary to show the composition of the vapor that is in equilibrium with the liquid on the same diagram. Figure 14-26 shows these curves for the ideal system benzene-toluene. Now one notices that, for the vapor to be relatively richer in the more volatile, i.e., *lower*-boiling, component, the liquid-composition curve lies below the vapor-composition curve. The exact shapes of the two curves on the boiling-point diagram, even for an ideal solution, are not so easily deduced as were the curves on the vapor-pressure diagram. The curves depend on the behavior of the system as a function of temperature, and this is less easy to generalize than the constant-temperature behavior of the vapor-pressure diagrams.

The boiling-point curves for the two types of nonideal systems are shown in Figs. 14-27 and 14-28. A minimum in the vapor-pressure–composition curve

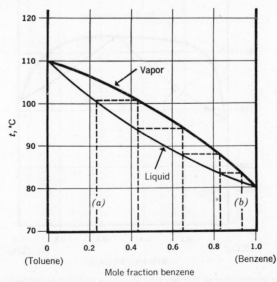

Fig. 14-26. The boiling-point diagram for the ideal system benzene-toluene at 1 atm pressure.

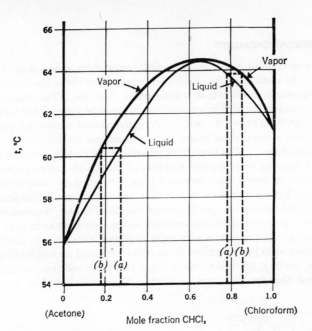

Fig. 14-27. The boiling-point diagram for the system chloroform-acetone at 1 atm pressure. (*Data from "International Critical Tables," McGraw-Hill Book Company, Inc., New York, 1926–1930.*)

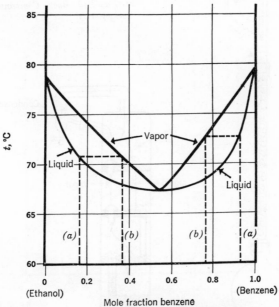

Fig. 14-28. The boiling-point diagram for the system ethanol-benzene at 750 mm pressure. (*Data from "International Critical Tables," McGraw-Hill Book Company, Inc., New York, 1926–1930.*)

results in a maximum in the boiling-point–composition curve, and vice versa. Also, as for the ideal solutions, the liquid-composition curve lies lower than the vapor-composition curve on a boiling-point diagram. The significance of these diagrams for any separation process can again be appreciated by following paths, such as those shown dashed, for the conversion of some of a liquid sample of composition a to its equilibrium vapor of composition b.

14-20. Distillation. The important process of distillation can now be investigated. From the boiling-point diagram of Fig. 14-26 one can see that, if a small amount of vapor were removed from a solution of composition a, the vapor would have a composition higher in the more volatile component than did the original solution a. Such a single step is, of course, inadequate for any appreciable separation of two components unless they have extremely different boiling points. In practice, a process of *fractional distillation* is used in which the separation step just described is, in effect, repeated by condensing some of the vapor, boiling off some vapor from this new solution, collecting and revaporizing this product, and so forth. This procedure has the effect of

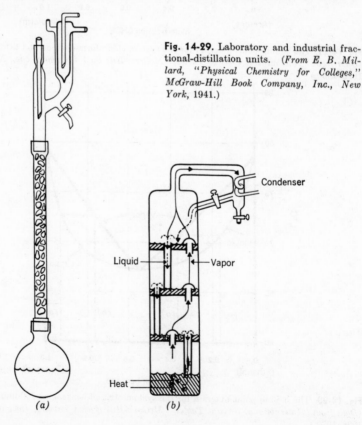

Fig. 14-29. Laboratory and industrial fractional-distillation units. (*From E. B. Millard, "Physical Chemistry for Colleges," McGraw-Hill Book Company, Inc., New York, 1941.*)

Condenser

Liquid — ← Vapor

Heat

(a)   (b)

stepping across the boiling-point diagram, as indicated by the dashed lines of Fig. 14-26.

Experimentally one arranges a distillation column so that such a stepwise process is automatically carried out. In the laboratory one ordinarily uses a more or less simple packed column, such as is illustrated in Fig. 14-29a. The assembly consists of the *pot*, which contains the sample to be separated, and the *column*, through which the vapor from the pot rises and comes in contact with descending liquid that has been condensed in the *head* of the column. The head is provided with a condenser, a thermometer, and an arrangement for withdrawing the distillate. In operation the system of ascending vapor and returning liquid is kept near equilibrium by removing only a fraction of the vapor condensed in the head. Most of the condensate is returned down the column as reflux.

An industrial column may reveal more clearly the stepwise operation that is intended in a distillation column. Figure 14-29b shows the rather common *bubble-cap column*. Each plate is designed so that the rising vapor will condense on the plate, and equilibrium vapor from this condensate will rise to the next plate.

The efficiency of a column, of either the packed or the plate type, is determined by the number of *theoretical plates* that the separation it performs corresponds to. A column supplied, for example, with a charge of composition a in Fig. 14-26 is operated at total reflux until equilibrium is established. A small sample of distillate is then drawn off and analyzed and, we shall assume, has composition b. The separation that has resulted corresponds to four ideal evaporations and condensations, and the column is said to have four theoretical plates.

In practice, a plate column is not perfectly efficient, and each plate behaves as less than one theoretical plate. For a packed column, one often uses the idea of the *height equivalent to a theoretical plate*, or *HETP*, to rate the efficiency of a column. For a laboratory column the HETP may be of the order of a few inches.

A complete study of the operation of fractional-distillation columns is beyond the scope of the present treatment. A number of complications arise when one deals with a multicomponent system, when one treats quantitatively the effect of drawing off appreciable amounts of distillate, of using a continuous rather than a batch process, and so forth.

It is necessary, however, to consider the situation that occurs when one tries to separate a binary solution which shows nonideal behavior. For a solution showing a maximum vapor pressure and a minimum boiling point the situation is indicated by the dotted lines of Fig. 14-28. Distillation in a fractional-distillation unit is seen, regardless of the initial solution, to result in a distillate of the composition of the maximum-boiling-point mixture. A separation into one or the other of the pure components could result only by working with the residue. The most important commercial solution that shows this behavior is the ethyl alcohol–water system. Fermentation proc-

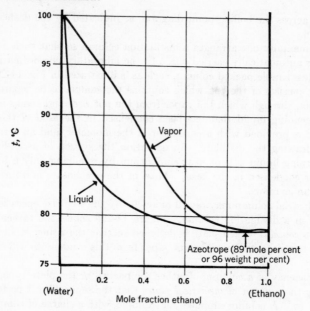

Fig. 14-30. The boiling-point diagram for the system water-ethanol at 1 atm. (*Data from "International Critical Tables," McGraw-Hill Book Company, Inc., New York, 1926–1930.*)

esses result in an ethyl alcohol concentration of about 10 per cent. The object of distillation is to increase this concentration and, possibly, to yield pure ethyl alcohol. The boiling-point diagram of Fig. 14-30 shows that distillation at atmospheric pressure can yield, at best, a distillate of 95 per cent ethyl alcohol. It is for this reason that 95 per cent ethyl alcohol is a fairly common chemical material. Absolute alcohol can be obtained by a distillation procedure using a three-component system, usually alcohol, water, and benzene.

A different situation arises with solutions that show a maximum in their boiling-point curves, as does the system of Fig. 14-27. If such a solution is merely boiled away, the residue will approach the composition corresponding to the maximum of the boiling-point curve and the boiling point will also approach that corresponding to this maximum. Once this solution and boiling point have been reached, the remaining solution will boil at this temperature and will not change its composition. Such a solution is known as a *constant-boiling mixture*, or an *azeotrope*. This same term is applied to a solution having the composition of the minimum of a boiling-point curve.

It is necessary to stress that, although we are dealing, in the case of an azeotrope, with a constant-temperature constant-composition boiling mixture, this mixture is not to be regarded as a compound formed between the two components. A change in the total pressure is usually sufficient to show that the azeotrope composition can be changed. It is true, however, that a maximum in the boiling-point curve corresponds to a minimum in the vapor-pressure curve, and, as discussed in Sec. 14-16, this situation arises when the components show a mutual attraction.

14-21. Distillation of Immiscible Liquids.   It seems desirable to include with our discussion of distillation the distillation of immiscible liquids.   The process usually makes use of water or steam and an insoluble organic material and is then referred to as *steam distillation.*

Consider two components which, though somewhat soluble in each other, separate into two layers on mixing.   Each layer will exert its own vapor pressure, and the pressure measured over such a mixture will be the sum of the two pressures.   As long as the two layers are present, they will have the same compositions: a layer of A saturated with B, and a layer of B saturated with A. It follows that the vapor pressure of each layer (and thus the total vapor pressure) will be independent of the amounts of the two layers.   These statements indicate that the boiling point of such a mixture and the equilibrium vapor composition will be constant as long as the two layers are present. Furthermore, the boiling point will be the temperature at which the total pressure is equal to 1 atm, and this will be at a lower temperature than the boiling point of either component.   Figure 14-31 shows a boiling-point diagram for immiscible liquids.   Any two-phase mixture of the liquids will boil at temperature T_M and produce vapor of composition M.   The lines AM and BM

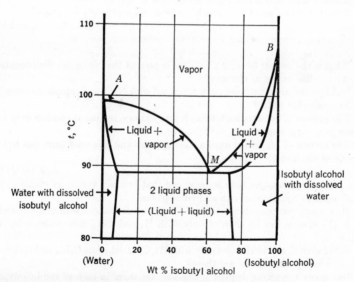

Fig. 14-31. Boiling-point diagram for a pair of immiscible liquids, water-isobutyl alcohol, at 1 atm pressure.   (*From Louis P. Hammet, "Introduction to the Study of Physical Chemistry," McGraw-Hill Book Company, Inc., New York, 1952.*)

correspond to the temperatures at which vapor mixtures would start to condense to give pure A or B.

It is the lowering of the boiling point that makes the process of steam distillation attractive. Many organic materials of high molecular weight boil at such a high temperature that they would decompose. These materials can be conveniently "cleaned up" by steam distillation. A mixture of the organic material and water is heated, usually by the direct addition of steam, and the two liquids distill over at a temperature of less than 100°C. They are collected in amounts that are proportional to their vapor pressure. It is this fact which sets a limit to the usefulness of the process since very high-boiling materials, having very low vapor pressures, come over in relatively small amounts compared with the amount of steam used. The distillate separates into the two immiscible layers, and the organic layer can be separated and dried. The process has considerable application but is most useful in the rough purification of organic materials and does not usually handle the same problems as do fractional distillations.

Problems

1. How many phases are there in:

(a) A sealed bulb half-filled with liquid water, the other half being air saturated with water vapor?

(b) A 1-liter bulb containing 2 g of water, and no air, at 100°C?

(c) A mixture of oil and water which has been dispersed into an emulsion?

Ans. (a), (b), and (c): 2.

2. How many components are there in the systems composed of:

(a) $N_2(g)$ plus $O_2(g)$?

(b) What is the answer to (a) if a catalyst is present that promotes the formation of the many possible oxides of nitrogen?

(c) $NaCl(s)$ and an aqueous solution saturated with NaCl and containing some HCl?

(d) Any salt plus water?

(e) The system of (d) at a high enough temperature so that it consists only of dry solid salt and water vapor?

(f) The system of (d) cooled until a solid appears and this solid turns out to be the hydroxide of the metal?

Ans. (b) 2; (c) 3.

3. A remarkable catalyst is to be imagined that brings a system containing carbon and hydrogen to equilibrium with all hydrocarbons.

(a) How many components are there if the system is charged with graphite and H_2?

(b) If the system can be charged only with H_2 and CH_4, how many components will there be?

(c) If the system can be charged only with H_2, CH_4, ethylene C_2H_4, and cyclohexane C_6H_{12}, how many components are there?

4. How many remaining degrees of freedom are there in each of the following systems? Suggest variables that could correspond to these degrees of freedom.

(a) Liquid water and water vapor in equilibrium at a pressure of 1 atm

(b) Liquid water and water vapor in equilibrium

(c) I_2 dispersed between liquid water and liquid CCl_4 at 1 atm pressure with no solid I_2 present

(d) The vapor equilibrium system of NH_3, N_2, and H_2

(e) An aqueous solution of H_3PO_4 and NaOH at 1 atm pressure

(f) A solution of H_2SO_4 in water in equilibrium with the solid hydrate $H_2SO_4 \cdot 2H_2O$ at 1 atm pressure

Ans. (a) 0; *(b)* 1.

5. Describe, in view of Fig. 14-4c, the phase situations that arise when nicotine is gradually added to a small quantity of water at 100°C until the system is transformed to nearly 100 per cent nicotine.

6. Describe, in view of Fig. 14-4c, the phase situations that arise when an aqueous solution that is 60 per cent by weight nicotine is heated from 50 to 250°C.

7. Estimate from Fig. 14-6 the weight of solution and of solid that will be present when 100 g of solution of composition b is cooled to point c.

8. Describe, with the help of Fig. 14-8, the phases that form and the temperatures at which phase changes occur when a 20 per cent copper in silver melt at 1000°C is cooled to 700°C.

9. Describe, with the help of Fig. 14-8, the phase changes when solid silver at 900°C is added to a silver-copper melt containing 40 per cent copper at 900°C.

10. At about 60 per cent $CaCl_2$ in the system $CaCl_2$-CaF_2, shown in Fig. 14-11, a peritectic point occurs at 737°C. If the pressure is assumed fixed at 1 atm, apply the phase rule to deduce the number of degrees of freedom at this point.

11. Describe the phases that appear and the temperature of their appearance when the solid compound $CaF_2 \cdot CaCl_2$ is heated from 400 to 1400°C at 1 atm pressure.

12. Verify that the sum of the three perpendicular distances from any point inside an equilateral triangle to the sides of the triangle is equal to the height of the triangle.

13. Estimate from Fig. 14-14 the weights of the three components that are present in 100 g of the one-phase system at point d. Estimate the compositions and the weights of the two phases that occur for 100 g of the system having the total composition of point a of Fig. 14-14.

14. Describe the phases that occur as water is added to an initially anhydrous mixture of 5 per cent of the salt B and 95 per cent of the salt C in Fig. 14-15.

15. Assuming ideal-solution behavior, calculate the equilibrium vapor pressure and the mole-fraction composition of the vapor in equilibrium, at 40°C, with a solution of carbon tetrachloride–cyclohexane that has 0.4753 mole fraction CCl_4. The vapor pressures at 40°C of pure CCl_4 and cyclohexane are 213.34 and 184.61 mm Hg, respectively. Compare with the measured values reported by Scatchard, Wood, and Mochel [*J. Am. Chem. Soc.*, **61**: 3206 (1939)] of 203.45 for the vapor pressure and 0.5116 for the mole fraction of CCl_4 in the vapor.

16. Liquid nitrogen and oxygen form an essentially ideal solution. Measurements on solutions of such components could best be made at low temperatures, say, at 70°K. Illustrate the heat, entropy, and free energy of mixing for the formation of 1 mole of solution at 70°K, as has been done in Fig. 14-18 for ideal solutions at 25°C.

17. It is found that the boiling point, at 1 atm pressure, of a solution of 0.6589 mole fraction benzene and 0.3411 mole fraction toluene is 88.0°C. At this temperature the vapor pressures of pure benzene and toluene are 957 and 379.5 mm, respectively. What is the vapor composition that boils off this liquid?

Ans. Mole fraction benzene = 0.830.

18. At 55°C a solution of mole fraction 0.2205 ethanol and 0.7795 cyclohexane has a

vapor pressure of 368.0 mm Hg and a vapor composition of 0.5645 mole fraction ethanol and 0.4355 cyclohexane. The vapor pressures of pure ethanol and cyclohexane at 55°C are 279.9 and 168.1, respectively. Plot a possible vapor-pressure diagram having liquid and vapor compositions that are compatible with these data.

19. At total reflux, samples from the pot and the still head are withdrawn from an experiment in which ethanol and benzene are refluxing in a packed distillation column operating at 75 mm pressure. The pot sample has 0.05 mole fraction benzene and the still head a composition of about 0.5 mole fraction benzene. According to Fig. 14-28, what would be the temperatures in the pot and head and how many theoretical plates does the column have?

20. Describe, with the help of Fig. 14-31, the phase changes, and the temperatures at which they occur, when a 40 per cent isobutyl alcohol 60 per cent water solution is heated from 50 to 100°C. Similarly describe the changes that occur when a vapor of this composition is cooled from 100 to 80°C.

21. Calculate the heat of solution of O_2 in water from the data of Table 14-4.

Ans. $\Delta H = -2.4$ kcal/mole.

15

Colligative Properties of Solutions

A number of important methods for studying solutes in all types of solvents stems from the validity of Raoult's law for the solvent of any dilute solution. The fractional vapor-pressure lowering, as was pointed out in Sec. 14-13, depends only on the mole fraction of the solute and on no other solute property. Thus, measurement of the vapor pressure or, as we shall see, of a number of related quantities for the addition of a nonvolatile solute to any solvent leads to information on the number of moles of solute per mole of solvent. Such information is valuable in that it, in effect, provides a count of the number of moles or molecules of the solute and can be used to deduce the molecular weight of the solute.

Since the addition of a solute lowers the free energy of the solution, other properties besides the vapor pressure will be expected to be affected. We shall see that, when solute is added, a solution is formed for which the boiling point is raised, the freezing point is depressed, and an osmotic pressure can be developed. All these changes have in common the fact that they are dependent only on the number of solute particles. They are grouped together as *colligative properties.*

The quantitative relations between each of these properties and the mole fraction of the solution will be developed. This will be done, at first, for solutes that are nonelectrolytes; i.e., the solutions can be thought of as organic solutes in organic solvents. Finally we shall study special effects that arise when the solute is an electrolyte and the solvent, like water, supports dissociation.

15-1. Effect of a Nonvolatile Solute on the Vapor Pressure of a Solution. The necessary equations for the vapor-pressure lowering according to Raoult's law have already been given in Sec. 14-17. They are repeated here with emphasis on the case of a nonvolatile solute. Since the solutions that will be dealt with may be either ideal or nonideal, the treatment will be limited to dilute solutions.

Consider a nonvolatile solute B added to a solvent A. The vapor pressure

495

P of the solution will be equal to the vapor pressure of component A. If the vapor pressure of pure A, that is, of an infinitely dilute solution, is represented by $P°$, Raoult's law becomes

$$P = x_A P° \tag{1}$$

and

$$\ln P = \ln x_A + \ln P° \tag{2}$$

For an infinitesimal change in x_A, brought about by such a change in x_B, we can write

$$d(\ln P) = d(\ln x_A)$$
$$= \frac{dx_A}{x_A} = -\frac{dx_B}{x_A} \tag{3}$$

For dilute solutions the mole fraction x_A of A will remain almost equal to unity, and Eq. (3) can be written approximately as

$$d(\ln P) = -dx_B \tag{4}$$

This differential form of Raoult's law corresponds to Eq. (14-8) if the logarithm term of Eq. (4) is written as dP/P.

The lowering of the vapor pressure is seen to depend only on the mole fraction of the solute and is, therefore, one of the colligative properties. Since it is not experimentally very easy to measure a vapor-pressure lowering accurately, little direct use is made of this result. We now turn to other colligative properties that can be treated in terms of the development of this section and that are more susceptible to measurement.

15-2. The Boiling-point Elevation. The boiling point is that temperature at which the vapor pressure of the liquid is equal to the external, usually atmospheric, pressure. The addition of a nonvolatile solute, which according to Raoult's law must lower the vapor pressure, requires a higher temperature to be reached before the solution vapor pressure is equal to the external pressure. The added solute produces therefore a *boiling-point elevation*. A quantitative expression for this quantity is now obtained.

The vapor-pressure curves for a pure solvent and for a solution consisting of an infinitesimal amount dx_2 of solute are represented, near the boiling point, in Fig. 15-1. The decrease in the logarithm of the vapor pressure due to the addition of the solute is given by Eq. (4) as

$$d(\ln P) = -dx_B$$

The solution can be made to boil by raising the temperature until the vapor pressure is increased by an amount that compensates for the lowering of Eq. (4). The temperature dependence of vapor pressure has been shown in Sec. 12-1 to be given by the Clausius-Clapeyron equation

$$\frac{d(\ln P)}{dT} = \frac{\Delta H_{\text{vap}}}{RT^2}$$

or

$$d(\ln P) = \frac{\Delta H_{\text{vap}}}{RT^2_{\text{bp}}} dT_{\text{bp}} \tag{5}$$

where the fact that we are dealing with the boiling point has been indicated by writing T_{bp}.

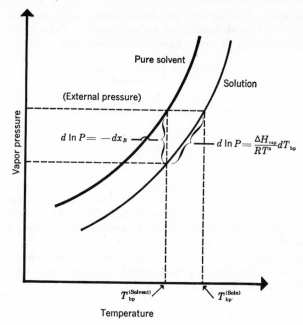

Fig. 15-1. The boiling-point elevation dT_{bp} produced by the addition of solute to a solvent.

The decrease in vapor pressure, due to the solute addition, can be balanced by the increase, due to the temperature rise.   Thus

$$[d(\ln P)]_{\text{solute}} + [d(\ln P)]_{\text{temp}} = 0$$

or

$$-dx_B + \frac{\Delta H_{\text{vap}}}{RT_{bp}^2} dT = 0$$

and

$$dT_{bp} = \frac{RT_{bp}^2}{\Delta H_{\text{vap}}} dx_B \tag{6}$$

For dilute solutions, ΔH_{vap} will have very nearly the value of the heat of vaporization of the pure solvent.   The boiling-point elevation for dilute solutions is therefore independent of all properties of the solute except its mole fraction in the solution.   Thus, the boiling-point elevation is another colligative property.

It is customary in colligative-property work to express the concentration of the dilute solutions that are encountered in terms of molality.   Molality, represented by m, was defined as the moles of solute per 1,000 g of solvent. *If n_A is the number of moles of solvent in 1,000 g of solvent, then*

$$x_B = \frac{m}{n_A + m} \cong \frac{m}{n_A} \tag{7}$$

where the final simplification results since, for dilute solutions, m is much less than n_A.   The quantity n_A, for any solvent A, is readily calculated as

$1,000/(\text{mol wt})_A$. Furthermore, for dilute solutions the molality m can be written in place of the differential of the molality.

In terms of molality the boiling-point elevation is written as

$$\Delta T_{\text{bp}} = \left[\frac{RT_{\text{bp}}^2}{n_A\, \Delta H_{\text{vap}}} \right] m \tag{8}$$

The expression in brackets is called the *boiling-point elevation constant*, or the *ebullioscopic constant*, and is frequently represented by K_{bp}. With this notation we have

$$\Delta T_{\text{bp}} = K_{\text{bp}} m \tag{9}$$

where

$$K_{\text{bp}} = \frac{RT_{\text{bp}}^2}{n_A\, \Delta H_{\text{vap}}} \tag{10}$$

Some results comparing the values of K_{bp} from Eq. (9) and measurements of the boiling-point elevation with the values obtained from Eq. (10) are shown in Table 15-1. This agreement can be expected to be good, however, only for solutes that are neither associated nor dissociated in solution. If either of these processes occurs, the number of solute particles per 1,000 g of solvent is not simply Avogadro's number times the molality. The boiling-point elevation, while then proportional to the molality, does not have the proportionality constant K_{bp} of Eq. (10).

One type of boiling-point apparatus that is used to measure boiling-point elevations is shown in Fig. 15-2. The principal difficulty in accurately determining the boiling-point elevation stems from the fact that it is the temperature of the boiling liquid and not, as in the case of pure liquids, the temperature of the refluxing vapor that must be measured. The vapor rising from the solution is essentially pure solvent, and this vapor will condense at the boiling point of the pure solvent. It is necessary, therefore, to arrange the apparatus so that the thermometer is drenched with representative samples of the solution and is not merely at the temperature of the condensing vapor. This requirement immediately introduces difficulties due to superheating of the liquid. Boiling-point-elevation devices, such as that of Fig. 15-2, attempt to overcome these problems. It is, however, difficult to obtain boiling-point-elevation results to better than about $\pm 0.01°\text{C}$.

The practical application of boiling-point-elevation measurements, and of other colligative properties, follows from their use in the determination of molecular weights. A sample calculation of a molecular weight illustrates

Table 15-1. Molal Boiling-point-elevation Constants at 1 Atm Pressure

Solvent	Bp (°C)	$K_{\text{bp}}(\text{obs}) = \dfrac{\Delta T_{\text{bp}}}{m}$	$K_{\text{bp}}(\text{calc})$ [Eq. (10)]
Water..............	100.0	0.51	0.51
Ethyl alcohol........	78.4	1.22	1.20
Benzene............	80.1	2.53	2.63
Ethyl ether.........	34.6	2.02	2.11
Chloroform.........	61.3	3.63	3.77

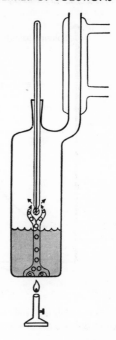

Fig. 15-2. The Cottrell boiling-point apparatus. (*F. Daniels, J. H. Mathews, J. W. Williams, and staff, "Experimental Physical Chemistry," 4th ed., McGraw-Hill Book Co., Inc., New York, 1949*).

this. A sample of unknown molecular weight is found to raise the boiling point of benzene by 1.04°C when 3.63 g of the material is added to 100 g of benzene. From the observed boiling-point elevation and the boiling-point-elevation constant for benzene from Table 15-1, the molality is calculated as

$$m = \frac{T_{bp}}{K_{bp}} = \frac{1.04}{2.57} = 0.396 \text{ mole}/1{,}000 \text{ g benzene}$$

The weight of the solute in 1,000 g of the solvent is obtained from the weights of the two components as

$$\frac{3.63}{100} \times (1{,}000) = 36.3 \text{ g}/1{,}000 \text{ g benzene}$$

These two results allow the calculation of the molecular weight, i.e., the weight per mole, as

$$\frac{36.3}{0.396} = 92 \text{ g/mole}$$

The practical difficulties inherent in boiling-point measurements, however, lead to the more frequent use of freezing-point depressions for such molecular-weight determinations.

15-3. The Freezing-point Depression. The lowering of the vapor pressure of a solution as a result of the addition of a small amount of nonvolatile solute changes the liquid-vapor equilibrium curve and the liquid-solid equilibrium curve in a manner indicated in Fig. 15-3. The normal freezing point is the

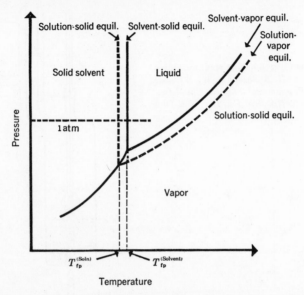

Fig. 15-3. The equilibria of solid-liquid and vapor phase for pure solvent and for solution as a function of the external pressure and temperature.

temperature at which the liquid and solid have equal vapor pressures when they are subjected to a pressure of 1 atm. The freezing-point depression can most easily be understood by considering a system open to the atmosphere in which the pressure on the condensed phases is 1 atm but in which the condensed phase or phases can exert a vapor pressure. In such a system, represented in Fig. 15-4, the vapor pressure as a function of temperature for the pure solvent and for the solution is shown near the freezing-point region. On this diagram it is clear that the solid, whose vapor pressure is unaffected by the solute in the solution, is in equilibrium with the solution at a lower temperature than that at which it is in equilibrium with the pure solvent. (It should be mentioned, however, that this behavior can be handled only when cooling of the solution leads to the formation of pure solid solvent. We are not dealing with systems in which a solid solution separates or in which the solute is so sparingly soluble that it separates.)

The quantitative relation between the added mole fraction of solute dx_B and the freezing-point lowering dT_{fp} can be obtained by calculating the vapor-pressure lowering from the solid-solvent equilibrium at A to the solid-solution equilibrium at B. This can be calculated, as Fig. 15-4 indicates, either as the vapor-pressure lowering of the solid as a result of the temperature lowering or as the combined effect of the addition of solute and the lowering of the temperature of the solution. Equating these two approaches, as indicated in

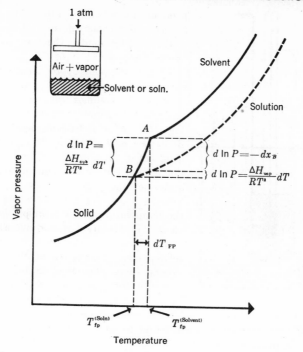

Fig. 15-4. The vapor-pressure diagram for the solvent and solution near the freezing point at a total pressure of 1 atm.

Fig. 15-4, we have

$$\frac{\Delta H_{\text{sub}}}{RT_{\text{fp}}^2} dT_{\text{fp}} = \frac{\Delta H_{\text{vap}}}{RT_{\text{fp}}^2} dT_{\text{fp}} - dx_B \tag{11}$$

The heat of sublimation ΔH_{sub} can be combined with the heat of vaporization ΔH_{vap} by recognizing that their difference is the heat of fusion ΔH_f; that is,

$$\Delta H_f = \Delta H_{\text{sub}} - \Delta H_{\text{vap}} \tag{12}$$

Rearrangement of Eq. (11), together with Eq. (12), gives

$$dT_{\text{fp}} = -\frac{RT_{\text{fp}}^2}{\Delta H_f} dx_B \tag{13}$$

Again this result can be written in terms of molality, and it then becomes

$$\Delta T_{\text{fp}} = -K_{\text{fp}}m \tag{14}$$

where

$$K_{\text{fp}} = \frac{RT_{\text{fp}}^2}{n_A \Delta H_f} \tag{15}$$

The constant K_{fp} is known as the *freezing-point-depression constant* and is clearly a function only of the solvent. The freezing point depression of dilute solutions is, therefore, a function of the properties of the solvent and is inde-

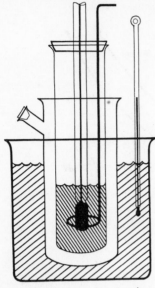

Fig. 15-5. The Beckmann freezing-point apparatus.

pendent of any feature of the solute except its concentration in the solution. The depression of the freezing point is therefore another colligative property.

The freezing-point depression can usually be measured much more easily and accurately than can the boiling-point elevation. A simple, usually suitable, apparatus is shown in Fig. 15-5. The procedure, described as the *Beckmann method*, for determining the freezing point of the pure solvent and of the solution is to fix the bath at some suitable temperature several degrees below the expected freezing point of the solution and to follow the temperature of the sample solution as it cools. The solution is continuously stirred, and particular care is taken to prevent the solvent from freezing out on the wall of the sample tube. The freezing point is determined by the appearance of solid particles or by a change in the slope of the cooling curve. The temperature is usually measured by a differential thermometer that can be set to provide an expanded scale in the region of the freezing point.

For very accurate determinations one measures the temperature with a multijunction thermocouple and adopts an equilibrium method whereby the solid solvent and the solution are agitated until equilibrium is obtained. This procedure prevents the troublesome supercooling that occurs in the Beckmann method.

Table 15-2 shows the accuracy with which freezing-point depressions can be measured and indicates the degree to which the dilute-solution freezing-point-depression equation is obeyed.

Table 15-2. Freezing-point Depressions for Solutions of Mannitol in Water*

Molality	Fp (°C)	$-\dfrac{\Delta T_{fp}}{m}$
0.00402	−0.0075	1.86
0.00842	−0.0157	1.86
0.01404	−0.0260	1.852
0.02829	−0.0525	1.856
0.06259	−0.1162	1.857

* From data of L. H. Adams, *J. Am. Chem. Soc.*, **37**: 481 (1915).

Table 15-3. Molal Freezing-point-depression Constants

Solvent	Fp (°C)	K_{fp}
Water.	0.00	1.86
Acetic acid.	16.6	3.90
Benzene.	5.5	5.12
Bromoform.	7.8	14.4
Cyclohexane.	6.5	20
Camphor.	173	40

The freezing-point-depression constants of a number of solvents that find use in this work are listed in Table 15-3. The choice of solvent is frequently dictated by the solubility and chemical reactivity of the substance whose molecular weight is to be determined. Increased accuracy results, of course, from the use of a solvent with a large freezing-point-depression constant.

Freezing-point-depression measurements find frequent use in molecular-weight determinations. In the field of organic chemistry it is frequently very helpful to have a value for the molecular weight of a newly synthesized or isolated material whose structure is being determined.

15-4. Osmotic Pressure. Osmotic pressure needs, perhaps, more of an introduction than did the properties of the preceding sections. The phenomenon of osmosis depends on the existence of *semipermeable membranes.* Such membranes are of a great variety, but they are all characterized by the fact that they allow one component of a solution to pass through them while they prevent the passage of another component. Cellophane and a number of animal or protein membranes, for example, are permeable to water but not to higher-molecular-weight compounds. The gelatinous deposit of copper ferrocyanide, $CuFe(CN)_6$, in the pores of a porous pot provide a semipermeable membrane that found considerable use in early experiments. Finally, mention can be made of the semipermeability of a palladium foil, which is permeable to hydrogen gas but not to nitrogen and other gases. With such a membrane osmosis can be studied in the vapor phase.

Two arrangements that have been used for the quantitative study of osmosis are shown in Fig. 15-6. Any osmosis apparatus depends on the separation of a solution from its pure solvent by means of a membrane, permeable to the solvent but impermeable to the solute. The essential features of either of the systems of Fig. 15-6 are shown schematically in Fig. 15-7. When such an arrangement is made, it is found that there is a natural tendency for the solvent to flow from the pure solvent chamber through the membrane into the solution chamber. This tendency can be opposed by applying pressure to the solution chamber. In the apparatus of Fuoss and Mead this balancing pressure results from the hydrostatic head that is developed. The excess pressure that must be applied to the solution to produce equilibrium is known as the *osmotic pressure* and is denoted by Π. It is through this quantity that the quantitative aspects of osmosis are studied.

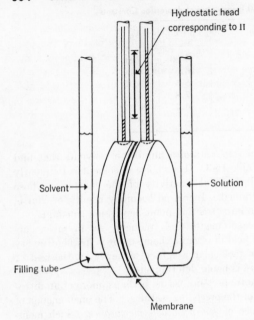

Hydrostatic head
corresponding to Π

Solvent →

← Solution

Filling tube →

Membrane

Fig. 15-6. The osmotic-pressure apparatus (schematic) of Fuoss and Mead [*J. Phys. Chem.*, **47**: 59 (1943)].

The osmotic pressure developed between any dilute solution and its solvent will be shown to be a colligative property. It is, therefore, dependent only on the concentration of the solution and on the properties of the solvent. It is important to recognize that the nature of the semipermeable membrane and the mechanism by which it allows solvent to pass through it but prevents the passage of solute is of no importance for the study of osmotic pressure as a colligative property.

The thermodynamic basis of the osmotic pressure can readily be seen. The

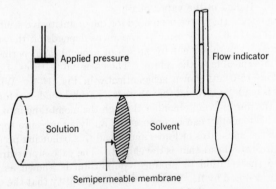

Applied pressure

Flow indicator

Solution

Solvent

Semipermeable membrane

Fig. 15-7. Schematic representation of an osmotic-pressure apparatus.

free energy of the solvent in the solution is less than the free energy of the solvent in pure solvent. There results, therefore, a spontaneous tendency for the solvent to move from the relatively high free-energy state of the pure solvent to the relatively low free-energy state of the solution. This tendency is balanced by increasing the free energy of the solution by subjecting it to an externally applied pressure. These ideas are now put in quantitative form.

The free-energy lowering *per mole of solvent* that results from the addition of solute is given in terms of the lowering of the equilibrium vapor pressure from $P°$ for the pure solvent to P for the solution as

$$\Delta G = RT \ln \frac{P}{P°} \tag{16}$$

It is this free-energy decrease which is balanced by the effect of the applied pressure. The dependence of free energy on pressure has been shown in Sec. 7-4 to be given by the relation

$$\left(\frac{\partial G}{\partial P}\right)_T = V \tag{17}$$

Since liquids are quite incompressible, the volume V of 1 mole of solvent in the solution can be assumed to be constant. The free-energy increase per mole of solvent, when it is subject to an excess pressure Π, is then given as

$$\Delta G = \Pi V \tag{18}$$

For equilibrium to be established, the decrease in free energy of the solution due to the solute addition must be balanced by the increase due to the applied pressure. This implies

$$\Pi V + RT \ln \frac{P}{P°} = 0$$

or
$$\Pi V = -RT \ln \frac{P}{P°} \tag{19}$$

For dilute solution a more generally useful result is obtained by recognizing that Raoult's law will be obeyed by the solvent, i.e., that $P/P° = x_A$. Substitution in Eq. (19) gives

$$\Pi V = -RT \ln x_A \tag{20}$$

This important thermodynamic result shows that the osmotic pressure Π is a function of the molar volume of the solvent, the temperature, and the concentration of the solution. It is therefore a colligative property. It should be pointed out that for dilute solutions the molar volume of solvent in the solution will be essentially equal to the more readily available quantity, the molar volume of the pure solvent.

A number of expressions can be obtained from Eq. (20), which, although more approximate than Eqs. (19) and (20) for other than infinitely dilute solution, are frequently encountered and will be mentioned briefly. The mole fraction of solute can be shown explicitly by substituting $x_B = 1 - x_A$, to give

$$\Pi V = -RT \ln (1 - x_B) \tag{21}$$

Furthermore, if x_B is much less than unity, as will be the case for a dilute solution, one can use the approximation

$$\ln (1 - x_B) \cong -x_B \tag{22}$$

to give

$$\Pi V = RTx_B \tag{23}$$

Now the mole fraction x_B can be written explicitly in terms of the moles of A and of B, in some given quantity of solution, as

$$x_B = \frac{n_B}{n_A + n_B} \cong \frac{n_B}{n_A} \tag{24}$$

Equation (23) becomes

$$\Pi(n_A V) = n_B RT \tag{25}$$

The quantity $n_A V$, the number of moles of A times the molar volume of A, is the volume of solvent which contains n_B moles of B. If Π is given in atmospheres and V in liters, the gas constant R must be used in liter atmospheres per degree.

Finally, one more approximate expression should be mentioned. In Eq. (25) the quantity $n_A V$ can, for dilute solutions, be considered, to a somewhat poorer approximation than our previous assumptions, to be the volume of *solution* containing n_B moles of solute. If this volume is represented by **V**, we arrive at the interesting-looking result, first obtained by van't Hoff,

$$\Pi \mathbf{V} = n_B RT \tag{26}$$

The similarity of this expression to the ideal-gas law led van't Hoff and others to some not very fruitful ideas that view the osmotic pressure as arising from a molecular-bombardment process. It is recognized here that Eq. (26) is merely an approximate form that is obtained from the thermodynamic results [Eqs. (19) and (20)].

A comparison of the observed osmotic pressure, as a function of concentration, with the behavior expected on the basis of some of the derived expressions is shown in Table 15-4.

To this discussion of the osmotic pressure as a colligative property can be added a few comments on the mechanism by which a semipermeable membrane operates. In some cases the membrane seems to act simply as a mechanical sieve, letting small molecules, like water, through, while preventing the passage of large molecules. Other membranes do not appear to pass and reject molecules on a simple size basis. In some of these cases a component appears to penetrate the membrane by dissolving in it, while another component that is not soluble in the membrane cannot pass through it. Probably the clearest example of this is the passage of hydrogen through palladium. The hydrogen molecules are probably dissociated to atoms on the surface of the palladium. These atoms can penetrate through the solid lattice and on the opposite surface can reunite into hydrogen molecules. Other molecules are not dissociated and cannot pass through the solid.

As previously mentioned, the mechanism of the process at the semipermeable membrane can be studied quite separately from the subject of colligative properties. The expressions for the osmotic pressure derived in this section

Table 15-4. The Osmotic Pressure of Aqueous Solutions of Sucrose at 20°C*

Molal conc.	Molar conc.	Obs. osmotic press. (atm)	Calc. osmotic press.		
			From Eq. (20)	From Eq. (25)	From Eq. (26)
0.1	0.098	2.59	2.44	2.40	2.36
0 2	0.192	5.06	5.46	4.81	4.63
0.3	0.282	7.61	7.82	7.21	6.80
0.4	0.370	10.14	10.22	9.62	8.90
0.5	0.453	12.75	12.62	12.0	10.9
0.6	0.533	15.39	15.00	14.4	12.8
0.7	0.610	18.13	17.40	16.8	14.7
0.8	0.685	20.91	18.77	19.2	16.5
0.9	0.757	23 72	22.15	21.6	18.2
1.0	0.825	26.64	24 48	24.0	19.8

* Osmotic-pressure data of Morse, reported by A. Findlay, "Osmotic Pressure," Longmans, Green & Co., Inc., New York, 1919.

will apply as long as a membrane is available that will pass solvent and will not pass solute. The procedure by which it accomplishes this is immaterial.

15-5. Osmotic-pressure Determination of Molecular Weights. The principal use of osmotic-pressure measurements is in the determination of the molecular weight of high-molecular-weight compounds. Solutions of high-molecular-weight compounds will have low molal concentrations even though they may be quite concentrated in terms of the weight of solute. The measurable osmotic pressure produced even by solutions of low molality makes it the most suitable of the colligative properties for the study of such compounds.

The physical chemistry of compounds of high molecular weight will be treated in more detail later. For the present it is enough to point out that two types of high-molecular-weight compounds, in which one is interested in the molecular weight, are the synthetic polymers and the naturally occurring materials such as proteins. An example of the first type will illustrate the use of osmotic pressure to obtain the molecular weight of a compound.

The expressions obtained for the osmotic pressure have so far been written in terms of mole fraction or molality. To study the osmotic pressure of a compound of unknown molecular weight, it is convenient to start with Eq. (26) and to write it, with the dilute-solution approximation of $n_A V$ equal to volume of solution, as

$$\Pi = \frac{(n_B)RT}{n_A V}$$

$$= \frac{(\text{wt of } B/\text{mol wt of } B)RT}{\text{vol of soln}} \qquad (27)$$

Introduction of the concentration unit of grams per cubic centimeter, represented by c, allows Eq. (27) to be written as

$$\frac{\Pi}{c} = \frac{RT}{\text{mol wt of solute}} \qquad (28)$$

If the osmotic pressure is given in atmospheres and c in grams per cubic centimeter, then the gas constant R must be in cubic centimeter atmospheres per degree.

Equation (28) can be expected to be valid only at infinite dilution. This follows, in addition to the approximations introduced in its derivation, from the fact that large-molecular-weight compounds tend to interact with one another at the concentrations at which the measurements are made. The procedure that must be used, therefore, is to measure Π/c as a function of c and to extrapolate these results to infinite dilution. The intercept of Π/c at zero concentration can then be taken as the value of $RT/(\text{mol wt of solute})$. From this value a valid molecular weight for the solute in solution is obtained.

The data of Table 15-5 show the osmotic pressures and concentrations of solutions of a polyisobutylene fraction in two different solvents. The extrapolations of these data in Fig. 15-8 lead to a value for Π/c of 0.097 atm cc/g at infinite dilution. With this value and Eq. (28), the molecular weight, or, as will be pointed out in Chap. 20, an average molecular weight, is calculated as

$$\text{Mol wt polyisobutylene} = \lim_{c \to 0} \frac{RT}{\Pi/c}$$
$$= \frac{(82.06)(298)}{0.097} = 250,000$$

It should be noticed that measurements of the osmotic pressure shown in Fig. 15-8 have been made down to molal concentrations of about 10^{-5}. At such concentration the boiling-point elevation and freezing-point depression would be much too small to be readily susceptible to measurement.

15.6. Colligative Properties of Electrolytes. Most of the physical-chemistry subjects with which we have yet to deal involve solutes which are more or less dissociated into ions; i.e., they are electrolytes. The solvent will almost always be water. One of the types of experiments that contributed to the early understanding of the nature of electrolytes in solution was the determination of the colligative properties of such solution. The first of these experiments were the determinations of osmotic pressures in 1885 by van't Hoff.

Table 15-5. Osmotic-pressure Results at 25°C for a Polyisobutylene Fraction*

Conc. (g/cc)	Π (atm)		Π/c (atm cc/g)	
	In benzene	In cyclohexane	In benzene	In cyclohexane
0.0200	0.00208	0.0117	0.104	0.585
0.0150	0.00152	0.0066	0.101	0.44
0.0100	0.00099	0.0030	0.099	0.30
0.0075	....	0.00173	.....	0.23
0.0050	0.00049	0.00090	0.098	0.18
0.0025	....	0.00035	.....	0.14

* Calculated from the data of P. J. Flory, *J. Am. Chem. Soc.*, **65**: 372 (1943).

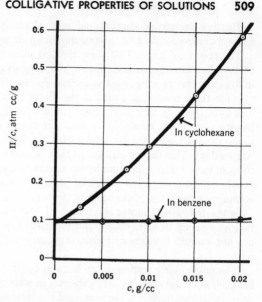

Fig. 15-8. The extrapolation of the osmotic pressure–concentration ratio to infinite dilution for a sample of polyisobutylene in cyclohexane and in benzene. (Data of Table 15-5.)

These studies were subsequently followed by measurements of the boiling-point elevations and freezing-point depressions of solutions of electrolytes.

Table 15-6 shows some results that have been obtained for the freezing-point-depression term $\Delta T_{fp}/m$ for a number of electrolytes as functions of their concentration in water. When it is recalled that a great variety of nonelectrolytes show the rather consistent freezing-point-depression constant of 1.86, these results are, at first, quite remarkable.

It was recognized by van't Hoff that the comparison of electrolyte and non-electrolyte colligative behavior could conveniently be made by writing the previous colligative-property equations in the more general form

$$T_{bp} = iK_{bp}m$$
$$T_{fp} = iK_{fp}m \qquad (29)$$
and
$$\Pi = i\Pi_0$$

where K_{bp}, K_{fp}, and Π_0 are quantities appropriate to nonelectrolytes. The value of i, called the *van't Hoff i factor*, shows explicitly the enhancement of the

Table 15-6. Observed Freezing-point-depression Terms, $K_{fp} = -\Delta T_{fp}/m$, for Electrolytes in Water

m	NaCl	HCl	CuSO$_4$	MgSO$_4$	H$_2$SO$_4$	Pb(NO$_3$)$_2$	K$_3$Fe(CN)$_6$
0.001	3.66	3.690	. . . .	3.38	. . . . .	5.368	7.10
0.01	3.604	3.601	2.703	2.85	4.584	4.898	6.26
0.1	3.478	3.523	2.08	2.252	3.940	3.955	5.30
1.0	3.37	3.94	1.72	2.02	4.04	2.435	

colligative properties encountered with electrolytes. Table 15-7 shows the i factors corresponding to the freezing-point depressions of Table 15-6.

The results of Table 15-7 show that, at least for the more dilute solutions, electrolytes are approximately two, three, or four times as effective per mole in lowering the freezing point as are nonelectrolytes. The qualitative explanation for these results, in terms of the dissociation of the electrolyte molecules into two, three, or four ions, is now quite obvious to the student. When such results were made available by van't Hoff in 1885, however, they provided much needed and dramatic support for the then recent dissociation theory of Arrhenius. This theory postulated that in solution electrolytes are dissociated to form ions. The approximate correlation of the van't Hoff i factors with the number of ions expected from the various electrolytes helped to win almost complete support for these ideas of Arrhenius.

In the following chapter the nature of ions and electrolytes in solution will be investigated in more detail, and there the fact that the van't Hoff i factors are not exactly integers and that they vary with concentration will be dealt with.

It is particularly important to keep in mind, in using colligative properties for such nonideal systems as electrolytes in water, that interaction between the solute particles, molecules or ions, and the solvent molecules can occur and the solvent, of dilute solutions, will still be expected to follow Raoult's law. Ions, as we shall see, are generally *hydrated* in aqueous solution. Thus, if sodium chloride is added to water, the solution that is obtained may best be described as containing

$$Na(H_2O)_x^+ \quad \text{and} \quad Cl(H_2O)_y^-$$

particles, where x and y are the numbers of water molecules solvating each Na^+ and Cl^- ion. In spite of the formation of such hydrates, however, there are as many hydrated particles in solution as there would have been if simple Na^+ and Cl^- ions existed. The number of water molecules withdrawn from the solvent to form the hydrated ions will have a negligible effect on the total number of solvent molecules as long as only dilute solutions are considered. Thus, in spite of such interactions, there will be the same ratio between the number of solute and solvent particles as there would be without such interactions. The previous colligative-property derivations and the interpretation of the van't Hoff i factors as the number of particles produced by a molecule of electrolyte are therefore valid.

Table 15-7. Van't Hoff i Factors Calculated from the Data of Table 15-6 and the Freezing-point-depression Constant of 1.86 for Water

m	NaCl	HCl	CuSO$_4$	MgSO$_4$	H$_2$SO$_4$	Pb(NO$_3$)$_2$	K$_3$Fe(CN)$_6$
0.001	1.97	1.98	....	1.82	....	2.89	3.82
0.01	1.94	1.94	1.45	1.53	2.46	2.63	3.36
0.1	1.87	1.89	1.12	1.21	2.12	2.13	2.85
1.0	1.81	2.12	0.93	1.09	2.17	1.31	

Interactions that upset these interpretations are those which occur among the solute particles themselves. Such interionic interactions will be absent at infinite dilution but, as we shall see, must be considered at any finite concentration.

Problems

1. What is the vapor pressure at 100°C of a solution containing 15.6 g of water and 1.68 g of sucrose, $C_{12}H_{22}O_{11}$?

Ans. 755.7 mm.

2. The boiling point of benzene is raised from its normal value of 80.1°C to 82.4°C by the addition of 13.76 g of biphenyl, $C_6H_5C_6H_5$, to 100 g of benzene.

What are the boiling-point-elevation constant and the heat of vaporization of benzene according to these data?

Ans. $\Delta H_{vap} = 7500$ cal/mole.

3. Make a scale diagram, like that of Fig. 15-1, in which is shown the solvent chloroform, which has a normal boiling point of 61.3°C, a heat of vaporization 7050 cal/mole, and a solution consisting of 0.1 mole of hexachloroethane, C_2Cl_6, dissolved in 1 mole of chloroform.

4. Equation (8) involves the quantity n_A, the moles of solvent in 1,000 g of solvent. Explain why, even if the heat to vaporize a given amount of solvent were measured, Eq. (8) could not be used to obtain the molecular weight of the solvent if a measurement of ΔT_{bp} were made with a solute of known molecular weight.

5. Benzene has a freezing point of 5.5°C, a heat of fusion of 2360 cal/mole, and a heat of vaporization of 7350 cal/mole. Plot, to scale, the curves corresponding to those of Fig. 15-4 for pure benzene and for a solution containing 1 g of anthracene, $C_{14}H_{10}$, in 50 g of benzene.

6. A newly synthesized organic compound is analyzed for carbon and hydrogen and found to contain 63.2 per cent, by weight, carbon, 8.8 per cent hydrogen, and the remainder oxygen. A solution of 0.0702 g of the compound in 0.804 g of camphor is found to freeze 15.3°C lower than the freezing point of the pure camphor. What are the molecular weight and the formula of the new compound?

Ans. $C_{12}H_{20}O_4$.

7. The osmotic pressure is measured between water and a solution containing 1 g of glucose, $C_6H_{12}O_6$, and 1 g of sucrose, $C_{12}H_{22}O_{11}$, in 1,000 g of water. The temperature is maintained at 25°C.

(a) What osmotic pressure would be expected?

(b) If this pressure were measured and it were not known that the solute was a mixture, what molecular weight would have been calculated?

(c) The measurement of the osmotic pressure gives an average molecular weight of the solute. What kind of average, i.e., number or weight, is this?

Ans. (b) 236.

8. Verify some of the calculated values in Table 15-4.

9. It is reasonable to expect that a number of water molecules, say, five, are bound quite strongly to a sucrose molecule by hydrogen bonding. This would have the effect of decreasing the number of solvent particles relative to the number of solute particles. Calculate what value of the osmotic pressure of the 1 M sucrose solution would be expected with this hydration assumption and Eq. (25). Compare with the observed value of Table 15-4.

10. At low concentration the freezing-point-depression constant, $-\Delta T_{fp}/m$, for one-to-one electrolytes in water approaches the limiting value of 3.72. At higher concentrations the values of $-\Delta T_{fp}/m$ deviate from this limit. Calculate what value would be expected for a 1 M solution as a result of the removal of water molecules from the total solvent by solvation of each of the ions by six water molecules.

In view of the results shown in Table 15-6, would such an explanation be able to account for the variations observed for $-\Delta T_{fp}/m$?

11. A solution of 2.58 g phenol in 100 g bromoform freezes at a temperature 2.374° lower than does pure bromoform.

(a) What is the apparent molecular weight of phenol at this concentration and temperature in benzene?

(b) Give a qualitative explanation for this molecular weight.

Ans. (a) 157.

12. The osmotic pressure of a dilute solution of KNO_3 in water is 357 mm Hg when measured against water at 25°C. What would be the vapor pressure at 25°C (the vapor pressure of pure water is 23.756 mm Hg at this temperature), the freezing point, and the boiling point of the solution?

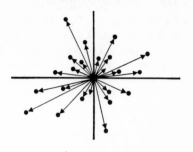

16

The Nature of Electrolytes in Solution

In our study of physical chemistry, so far, we have learned much about the details of atomic and molecular systems and have used this information to understand better a number of chemical and physical properties.   It is a fact, however, that many of the phenomena that interest chemists deal with electrolytes in aqueous solutions.   It was in studies of such systems by Ostwald, van't Hoff, Kohlrausch, Arrhenius, and others that the subject of physical chemistry had its beginnings.   Our knowledge of the behavior of free, independent molecules is not an adequate basis on which to understand systems in which charged particles are immersed in a far from inert medium.

It is necessary to start our study at a state of ignorance that corresponds to views about gases before the advent of the kinetic-molecular theory.   The early interpretations that gave basic, molecular-scale details of solutions will first be followed.   Later, and still continuing, investigations of the finer details of the molecular behavior in these systems will then be considered.   Again, it will be apparent that the molecular approach leads to an easier comprehension of the macroproperties.

An essentially thermodynamic treatment of solutions of electrolytes will be postponed until the following two chapters.   It is more satisfactory to obtain first a few ideas about the nature of these solutions.   The two empirical approaches that contributed greatly were measurements of the colligative properties and measurement of the electrical conductivity of such solutions. Historically it was the conductivity results that were first available, and it was primarily these results that stimulated the important theory of Arrhenius.   Our study starts, therefore, with a discussion of such conductivity measurements.

16-1. Electrical Conductivity of Solutions.   The experimental arrangement and the treatment of the experimental data that lead to quantities measuring the readiness, or ease, with which a current is carried through a solution will now be given.   The schematic diagram of Fig. 16-1 shows the typical arrangement

513

for such studies.   The setup has a *conductivity cell* in one arm of a Wheatstone-bridge circuit that allows the measurement of the electrical resistance provided by the cell.   The measurement consists in altering the variable resistances until no current flows through the detecting circuit containing the earphones. When this state of balance is achieved, the potential at D must be the same as that at E.   For equal potential drops from A to D and from A to E one writes

$$I_1 X = I_2 R_1 \tag{1}$$

and for equal drops from D and from E to B one has

$$I_1 R_3 = I_2 R_2 \tag{2}$$

Combination of these equalities gives

$$\frac{X}{R_3} = \frac{R_1}{R_2} \quad \text{or} \quad X = R_3 \frac{R_1}{R_2} \tag{3}$$

Knowledge of the values of the three variable resistances for a state of balance

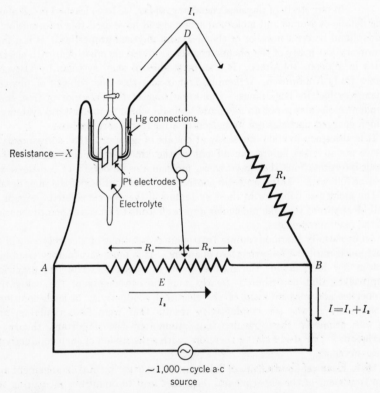

Fig. 16-1. Schematic diagram of conductivity apparatus.

allows the calculation of the resistance of the conductivity cell containing the electrolyte.

Some special care must be taken for this measured resistance to be meaningful.   If a direct current, for example, is used, the apparent resistance of the cell changes with time.   This can be attributed to a *polarization* effect in which the positive ions are somewhat displaced toward the negative electrode.   The acquired polarity of the solution greatly affects the ease of current flow through the cell.   This effect can be overcome and the resistance of the solution, undisturbed by polarization effects, can be obtained by using an alternating current of several thousand cycles per second.   The other necessary precaution concerns the nature of the platinum electrodes.   These normally consist of platinum sheets of about 1 sq cm area which are attached to the electrode wires and are separated from each other by about 1 cm.   A clear, reproducible state of balance on the Wheatstone bridge is usually obtained only when the electrodes are coated with platinum black.

When these two precautions are taken, it is found that the conductivity cell filled with a solution of an electrolyte obeys Ohm's law; i.e., the current is proportional to the applied voltage.   It is possible therefore to assign a resistance of so many ohms to such a cell in the same manner as one assigns a resistance to a metallic conductor.

It is, however, more convenient to focus our attention on the *conductance* of an electrolytic solution rather than on its *resistance*.   These quantities are reciprocally related, and the conductance, denoted by L, is calculated from the measured resistance-as

$$L = \frac{1}{R} \tag{4}$$

where R is the resistance in ohms and L has the units, therefore, of the reciprocal ohm; sometimes called "mho."   As for metallic conductors, the resistance, and therefore the conductance, depends on the cross-section area A and the length l of the conductivity cell, i.e., of the region between the electrodes. Just as for a metallic conductor one has

$$R = \rho \, \frac{l}{A} \tag{5}$$

where ρ is the *specific resistance* and is the proportionality factor that corresponds to the resistance of a cell of 1 sq cm cross section and 1 cm length. Similarly

$$L = \kappa \, \frac{A}{l} \tag{6}$$

where κ is the *specific conductance* and again can be thought of as the conductance of 1 cc of the solution of electrolyte.   It is κ, therefore, that characterizes the electrical conductivity of the solution.

The specific conductance can, in principle, be obtained from the measured value of R, which gives $L = 1/R$, and of l and A of the cell.   In practice, it is more convenient to deduce l and A, or rather the *cell constant* l/A, from a measurement of L when the cell is filled with a solution of known specific conductance. With such a measurement and datum one can use the equation

$$\kappa = \frac{l}{A} L = (\text{cell const})L \tag{7}$$

to calculate a value for the cell constant. Once this geometric factor has been obtained for a cell, it can be used to deduce κ for an unknown solution from a measured value of L and Eq. (7).

The cell constant is almost always determined by using a solution of KCl. Some specific conductances of these reference solutions are shown in Table 16-1. These absolutely determined conductances come from measurements with rather elaborately designed electrodes which avoid the usual ambiguity about the exact cross section of the solution that is effective in the current-carrying process. One should notice that the data of Table 16-1 show a marked temperature dependence. Since this dependence is characteristic of all conductance results, it is necessary to make measurements of conductances in well-thermostated cells.

Although the specific conductance is a measure of the ease with which a current flows through a 1-cm cube of solution, it is not a convenient quantity for the discussion of the conduction process of solutions of electrolytes. Solutions of different concentrations, for example, will have very different specific conductances simply because 1 cc of the different solutions will contain different amounts of electrolyte. Since it will be of particular interest to compare the current-carrying ability of a given number of electrolyte charges at different concentrations, it is helpful to define yet another measure of conductance.

16-2. Equivalent Conductance. An equivalent weight of an electrolyte is that amount which, for complete dissociation, would lead to ions with total positive and negative charges of $+eN$ and $-eN$, where e is the electronic charge. Thus an equivalent of NaCl gives an Avogadro's number of Na^+ ions and of Cl^- ions; an equivalent of $MgSO_4$ gives half an Avogadro's number of Mg^{++} ions and of $SO_4^=$ ions; and so forth. One equivalent of any electrolyte would, on complete dissociation, provide the same effective number of charge-carrying particles. The conductance that would be conveniently dealt with, therefore, is that which would be given by a conductance cell with electrodes

Table 16-1. Specific Conductance of KCl Solutions*

Concentration (equivalents/liter)	In ohms^{-1}/cm		
	0°C	18°C	25°C
1	0.06543	0.09820	0.11173
0.1	0.007154	0.011192	0.012886
0.01	0.0007751	0.0012227	0.0014114

* From G. Kortum and J. O'M. Bockris, "Textbook of Electrochemistry," vol. 1, Elsevier Press, Inc., Houston, Tex., 1951.

1 cm apart and of large enough cross sections so that the volume of solution containing one equivalent of the electrolyte would be held between the electrodes. This conductance, known as the *equivalent conductance* and designated by Λ, would measure the current-carrying ability of an equivalent of solute.

The volume of solution of concentration c equivalents per liter that holds 1 equivalent is $1/c$ liters, or $1,000/c$ cc. The conductance of a cell with plates 1 cm apart and of area $1,000/c$ sq cm is

$$\Lambda = \frac{1,000}{c}\kappa \tag{8}$$

This relation defines the equivalent conductance in terms of the specific conductance. The concept of the cell holding solution of volume $1,000/c$ is introduced only to suggest the definition of Eq. (8), and one should recognize that, in practice, one uses any convenient conductance cell, measures R, and calculates $L = 1/R$. With this datum one obtains $\kappa = (\text{cell const})L$, and, finally, Λ from Eq. (8).

Many precise measurements of equivalent conductances were made by Kohlrausch and his coworkers between about 1860 and 1880. The data of Table 16-2 are typical of these measurements. On the basis of such data and in the absence of any satisfactory theory as to the nature of conduction in these solutions, some valuable empirical relations were deduced.

16-3. Empirical Equivalent-conductance Relations. It was recognized empirically by Kohlrausch that plotting the equivalent conductance of an electrolyte at a fixed temperature against the square root of the concentration led, for some electrolytes, to plots which, at the lower concentrations, conformed very closely to straight lines. Such plots for a few electrolytes are shown in Fig. 16-2. It is clear from this figure that two different types of behavior are exhibited. Those electrolytes which lead to essentially linear plots are now classed as *strong electrolytes*, while those which seem to approach the dilute-solution limit almost tangentially are classed as *weak electrolytes*.

An important relation can be deduced from the extrapolations of the strong-electrolyte data to infinite dilution to give what are known as *limiting equivalent*

Table 16-2. Equivalent Conductances in Aqueous Solution at 25°C*

c (equivalents/liter)	NaCl	KCl	HCl	NaAc	CuSO$_4$	BaCl$_2$	H$_2$SO$_4$	HAc	NH$_4$OH
0.0000	126.45	149.86	426.16	91.0	133	139.98	429.6	(390.7)	(271.4)
0.0005	124.50	147.81	422.74	89.2	.....	135.96	413.1	67.7	47
0.001	123.74	146.95	421.36	88.5	115.2	134.34	399.5	49.2	34
0.010	118.51	141.27	412.00	83.76	83.3	123.94	336.4	16.3	11.3
0.100	106.74	128.96	391.32	72.80	50.5	105.19	250.8	.....	3.6
1.000	.....	111.9	332.8	49.1	29.3	80.5			

* Data mostly from D. A. MacInnes, "The Principles of Electrochemistry," Reinhold Publishing Corporation, New York, 1939.

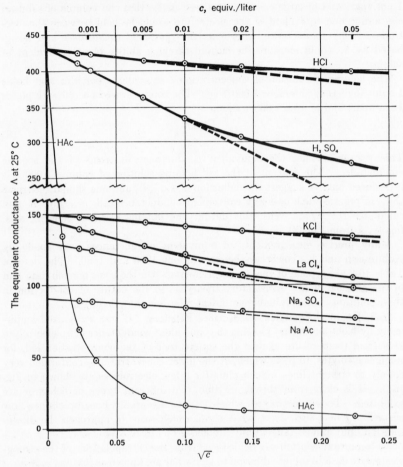

Fig. 16-2. The equivalent conductance versus $\sqrt{c}$ for some electrolytes in water at 25°C.

conductances. These conductances, denoted by Λ_0, are the basis for *Kohlrausch's law of the independent migration of ions.* The law is more easily stated and understandable if some later ideas are anticipated and the conductance of an electrolyte at infinite dilution is treated as being made up of contributions from the individual ions of the electrolyte. In this way one introduces *equivalent ionic conductances* and writes for the limit of infinite dilution

$$\Lambda_0 = \lambda_0^+ + \lambda_0^- \tag{9}$$

The law of Kohlrausch now suggests that at infinite dilution the conductance of an electrolyte, NaCl, for example, depends on independent contributions from Na^+ and from Cl^-.   The independence of these contributions is judged by a comparison of pairs of electrolytes containing a common ion as shown in Table 16-3.   The differences show the value of $\lambda_0^{K^+} - \lambda_0^{Li^+}$ and $\lambda_0^{Cl^-} - \lambda_0^{NO_3^-}$, and these differences are seen to be independent of the other ionic species present.   Kohlrausch's law gives, it should be noted, no way of deducing the contributions of the individual ions.

The immediate practical application of the idea of the independent contribution of the ions at infinite dilution is a method for deducing the limiting equivalent conductance of weak electrolytes.   For acetic acid, for example, one can write

$$\Lambda_0(HAc) = \Lambda_0(NaAc) + \Lambda_0(HCl) - \Lambda_0(NaCl)$$

because the right side can be interpreted as

$$\lambda_0^{Na^+} + \lambda_0^{Ac^-} + \lambda_0^{H^+} + \lambda_0^{Cl^-} - \lambda_0^{Na^+} - \lambda_0^{Cl^-} = \lambda_0^{H^+} + \lambda_0^{Ac^-} = \Lambda_0(HAc)$$

In this way, the value, at 25°C, of

$$\Lambda_0(HAc) = 91.0 + 426.2 - 126.5 = 390.7 \tag{10}$$

is found, and it is clear from Fig. 16-2 that no reliable value could have been determined by a graphical extrapolation.

The availability of limiting equivalent conductances for all types of electrolytes was a prerequisite for the development of the theory for the nature of electrolytes in solution, which followed closely the experimental studies of Kohlrausch.

16-4. The Arrhenius Theory of Dissociations.   Prior to the development of the important theory of Arrhenius, about 1887, a number of suggestions had been made to explain the fact that solutions of electrolytes were conductors of electricity.   It is difficult for the modern student, who is brought up with the idea that salts and strong acids and bases are completely ionized in water, to appreciate the early difficulties in recognizing that such solutions of ions could exist.   In the nineteenth century chemists were very much impressed with the difficulty of breaking apart stable molecules, and they could not accept the idea that a molecule, like HCl, could be dissociated except at a very high

Table 16-3. The Basis for Kohlrausch's Law of Independent Migration of Ions*
(Data for 25°C)

	Λ_0	$\Delta(= \lambda_0^{K^+} - \lambda_0^{Li^+})$		Λ_0	$\Delta(= \lambda_0^{Cl^-} - \lambda_0^{NO_3^-})$
KCl	149.86		LiCl	115.03	
LiCl	115.03	34.83	LiNO$_3$	110.1	4.9
KClO$_4$	140.04		KCl	149.86	
LiClO$_4$	105.98	35.06	KNO$_3$	144.96	4.90
			HCl	426.16	
			HNO$_3$	421.3	4.9

* Data from H. S. Harned and B. B. Owen, "The Physical Chemistry of Electrolytic Solutions," Reinhold Publishing Corporation, New York, 1950.

temperature.   It must be remembered also that at this time solid salts had not been represented as an array of ions in the crystal lattice.

It was Arrhenius who made the then bold postulate that the dissolving of an electrolyte in an aqueous solution could lead to electrolytic dissociation and, even at ordinary temperatures, the conversion of an appreciable fraction of the electrolyte to free ions.   Basic to the theory was the explanation offered by Arrhenius for the observed variation of conductance with concentration, as illustrated by the data of Fig. 16-2 and Table 16-2.   The decrease of equivalent conductance with increasing concentration, observed in dilute solutions of all electrolytes, was attributed by him to the partial dissociation of the electrolyte. A chemical equilibrium between undissociated electrolyte molecules and the ions that result from dissociation always leads to an increase of the ion concentration for more dilute solutions.   Since it seemed likely that the conductance could be related to the concentration of charged species, a qualitative explanation for the concentration variation of conductance was immediately reached.

These ideas of Arrhenius led him to a method for the calculation of the degree of dissociation of an electrolyte from the conductivity data.   The supposition of a dissociation equilibrium implies that at infinite dilution all electrolytes are completely dissociated.   [This general result depends on the fact that the products contain more particles than do the reactants.   Equations (18) and (20), to be obtained in the following section, illustrate that, as $c \to 0$, the degree of dissociation α must approach unity.]   A comparison of the equivalent conductance at some finite concentration with that at infinite dilution gives therefore a measure of the fraction of electrolyte dissociated at the higher concentration.   One introduces α, the *degree of dissociation*, and writes

$$\alpha = \frac{\Lambda}{\Lambda_0} \tag{11}$$

In this way Arrhenius could calculate results for the degree of dissociation, such as are shown in Table 16-4 for HCl and acetic acid.   One notices that Arrhenius treats strong and weak electrolytes in essentially the same way, the apparent different behavior revealed in Fig. 16-2 being interpreted merely as a difference in degree of dissociation.   It should, however, be mentioned that later ideas tend to substantiate the previous suggestion of two essentially different behaviors being exhibited in Fig. 16-2.

The Arrhenius theory and the deduced degrees of dissociation were received with considerable skepticism, and it was still generally held to be unlikely that the mere solution of an electrolyte could break up the molecules into separate ions.   At this stage the measurements of colligative properties by van't Hoff, which were presented in Chap. 15, became available.   The interpretation of these results by the electrolytic-dissociation theory of Arrhenius swung support almost completely over to this new theory.

16-5. The Degree of Dissociation from van't Hoff i Factors.   The van't Hoff i factors given in Table 15-8 are clearly in qualitative accord with the view that

Table 16-4. Degrees of Dissociation for a Strong and a Weak Electrolyte Calculated
According to the Arrhenius Theory
(The temperature is 25°C)

c (equivalents/liter)	Λ	$\alpha = \dfrac{\Lambda}{\Lambda_0}$	$K_\Lambda = \dfrac{c\alpha^2}{1-\alpha}$	i	$\alpha = \dfrac{i-1}{2-1}$	$K_i = \dfrac{c\alpha^2}{1-\alpha}$
			HCl			
0	(426.16)	1.00				
0.001	421.36	0.99	0.10	1.98	0.98	0.05
0 005	415.80	0.98	0.24	1.95	0.95	0.09
0.01	412.00	0.97	0.31	1.94	0.94	0.15
0.05	399.09	0.94	0.73	1.90	0.90	0.40
0.1	391.32	0.92	1.1	1.89	0.89	0.72
0.5	359.2	0.84	2.2			
1.0	332.8	0.78	2 8	2.12	1.12	−10.4
			Acetic acid			
0	(390.7)	1.000				
0.001	49.2	0.126	1.82×10^{-5}			
0.005	22.9	0.058	1.78			
0.01	16.3	0.042	1.84			
0.05	7.4	0.019	1.84			
0.1	5.2	0.013	1.71			
0.5						
1.0						

electrolytes are more or less dissociated in solution. Since, for noninteracting solute particles, the colligative measurements give the number of particles in solution, it is apparent that the strong electrolytes behave as though there are about two, three, or four times as many particles as might have been expected. The numbers, furthermore, correspond to the number of ions that would be expected to result from the dissociation of the electrolyte molecule. The colligative-property results provided by van't Hoff gave a virtual proof to the Arrhenius idea of appreciable dissociation of electrolytes in aqueous solution.

It is necessary, however, to look more closely at the results and to see whether or not the Arrhenius theory can provide an explanation for the fact that the i factors tend to be less than the integer expected for complete dissociation. A quantitative explanation can be attempted in terms of incomplete dissociation, and it will be of interest to compare the degree of dissociation computed from van't Hoff i factors with the corresponding results from conductivity data.

Consider the general electrolyte A_aB_b, which can dissociate to form a positive ions and b negative ions according to the equation

$$A_aB_b \rightleftharpoons aA^{(+)} + bB^{(-)}$$

It is necessary to calculate the net number of particles that result from a degree of dissociation α. If the molality of the electrolyte is m and the degree of dissociation is α, the concentration of undissociated electrolyte will be $m - \alpha m = m(1 - \alpha)$. In addition there will be $a\alpha m$ of $A^{(+)}$ and $b\alpha m$ of $B^{(-)}$ The concentration of particles, regardless of their kind, is, therefore,

$$m(1 - \alpha) + a\alpha m + b\alpha m \qquad (12)$$

It is customary to let ν be the total number of ions yielded by complete dissociation of a molecule, i.e.,

$$\nu = a + b \qquad (13)$$

With this notation the molality of particles for the partially dissociated electrolyte is

$$m(1 - \alpha) + \alpha\nu m \qquad (14)$$

rather than the value of m expected for no dissociation.

The definition of the van't Hoff i factor given in Chap. 15 shows that it is to be identified with the ratio

$$i = \frac{m(1 - \alpha) + \alpha\nu m}{m}$$

$$= 1 - \alpha + \alpha\nu \qquad (15)$$

From this interpretation of i, one obtains

$$\alpha = \frac{i - 1}{\nu - 1} \qquad (16)$$

This important result provides an alternative way to that given by Eq. (11) for calculating the degree of dissociation of an electrolyte. The results of such calculations for HCl and acetic acid are included in Table 16-4.

For rather dilute solutions the two methods of calculating α lead to fair agreement, and in the early stages of the theory such agreement could be accepted as support for the interpretation of the conductivity and the i-factor data in terms of incomplete dissociation. The modern view, it should be mentioned, does not accept the idea of only partial dissociation of strong electrolytes.

A further test of the Arrhenius theory is possible with the data of Table 16-4. If the equilibria postulated by Arrhenius are, in fact, set up and if this is the only feature of ionic solutions that need be considered, it should be possible to calculate a good equilibrium constant from the deduced degrees of dissociation.

16-6. Dissociation Equilibria.   No convenient general expression can be set up for the equilibrium constant of the dissociation reaction in terms of the degree of dissociation for all types of electrolytes. For a particular type of electrolyte such a relation can be easily deduced, as two examples will show.

No thermodynamic derivation of the equilibrium-constant expression for a reaction involving solids or liquids has so far been obtained. It is sufficient for the present merely to state that for solutes it is often satisfactory to write molar concentrations in the same form as the pressure terms of Eq. (7-35). This procedure will be justified in the following chapter.

For a simple one-to-one electrolyte AB with a degree of dissociation α at a concentration of c moles/liter, the amount of the dissociated species will be

$c\alpha$ and the remaining undissociated electrolyte will be $c - c\alpha$. Thus one can write the dissociation reaction and the equilibrium concentrations as

$$AB \quad \rightleftharpoons A^+ + B^-$$

Equil. concs. $c(1 - \alpha)$ $c\alpha$ $c\alpha$

The equilibrium-constant expression

$$K = \frac{[A^+][B^-]}{[AB]} \tag{17}$$

can therefore be written as

$$K = \frac{(c\alpha)(c\alpha)}{c(1 - \alpha)} = \frac{c\alpha^2}{1 - \alpha} \tag{18}$$

With this expression, a value of K can be calculated for an electrolyte of the type AB for any concentration for which a value of α is available. Results for such calculations are shown for the data of Table 16-4.

For an electrolyte of the type A_2B one writes

$$A_2B \quad \rightleftharpoons 2A^+ + B^=$$

Equil. concs. $c(1 - \alpha)$ $2c\alpha$ $c\alpha$

The equilibrium-constant expression is

$$K = \frac{[A^+][B^=]^2}{[A_2B]} \tag{19}$$

and substitution of the equilibrium concentrations gives

$$K = \frac{(2c\alpha)^2(c\alpha)}{c(1 - \alpha)} = \frac{4c\alpha^3}{1 - \alpha} \tag{20}$$

Similar relations between K and α can be worked out for any other type of electrolyte.

Representative results for the calculated equilibrium constants as a function of concentration are shown in Table 16-4. Such results are confusing if one seeks evidence for or against the Arrhenius theory. The two examples are representative of the fact that those electrolytes previously classified as weak electrolytes give quite constant values for K, while strong electrolytes give the unsatisfactory results of which those for HCl are representative.

It is now necessary to sum up the ideas that were held in the forty years that followed the publication of the Arrhenius theory. This summation should make clear that the Arrhenius theory led to a great advance in our knowledge of the molecular behavior of solutions of electrolytes. However, just as the simple kinetic-molecular theory left the details of the behavior of real gases unexplained, so also did the Arrhenius theory fail to allow for some rather important effects that are operative in solution of electrolytes.

16-7. Difficulties of the Arrhenius Theory and Some Aspects of Ionic Solutions. Although almost all the calculations of the previous section seemed at first to lend support to the basic idea of the Arrhenius theory, it began to be apparent in the early years of the twentieth century that the theory led to some serious difficulties especially when applied to strong electrolytes.

First, the degree-of-dissociation results of Table 16-4 from the conductivity measurements are, for the higher concentrations, in very poor agreement with those from the van't Hoff i factor.   Furthermore, values of α greater than even unity appear.

Second, the calculated values for the equilibrium constants of strong electrolytes, as illustrated by the data for HCl in Table 16-4, vary with concentration in a way that raised questions as to the existence of the equilibria assumed by Arrhenius.

A third criticism was based on the data on the heats of mixing of electrolyte solutions.   Arrhenius had originally claimed support for his theory of dissociation from the fact, noted earlier by Hess, that little heat was evolved or absorbed when solutions of strong electrolytesw ere mixed.   This generalization supported the idea that the electrolytes are very largely dissociated and that mixing produced no new chemical reaction.   A more careful consideration of the data shows that, even where the Arrhenius theory predicts an appreciable fraction of undissociated molecules, the heat evolved or absorbed is very much less than would be expected for the combining of solutions of different electrolytes.

A fourth criticism centered around the newly deduced crystal structure of NaCl by Bragg in 1912 in which no molecules, in the Arrhenius understanding of the word, were present.   It becomes difficult to see why the process of solution should cause such an ionic salt to *form* molecules!   This criticism, though a historical fact, is perhaps misleading.   The interpretation of the NaCl molecule as an ion pair, such as exists in the vapor, which would not contribute to the electrical conductivity, would allow the Arrhenius view of undissociated molecules to be maintained without serious conflict with the deductions drawn from the crystal structure.

It is interesting to note that the early criticisms that were raised against Arrhenius's theory were that it postulated ions for situations in which everyone had felt molecules existed.   It overcame these criticisms only to end up by being attacked because it postulated molecules where its critics now insisted only ions existed!

Before proceeding to the theory that, at least for strong electrolytes, was finally to supplant that of Arrhenius, we should look at some of the features of solutions of electrolytes on which the attention of the chemist concerned with these systems began to be focused.

It was recognized that a remarkable feature of the Arrhenius theory is that, although it attributes the dissociation process to the solution of the electrolyte, it proceeds to ignore the role of the solvent or, rather, treats the solvent as if it were an inert medium.   A detailed understanding of the molecular nature of ionic solutions must clearly investigate the very important role played by the solvent.   It is necessary, for instance, to understand why water is such a unique solvent for ionic systems.

In this regard two aspects of solvent behavior are important.   The first of these is the tendency of the solvent molecules to interact with, or to *solvate*, solute species.   Of particular importance is the solvation of charged species.   The water molecules can be looked upon as dipole units that can arrange themselves about either positive or negative solute particles, as indicated in Fig. 16-3. The question of just how many water molecules can arrange themselves directly around an ion, in what is called the *first solvation layer*, is difficult to answer. About six molecules might be expected to fit. Clearly, however, this will be a rather flexible arrangement, and there will be other, less tightly bound molecules in secondary, or outer, solvation layers. It seems certain, however, that an ion in aqueous solution must be looked upon as surrounded by a considerable number of more or less bound water molecules.

Some idea of the energy of this solvation can be obtained by considering the heat evolved when an Avogadro's number of Na^+ ions and of Cl^- ions is taken from the gas phase to an infinitely dilute aqueous solution.

In Sec. 13-1 it was found that

$$NaCl(cryst) \rightarrow Na^+(g) + Cl^-(g) \qquad \Delta E = +184 \text{ kcal}$$

The heat of solution of crystalline NaCl is easily measured, and this quantity can be identified with little error with the internal-energy change. Thus

$$NaCl(cryst) \xrightarrow{H_2O} Na^+(aq) + Cl^-(aq) \qquad \Delta E = 1.3 \text{ kcal}$$

Combination of these reactions gives

$$Na^+(g) + Cl^-(g) \xrightarrow{H_2O} Na^+(aq) + Cl^-(aq) \qquad \Delta E = -183 \text{ kcal}$$

The liberation of this amount of heat corresponds to a value per solvating water molecule that must be less than that of chemical binding but much greater than that of van der Waals' forces and greater even than that of typical hydrogen-bond energies, if something like six water molecules are involved per ion. It should be recognized that the separate solvation energies of the Na^+ and Cl^- ions cannot, unfortunately, be obtained.

An extreme example of solvation is presented by that of the proton in aqueous solutions. The properties of acidic solutions are not those expected for a system of bare protons. Spectroscopic evidence, moreover, indicates that the species H_3O^+, the hydronium ion, does exist. The writing of the hydrated proton, i.e., of H_3O^+, and at the same time the use of symbols such as

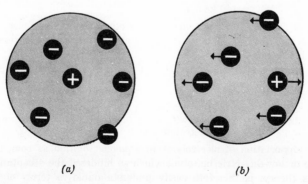

(a)   *(b)*

Fig. 16-3. Representation of ion atmosphere for ion $\oplus$. (a) At rest. (b) Moving.

Na⁺, Cl⁻, OH⁻, and so forth, tends to obscure the fact that all ions are associated with solvent molecules and that the proton may be an extreme, rather than a special, case.

Many attempts have been made to deduce the number of water molecules that are presumed to be bound to various ions. No satisfactory results have as yet been obtained. The difficulty undoubtedly stems from the fact that the concept of solvation has not been carefully defined. Since at least some of the solvating water molecules can be expected to be in rapid equilibrium with the molecules of the bulk of the liquid, while others may be tightly and more permanently bound to the ion, the extent of solvation would appear to be a concept of some complexity.

The second important role of the solvent is the decrease in electrostatic interactions that it produced as a result of its *dielectric effect*. The electrostatic force of attraction between ions of charge Z^+ and Z^- is given by Coulomb's law as

$$f(r) = \frac{e^2 Z^+ Z^-}{\epsilon r^2} \tag{21}$$

where r is the distance between the ions and ϵ is the dielectric constant of the medium in which the ions are immersed. The high value of 78 for the dielectric constant for water plays, along with its special solvating ability for both positive and negative ions, a decisive role in making water an exceptional medium for electrolytes. The solubility of salts in water compared with almost all other solvents is perhaps the most dramatic illustration of these special properties. The importance of the dielectric constant can be illustrated by the calculation of the electrostatic energy required to pull apart an NaCl molecule. Studies of such a molecule in the gas phase, where individual NaCl molecules do occur, show that it can be treated approximately as a pair of ions that have an equilibrium internuclear separation of 2.36 A. To overcome this electrostatic binding, an amount of energy must be spent that is given by

$$\Delta E = \int_{r=2.36\,\text{A}}^{r=\infty} f \, dr = \int_{r=2.36}^{r=\infty} \frac{e^2}{r^2} \, dr = -\frac{e^2}{r} \Big]_{2.36}^{\infty}$$
$$= +0.97 \times 10^{-11} \text{ erg}$$
$$= 140 \text{ kcal/mole}$$

This amount, less the repulsion energy at the equilibrium internuclear distance, as is shown in Fig. 8-5, is approximately the energy for the dissociation of NaCl into ions in the vapor state.

In the presence of a medium with a dielectric constant of 82 this electrostatic energy amounts to only

$$\Delta E = \int_{r=2.36}^{r=\infty} \frac{e^2}{\epsilon r} \, dr = 1.19 \times 10^{-13} \text{ erg}$$
$$= 1.7 \text{ kcal/mole}$$

The easy dissociation of electrolytes in aqueous solution as compared with gas-phase or low-dielectric material, which so hindered the acceptance of the Arrhenius theory, is therefore easily understandable in terms of the high dielectric constant of water. The initial criticisms raised against the Arrhenius theory remain, however, valid arguments against any theory postulating appreciable dissociation to form free ions in solvents of low dielectric constant.

A calculation such as that given for NaCl suggests that water is a solvent that will allow, or will affect, dissociation. It is, however, not valid to conclude that the dielectric constant is such that all interactions between charged species will be eliminated. The Arrhenius theory is based on the idea that the ions are completely noninteracting and that their contribution to the conductivity is simply proportional to their concentration.

It is illustrative to estimate, first, the average distance between nearest ionic neighbors in a 1 M solution of, for example, NaCl. On the basis of a simple lattice, as for the calculation for the NaCl crystal, one deduces that about $\sqrt[3]{12 \times 10^{23}}$ ions would be spaced irregularly along a distance of $\sqrt[3]{1,000}$ cc. Working with these figures one estimates that a nearest neighbor is about 9 A away. A similar calculation for a gas shows that the pressure would have to be about 50 atm for the gas molecules to be as closely spaced. The ions of all but the most dilute solutions are therefore not far removed from their nearest neighbors.

The importance of this nearness of ions is even more apparent when one compares the electrostatic energy of interaction between ions with the van der Waals' interaction between neutral molecules at the same distance. At 10 A separation, for example, the electrostatic energy of attraction of oppositely charged ions, compared with infinite separation, is

$$\frac{e^2}{r} = \frac{(4.8 \times 10^{-10})^2}{10 \times 10^{-8}} = 2.3 \times 10^{-12} \text{ erg}$$
$$= 33 \text{ kcal/mole}$$

This gas-phase value reduces to $\frac{33}{78} = 0.4$ kcal if the ions are immersed in a dielectric medium like water. For typical small neutral molecules in the gas phase at such a distance, the data of Table 12-4 indicate that the van der Waals' interaction would be of the order of only 0.003 kcal/mole.

It will be recalled that the interactions between gas molecules led to appreciable changes in the simple theory of gases and that these changes led us to a more detailed understanding of the nature of gases. From the calculations that have been introduced here, it seems unlikely that the interactions between ions can be ignored. They would be expected to influence the behavior of all but infinitely dilute ionic solutions. This is, in fact, found to be so.

The discussion of this section recapitulates the attitudes that were prevalent in the years after the publication of the theory of Arrhenius. First, the defects of the Arrhenius theory were more and more emphasized. Second, the specific role played by the solvent, in terms of solvation and dielectric effects, was appreciated. Finally, the fact that interactions between the ions of all but infinitely dilute solutions would be appreciable was recognized. Attempts to improve the Arrhenius theory by recognizing the role of the solvent and that of interionic attractions were made in the early 1900s by van Laar, Noyes, Bjerrum, Milner, and G. N. Lewis. The effects that these and other workers recognized as being important were handled by the important theoretical development of Debye and Hückel in 1923.

16-8. Interpretation of Conductance Results by the Debye-Hückel Theory.   The effect of ion solvation and interionic attractions on the behavior of dilute solutions of electrolytes was successfully treated by Debye and Hückel.   These features, as we shall see, are not easily handled, and the Debye-Hückel theory is really satisfactory only for rather dilute solutions, i.e., below about 0.01 M. In the following chapter some of the thermodynamic features of ionic solutions predicted by the Debye-Hückel theory will be derived in some detail.   An introduction to the theory and the qualitative aspects of its explanation for the strong-electrolyte conductance curves of Fig. 16-2 will be given here.

The most dramatic result of the Debye-Hückel theory is that, for rather dilute solutions, the behavior of strong electrolytes can be understood on the basis of *complete dissociation*.   The behavior of these electrolytes that had led the Arrhenius theory to calculate degrees of dissociation is interpreted by the Debye-Hückel theory in a way that is more satisfactory with regard to some of the features pointed out in the previous section.   The ions of weak electrolytes, it should be mentioned, were also considered to be subject to the effects of solvation and ionic interactions, but the behavior of weak electrolytes was such that they were still postulated to be only partially dissociated, to much the same extent as given by the Arrhenius theory.

The first factor that the Debye-Hückel theory evaluated to explain the curves of Fig. 15-2 was the effect of interionic attractions.   Although the ions move in a random manner, it was shown that, if one focused one's attention on one ion, that ion would be surrounded more by oppositely charged ions than by like charges.   An ion has therefore an oppositely charged *ion atmosphere*, as indicated in Fig. 16-3.   The ionic distribution can be looked on as like an expanded and loosely held NaCl crystal; for example, the over-all arrangement places each ion among nearest neighbors of the opposite charge. This ion atmosphere around each ion is, of course, better formed at higher concentrations.

The application of an electric field, as in a conductance experiment, results initially in the movement of the central ion away from the center of the oppositely charged sphere, as shown in Fig. 16-2.   The distorted ion atmosphere tends to oppose the applied field, and this decreases the current produced by a given applied electric field.   Since the ion atmosphere is more important at higher concentrations, this decrease becomes more important at higher concentrations.   Debye and Hückel evaluated this factor quantitatively and showed that it contributed to the observed $\sqrt{c}$ dependence of the equivalent conductance.   This effect is further enhanced by the tendency of the oppositely charged ions that predominate in the ion atmosphere to move in the opposite direction.

The ionic-atmosphere drag depends on the fact that the atmosphere does not instantaneously adjust itself to the new positions of the central ion.   One says that the ionic atmosphere has a *relaxation time;* i.e., when a stress is applied, it takes a finite time for the atmosphere to relax, or to be re-established. The mechanism by which this occurs, as the central ion moves, is better thought of as a building of new ions on the front of the atmosphere and the dropping of some off the back rather than a maintaining of the same set of ions, which move to keep up with the central ion.

The second factor that acts to decrease the conductance at higher concentrations is an enhanced frictional drag that sets in. When an electric field is applied, the ions set off to the oppositely charged electrodes. Each ion moves with a velocity that depends on a balance between the electrical force and the viscous drag. The average velocity, and, therefore, the current, is concentration-dependent because the ions can be thought of as carrying along with them their many solvating molecules and at higher concentrations an ion seems to swim against the current produced by the oppositely charged, solvated ions moving in the opposite direction. Again Debye and Hückel evaluated this effect, and it likewise depended on the square root of the concentration.

The theory of Debye and Hückel has been used to draw the slopes of the straight, dashed lines of Fig. 16-2. It is apparent that the effects considered by the theory are adequate to explain the conductance behavior of strong electrolytes up to concentrations of about 0.01 M. Thus the Arrhenius assumption that a decrease in conductance must be interpreted as a decreased number of conducting particles cannot be maintained, and the relation $\alpha = \Lambda/\Lambda_0$ can be applied only when the Debye-Hückel effects are not appreciable or are corrected for. Only for solutions with low ionic concentrations will these effects be small. For weak electrolytes, therefore, one can still rely on Λ/Λ_0 to give a value that can be interpreted primarily in terms of a degree of dissociation.

Higher concentrations, i.e., in the 0.1 and 1 M regions, are not dealt with by the Debye-Hückel theory and are still not susceptible to any satisfactory-theoretical treatment. The effects dealt with by the Debye-Hückel theory will still exist, but they are not easily evaluated quantitatively. Furthermore, new features become important, and, of these, attention is often directed to the formation of *ion pairs* or *ion triplets*. Primarily as a result of the work of Bjerrum and Fuoss, it has been recognized that a more specific attraction between oppositely charged ions must be recognized at concentrations in the molar range. Bjerrum has calculated that, for a monovalent strong electrolyte with ions of about 2 A diameter, about 20 per cent of the ions, on the average, may be present as ion pairs; i.e., the random motion of the ions in solution will be affected by the electrostatic attractions such that at any time 20 per cent of the ions will be making "sticky" collisions with oppositely charged ions. Such ion pairs will affect the conductance and other electrolyte properties. The recognition of these ion pairs is particularly important in solvents of low dielectric constant. In a solvent like chloroform, for example, the neutralization reaction between an acid and a base leads almost exclusively to the formation of ion pairs. One has, for example,

$$HAc + NEt_3 \rightarrow CH_3 - \overset{\overset{\textstyle O}{\|}}{C} - O^- \cdots H - \overset{+}{N}Et_3$$

The recognition of the importance of ion pairs is to some extent a return to the Arrhenius view. For an electrolyte like NaCl, the ion pair that is postulated in the more concentrated solutions might equally well be called an undissociated NaCl molecule. These molecules are present, however, to a much less extent and only in much more concentrated solutions than expected by Arrhenius. The distinction between an ion pair and a molecule becomes more real when one thinks of a strong acid. The ion pair, of HCl, for example, would be depicted as

$$\begin{array}{c} H \\ \diagdown \\ \overset{+}{O}-H\cdots Cl^{-} \\ \diagup \\ H \end{array}$$

whereas the solvated undissociated molecule would be represented as

$$\begin{array}{c} H \\ \diagdown \\ O\cdots H-Cl \\ \diagup \\ H \end{array}$$

As with the extent of solvation, the nature of an ion pair, or the formation of undissociated molecules in solutions of strong electrolytes, must be treated with some care. A very short lifetime of an ion pair is, for example, better treated as a collision between the ions rather than as molecule formation. In these terms the distinction between colliding species and molecules can become poorly defined and will vary with the experimental approach.

With this section, the information about the molecular-scale behavior of electrolytic solutions that can be derived from conductivities and from van't Hoff i factors is completed. The theories of Arrhenius and of Debye and Hückel have led to some understanding of the experimental results. At the same time our knowledge of the ionic world has been considerably enlarged. Strong electrolytes are interpreted as being completely dissociated into ions, but at higher concentrations these ions appear to be associated into ion pairs or undissociated molecules. Furthermore, it is known that ions are solvated and that solvation along with interionic attractions are important factors.

This information, however, falls far short of the detailed, precise data obtained for the molecular world. Now we proceed with some further experimental results that will lead us to a more thorough understanding of how ions in solution behave.

16-9. Electrolysis and the Electrode Process. The variations of equivalent conductance with concentration have been the principal data for the theories of the preceding sections. Much additional information is obtained from studies of the passage of a direct current through a cell containing a solution of an electrolyte. One is able to investigate some further features of the way in which the current is carried through the solution by the electrolyte. Since d-c experiments involve chemical reactions at the electrodes, a feature that is avoided in conductivity studies by the use of an alternating current, it is first necessary to describe and classify these electrode processes.

When electrodes are inserted in a solution of electrolyte and a sufficient potential, of the order of several volts, is applied, chemical reactions are observed at the electrodes. *Electrolysis* is said to be occurring. The electrode that is charged positively, i.e., that has a deficit of electrons, by the applied potential is called the *anode* while that charged negatively, i.e., that has an excess of electrons, is called the *cathode*. The electrodes consist of conductors that introduce the source and sink of electrons into the solution. In classifying the reactions that occur as a result of the charged electrodes, it is convenient to distinguish *inert electrodes*, usually a platinum wire, that serve only to transfer electrons to and from the solution, from *reacting electrodes* that enter chemically into the electrode reaction. Most simply, the reacting electrode is a metal that either contributes metal ions to the solution or accepts discharged metal ions from the solution.

Only a few basically different types of electrode reactions occur. Three important types are of interest here, and these will be introduced through several examples.

Consider first the electrolysis of a solution of HCl between platinum electrodes. A cell that allows the study of the electrode reactions is illustrated in Fig. 16-4. With a voltage of about 1.3 volts, its value depends, among other things, on the HCl concentration; it is found that H_2 is evolved at the cathode and Cl_2 at the anode.

It is instructive to investigate how the current flows across various parts of the circuit. Through the external metallic conductor the electrons flow, as a result of the driving force of the battery, in the direction indicated to maintain the negative charge on the cathode and the positive charge at the anode.

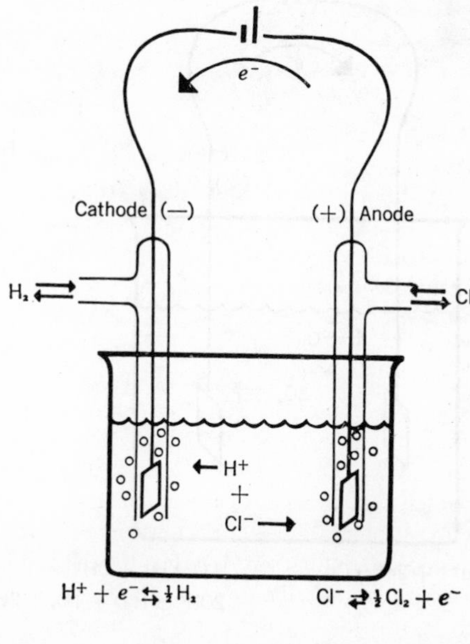

Fig. 16-4. Electrolysis of a hydrochloric acid solution.

$$H^+ + e^- \rightleftarrows \tfrac{1}{2}H_2 \qquad\qquad Cl^- \rightleftarrows \tfrac{1}{2}Cl_2 + e^-$$

Through the bulk of the solution this flow of current is maintained by motion of the principal charged species H^+ (or H_3O^+ if preferred) to the left and Cl^- to the right; i.e., the Cl^- ions flow in the same direction as the negative particles of the external circuit, while the positive particles flow in the opposite direction.

How does the current get from the metal conductors to the solution?   At the cathode the product H_2 can be accounted for simply by the discharge of H^+ ions according to the reaction

$$H^+ + e^- \rightarrow \tfrac{1}{2}H_2$$

The detailed mechanism as to how two H^+ ions are discharged and come together to form H_2 is, however, not easily depicted.   At the anode the current can get across the boundary by means of the removal of electrons from Cl^- ions according to the equation

$$Cl^- \rightarrow \tfrac{1}{2}Cl_2 + e^-$$

The battery can be thought of, therefore, as an electron pump that keeps pumping electrons from the positive well at the anode, which tends to fill up as Cl^- ions are discharged, over to the reservoir at the cathode, which the H^+ ions tend to deplete.   Since addition of electrons to a chemical species is called *reduction* and removal is called *oxidation,* one recognizes that in electrolysis *reduction occurs at the cathode and oxidation at the anode.*

The HCl electrolysis represents the first type of electrode reaction: *current-carrying ions are discharged at the electrode.*

Consider now the electrolysis of a solution of copper sulfate as indicated in

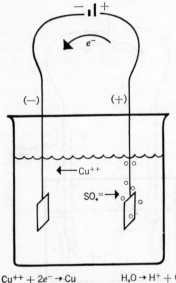

Fig. 16-5. Electrolysis of $CuSO_4$ solution.

$Cu^{++} + 2e^- \rightarrow Cu$ $H_2O \rightarrow H^+ + OH^-$

$2OH^- \rightarrow H_2O + \tfrac{1}{2}O_2 + 2e^-$

Fig. 16-5. The flow of electrons occurs as before, but the most important ions are now Cu^{++} and $SO_4^=$, and they are responsible for the current flow through the solution. At the cathode one now finds the deposition of metallic copper, and the equation

$$\tfrac{1}{2}Cu^{++} + e^- \rightarrow \tfrac{1}{2}Cu$$

indicates that the reaction can be put in the same class as the formation of gases in the previous example.

At the anode O_2 gas is evolved, and the solution around the electrode is found to contain sulfuric acid. These products can be understood by recognizing that, although the $SO_4^=$ ions are the important carriers of current through the solution, they are not necessarily the species that is discharged to accomplish the transfer of current between the solution and the electrode. The products are explained if it is assumed that the OH^-, present in low concentration from the dissociation of water, is discharged more easily than is the $SO_4^=$ ion. The anode reaction can then be written as

$$H_2O \rightleftharpoons H^+ + OH^-$$

and

$$OH^- \rightarrow \tfrac{1}{2}H_2O + \tfrac{1}{4}O_2 + e^-$$

or the two equations can be combined and the electrode reaction represented as

$$\tfrac{1}{2}H_2O \rightarrow H^+ + \tfrac{1}{4}O_2 + e^-$$

The migration of $SO_4^=$ ions to the anode region, as will be shown in more detail later, produces, with the H^+ ions, the observed sulfuric acid.

An alternative mechanism might suggest itself. One might postulate the initial discharge of $SO_4^=$ ions and the subsequent reaction with water to give

$$SO_4^= \rightarrow SO_4 + 2e^-$$
$$SO_4 + H_2O \rightarrow 2H^+ + SO_4^= + \tfrac{1}{2}O_2$$

Although the correct products are predicted, this mechanism depends on the existence of the uncharged SO_4 group. Since no substantiating evidence for this group exists, it seems more satisfactory to interpret the electrode reaction as an initial discharge of hydroxide ions.

This anode reaction represents the second type of electrode process. *A difficultly discharged negative ion, or anion, leads to the decomposition of water at the anode to give H^+, O_2, and electrons.*

The third type of electrode reaction is illustrated when the cation of the electrolyte is difficult to discharge. Thus, in the electrolysis of an NaCl solution, one observes, at the cathode, the evolution of H_2 and the accumulation of NaOH in the solution around the cathode. Again the explanation is that the principal current-carrying cation is less easily discharged than is an ion from water. The cathode reaction can be represented as

$$H_2O \rightarrow H^+ + OH^-$$

and

$$H^+ + e^- \rightarrow \tfrac{1}{2}H_2$$

or again in a combined manner as

$$H_2O + e^- \rightarrow OH^- + \tfrac{1}{2}H_2$$

The migration of Na^+ ions produces the observed NaOH. Thus, *a difficultly discharged cation leads to the decomposition of water at the cathode by the uptake of electrons and the production of* OH *and* H_2.

More complicated electrode reactions do occur, but the features of electrolytic solutions that are to be studied in this chapter can be dealt with in terms of electrode reactions of these three types.

Electrolyses of the type illustrated here were extensively and quantitatively studied as early as 1820 by Faraday. He was led to the important conclusion that *one equivalent of product is produced by the passage of* 96,500 *coulombs of current for an electrolyte and for any electrode reaction*. Now it can be recognized that 96,500, *or more accurately* 96,493, *coulombs is the charge of an Avogadro's number of electrons*. Faraday's result is understandable because an Avogadro's number of electrons added to or removed from a reagent will produce an equivalent weight of product.

The quantity of charge that corresponds to a chemical equivalent is of enough importance to merit a name, and the unit of a faraday is introduced as

$$1 \text{ faraday} = 96,493 \text{ coulombs}$$

A faraday is an Avogadro's number of electrons just as a mole is an Avogadro's number of molecules. The principal significance of the faraday is that it is the amount of charge that produces an equivalent of chemical change.

This electrochemical quantity can be related to our often used value of 4.8×10^{-10} esu as the charge of an electron. An esu of charge is related to the coulomb through the velocity of light; i.e.,

$$1 \text{ coulomb} = 3 \times 10^{10} \text{ esu}$$

The value of the electronic charge can therefore be calculated from the value of the faraday and Avogadro's number as

$$e = \frac{96,493 \times 3 \times 10^{-10}}{6.023 \times 10^{23}} = 4.80 \times 10^{-10} \text{ esu}$$

Before leaving this introduction to electrolysis, it seems necessary, in view of the analyses to follow, to emphasize that in all electrochemical processes all parts of the chemical system remain essentially neutral. This can be illustrated by a simple calculation of the force that would be necessary to hold an Avogadro's number of positively charged ions a distance of 1 cm from an equal number of negative ions. The force of attraction between a positive ion and a negative ion, immersed in water, is

$$\frac{(e)(e)}{\epsilon r^2}$$

and that between all the positive and all the negative particles is

$$\frac{(Ne)(Ne)}{\epsilon r^2}$$

$$\frac{(4.8 \times 10^{-10})^2 (6.02 \times 10^{23})^2}{(78)(1)^2} = 1 \times 10^{27} \text{ dynes}$$

Recollection of the relation 1 atm $\cong 10^6$ dynes/sq cm shows that this force is 10^{21} atm, or about 10^{22} lb/sq in. No such force could be maintained between different parts of a solution. It must be concluded that such a charge separation can occur only at molecular dimensions, as in an NaCl ion pair, and that no macroscopic charge separations are produced in solution.   It is sometimes helpful to check that an analysis of an electrochemical process obeys this neutrality rule.

16-10. Transference Numbers.   Now that the general features of electrode processes have been mentioned, the details of the passage of the electric current through the body of the solution can be investigated.   The flow of either the positive ions or the negative ions, or both, might be responsible for conduction processes, and the first goal is the determination of the fraction of the current carried by each ion in a given electrolyte.   For this purpose the *transference numbers* t_+ and t_- are introduced according to the definitions

t_+ = fraction of current carried by cation

t_- = fraction of current carried by anion

These definitions imply the relation

$$t_+ + t_- = 1 \tag{22}$$

In metal conductors all the current is carried by the electrons, and for such conductors one could write $t_- = 1$ and $t_+ = 0$.   For solutions of electrolytes it is clearly difficult to guess what fraction of the current is carried past some position in the electrolyte by the cations and what fraction by the anions. One method, known as the *Hittorf method*, for measuring transference numbers will now be illustrated by two examples.

A schematic diagram of a cell marked off into three compartments is shown in Fig. 16-6.   In practice a cell of the type shown in Fig. 16-7 can be used, and the three compartments that can be drained off correspond to those marked off by the dotted lines of Fig. 16-6.   The following treatment will show that transference numbers can be deduced from the analysis for the amount of electrolyte in the separate compartments following passage of a measured amount of current through the cell.

Consider an experiment in which a cell such as that of Fig. 16-6 or 16-7 is filled with an HCl solution and 1 faraday of charge is passed through the cell. The electrode processes, indicated in Fig. 16-6, were given in the preceding

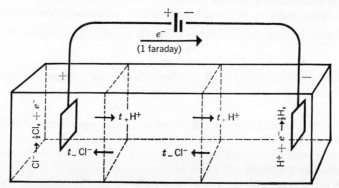

Fig. 16-6. Transference numbers for HCl by the Hittorf method.

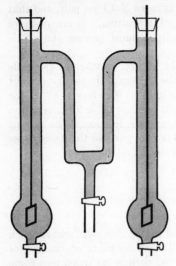

Fig. 16-7. Hittorf transference-number apparatus.

section. The current is carried across the dotted sections by the flow of ions, and, in view of the definitions of t_+ and t_-, the passage of 1 faraday of charge across these sections is accomplished by the flow of t_+ equivalents of H^+ to the right and t_- equivalents of Cl^- to the left. The net flow across these sections is then $t_+ + t_- = 1$ equivalent of ions, which corresponds to 1 faraday of charge. It is clear from Fig. 16-6 that the number of equivalents of HCl in the central compartment should not be changed by the passage of current.

Consider now the changes that occur in the cathode portion. The change in equivalents of H^+ and Cl^- due to ion migrations is shown by the transfers across the dotted line. In addition to migration, however, there is a removal of one equivalent of H^+ at the electrode by the reaction

$$H^+ + e^- \rightarrow \tfrac{1}{2}H_2$$

The net cathode-compartment changes for the passage of 1 faraday are calculated as

Change in equivalents of H^+ = electrode reaction + migration effect
$$= -1 + t_+$$
$$= t_+ - 1 = -t_- \text{ equivalents}$$
Change in equivalents of Cl^- = electrode reaction + migration effect
$$= 0 - t_-$$
$$= -t_-$$

Passage of 1 faraday of current results, therefore, in the removal of t_- equivalents of HCl from the cathode portion.

In a similar manner, the changes in the anode compartment are calculated as

Change in equivalents of H^+ = electrode reaction + migration effect
$$= 0 - t_+$$
$$= -t_+$$
Change in equivalents of Cl^- = electrode reaction + migration effect
$$= -1 + t_-$$
$$= t_- - 1 = -t_+$$

The net effect around the anode is the removal of t_+ equivalents of HCl.

It should be noticed that the analysis is in terms of the changes in the number of equivalents, and not concentration. The volume of the compartments is, as we shall see, not critical.

This calculation suggests a method introduced by Hittorf for determining transference numbers. The procedure consists in filling a cell like that of

Fig. 16-7 with the HCl solution and, first, without passage of current, draining the compartments and analyzing for the number of equivalents of HCl in each compartment.   The number of equivalents would be calculated from the concentrations and compartment volumes.   The cell is then refilled with the same solution, and a measured number of coulombs of current are passed.   The compartments are then drained and analyzed to give the number of equivalents in each and, from this, the change in equivalents in each compartment.

If not too large an amount of current is passed and if no mixing of the compartment solutions occurs, it will be found, in accordance with the previous treatment, that the number of equivalents in the central compartment will be unchanged.   The changes in the number of equivalents in either of the electrode compartments allow the determination of the transference numbers of H^+ and Cl^-.

In practice, of course, an amount of current much less than 1 faraday is passed through the cell.   The observed changes in the electrode compartments can, however, be used to calculate the change expected per faraday of charge passed through the cell.   These data can then be used directly with the type of analysis indicated above to give t_+ and t_-.

The treatment is much the same when more complicated electrode processes occur.   The electrolysis of a solution of $CuSO_4$ will illustrate this.   Again consider the effect of the passage of 1 faraday of charge.   The electrode reactions and transfers between the compartments are shown in Fig. 16-8. Again the middle compartment will experience no net change.

At the cathode the addition of 1 faraday of charge discharges one equivalent of Cu^{++} according to the electrode reaction

$$\tfrac{1}{2}Cu^{++} + e^- \rightarrow \tfrac{1}{2}Cu$$

The changes in the number of equivalents of the species involved in the cathode compartment are

$$\text{Change in equivalents of } Cu^{++} = \text{electrode reaction} + \text{migration effect}$$
$$= -1 + t_+$$
$$= t_+ - 1 = t_-$$

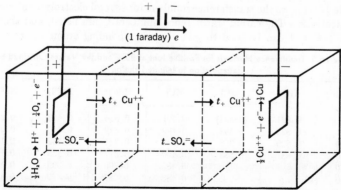

Fig. 16-8. Transference numbers for $CuSO_4$ by the Hittorf method.

Change in equivalents of $SO_4^=$ = electrode reaction + migration effect
$$= 0 - t_-$$
$$= -t_-$$

The net effect is the loss of t_- equivalents from the cathode compartment per faraday of charge passed through the cell.

At the anode the electrode reaction was seen to be

$$\tfrac{1}{2}H_2O \rightarrow \tfrac{1}{4}O_2 + H^+ + e^-$$

and the changes in all ionic species affected by the passage of current can be deduced as

Change in equivalents of Cu^{++} = electrode reaction + migration effect
$$= 0 - t_+$$
$$= -t_+$$

Change in equivalents of $SO_4^=$ = electrode reaction + migration effect
$$= 0 + t_-$$
$$= +t_-$$
$$= 1 - t_+$$

Change in equivalents of H^+ = electrode reaction + migration effect
$$= +1 + 0$$

These ionic changes can be expressed as the gain of one equivalent of H_2SO_4 and the loss of t_+ equivalent of $CuSO_4$. One sees that this corresponds to a net change of $1 - t_+$ equivalents of $SO_4^=$. An analysis for the change, in the number of equivalents either of Cu^{++} or of $SO_4^=$, could be used to calculate the transference numbers. Thus the decrease in number of equivalents of Cu^{++} per faraday of charge gives t_+, from which one obtains $t_- = 1 - t_+$. Alternatively, the increase in the number of equivalents of $SO_4^=$ per faraday of charge gives t_-, from which $t_+ = 1 - t_-$ is also calculated.

Other methods are available for the determination of transference numbers, but the detailed look at the conduction process that the Hittorf method requires makes this method sufficient to illustrate the determination of these quantities.

Table 16-5 shows the transference numbers for several electrolytes at various concentrations. The cation transference numbers t_+ are listed, and the relation $t_+ + t_- = 1$ can be used to give the corresponding anion values. This

Table 16-5. Transference Numbers for Positive Ions at 25°C and the Values Obtained by Extrapolation to Infinite Dilution*

Normality	HCl	NaCl	KCl	LiCl	BaCl₂	NaOH
0	0.821	(0.394)	0.491	0.336	0.443	0.290
0.01	0.825	0.392	0.490	0.329	0.440	0.203
0.05	0.829	0.388	0.490	0.321	0.432	0.189
0.10	0.831	0.385	0.490	0.317	0.425	0.183
0.50	.....	....	0.489	0.300	0.399	0.169
1.00	.....	....	0.488	0.287	0.379	0.163

* From L. G. Longsworth, *J. Am. Chem. Soc.*, **57**: 1185 (1935); **60**: 3070 (1938).

table shows that both positive and negative ions carry the current through the solution and that they do so to approximately the same extent.

It is important to notice that the transference numbers show some concentration dependence, particularly for electrolytes with highly charged ions. The relative conductance contributions of the ions are therefore a function of concentration, as would be expected, for example, from ionic interactions such as are recognized by the Debye-Hückel theory.

Knowledge of the values of transference numbers lets us proceed to a discussion of other ionic properties.

16-11. Ionic Conductances.   Values can now be obtained for the contributions that the individual ions of an electrolyte make to the equivalent conductance.   The empirical law of Kohlrausch implies that at infinite dilution the equivalent conductance can be interpreted in terms of such ionic contributions and that the contributions of an ion are independent of the other ion of the electrolyte.

At infinite dilution, therefore, it is profitable to write

$$\Lambda_0 = \lambda_0^+ + \lambda_0^- \tag{23}$$

where λ_0^+ and λ_0^- are the *equivalent ionic conductances at infinite dilution*. Since the transference numbers give the fraction of the total current carried by each ion, i.e., the fraction of the total conductance that each ion contributes, we can write

$$\lambda_0^+ = t_+^0 \Lambda_0 \quad \text{and} \quad \lambda_0^- = t_-^0 \Lambda_0 \tag{24}$$

where t_+^0 and t_-^0 are the transference numbers extrapolated to infinite dilution.

Table 16-6 shows some values for these limiting equivalent ionic conductances.   An immediate use of such tabulated values is the calculation of the limiting equivalent conductance of a weak electrolyte without the addition and subtraction procedure of Sec. 16-3.

In a formal manner one can use the data for the equivalent conductance and the transference numbers at concentrations other than that of infinite dilution to obtain values of λ^+ and λ^- at these higher concentrations.   At such concentrations, however, the law of independent migration of the ions fails,

Table 16-6. Equivalent Ionic Conductances and Ionic Mobilities at Infinite Dilution and 25°C*
[Sq cm/(sec)(volt)]

Ion	λ_0^+	v_+^0	Ion	λ_0^-	v_-^0
H^+	349.82	36.3×10^{-4}	OH^-	198.0	20.5×10^{-4}
Li^+	38.69	4.01×10^{-4}	Cl^-	76.34	7.91×10^{-4}
Na^+	50.11	5.19×10^{-4}	I^-	76.8	7.95×10^{-4}
K^+	73.52	7.61×10^{-4}	CH_3COO^-	40.9	4.23×10^{-4}
Ag^+	61.92	6.41			
NH_4^+	73.4	7.60×10^{-4}	SO_4^-	79.8	8.27×10^{-4}
Ca^{++}	59.50	6.16×10^{-4}			
La^{3+}	69.6	7.21×10^{-4}			

* Data from D. A. MacInnes, "The Principles of Electrochemistry," Reinhold Publishing Corporation, New York, 1939.

and the conductance is really a property of the electrolyte rather than of the individual ions of the electrolyte. This means that an ionic conductance calculated for a Cl⁻ ion, for example, in a 1 M HCl solution, will be different from that deduced for the Cl⁻ ion in a 1 M NaCl solution. The concept of ionic conductances is really valuable therefore only at infinite dilution.

Rather than trying to understand the different current-carrying properties of the ions of Table 16-6 in terms of ionic conductances, we proceed now to obtain an even more fundamental ionic property: the velocity with which the ions travel through the solution under the influence of the applied electric field.

16-12. Ionic Mobilities. Consider a cell of the type used to introduce the concept of equivalent conductance. Such a cell, it will be recalled, consists of two electrodes 1 cm apart and of cross-section area A such that an amount of solution that contains one equivalent of electrolyte is held between the electrode. A distorted picture of such a cell is shown in Fig. 16-9.

For an applied voltage $\mathcal{U}$ a current I will flow through the cell. These electrical quantities are related by

$$I = \frac{\mathcal{U}}{R} \qquad \text{or} \qquad I = \Lambda\mathcal{U} \tag{25}$$

since the conductance of such a cell is the equivalent conductance of the electrolyte. At infinite dilution the current can be attributed to the independent flow of positive and negative ions, and one can write

$$\begin{aligned} I &= \Lambda_0\mathcal{U} = (\lambda_0^+ + \lambda_0^-)\mathcal{U} \\ &= \lambda_0^+\mathcal{U} + \lambda_0^-\mathcal{U} \\ &= I_+ + I_- \end{aligned} \tag{26}$$

This flow of current through the cell can also be analyzed in terms of the details of the ion movements in the cell. Since the cell contains one equivalent of electrolyte, there will be N/Z_+ positive ions present and N/Z_- negative ions present, where N is Avogadro's number and Z_+ and Z_- are the charges of the ions of the electrolyte. The average velocities with which the ions

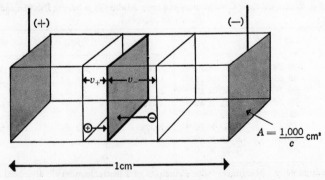

Fig. 16-9. Diagram for ionic-mobility calculation.

move to their respective electrodes under the influence of the applied voltage are represented by v_+ and v_-. The current passing a cross section of the cell can now be obtained in terms of these ionic quantities and the applied voltage.

For an ion to cross the shaded cross section of Fig. 16-9 within 1 sec it must start within a distance v_+ or v_- cm from the cross section. (The ions travel a distance v_+ or v_- in 1 sec.) In 1 sec, therefore, all the positive ions in the right rectangular compartment and all the negative ions in the left compartment will have crossed the boundary. Since these rectangular volumes have widths v_+ and v_- and the cell has a width of 1 cm, the volumes will contain fractions $v_+/1$ and $v_-/1$ of the total number of positive and negative ions in the cell. We can write, therefore,

$$\text{(No. positive ions crossing boundary)}/\text{sec} = \frac{N}{Z_+}\frac{v_+}{1} = \frac{Nv_+}{Z_+}$$

$$\text{(No. negative ions crossing boundary)}/\text{sec} = \frac{N}{Z_-}\frac{v_-}{1} = \frac{Nv_-}{Z_-}$$

The current corresponding to these flow rates is obtained by multiplying by the ion charges eZ_+ and eZ_- to give

$$\text{(Positive charge crossing)}/\text{sec} = I_+ = eZ_+\frac{Nv_+}{Z_+} = eNv_+$$

$$\text{(Negative charge crossing)}/\text{sec} = I_- = eZ_-\frac{Nv_-}{Z_-} = eNv_-$$

For an infinitely dilute solution, if the average ionic velocities in the electric-field direction are represented as v_+^0 and v_-^0, comparison with Eq. (26) gives

$$\mathcal{V}\lambda_0^+ = eNv_+^0 \qquad \text{and} \qquad \mathcal{V}\lambda_0^- = eNv_-^0 \tag{27}$$

Furthermore, the substitution $eN = \mathcal{F}$ can be made to yield, finally,

$$v_+^0 = \frac{\lambda_0^+\mathcal{V}}{\mathcal{F}} \qquad \text{and} \qquad v_-^0 = \frac{\lambda_0^-\mathcal{V}}{\mathcal{F}} \tag{28}$$

The average velocity with which an ion moves toward an electrode under the influence of a potential of 1 volt applied across a 1-cm cell is known as the *ionic mobility*. The ionic mobility is calculated, as Eq. (28) shows, by dividing the ionic conductance, as listed in Table 16-6, by the value of the faraday. These mobility results are also shown in Table 16-6.

The most remarkable feature of the data of Table 16-6 is, perhaps, the high values for the mobilities of the H^+ and OH^- ions compared with those of all the other ions. Since the proton is present as an H_3O^+ ion and since both the H_3O^+ and OH^- ions are expected to be highly solvated, an explanation cannot be given in terms of the size of these ions. A mechanism of the type suggested originally by von Grotthuss in 1805 to explain conduction by all electrolytes appears now to be applicable, but only to the H_3O^+ and OH^- ions. Figure 16-10 shows how a series of transfers of protons between neighboring water molecules can have the effect of moving either an H^+ or an OH^- through the solution. The high mobilities of H^+ and OH^- and the fact that they are the dissociation products of the solvent are seen to be related. In other solvents, where such a mechanism could not operate, these ions would show mobilities more in line with those of the other ions.

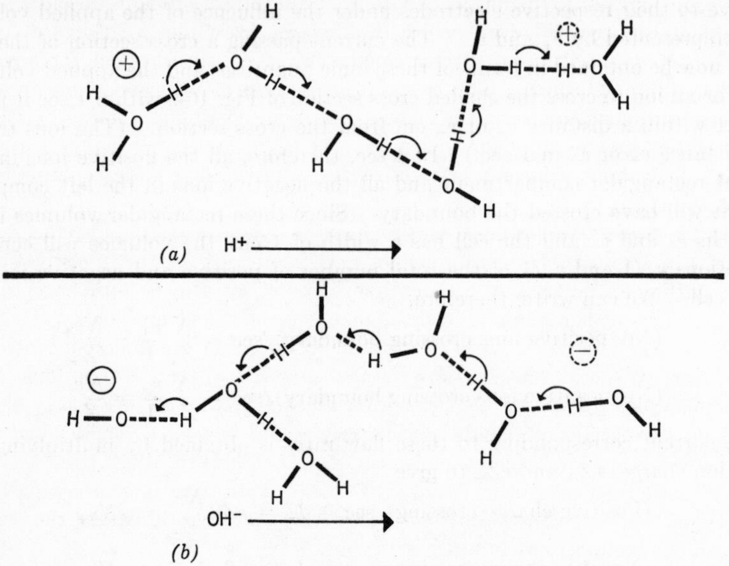

Fig. 16-10. Movement of (a) H⁺ and (b) OH⁻ by the Grotthuss mechanism. The charges outlined by dotted circles are formed as a result of the series of proton transfers.

The actual values of the mobilities of the other ions in aqueous solution are difficult to understand. The high degree of solvation expected for the small ions, such as Li^+, and for the highly charged ions, such as La^{3+}, apparently works against the expected dependence of mobility on size and charge. A better understanding of the ionic world than we now have would be necessary before the fairly small variation of mobility such as that shown in Table 16-6, except for H⁺ and OH⁻, could be interpreted in terms of the properties of the solvated ions.

It is interesting to compare the mobilities of ions with the velocities previously found for molecules of a gas. For a voltage of 100 volts placed across electrodes 1 cm apart, for instance, ions would migrate according to the mobility data of Table 16-6, with a velocity of about 0.05 cm/sec. It would take a typical ion 20 sec to travel the distance of 1 cm. This quantity is to be compared with molecular speeds in gases of about 10,000 cm/sec, as deduced in Chap. 2. We conclude, therefore, that the path of an ion under the influence of an electric field is a slow, devious trek of a cumbersome solvated ion through the interfering solvent molecules. This would be explained also by saying that the electric field that is conveniently applied to a solution is not an overwhelming factor in the affairs of ions. The ions are to be thought of as having only a slight directional component imposed on their random motions.

This takes us as far as we can go in our nonthermodynamic study of the behavior and nature of ions in solution. Many facets remain obscure. The problems that existed even before the days of Arrhenius with regard to the extent of dissociation of strong electrolytes are still unsolved for any but rather dilute solutions. The extent of solvation of ions and even an exact interpretation of this term, in view of the rapid coming and going of solvent molecules, remain an open question. Thus, although we have learned a great deal about solutions of electrolytes, a great deal more remains to be discovered.

16-13. Some Applications of Conductance Measurements. Previously the results of conductance measurements have been used for the investigation of the nature of electrolytes in solution. There are also a number of direct applications of conductance measurements to chemical problems. The usefulness of conductance arises from its dependence on the ionic concentration and from its special sensitivity to the concentration of H^+ and OH^- ions. The complications recognized by Debye and Hückel that stand in the way of simple interpretations of conductance experiments can be avoided when solutions with very low ionic concentrations are studied. In other cases conductance measurements can be used without a quantitative interpretation being made of the ionic concentrations. Three examples will illustrate the uses to which conductance measurements are put.

Example 1. *Conductimetric Titrations.* An acid-base titration, using HCl and NaOH, for example, can be performed in a conductivity cell and the change of conductance followed as the base is added to the acid. Results such as those shown in Fig. 16-11 are obtained. This behavior depends on

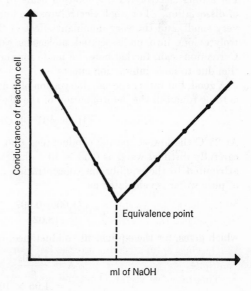

Fig. 16-11. The form of the conductimetric titration curve of HCl with NaOH.

Conductance of reaction cell

Equivalence point

ml of NaOH

the high ionic conductances of H^+ and OH^- compared with the salt ions Na^+ and Cl^-. Initially the H^+ concentration is large, and as the titration proceeds, the concentration of this ion decreases up to the equivalence point and is replaced by the less conducting Na^+ ion. At the equivalence point, where for a strong acid and base the concentration of H^+ and OH^- are both only 10^{-7}, the conductance is due to the Na^+ and Cl^- ions. As further base is added, the OH^- concentration builds up and the conductance increases.

If the base is added as a concentrated solution so that the volume does not change appreciably during the titration, the concentration of H^+ and OH^- will vary, except very near the equivalence point, in a linear manner with the amount of base added. The equivalence point can then be conveniently taken as the intersection of the two straight lines that can be drawn.

For titrations involving a weak acid or a weak base the behavior is not quite so simple, but the conductance still provides a useful means for following the titration.

Of particular value is the fact that the conductance is derived from the measured resistance of the cell. The change in resistance as the titration proceeds can be used in an instrumental method for following the course of the titration automatically.

Example 2. Degree of Ionization of Weak Electrolytes. The complications of ionic interactions and solvation tend to spoil the Arrhenius relation

$$\alpha = \frac{\Lambda}{\Lambda_0}$$

For strong electrolytes this relation leads to erroneous values for the degree of dissociation. For weak electrolytes the ionic concentrations are sometimes very small, and the very dominant effect of the association of the weak-electrolyte ions into undissociated molecules can be studied with little error. Corrections can, furthermore, be made for the variation of Λ with concentration due to ionic interaction effects.

A good, but rather special, illustration of a use of conductance measurements is to be found in the determination of the dissociation constant of water

$$H_2O \rightleftharpoons H^+ + OH^-$$

At 25°C the lowest specific conductance that can be obtained with the most carefully distilled water is 0.58×10^{-7} ohm^{-1}, and this conductance must be attributed to the equilibrium concentration of H^+ and OH^-. The molarity of pure water is calculated as

$$c = \frac{(1,000)(0.997)}{18.02} = 55.3$$

which gives, for the equivalent conductance, the result

$$\Lambda = \frac{1,000\kappa}{c}$$
$$= 1.05 \times 10^{-6}$$

The equivalent conductance expected for completely dissociated water is calculated as

$$\Lambda_0 = \lambda_0^{H^+} + \lambda_0^{OH^-}$$
$$= 547.8$$

The degree of dissociation of water at 25°C is therefore

$$\alpha = \frac{\Lambda}{\Lambda_0} = \frac{1.05 \times 10^{-6}}{547.8} = 1.9 \times 10^{-9}$$

and the ionic concentrations are

$$[H^+] = [OH^-] = \alpha c = 1.05 \times 10^{-7}$$

The familiar ion product for water is then determined as

$$K_w = [H^+][OH^-] = 1.1 \times 10^{-14}$$

The very low concentration of ions makes the Arrhenius relation $\alpha = \Lambda/\Lambda$ quite valid, and the value obtained for K_w is therefore reliable.

Example 3.   The Ionic Concentrations Produced by Sparingly Soluble Salts. A large number of salts are sufficiently insoluble in water to make a chemical analysis of their solubility quite difficult.   Information on the concentration of the ions in solution in equilibrium with the solid can be obtained from measurements of the conductance of a saturated solution.   For the salt **MX**, for example, the solubility product

$$[M^+][X^-]$$

can then be deduced.   For very insoluble salts the concentration of ions in solution will again be low enough so that the conductance can be taken as a measure of ionic concentrations.

The frequently referred to example of an insoluble salt that can be studied in this way is AgCl.   The specific conductance of a saturated solution at 25°C is given, after subtraction of the specific conductance of the water itself, as

$$\kappa = 2.28 \times 10^{-6} \text{ ohm}^{-1}$$

The conductance of one equivalent at infinite dilution is obtained from the data of Table 16-6, which are deduced from measurements on more soluble electrolytes.   Thus

$$\Lambda_0 = \lambda_0^{Ag^+} + \lambda_0^{Cl^-}$$
$$= 61.9 + 76.3 = 138.2 \text{ ohm}^{-1}$$

Since the solubility of AgCl is quite low, the equivalent conductance of a saturated solution will be little different from that at infinite dilution.   Thus one can use Eq. (8) to write, for the saturated solution,

$$\Lambda = \Lambda_0 = \frac{1,000\kappa}{c}$$

or

$$c = \frac{1,000\kappa}{\Lambda_0} = \frac{1,000(2.28 \times 10^{-6})}{138.2} = 1.65 \times 10^{-5}$$

The solubility product is then calculated as

$$K_{sol} = [Ag^+][Cl^-] = (1.65 \times 10^{-5})^2 = 2.72 \times 10^{-10}$$

Such a calculation assumes that the Debye-Hückel effects are negligible, a good assumption at ion concentrations of 10^{-5}, and that the conducting ionic species are Ag^+ and Cl^-. Such a treatment is disturbed if, for example, complex ions such as Ag_2Cl^+ or $AgCl_2^-$ are present but is not affected by any ion pairs or higher neutral association species. If such species are important, however, the solubility of the electrolyte would not be simply given by the concentrations of the Ag^+ or Cl^- ions.

Problems

1. The specific conductance of a 0.1 M KCl solution at 25°C is 0.01289 ohm^{-1}/cm. What are the conductance and the resistance of a conductance cell for which the electrodes have an effective area of 2.037 sq cm and are separated by a distance of 0.531 cm?

Ans. 20.2 ohms.

2. The resistance of a conductance cell filled with 0.01 M KCl solution is found to be 8.30 ohms at 25°C. What is the cell constant l/A for the cell?

3. A cell, whose resistance when filled with 0.1 M KCl is 192.3 ohms, is measured to be 6,363 ohms when filled with 0.003186 M NaCl solution. All measurements are at 25°C. What are the specific and the equivalent conductance of the NaCl solution?

Ans. $\Lambda = 122.2$ ohm^{-1}.

4. The limiting equivalent conductance of NH_4Cl at 25°C is 149.7; that of NaOH is 247.8. Calculate, with the aid of Table 16-2, the limiting equivalent conductance of NH_4OH, and compare with the value reported in Table 16-2.

5. Show, from the expression for the equilibrium constant in terms of the concentration of the electrolyte and the degree of dissociation α for an electrolyte AB, that as the concentration approaches zero the value of α approaches unity regardless of the value of K.

6. The limiting equivalent conductance of NaOH is 247.8. With this datum and the results of Table 16-2 calculate what the equivalent conductance of a completely ionized mole of water, at infinite dilution in the solvent water at 25°C, would be.

Ans. 547.6.

7. Calculate, according to the Arrhenius theory, the degree of dissociation and the dissociation equilibrium constants for $CuSO_4$ up to a 1 M concentration at 25°C, from the data of Table 16-2.

8. Calculate, according to the Arrhenius theory, the degree of dissociation and the dissociation equilibrium constants for the reaction $H_2SO_4 \rightleftharpoons 2H^+ + SO_4^=$, up to a 0.1 M concentration, from the data of Table 16-2.

9. Calculate the degree of dissociation and the equilibrium constants for the dissociation of $CuSO_4$ from the van't Hoff i factors of Table 15-7, and compare with the results of Prob. 7.

10. Calculate the degree of dissociation and the equilibrium constants for the dissociation of H_2SO_4 from the van't Hoff i factors of Table 15-7, and compare with the values obtained in Prob. 8.

11. Calculate the degree of ionization and the dissociation equilibrium constants for $K_3Fe(CN)_6$ from the data of Table 15-7.

12. Calculate the energy required to dissociate 1 mole of NaCl in the solvents acetonitrile and benzene, which have dielectric constants 39 and 2.3, respectively. Ignoring the entropy change accompanying dissociation, and the solvation of the ions, which is in fact very important in the polar solvents, use Boltzmann's distribution to deduce the relative amounts of dissociated and undissociated NaCl in benzene, in acetonitrile, and in water at 25°C.

13. Using data given in previous tables and the result that 17.8 kcal of heat is liberated when 1 mole of HCl is added to a large amount of water, calculate the energy change for the reaction

$$H^+(g) + Cl^-(g) \xrightarrow{H_2O} H^+(aq) + Cl^-(aq)$$

What is the difference in the hydration energy of Na^+ and H^+ in dilute aqueous solutions?

Ans. $\Delta H = -345$ kcal, 162 kcal.

14. Show by a diagram the process by which current is carried through a solution of NaCl, and show the electrode reactions that carry the current between the solutions and the electrodes when an aqueous solution of NaCl is electrolyzed.

15. Show by a diagram the conduction process through an aqueous solution and at the electrodes when an aqueous solution of Na_2SO_4 is electrolyzed between inert electrodes.

Write the electrode reactions.

If 0.342 amp is passed through such a cell for 4.80 min, how many equivalents and how many moles of the products of electrolysis will be obtained?

Ans. Equiv. of $O_2 = 0.00102$; moles of $O_2 = 0.00025$.

16. What volumes of gases, measured at 1 atm pressure and 0°C, will be obtained at the electrodes when 1,000 coulombs of charge is passed through an aqueous NaOH solution?

17. What weight of copper will be deposited at the cathode by the passage of 0.473 amp of current through a solution of copper sulfate for 5 min?

Ans. 0.0467 g.

18. A determination of the transference numbers of cadmium and iodide ions by Hittorf gave the following data:

A stock solution of CdI_2 was prepared, and its concentration was determined, by precipitation of iodide as AgI, to be 0.002763 g of CdI_2 per gram of solution.

Another sample of this solution was placed in a Hittorf transference-number cell, and current was passed through the cell. It was found that 0.03462 g of cadmium was deposited at the cathode by the passage of the current. Furthermore, analysis of the anode-compartment solution, which weighed 152.643 g, indicated the presence of 0.3718 g of cadmium iodide.

(a) What are the electrode reactions?

(b) Indicate diagrammatically, using t_+ and t_- to represent the transference numbers, the changes in the amounts of the ions in the anode and cathode compartments as a result of migration and electrode reactions.

(c) How many coulombs of charge were passed through the cell in the experiment?

(d) What are the transference numbers of Cd^{++} and I^- in this CdI_2 solution?

(e) What was the change in the equivalents of CdI_2 in the cathode compartment?

Ans. (d) $t_+ = 0.443$.

19. A solution is prepared so that it is 0.01 M in HCl and 0.1 M in NaCl.

(a) Can the fraction of current carried by the various ions of this solution be rigorously deduced from any of the data given in this chapter?

(b) Estimate a value for the fraction of the current carried by each of the ions.

20. In aqueous solutions chlorine is hydrolyzed, to some extent, according to the reaction

$$Cl_2 + H_2O \rightleftharpoons H^+ + Cl^- + HOCl$$

The hypochlorous acid is not appreciably dissociated. At 25°C the specific conductance of a 0.0246 M chlorine solution was found to be 0.0068 ohm^{-1}/cm. What is the fraction of Cl_2 that has been hydrolyzed?

Ans. 0.65.

21. The following equivalent conductances of sodium propionate at 25°C have been reported by Belcher [*J. Am. Chem. Soc.*, **60**: 2746 (1938)]:

Conc. (moles/liter)	0.002178	0.004180	0.007870	0.01427	0.02597
A	82.53	81.27	79.72	77.88	75.64

(a) What is the limiting conductance of sodium propionate?

(b) What, in view of the data of Table 16-2, is the limiting conductance of propionic acid?

(c) At a concentration of 1 M the equivalent conductance of propionic acid is 1.4 cm^2 ohm^{-1}. What is the degree of dissociation of propionic acid in this solution?

(d) Estimate from the curves of Fig. 16-2 or the data of Table 16-2 what effect the interionic interaction would have on this conductance measurement.

(e) Deduce a dissociation constant for propionic acid.

22. Calculate the ionic mobility of the Cl^- ion at an ionic concentration of 0.1 g ion/liter from the transference numbers for the electrolytes HCl, NaCl, KCl, and $BaCl_2$ of Table 16-5 and the equivalent conductances of Table 16-2. Recognize that only at infinite dilution is the ionic conductance a property of the ion rather than the electrolyte.

23. The specific conductance, at 18°C, of a saturated silver iodide solution is 1.19 × 10^{-5} greater than the water used to prepare the solution. The sum of the limiting equivalent conductances of Ag^+ and IO_3^- is found, from measurements on more soluble salts, to be 87.3. Calculate the solubility product $[Ag^+][IO_3^-]$ at 18°C. What value of the solubility is obtained if it is assumed that no species other than Ag^+ and IO_3^- are present in the solution?

24. At 18°C the specific conductance of water saturated with CaF_2 is 3.86 × 10^{-5} and that of the water used in the preparation of this solution is 0.15 × 10^{-5}. The equivalent ionic conductances at infinite dilution of Ca^{++} and F^- are 51.0 and 47.0, respectively. Calculate the solubility product for CaF_2 and, assuming only Ca^{++} and F^- ions in solution, the solubility of CaF_2.

Ans. Solubility = 0.0148 *g*/liter.

17

The Thermodynamics of
Nonideal Systems

Most of the detailed applications of thermodynamics have so far been restricted to systems that can be said to be ideal. The equilibrium state of a system has been dealt with in Sec. 7-5, for example, on the assumption that the reacting species could be treated as ideal gases. Now that we are engaged in the study of condensed phases, it is desirable to be able to extend the methods of thermodynamics to such systems. For solutions, and particularly for solutions of electrolytes, deviations from ideal behavior are almost always very large. It is particularly important, therefore, that an introduction be given to the way in which thermodynamic treatments can be applied to such systems.

The empirical criterion for ideal behavior is obedience of the system to some relatively simple and general law. Adherence to the ideal-gas law $PV = nRT$ or Raoult's law $P = P°N$, for example, is taken as constituting ideal behavior. For systems obeying such laws one finds correspondingly simple thermodynamic relations. Of particular importance is the dependence of free energy on the state of the system. For 1 mole of an ideal gas, for example, the dependence of free energy on pressure was found to be simply given by

$$G_2 - G_1 = RT \ln \frac{P_2}{P_1} \tag{1}$$

Similar simple free-energy relations occur for solutions that are said to be ideal.

The molecular basis for ideal behavior can be recognized from our previous discussions of ideal gases and ideal solutions. Either an absence of all interactions between the particles of the system or an absence of all special interactions between the particles of the components of the system was seen to be necessary. Deviations from the ideal laws occur, for example, when the

549

van der Waals' factors become appreciable in gases or when the solute molecules of solutions interact with one another. Our recognition of the importance of ionic interactions in electrolytic solutions in the previous chapter indicates that nonideal behavior is to be expected for all but infinitely dilute electrolyte solutions. Such infinitely dilute solutions can, as we shall see, be said to behave ideally, and this behavior in no way requires an absence of solute-solvent interactions. The principal subject of study in this chapter on non-ideality will be aqueous solutions of electrolytes.

As in previous thermodynamic treatments a molecular explanation of the thermodynamic quantities will be introduced. In particular, the theory of Debye and Hückel will lead to an understanding of the way in which ionic interactions act to cause ionic solutions to deviate from ideal behavior.

Again it is necessary to emphasize that such molecular interpretations are not essential to the thermodynamic development. Such a development can be made without any inquiry into the molecular reason for the behavior of the system. Attempts to understand the thermodynamic functions introduced to handle nonideal systems lead us, however, to a better understanding of molecular and ionic interactions.

The thermodynamic methods that are used to treat nonideal effects will, at first, appear to be unnecessarily devious. The working out of a few problems should, however, make the new features familiar and should reveal the merits of the system. The behavior of gases, solvents, and solutes will be treated separately. It will be recognized that the procedure is essentially the same for all three cases.

NONIDEAL GASES

17-1. Relation of Free Energy to Pressure. The starting point for most of the derivations of this chapter is the equation relating free energy to pressure. This relation is therefore derived again.

The defining equations for free energy and enthalpy give, for 1 mole of any system,

$$G = H - TS \tag{2}$$
$$G = E + PV - TS \tag{3}$$

For any infinitesimal change in the system one has

$$dG = dE + P\,dV + V\,dP - T\,dS - S\,dT \tag{4}$$

For such a process performed reversibly $T\,dS = dq$, and for one in which the only work done is that of expansion $P\,dV = dw$. Equation (4) then reduces, with the use of the first law, to

$$dG = V\,dP - S\,dT \tag{5}$$

Of particular interest at the moment are constant-temperature processes. For these, Eq. (5) can be put in the form

$$\left(\frac{\partial G}{\partial P}\right)_T = V \tag{6}$$

Thus, if the pressure of a system is changed and if this pressure change is performed reversibly and is accompanied by no temperature change and only $P\, dV$ work, the free energy change can be calculated according to Eq. (6).

The integral form of Eq. (6), for the free-energy difference at two pressures P_1 and P_2, is

$$\Delta G = G_2 - G_1 = \int_{P_1}^{P_2} V\, dP \tag{7}$$

It is important to recognize that so far we have depended only on the first and second laws of thermodynamics and that stipulations have been made as to the kind of process but not as to the nature of the system, which may be gaseous, liquid, or solid and ideal or nonideal.

17-2. Ideal Gases. A review of the free-energy development that follows the assumption of the ideal-gas laws will help to clarify the procedure to be adopted in later sections.

For 1 mole of an ideal gas one has the equation of state

$$V = \frac{RT}{P} \tag{8}$$

If this relationship can be assumed, Eq. (7) can be integrated to give

$$\Delta G = G_2 - G_1 = RT \int_{P_1}^{P_2} \frac{dP}{P} = RT \ln \frac{P_2}{P_1} \tag{9}$$

In Chap. 7 we found it convenient to tabulate the free energies of gases measured at 1 atm pressure. These free energies were called *standard free energies*, and the state of 1 atm pressure is known as the *standard state*. Thus we arbitrarily chose the *standard state for ideal gases to be that of* 1 *atm pressure*.

Free energies at other pressures are obtained from the tabulated standard free energies by means of Eq. (9). If the standard free energy is represented by $G°$ and the free energy at some pressure P is denoted by G, one writes Eq. (9) as

$$G - G° = RT \ln \frac{P}{1} = RT \ln P$$

or

$$G = G° + RT \ln P \tag{10}$$

where P must be expressed in atmospheres since the term really implies P divided by 1 atm.

It is this expression, it will be recalled, that led to the very important relation between the free-energy change of a reaction and the equilibrium constant in Sec. 7-5.

Now we must attempt to obtain a relation for the free energy of a gas that does not obey the $PV = RT$ law.

17-3. Nonideal Gases: The Fugacity. A straightforward treatment of nonideal gases would use a suitable equation of state, such as van der Waals' equation, to allow the integration of Eq. (7) to be performed. Such a procedure, however, results in an expression for ΔG that is a complicated and unwieldy function of P. Such a function is not at all suitable, for example, for the deduction of the free-energy–equilibrium-constant relation that corresponds to Eq. (34) of Chap. 7.

A more satisfactory procedure is to introduce a new function called the *fugacity* and denoted by f, which is *defined* so that for any gas

$$G_2 - G_1 = RT \ln \frac{f_2}{f_1} \tag{11}$$

Comparison of this expression with Eq. (9) shows that for an ideal gas the fugacity is exactly equal to the pressure. For a nonideal gas the fugacity will be a function similar to, but not equal to, the pressure.

The procedure insists on the free-energy equation having the convenient form of Eq. (11). The nonideal complications are hidden in the fugacity. It is necessary now to show how the fugacity can be deduced for nonideal gases.

A number of manipulations are necessary. The thermodynamic equation

$$G_2 - G_1 = \int_{P_1}^{P_2} V \, dP \tag{9}$$

is valid for all types of systems and can be used here. The quantity RT/P can be added to and subtracted from the right side of Eq. (9) to give

$$
\begin{aligned}
G_2 - G_1 &= \int_{P_1}^{P_2} \left(\frac{RT}{P} + V - \frac{RT}{P} \right) dP \\
&= \int_{P_1}^{P_2} \frac{RT}{P} \, dP + \int_{P_1}^{P_2} \left(V - \frac{RT}{P} \right) dP \\
&= RT \ln \frac{P_2}{P_1} + \int_{P_1}^{P_2} \left(V - \frac{RT}{P} \right) dP
\end{aligned}
\tag{12}
$$

Fugacities are defined by Eq. (11) so that

$$G_2 - G_1 = RT \ln \frac{f_2}{f_1}$$

and comparison of Eq. (12) and Eq. (11) gives

$$RT \ln \frac{f_2}{f_1} = RT \ln \frac{P_2}{P_1} + \int_{P_1}^{P_2} \left(V - \frac{RT}{P} \right) dP$$

or

$$RT \ln \frac{f_2/P_2}{f_1/P_1} = \int_{P_1}^{P_2} \left(V - \frac{RT}{P} \right) dP \tag{13}$$

Now it can be recognized that all gases tend to become ideal as the pressure approaches zero. That is

$$\frac{f}{P} \to 1 \quad \text{as} \quad P \to 0$$

If we let P_1 go to zero, f_1/P_1 becomes unity. Furthermore, if P and f are written instead of P_2 and f_2 for the general pressure and fugacity in Eq. (13), we have

$$RT \ln \frac{f}{P} = \int_{P=0}^{P=P} \left(V - \frac{RT}{P} \right) dP \tag{14}$$

It is this expression that allows, if sufficient data on the values of V as a function of pressure are available, the determination of f/P and therefore of f at some pressure P.

Before preceeding to an illustration of the evaluation of fugacities it is necessary again to recognize that a reference, or standard, state is a useful concept.

17-4. The Standard State for Nonideal Gases: The Activity and Activity Coefficient.

In a formal manner one can again identify the standard state by the superscript ° and write

$$G - G° = RT \ln \frac{f}{f°} \tag{15}$$

where $G°$ and $f°$ are the free energy per mole and the fugacity at the standard state. The ratio $f/f°$ is sufficiently frequently encountered to merit a name and symbol. The *activity* is introduced and is represented by a. It is defined as

$$a = \frac{f}{f°} \tag{16}$$

With this notation Eq. (15) becomes

$$G - G° = RT \ln a \tag{17}$$

Just as the reference, or standard, state could be arbitrarily chosen for ideal gases, so also can it be for nonideal gases. It is convenient to choose the standard state as that for which *the fugacity is* 1 *atm.* This corresponds to the treatment for ideal gases. Furthermore, since many gases are essentially ideal at 1 atm pressure, the state with unit pressure will be the same as that with unity fugacity for these gases.

With the definition $f° = 1$ atm, the activity becomes numerically equal to fugacity since

$$a = \frac{f}{f°} \qquad \text{becomes} \qquad a = \frac{f}{1} = f$$

The standard free energy $G°$, such as appears in Eq. (15), for example, is interpreted as the free energy per mole of gas when the gas is at a fugacity of 1 atm.

Comparison of the equations

$$G - G_{f=1} = RT \ln a \qquad \text{real gases} \tag{17}$$
$$G - G_{P=1} = RT \ln P \qquad \text{ideal gases} \tag{10}$$

suggests the introduction of the *activity coefficient* γ defined as

$$\gamma = \frac{a}{P} \qquad \text{and} \qquad a = \gamma P \tag{18}$$

where again it must be remembered that a is dimensionless and P is really $P/1$ atm so that γ is dimensionless. The thermodynamic expression for real gases can then be written as

$$G - G° = RT \ln \gamma P \tag{19}$$

The special convenience of γ is that it shows explicitly the importance of the nonideality. For ideal gases the activity coefficient is always unity since then $f = P$ and $a = f/f° = P/P° = P/1 = P$. The deviation of γ from unity shows directly the nonideality of the gas.

Evaluation of γ, or of a, can be done through Eq. (14). The choice of the standard state of 1 atm fugacity makes $a = f/1$, and therefore $\gamma = a/P = f/P$. Equation (14) becomes

$$RT \ln \gamma = \int_0^P \left(V - \frac{RT}{P} \right) dP \tag{20}$$

A considerable manipulation, some of it unnecessary, has been done. One should recognize that only the fugacities need have been introduced. The activity is convenient because it relates the fugacity to that at the standard state. The activity coefficient is convenient because it shows explicitly the nonideality of the system. In practice all three quantities f, a, and γ are encountered.

17-5. Evaluation of Activity Coefficients. Any of the three functions f, a, or γ can be evaluated. Most convenient of these is γ, and Eq. (20) can be used for its evaluation. Data must be available for the actual molar volumes V as a function of pressure up to the pressure at which the activity coefficient is desired. Such data can be fitted by an equation of state and this equation used to replace V in Eq. (20) by a function of P and T. Integration over the pressure range then gives the desired result.

In practice it is often more satisfactory to perform the integration graphically. The activity-coefficient data of Table 17-1 have been obtained, for example, from the listed values of V and P by the graphical evaluation of the integrals of column 4.

A very convenient condensation of the gas-imperfection data necessary for

Table 17-1. The Activity Coefficients for Methane at $-50°C$*

P (atm)	V (liters/mole)	$\dfrac{RT}{P}$	$V - \dfrac{RT}{P}$	$\displaystyle\int_0^P \left(V - \frac{RT}{P} \right) dP$	γ
1	18.3	18.3	0	0.00	1.000
10	1.747	1.830	−0.083	−0.41	0.980
20	0.830	0.915	−0.085	−1.54	0.920
40	0.366	0.458	−0.092	−3.27	0.835
60	0.208	0.305	−0.097	−5.16	0.755
80	0.129	0.229	−0.110	−7.28	0.672
100	0.092	0.183	−0.091	−9.35	0.600
120	0.076	0.153	−0.077	−11.03	0.548
160	0.064	0.114	−0.055	−13.49	0.479
200	0.0591	0.0915	−0.0324	−15.15	0.436
300	0.0525	0.0610	−0.0085	−17.10	0.393
400	0.0491	0.0458	+0.0033	−17.27	0.388
600	0.0451	0.0305	+0.0146	−15.36	0.432
800	0.0427	0.0229	+0.0198	−11.89	0.522
1,000	0.0410	0.0183	+0.0227	−7.59	0.661

* Data from "Chemical Engineers' Handbook," 3rd ed., McGraw-Hill Book Company, Inc., New York, 1950.

the integration of Eq. (20) is furnished by the law of corresponding states discussed in Sec. 1-11.   This law states that, in terms of the reduced variables P_R, V_R, and T_R, all gases follow the same equation of state.   This means that at the same value of P_R and T_R all gases have the same imperfection and therefore the same activity coefficient.   Furthermore the variation of the compressibility factor Z with the reduced pressure has been represented for various values of T_R in Fig. 1-9.   These data are all that are necessary for the integration of Eq. (20).   Figure 1-9 gives values of

$$Z = \frac{PV}{RT} \tag{21}$$

from which one obtains

$$V = \frac{RT}{P} Z \tag{22}$$

and Eq. (20) can be written as

$$RT \ln \gamma = \int_0^P \left(\frac{RT}{P} Z - \frac{RT}{P} \right) dP$$

$$= RT \int_0^P (Z - 1) \frac{dP}{P}$$

or

$$\ln \gamma = \int_0^P (Z - 1) \frac{dP}{P}$$

$$= \int_0^P (Z - 1) \frac{dP_R}{P_R} \tag{23}$$

The data of Z as a function of P_R, for a given value of T_R, allows graphical integrations to be performed to give the curves of Fig. 17-1.

17-6. Equilibrium Constants for Systems of Real Gases.   It will be recalled that in Sec. 7-5 the equilibrium constant for the reaction

$$aA + bB \rightleftharpoons cC + dD \tag{24}$$

was related to the standard free energies and the pressures of the reagents, all assumed to be ideal gases.   The derivation started with the ideal-gas expression,

$$G = G° + RT \ln P \tag{10}$$

for each component and deduced that the usual equilibrium-constant expression involving the gas pressures should be a constant, i.e.,

$$\frac{(P_C)^c (P_D)^d}{(P_A)^a (P_B)^b} = K_p \tag{25}$$

For gases that are not necessarily ideal the corresponding free-energy relation for each of the reagents is

$$G = G° + RT \ln a \tag{17}$$

and repetition of the derivation of Sec. 7-5 leads to the expectation that the expression that must be constant is

$$\frac{(a_C)^c (a_D)^d}{(a_A)^a (a_B)^b} = K_{th} \tag{26}$$

where K_{th} is written as the value of this term since it represents the thermo-

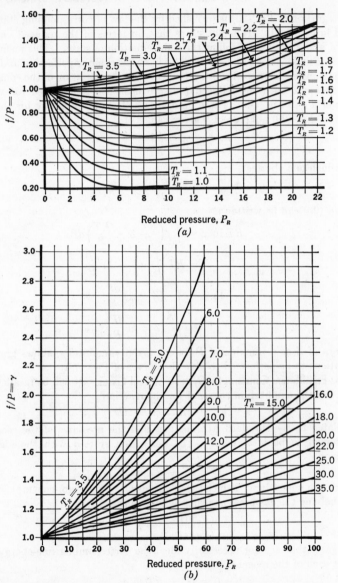

Fig. 17-1. The activity coefficient for gases as a function of the reduced pressure $P_R = P/P_C$ and the reduced temperature $T_R = T/T_C$. [*From R. H. Newton, Ind. Eng. Chem.,* **27**: 302 (1935).] (a) At pressures and temperatures near the critical point. (b) At high temperatures and pressures. (*"Chemical Engineers' Handbook,"* 3d ed., *McGraw-Hill Book Company, Inc., New York, 1950.*)

dynamic equilibrium constant and is independent of any assumption of the behavior of the gaseous reagents.

This thermodynamically exact expression is more frequently used with the substitution, for each of the components, of the relation $a = \gamma P$, which gives

$$K_{th} = \frac{(\gamma_C P_C)^c(\gamma_D P_D)^d}{(\gamma_A P_A)^a(\gamma_B P_B)^b}$$

$$= \frac{(\gamma_C)^c(\gamma_D)^d}{(\gamma_A)^a(\gamma_B)^b} K_p \qquad (27)$$

Only for ideal gases will all the activity coefficients be unity, and only then will $K_{th} = K_p$. Furthermore the activity-coefficient term may well change as the pressure of the system or as the individual pressures change. Then only K_{th} can be expected to be a constant for any arrangement of pressures and the pressure term K_p will be a nonconstant "equilibrium constant."

An illustration of the effects of nonideality on the equilibrium constant is provided by the industrially important reaction

$$\tfrac{1}{2}N_2 + \tfrac{3}{2}H_2 \rightleftharpoons NH_3$$

The reaction is generally carried out at high pressures and at a temperature of about 450°C. One is interested in knowing the equilibrium pressure of NH_3 for various pressures of N_2 and H_2.

The data of Table 17-2 for the pressure expression K_p have been calculated from the measured partial pressures of the components at equilibrium. It is clear that at these pressures nonideal effects are important and that use of the ideal expression K_p is not satisfactory.

For the individual reagents the activity coefficients can be calculated, as indicated in the previous section, from the critical data. In this way one can obtain the activity-coefficient expression listed in Table 17-2 and the results for K_{th}. A considerable improvement in constancy is seen to result from the use of activities rather than pressures.

The result at the highest pressure indicates that our treatment as entered in Table 17-2 is still somewhat approximate. This does not imply any approximation in the formation of K_{th} but stems from the evaluation of the activity coefficients for the individual gases as if they were pure gases at the

Table 17-2. Equilibrium Constants for the Reaction $\tfrac{1}{2}N_2 + \tfrac{3}{2}H_2 \rightleftharpoons NH_3$ at 450°C*

Total pressure (atm)	Equilibrium pressures (atm)			K_p	$\dfrac{\gamma_{NH_3}}{\gamma_{N_2}^{1/2}\gamma_{H_2}^{3/2}}$	K_f
	NH$_3$	N$_2$	H$_2$			
10	0.204	2.44	7.35	0.0066	0.99	0.0065
50	4.58	11.3	34.1	0.0068	0.94	0.0064
100	16.35	20.9	62.7	0.0072	0.88	0.0063
300	106.5	48.4	145	0.0088	0.69	0.0061
600	322	69.5	208	0.0129	0.50	0.0064
1,000	694	76.5	229	0.0231	0.43	0.0099

* Data from A. T. Larson, *J. Am. Chem. Soc.*, **46**: 367 (1924).

total pressure of the reaction system. A correct treatment would make use of PVT data on nonreacting gas mixtures so that the activity coefficients of the components in the mixture could be evaluated. The treatment illustrated in Table 17-2 is, however, satisfactory at all but very high pressures.

SOLVENTS

17-7. Solvents in Ideal Solutions. Again it is helpful to recall the treatment that is applied to ideal systems. For ideal solutions, and for the solvent of dilute nonideal solutions, Raoult's law relates the vapor pressure of the solvent to the mole fraction of the solvent according to

$$P = xP^\circ \tag{28}$$

where, since only solvents are considered here, the subscript has been dropped and P is the vapor pressure of the solvent in the solution of solvent mole fraction x and P° is that of the pure solvent.

An appreciable simplification is introduced by making the often satisfactory assumption that the equilibrium vapor behaves as an ideal gas. The free energy of the vapor is equal to that of the solution with which it is in equilibrium, and, for two solutions having vapor pressure P_1 and P_2, one can write for the free-energy difference for 1 mole of the solvent in the solutions

$$G_2 - G_1 = RT \ln \frac{P_2}{P_1} \tag{29}$$

Raoult's law allows the substitutions $P_1 = x_1 P^\circ$ and $P_2 = x_2 P^\circ$ to be made. For ideal behavior, therefore, one has, for 1 mole of solvent,

$$G_2 - G_1 = RT \ln \frac{x_2}{x_1} \tag{30}$$

For solvents the usual interest is in the change of the free energy of the solvent from the value for the pure material. It is convenient, therefore, to take *the pure solvent as the standard state*. The free energy for $x = 1$ is therefore denoted by G°, and Eq. (30) gives the free energy G for the solvent in a solution of mole fraction x as

$$G - G^\circ = RT \ln \frac{x}{1}$$
$$= RT \ln x$$

or $$G = G^\circ + RT \ln x \tag{31}$$

Again the ideal behavior and the choice of standard state lead to a convenient, simple expression for the free energy of the solvent.

17-8. Nonideal Solutions: The Fugacity, Activity, and Activity Coefficient. Solutions that do not obey Raoult's law, and therefore solutions for which Eq. (30) cannot be written, must now be dealt with. As for gases, a convenient form for the free-energy equation is insisted upon by writing

$$G_2 - G_1 = RT \ln \frac{f_2}{f_1} \tag{32}$$

and thereby defining the fugacity function. For ideal solutions the fugacity can be equal to the mole fraction of the solvent, but for nonideal solutions it will be somewhat different.

Comparison of the free energy of the solvent with some reference solution, which will be the pure solvent, leads to the notation

$$G - G^\circ = RT \ln \frac{f}{f^\circ} \tag{33}$$

where G° and f° are the free energy and fugacity of the reference, or standard, state. Again it is a matter of convenience to introduce the *activity*, which is defined as

$$a = \frac{f}{f^\circ} \tag{34}$$

and leads to the expression

$$G - G^\circ = RT \ln a \tag{35}$$

As for ideal solutions it is convenient to choose the pure solvent as the standard state. With this choice, G° is the free energy of 1 mole of pure solvent, and the activity of the solvent in a solution is the fugacity compared with the fugacity of the pure solvent. The treatment is a little different from that applied to gases. There the standard state was that of unit fugacity. Now the fugacity of the standard state is not specified, but the standard state is described. Thus the quantity $a = f/f^\circ$ can be used without a statement as to the value of f°.

Comparison of the ideal-solution equation

$$G - G^\circ = RT \ln x \tag{31}$$

with the thermodynamic, general expression

$$G - G^\circ = RT \ln a \tag{35}$$

suggests the introduction of an activity coefficient defined by

$$\gamma = \frac{a}{x} \qquad \text{or} \qquad a = \gamma x \tag{36}$$

Again the activity coefficient shows, by its variation from unity, the nonideality of the solution. Since the solvents of all solutions that are sufficiently dilute obey Raoult's law, and, therefore, Eq. (31), the value of γ approaches unity for the solvent of any solution as the solute concentration approaches zero.

The most direct way of evaluating the fugacity ratio f/f°, that is, the activity a, or the activity coefficient γ is to measure the partial pressure of the solvent over the solution and the vapor pressure of the pure solvent. If the vapor behaves as an ideal gas, one can measure the partial pressure of the equilibrium solvent vapor and obtain the free energy of 1 mole of solvent as

$$G - G^\circ = RT \ln \frac{P}{P^\circ} \tag{37}$$

Combination with the alternative expression for this free energy difference

$$G - G^\circ = RT \ln a \tag{35}$$

gives

$$a = \frac{P}{P^\circ} \tag{38}$$

from which, if desired, one can calculate

$$\gamma = \frac{1}{x} \frac{P}{P^\circ} \tag{39}$$

The vapor-pressure data of the liquid-vapor equilibrium diagrams of Chap. 14 provide the necessary data for such a calculation of activity coefficients. Some activities for systems that were studied previously are shown in Table 17-3. It should be apparent that the previous discussion of the factors that

Table 17-3. The Activity Coefficients of Solvents on the Assumption of Ideal-vapor-phase Behavior*

Solvent, benzene; solute, toluene, 20°C		Solvent, toluene; solute, benzene, 20°C	
Mole fraction, benzene	Activity, benzene	Mole fraction, toluene	Activity, toluene
1.00	1.00	1.00	1.00
0.67	0.65	0.77	0.78
0.55	0.54	0.57	0.55
0.43	0.46	0.45	0.47

Solvent, acetone; solute, CHCl₃, 35°C		Solvent, CHCl₃; solute, acetone, 35°C	
Mole fraction, acetone	Activity, acetone	Mole fraction, CHCl₃	Activity, CHCl₃
1.00	1.00	1.00	1.00
0.94	0.94	0.92	0.91
0.88	0.87	0.81	0.76
0.73	0.70	0.66	0.55
0.63	0.57	0.58	0.48
0.51	0.42	0.49	0.38

Solvent, CH₃OH; solute CCl₄, 35°C		Solvent, CCl₄; solute, CH₃OH, 35°C	
Mole fraction, CH₃OH	Activity, CH₃OH	Mole fraction, CCl₄	Activity, CCl₄
1.00	1.00	1.00	1.00
0.91	0.95	0.98	0.99
0.79	0.88	0.87	0.97
0.66	0.84	0.64	0.94
0.49	0.80	0.51	0.92
0.36	0.78	0.34	0.87

* The data are from T. Bell and R. Wright, *J. Phys. Chem.*, **31**: 1884 (1927); J. von Zawidzki, *Z. physik. Chem.*, **35**: 129 (1900); J. Timmermans, "Physico-chemical Constants of Binary Systems," vol. 2, Interscience Publishers, Inc., New York, 1959.

act in nonideal solutions to raise or lower the free energy compared with that of an ideal solution could equally well have been used to explain the deviations of the activity coefficients from unity.

SOLUTES

17-9. Solutes of Dilute Solutions.   The behavior expected for a nonelectrolyte solute of any dilute solution is obedience to Henry's law,

$$P = kc \tag{40}$$

relating the solute vapor pressure to the solute concentration through an empirical constant k.   For dilute solutions any concentration units can be used and here molar concentrations will be assumed.   Obedience to Henry's law gives, for the free energy of a solute at concentration c_2 compared with that at c_1, the relation

$$G_2 - G_1 = RT \ln \frac{P_2}{P_1}$$

$$= RT \ln \frac{c_2}{c_1} \tag{41}$$

The reference state for solutes of solutions that satisfactorily obey this relation up to molar concentrations is that of *unit molar concentration*.   Thus one writes

$$G - G^\circ = RT \ln \frac{c}{c_0} \tag{42}$$

and $c_0 = 1$ to give

$$G - G^\circ = RT \ln \frac{c}{1\ M}$$

$$= RT \ln c \tag{43}$$

where G° is the free energy per mole of solute at a concentration of $1\ M$.

Obedience to Henry's law is therefore sufficient to lead to another convenient free-energy relation.

17-10. Solutes in Nonideal Solutions.   The free energy of solutes at two different concentrations in solutions that may be too concentrated to conform to Raoult's law can be formally written as

$$G_2 - G_1 = RT \ln \frac{f_2}{f_1} \tag{44}$$

The fugacity is again a function that is defined so that the convenient form of the free-energy equation is maintained.   For solutions obeying Raoult's law the fugacity can be identified with the molar concentration.

In terms of some standard state with free energy G° and fugacity f°, the free energy of the solute in some solution of different concentration for which the solute fugacity is f can be expressed as

$$G - G^\circ = RT \ln \frac{f}{f^\circ} \tag{45}$$

Since it is this difference between the solute free energy in some solution and that of the solute in the standard-state solution that is most frequently of interest, it is again convenient to introduce the activity a as

$$a = \frac{f}{f^\circ} \tag{46}$$

which allows Eq. (45) to be written as

$$G - G^\circ = RT \ln a \tag{47}$$

The value of G° has not yet been given since the standard state has not been specified. In a way that corresponds to the treatment of gases, one chooses *the standard state, for free-energy determination, as that for which the solute has a fugacity of 1 mole/liter*. The free energy G° is therefore that of 1 mole of solute in a solution for which the solute fugacity is unity. For an ideal solution the fugacity can be taken as equal to the molar concentration so that this procedure becomes identical to that adopted for Henry's-law solutes. For solutes in general the fugacity will be something like the molar concentration.

The standard states that are encountered in all types of systems can now be summarized. This is done in Table 17-4.

Comparison of the dilute-solution result

$$G - G^\circ = RT \ln c \tag{43}$$

with the more general thermodynamic expression

$$G - G^\circ = RT \ln a \tag{47}$$

suggests again the introduction of the *activity coefficient* defined as

$$\gamma = \frac{a}{c} \quad \text{or} \quad a = \gamma c \tag{48}$$

which leads to the free-energy equation

$$G - G^\circ = RT \ln \gamma c \tag{49}$$

For Henry's-law solutions $\gamma = 1$, but more generally the value will depend on the solute interactions and will deviate from unity.

For solutions in which γ for the solute takes on values different from unity, the concentration that gives unit fugacity is not immediately known. A number of methods will be dealt with later that determine both the free energy of the standard state and the activity coefficients of solutions of various concentrations.

Prime interest will be centered around ionic solutions. A number of special features are introduced when the solute is a dissociated electrolyte. Several sections must therefore be spent considering some aspects of these solutions.

17-11. Ion Activities. Because the ions of an electrolyte are looked upon as being the dissociation products of a neutral molecule, the activities and activity coefficients of the ions are given a special treatment.

Table 17-4. The Standard States for Use in Free-energy Calculations

Ideal gas	Pressure of 1 atm
Real gas	Fugacity of 1 atm
Pure liquid	Liquid at 1 atm pressure
Pure solid	Solid, in stable modification, at 1 atm pressure
Solvent of an ideal soln	Pure liquid solvent at 1 atm pressure
Solvent of a real soln	Pure liquid solvent at 1 atm pressure
Solute of an ideal soln	Solution in which the solute is at unit concentration
Solute of a real soln	Solution in which the solute has unit fugacity

Consider, to begin with, a simple electrolyte AB that dissociates as

$$AB \rightarrow A^+ + B^-$$

If one recalls the form of the equations written for the equilibria of such an electrolyte, the ionization of a weak acid or a weak base or the solubility of an insoluble salt, one recognizes that only the product

$$[A^+][B^-]$$

appears and that no thermodynamic study leads to the occurrence of a term involving only $[A^+]$ or only $[B^-]$. In a similar manner, if one deals with the thermodynamically more exact functions, the activities, one finds only the product

$$(a_{A^+})(a_{B^-})$$

usually written as

$$a_+ a_-$$

In view of the absence of any other arrangement of the activities it is convenient to introduce an average, or *mean activity* of the ions. A geometric mean is appropriate, and one writes

$$a_\pm = \sqrt{a_+ a_-} \tag{50}$$

so that
$$a_+ a_- = (a_\pm)(a_\pm) = (a_\pm)^2 \tag{51}$$

A similar treatment holds for activity coefficients. Since $a = \gamma c$, we have

$$a_+ a_- = (\gamma_+ c_+)(\gamma_- c_-) = \gamma_+ \gamma_- [A^+][B^-] \tag{52}$$

The activity coefficients also occur only as the product $\gamma_+ \gamma_-$, and the mean-activity coefficient is introduced as

$$\gamma_\pm = \sqrt{\gamma_+ \gamma_-} \tag{53}$$

More generally an electrolyte dissociates according to

$$A_x B_y \rightarrow x A^{(+)} + y B^{(-)}$$

The concentration term that occurs in thermodynamic treatments is

$$[A^{(+)}]^x [B^{(-)}]^y$$

and the corresponding activity term is written as

$$(a_+)^x (a_-)^y$$

Now the geometric mean gives the mean activity as

$$a_\pm = [(a_+)^x (a_-)^y]^{1/(x+y)}$$

or
$$(a_\pm)^{x+y} = (a_+)^x (a_-)^y \tag{54}$$

Similarly
$$\gamma_\pm = (\gamma_+^x \gamma_-^y)^{1/(x+y)}$$

or
$$\gamma_\pm^{x+y} = \gamma_+^x \gamma_-^y \tag{55}$$

A salt like Na_2SO_4, for example, would introduce into thermodynamic treatments the activity expression

$$(a_{Na^+})^2 (a_{SO_4^-})$$

which could be replaced by $(a_\pm)^3$. Similarly the activity-coefficient expression

$$\gamma_{Na^+}^2 \gamma_{SO_4^-}$$

could be replaced by the mean-activity-coefficient expression $\gamma_\pm^3$.

We shall see that these mean activities and activity coefficients are a considerable convenience and that their use loses nothing that is of thermodynamic concern. Furthermore, no thermodynamically exact method has been devised that allows the determination of the individual ion activities or activity coefficients.

17-12. Dependence of Activity Coefficients on Ionic Strength. Evaluation of activity coefficients for many systems, by means that we shall consider later, led Lewis and Randall to recognize that the mean-activity coefficient of the ions of an electrolyte can be related to a function of the concentration of charged particles in the solution. That such a relation exists reflects the fact that it is the ionic interactions that are primarily responsible for the nonideality of ionic solutes. Lewis and Randall introduced the *ionic strength* as a measure of the nonideality that the solution imposes on any dissociated electrolyte in the solution. Recognition of this function will, as we shall see, simplify our thermodynamic determinations of activity coefficients.

The ionic strength, denoted by μ, is a characteristic of the solution and is defined as

$$\mu = \frac{1}{2} \sum_i c_i Z_i^2 \tag{56}$$

where c_i is the concentration of the ith ion, Z_i is its charge, and the summation extends over all the ions in the solution. It is found empirically, and substantiated for dilute solutions by the theory of Debye and Hückel, that the ionic strength is a good measure of the interactions of all the ions of a solution with the ions of an electrolyte of the solution.

A few examples will illustrate the calculation of ionic strengths. In a solution containing only 0.01 M NaCl

$$\mu = \tfrac{1}{2}[(0.01)(1)^2 + (0.01)(1)^2] = 0.01$$

and for a single one-to-one electrolyte the ionic strength is therefore equal to the concentration. In a solution containing only 0.01 Na_2SO_4, where the concentration of Na^+ is 0.02 and that of SO_4^- is 0.01,

$$\mu = \tfrac{1}{2}[(0.02)(1) + (0.01)(2)^2] = 0.03$$

For a solution containing both 0.01 M NaCl and 0.01 M Na_2SO_4 the concentration of Na^+ is 0.03, of Cl^- is 0.01, and of SO_4^- is 0.01. The ionic strength of the solution is therefore

$$\mu = \tfrac{1}{2}[(0.03)(1)^2 + (0.01)(1)^2 + (0.01)(2)^2] = 0.04$$

It is important to keep in mind that the ionic strength is a property of the solution and is not a property of any particular ion in the solution.

Lewis and Randall were able to generalize their determinations of activity coefficients of ions of electrolytes into the following empirical statement: *In dilute solutions the activity coefficient of a given strong electrolyte is the same in all solutions of the same ionic strength.* In view of the tremendous number of different electrolyte solutions one might deal with, this rule is of great aid. Later we shall see how thermodynamic deductions of activity coefficients confirm this statement. We are now prepared to proceed with thermodynamic determinations of activity coefficients, but first a considerable digression is made in order to show how the Debye-Hückel theory leads to a theoretical expression for the mean-activity coefficient of an electrolyte in terms of the ionic strength of the solution.

For those who cannot afford the time that this digression requires it is enough to state that the Debye-Hückel theory recognizes the stabilizing effect on a particular ion of the excess of oppositely charged ions that tend, in spite of the random movement of the ions, to preferentially surround an ion of the opposite charge. The net result of the analysis for dilute solutions, less than about 0.01 M, is the important expression for the mean-activity coefficient of an electrolyte with anion charge Z_- and cation charge Z_+

$$\log \gamma_\pm = +0.5091 Z_+ Z_- \sqrt{\mu}$$

where Z_- is to be written as a negative number. Thus the Debye-Hückel theory predicts that $\log \gamma_\pm$ is negative and, therefore, that $\gamma_\pm$ is less than unity. The experimental results, for solutions of sufficiently low ionic strength, as shown in Sec. 14 and in the following chapter, are in good agreement with this theoretical expression.

*17-13. The Debye-Hückel Theory of Activity Coefficients. When some experimental determinations of activity coefficients are dealt with in the next section, it will be found that for fairly dilute solutions the activity coefficients are invariably less than unity. The free energy of a dissociated electrolyte in solution is therefore less than might be expected on the basis of its concentration. The Debye-Hückel theory attributes this free-energy lowering to an electrostatic stabilization of each ion, treated as a point charge, by the other ions that are present in the solution. This idea led Debye and Hückel to a quantitative explanation for the activity coefficients of ions in rather dilute solutions, i.e., less than about 0.01 M. The theory might appear to have had very limited success, being applicable only to such dilute solutions. It has, however, greatly influenced all subsequent ideas about ionic solutions. It is very worthwhile, therefore, to follow through the Debye-Hückel derivation in some detail.

It is necessary to present here only a very condensed version that takes in the important features of the theory but ignores many of the subtleties that are involved. Even so, the treatment is somewhat lengthy, but this is due to the use of simple steps rather than reliance on some useful but rather advanced mathematical relationships. The Debye-Hückel theory that leads to values for the activity coefficients of dissociated electrolytes in solution can be conveniently divided into several parts.

The Electrical Potential Surrounding a Charged Particle. We can start with the result of Sec. 10-7 that there are 4π lines of force emanating from a unit positive charge in vacuum. For a charge q in a dielectric ϵ the lines of force become, according to Sec. 10-8, $4\pi q/\epsilon$. Since one line of force per square centimeter corresponds to a unit electric field, the electric-field strength $\mathcal{E}$ at a distance r from the charge can be written as

$$\mathcal{E} = \frac{\text{lines of force}}{\text{cross-section area}}$$
$$= \frac{4\pi q/\epsilon}{4\pi r^2} = \frac{q}{\epsilon r^2} \tag{57}$$

A more detailed treatment shows that a similar result is obtained for the electric field at the surface of the sphere even if the charge q instead of being at the center of the sphere is spread out or dispersed within the sphere of radius r. Therefore for these spherically symmetric arrangements one can express the electric field at a distance r from a central point as

$$\mathcal{E} = \frac{\text{enclosed charge}}{\epsilon r^2} \tag{58}$$

If a uniform charge density ρ is assumed, the enclosed charge is $\frac{4}{3}\pi r^3 \rho$ and the electric-field intensity at r is

$$\mathcal{E} = \frac{\frac{4}{3}\pi r^3 \rho}{\epsilon r^2} = \frac{4}{3}\frac{\pi r \rho}{\epsilon} \tag{59}$$

A desired relation is obtained by multiplying both sides by r^2 and differentiating with respect to r to obtain

$$\frac{dr}{d}(r^2 \mathcal{E}) = \frac{d}{dr}\left(\frac{4}{3}\frac{\pi r^3 \rho}{\epsilon}\right) = \frac{4\pi r^2 \rho}{\epsilon}$$

or

$$\frac{1}{r^2}\frac{d}{dr}(r^2 \mathcal{E}) = \frac{4\pi \rho}{\epsilon} \tag{60}$$

Now the relation

$$\mathcal{E} = -\frac{d\mathcal{V}}{dr} \tag{61}$$

from Sec. 10-7 can be inserted to give the electrical potential $\mathcal{V}$ as a function of r and the charge density, i.e.,

$$\frac{1}{r^2}\frac{d}{dr}\left(r^2 \frac{d\mathcal{V}}{dr}\right) = -\frac{4\pi \rho}{\epsilon} \tag{62}$$

This expression might be recognized as the form of the Poisson equation appropriate to a spherically symmetric problem.

This result gives the potential in terms of a general charge distribution ρ. It is now necessary to consider the situation that arises for discrete charged particles such as occur in ionic solutions.

The Charge Distribution about the Reference Ion.   We consider now how the ions in a solution distribute themselves relative to one another. The two factors that play roles are the thermal jostlings and the electrical attractions between oppositely charged particles. Suppose that on the average there are n_i ions of the i type per unit volume. Around any positive ion there will be an increase in the concentration of negative ions and a decrease in the concentration of positive ions. These changes result from the ions moving to the energetically more favored regions, i.e., those in which their potential energy is low, and the tendency for this movement must compete with the random thermal motion.

Boltzmann's equation can be used to give the number of ions that on the average are a distance r from the positive charge. The energy of ions of charge $Z_i e$ in a potential of value $\mathcal{V}$ is $(eZ_i)\mathcal{V}$. If Z_i is positive, the energy is higher near the reference positive charge, and if Z_i is negative, the energy is lower, as illustrated in Fig. 17-2. Boltzmann's equation gives

$$n_i(r) = n_i e^{-(eZ_i \mathcal{V})/kT} \tag{63}$$

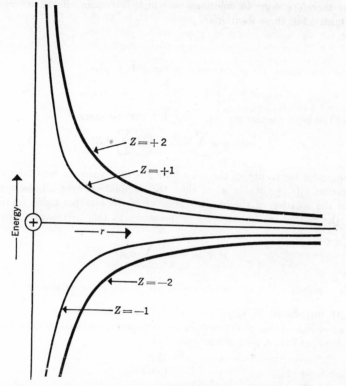

Fig. 17-2. The potential energy of charges as a function of their distances from a unit positive test charge.

where $n_i(r)$ is the number, or density, of ions at a distance r from the reference positive charge.

The charge density at a distance r from the unit positive charge can now be written as the ion density times the ion charges. This gives the charge density, which is a function of r, as

$$\rho(r) = (eZ_i)n_i(r)$$
$$= e\sum_i n_i Z_i e^{-eZ_i \mathcal{U}/kT} \tag{64}$$

The treatment is mathematically tractable, and the development is physically reasonable only if it is assumed that

$$eZ_i\mathcal{U} \ll kT \tag{65}$$

i.e., that the ionic interactions are less than the average thermal energy. Such is the case for dilute solutions. For more concentrated solutions the interionic attractions can more effectively overcome the thermal motion and associations occur that are not easily treated. The Debye-Hückel treatment applies therefore only to solutions in which interionic effects are not too important. For these solutions

$$\frac{eZ_i\mathcal{V}}{kT} \ll 1 \tag{66}$$

and one can expand the exponential of Eq. (64) to give

$$e^{-eZ_i\mathcal{V}/kT} = 1 - \frac{eZ_i\mathcal{V}}{kT} + \text{higher terms} \tag{67}$$

If all the higher terms are neglected, Eq. (64) becomes

$$\rho(r) = e \sum_i n_i Z_i - \frac{e^2\mathcal{V}}{kT} \sum_i n_i Z_i^2 \tag{68}$$

The electrical neutrality of the solution leads to a value of zero for the first summation. It is nothing more than the summation over all the types of ions in the solution of the average number of ith ions per cubic centimeter times the charge of the ith ion. Elimination of this necessarily zero term leaves

$$\rho(r) = -\frac{e^2\mathcal{V}}{kT} \sum_i n_i Z_i^2 \tag{69}$$

The expression $\sum_i n_i Z_i^2$ is very similar to, and can be related to, the ionic strength introduced by Lewis and Randall on an empirical basis. Since the number of ions of the ith type per cubic centimeter is related to the number of gram ions per liter c_i by the relation

$$n_i = \frac{Nc_i}{1{,}000} \tag{70}$$

where N is Avogadro's number, we have

$$\sum_i n_i Z_i^2 = \frac{N}{1{,}000} \sum_i c_i Z_i^2$$
$$= \frac{2N}{1{,}000} \mu \tag{71}$$

where μ is the ionic strength defined previously as

$$\mu = \frac{1}{2} \sum_i c_i Z_i^2 \tag{72}$$

With this notation the charge distribution about the central positive-reference ion is written, from Eq. (69), as

$$\rho(r) = -\frac{2Ne^2\mu\mathcal{V}}{1{,}000kT} \tag{73}$$

This relation, deduced from the specific considerations of the thermal agitation of ions counteracting the tendency of oppositely charged ions to attract one another, can be introduced into the more general equation [Eq. (62)] to eliminate $\rho(r)$ and give a relation for $\mathcal{V}$ in terms of the concentrations and ionic strength.

The Potential of the Reference Ion. Elimination of $\rho(r)$ from Eq. (62) by means of Eq. (73) leads to the relation

$$\frac{1}{r^2}\frac{d}{dr}\left(r^2\frac{d\mathcal{V}}{dr}\right) = \frac{8\pi Ne^2\mu\mathcal{V}}{1{,}000\epsilon kT} \tag{74}$$

or

$$\frac{d}{dr}\left(r^2\frac{d\mathcal{V}}{dr}\right) = \frac{8\pi Ne^2\mu}{1{,}000\epsilon kT}r^2\mathcal{V}$$
$$= \beta r^2\mathcal{V} \tag{75}$$

where β has been introduced as

$$\beta = \frac{8\pi Ne^2\mu}{1{,}000\epsilon kT} \tag{76}$$

Equation (75), known as the *Poisson-Boltzmann equation,* is a differential equation that can be solved to give $\mathcal{V}$ as a function of r. A certain amount of manipulation is necessary to put Eq. (75) in an easily soluble form.

Introduction of the function u, defined as

$$u = r\mathcal{V} \tag{77}$$

together with the relation

$$\frac{d\mathcal{V}}{dr} = \frac{d}{dr}\left(\frac{u}{r}\right) = \frac{1}{r}\frac{du}{dr} - \frac{u}{r^2} \tag{78}$$

gives

$$\frac{d}{dr}\left(r^2\frac{d\mathcal{V}}{dr}\right) = \frac{d}{dr}\left(r\frac{du}{dr} - u\right) = \frac{r\,d^2u}{dr^2} + \frac{du}{dr} - \frac{du}{dr} = r\frac{d^2u}{dr^2} \tag{79}$$

Substitution of this result for the left side of Eq. (75) and the relation $u = r\mathcal{V}$ in the right gives

$$\frac{d^2u}{dr^2} = \beta u \tag{80}$$

The solution of this form of Eq. (75) can be immediately verified to be of the form

$$u = Ae^{-\sqrt{\beta}r} + Be^{\sqrt{\beta}r} \tag{81}$$

which implies that the potential $\mathcal{V}$ has the form

$$\mathcal{V} = \frac{A}{r}e^{-\sqrt{\beta}r} + \frac{B}{r}e^{\sqrt{\beta}r} \tag{82}$$

At an infinite distance from the reference charge the ionic distribution will be undisturbed from neutrality, and the potential must be zero. This boundary condition requires $B = 0$ since

$$\lim_{r\to\infty}\frac{e^{\sqrt{\beta}r}}{r} \neq 0$$

Equation (82) can therefore be reduced to

$$\mathcal{V} = \frac{A}{r}e^{-\sqrt{\beta}r} \tag{83}$$

The constant A can be evaluated by recognizing that when the ionic strength is zero, and therefore $\sqrt{\beta}$ is zero, the potential about the reference positive charge is simply

$$\mathcal{V}_{\mu=0} = \frac{Ze}{\epsilon r} \tag{84}$$

where the positive charge is assumed now to have a charge Ze.

With $\beta = 0$, Eq. (83) gives

$$\upsilon = \frac{A}{r}\, e^{-(0)r} = \frac{A}{r}$$

and comparison with Eq. (83) shows that A must be identified as

$$A = \frac{Ze}{\epsilon} \tag{85}$$

The solution to the differential equation is therefore

$$\upsilon = \frac{Ze}{\epsilon r}\, e^{-\sqrt{\beta}\,r} \tag{86}$$

For dilute solutions the ionic strength will be small, and near the reference ion, which is the only region that is of interest,

$$\sqrt{\beta}\, r \ll 1$$

The exponential of Eq. (86) can therefore be expanded to give

$$\upsilon = \frac{Ze}{\epsilon r} (1 - \sqrt{\beta}\, r + \cdots) \tag{87}$$

$$\cong \frac{Ze}{\epsilon r} (1 - \sqrt{\beta}\, r) \tag{88}$$

or $$\upsilon = \frac{Ze}{\epsilon r} - \frac{\sqrt{\beta}\, Ze}{\epsilon} \tag{89}$$

We have obtained finally an expression for the potential-energy function about an ion in an ionic solution. It must be remembered that the potential function is defined as the work required to bring a unit positive charge to a distance r from the reference charge. For the present purpose this statement is better turned around to say that υ is the work that a unit positive charge can do as a result of its proximity to the reference charge. For an ion in a dielectric this available work is simply $Ze/\epsilon r$, the first term on the right of Eq. (89). The additional term on the right of Eq. (89) then must give the change in the amount of available work that is produced by the other ions in the solution. It is this term to which the Debye-Hückel theory has led. It is now necessary to relate this potential-energy term to the activity coefficient of the reference ion.

Relation of the Change in Potential Energy to the Activity Coefficient. The free energy of 1 mole of reference ions is written, in thermodynamic terms, as

$$\begin{aligned}
G - G^\circ &= RT \ln a \\
&= RT \ln c\gamma \\
&= RT \ln c + RT \ln \gamma
\end{aligned} \tag{90}$$

The right side suggests that the free energy, compared with the standard state, be thought of in terms of an ideal contribution corresponding to $RT \ln c$ and a nonideal contribution corresponding to $RT \ln \gamma$. Thus, one might write

$$G_{\text{ideal}} - G^\circ = RT \ln c \tag{91}$$

and $$\Delta G_{\text{nonideal}} = RT \ln \gamma \tag{92}$$

so that $$G = G_{\text{ideal}} + \Delta G_{\text{nonideal}}$$

It is the term for the nonideal-free-energy contribution that measures the change in free energy of the reference ions as a result of the nonideal effects. If the potential energy due to the ionic interactions can be related to a free-energy effect, this quantity can be identified with $RT \ln \gamma$.

The energy of any charge Q is given by the expression $\frac{1}{2}Q\mathcal{U}$, where $\mathcal{U}$ is the potential of the charge. This general electrostatic relation can be seen as follows: Imagine a charge and the potential associated with it to be gradually created. The work done in adding to the charge an amount dQ when the potential is $\mathcal{U}$ is given by

$$dw = \mathcal{U} \, dQ \tag{93}$$

This expression is analogous to the more frequently encountered result $dw = Q \, d\mathcal{U}$ in which a fixed charge moves through a potential difference. The potential in Eq. (93) is related to the charge, and it is sufficient here to write the proportionality equation

$$\mathcal{U} = (\text{const})Q \tag{94}$$

Substitution in Eq. (93) gives

$$dw = (\text{const})Q \, dQ \tag{95}$$

and

$$w = (\text{const}) \int_0^Q Q \, dQ = \frac{\text{const}}{2} Q^2 = \frac{1}{2}\mathcal{U}Q \tag{96}$$

The work that can be identified with the nonideal free energy is that which arises from the final term in the potential-energy expression for an ion in an ionic solution. One identifies w of Eq. (96) with $\Delta G_{\text{nonideal}}$, Q with the reference ion charge Ze, and $\mathcal{U}$ with the second term of Eq. (89). For an Avogadro's number of reference ions, therefore,

$$\Delta G_{\text{nonideal}} = \frac{1}{2}(Ze)\left(- \frac{\sqrt{\beta}\, Ze}{\epsilon} \right) N$$

$$= -\frac{1}{2} \frac{Z^2 e^2 \sqrt{\beta}\, N}{\epsilon} \tag{97}$$

This free-energy term is related to the activity coefficient [Eq. (92)]. Thus

$$\ln \gamma = -\frac{Z^2 e^2 \sqrt{\beta}\, N}{2RT\epsilon} \tag{98}$$

On substitution of the expression for β one obtains

$$\ln \gamma = -\left(\frac{e^2}{\epsilon kT} \right)^{\frac{3}{2}} \sqrt{\frac{2\pi N}{1{,}000}}\, Z^2 \sqrt{\mu} \tag{99}$$

This is the important limiting law, i.e., for dilute solutions, obtained by Debye and Hückel in 1923. It shows how the activity coefficient of an ion of charge Z can be calculated. It should be mentioned that our derivation has assumed a positive reference charge. The same result is obtained for a negative charge. Thus a positive value of Z or a negative value can be used in Eq. (99), and the same calculated value of the activity coefficient of the positive or negative ion will be obtained.

It is convenient to put numerical values in Eq. (99) for the special case of aqueous solutions at 25°C. Substituting values for the constants, and converting to logarithms to the base 10, gives

$$\log \gamma = -0.5091 Z^2 \sqrt{\mu} \tag{100}$$

More explicitly one writes the important results

$$\log \gamma_+ = -0.5091 Z_+^2 \sqrt{\mu} \tag{101}$$

and

$$\log \gamma_- = -0.5091 Z_-^2 \sqrt{\mu}$$

The Mean-activity Coefficient.   The thermodynamic expressions have been set up in terms of the mean-activity coefficient, and it is necessary therefore to have the Debye-Hückel prediction of the mean-activity coefficient as well as the predictions for individual ions.   Some manipulation is necessary.

The definition of a mean coefficient for an electrolyte $A_x B_y$, where the charge of A is Z_+ and that of B is Z_-, has been written as

$$\gamma_\pm = (\gamma_+^x \gamma_-^y)^{1/(x+y)} \tag{102}$$

which gives the logarithm of the mean coefficient as

$$\log \gamma_\pm = \frac{1}{x + y} \log (\gamma_x^x \gamma_-^y)$$

$$= \frac{1}{x + y} (x \log \gamma_+ + y \log \gamma_-) \tag{103}$$

The Debye-Hückel predictions for $\log \gamma_+$ and $\log \gamma_-$, if the charge of A is Z_+ and that of B is Z_-, can be inserted to give

$$\log \gamma_\pm = -\frac{0.5091 \sqrt{\mu}}{x + y} (x Z_+^2 + y Z_-^2) \tag{104}$$

Simplification results from the electrical-neutrality requirement for the electrolyte, i.e.,

$$x(Z_+) + y(Z_-) = 0 \tag{105}$$

A rearrangement trick consists in multiplying Eq. (105) by Z_+ to give

$$x Z_+^2 + y Z_+ Z_- = 0 \tag{106}$$

and Eq. (105) by Z_- to give

$$x_+ Z_+ Z_- + y Z_-^2 = 0 \tag{107}$$

Addition of these last two expressions and rearrangement gives

$$x Z_+^2 + y Z_-^2 = -Z_+ Z_-(x + y) \tag{108}$$

Use of this relation in Eq. (104) leads to the desired Debye-Hückel limiting-law prediction for the mean-activity coefficient for an electrolyte in aqueous solution at 25°C as

$$\log \gamma_\pm = +0.5091 Z_+ Z_- \sqrt{\mu} \tag{109}$$

It is understood that Z_- is a negative number and therefore that $\log \gamma_\pm$ is always negative and $\gamma_\pm$ is less than unity.

An example will illustrate the use of the Debye-Hückel equations for activity coefficients.   The thermodynamics of a salt such as $BaCl_2$ will introduce the expression

$$(a_{Ba^{++}})(a_{Cl^-})^2$$

or

$$\gamma_+ \gamma_-^2 [Ba^{++}][Cl^-]^2$$

which can also be written as

$$\gamma_\pm^3 [Ba^{++}][Cl^-]^2$$

The activity-coefficient term can be calculated, for solutions of low enough ionic strength.   As an example, assume a solution of $\mu = 0.01$.

First let us proceed by calculating the individual ionic activity coefficients. Thus, from Eq. (101),

$$\log \gamma_+ = -(0.5091)(2)^2 \sqrt{0.01} = -0.2036 = 0.7964 - 1$$

and $\gamma_+ = 0.626$

$$\log \gamma_- = -(0.5091)(-1)^2 \sqrt{0.01} = -0.0509 = 0.9491 - 1$$

and $\gamma = 0.890$

These give the activity-coefficient term

$$\gamma_+ \gamma_-^2 = (0.626)(0.890)^2 = 0.497$$

Calculation of the mean-activity coefficient directly from Eq. (109) gives

$$\log \gamma_\pm = (0.5091)(2)(-1) \sqrt{0.01} = -0.1018 = 0.8982 - 1$$

and $\gamma_\pm = 0.792$

The activity-coefficient term is then, as before,

$$\gamma_\pm^3 = 0.497$$

By either method the theory predicts that in a solution of 0.01 ionic strength

$$(a_{Ba^{++}})(a_{Cl^-})^2 = 0.497[Ba^{++}][Cl^-]^2 \tag{110}$$

The Debye-Hückel limiting law will be seen, when some experimental determinations of activity coefficients are presented, to be applicable only to solutions that have ionic strengths less than about 0.01.   The success of the Debye-Hückel theory for these dilute solutions, where, as the $BaCl_2$ calculation just given shows, the nonideality is far from negligible, must be looked upon as a great triumph.   An ionic solution cannot be understood simply in terms of the individual ions.   The interactions between the ions are important and determine the properties of the electrolyte in somewhat the same way as the interactions between gas molecules determine the properties of a nonideal gas.

Solutions with higher ionic strengths present a very difficult problem. Some attempts to understand the ionic behavior, and therefore the activity coefficients, of these more concentrated solutions will be given after some thermodynamic methods are presented for evaluating mean-activity coefficients.

17-14. Two Methods for the Determination of Mean-activity Coefficients. A number of experimental methods are available for the determination of activity coefficients of electrolytes in solution.   These methods depend on situations in which the nonideality of the ionic solution affects some measurable quantity.   Here we shall study the influence of nonideality on the dissociation of a weak acid and on the solubilities of slightly soluble salts.   These studies will lead to two ways for determining activity coefficients.   The most general method depends on the measurement of the emf of an electrochemical cell, and this will be dealt with in the following chapter.

Activity Coefficients from the Dissociation of a Weak Electrolyte. A convenient weak electrolyte to be used as an example is acetic acid, which, in aqueous solution, sets up the equilibrium

$$HAc \rightleftharpoons H^+ + Ac^- \tag{111}$$

The thermodynamic equilibrium constant is

$$K_{th} = \frac{(a_{H^+})(a_{Ac^-})}{a_{HAc}} \tag{112}$$

which can also be written as

$$K_{th} = \frac{\gamma_+ \gamma_-}{\gamma_{HAc}} \frac{[H^+][Ac^-]}{[HAc]} \tag{113}$$

This expression is simplified when it is realized that the electrostatic interactions are primarily responsible for the nonideality which produces activity coefficients different from unity. The uncharged HAc molecule should therefore behave relatively ideally, and we can set $\gamma_{HAc} = 1$. Introduction of $\gamma_\pm^2$ for $\gamma_+ \gamma_-$ and rearrangement gives

$$\log \frac{[H^+][Ac^-]}{[HAc]} = \log K_{th} - 2 \log \gamma_\pm \tag{114}$$

The concentration expression is that for the equilibrium constant in terms of concentrations, and introduction of the degree of dissociation allows the equation to be written as

$$\log \frac{c\alpha^2}{1 - \alpha} = \log K_{th} - 2 \log \gamma_\pm \tag{115}$$

For solutions that are very dilute in ions one can still use the Arrhenius expression

$$\alpha = \frac{\Lambda}{\Lambda_0} \tag{116}$$

to obtain the degree of dissociation from the conductivity. More accurately one can correct for the effect of ion concentration on conductance. In this way, the left side of Eq. (115) is determined for various acetic acid concentrations.

The right side consists of a constant term $\log K_{th}$ and a term which the Debye-Hückel theory of the previous section suggests will, at low ionic concentrations, be proportional to the square root of the ionic strength. If the solution contains only the H^+ and Ac^- ions from the dissociation of HAc, one has

$$\mu = \tfrac{1}{2}[(c\alpha)(1)^2 + (c\alpha)(1)^2] = c\alpha \tag{117}$$

and

$$\sqrt{\mu} = \sqrt{c\alpha}$$

It might be informative therefore to plot, as is done in Fig. 17-3, the left side of Eq. (115) against $\sqrt{c\alpha}$. At low concentrations the points do seem to fall along a straight line, in agreement with the prediction of the Debye-Hückel theory. The theory predicts, furthermore, that the last term of Eq. (115) should be

$$-2 \log \gamma_\pm = +(2)(0.5091) \sqrt{c\alpha}$$

and the line of Fig. 17-3, drawn with slope $+1.018$, fits the data satisfactorily.

Extrapolation to zero ionic strength, where $\gamma_\pm = 1$ and $\log \gamma_\pm = 0$, gives

$$\log K_{th} = -4.7565$$

and

$$K_{th} = 1.752 \times 10^{-5}$$

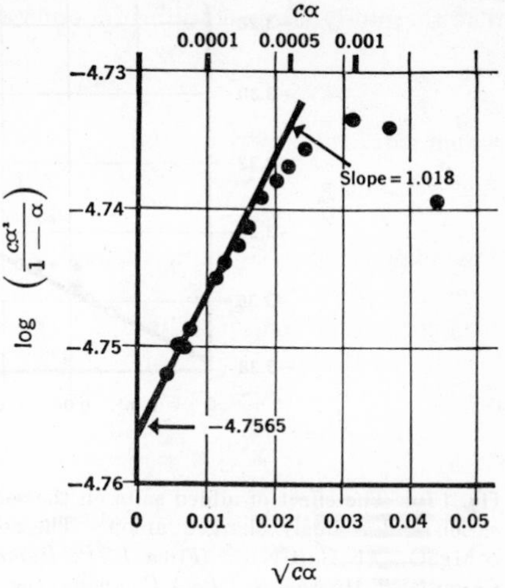

Fig. 17-3. The extrapolation of the logarithm of the concentration-equilibrium-constant expression, $\log (c\alpha^2/1 - \alpha)$, to zero ionic strength according to the plot suggested by the Debye-Hückel theory.

Equation (115) can now be rearranged to give

$$\log \gamma_\pm = \frac{1}{2} \log K_{th} - \frac{1}{2} \log \frac{c\alpha^2}{1 - \alpha}$$

$$= -2.3782 - \frac{1}{2} \log \frac{c\alpha^2}{1 - \alpha} \tag{118}$$

From this equation we can determine $\gamma_\pm$ for the dissociation products of HAc at any concentrations for which values of α can be obtained.

Activity Coefficients from Solubility Measurements. A one-to-one salt AB goes into solution and, possibly among a number of reactions, establishes the equilibrium

$$AB(s) \rightleftharpoons A^+ + B^- \tag{119}$$

The thermodynamic-equilibrium constant, the solubility product, is

$$K_{th} = (a_{A^+})(a_{B^-}) = \gamma_+\gamma_-[A^+][B^-]$$
$$= \gamma_\pm^2[A^+][B^-] \tag{120}$$

Taking logarithms and rearranging, one gets

$$\log [A^+][B^-] = \log K_{th} - 2 \log \gamma_\pm \tag{121}$$

The solubility s of such a salt is equal to the moles per liter of the salt that dissolve, which, if no species from the electrolyte AB other than A^+ and B^- exist in solution, gives

$$[A^+] = [B^-] = s$$

Thus

$$\log s^2 = \log K_{th} - 2 \log \gamma_\pm$$

or

$$\log s = \tfrac{1}{2} \log K_{th} - \log \gamma_\pm \tag{122}$$

Now consider the data that are obtained when a sparingly soluble salt is dissolved in solutions that contain various amounts of nonreacting electrolytes that do not contain the ions A^+ or B^-. The Debye-Hückel theory again suggests that at low ionic strengths the $\log \gamma_\pm$ term of the sparingly soluble elec-

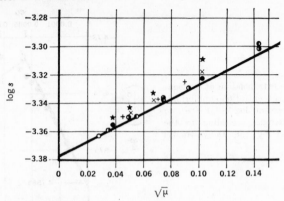

Fig. 17-4. The effect of added salts on the solubility of a salt containing a singly charged cation and a singly charged anion. The added salts are: ◑ NaCl, ◐ KNO₃, +BaSO₄, ×MgSO₄, ★K₃Co(CN)₆. (*From L. P. Hammett, "Introduction to the Study of Physical Chemistry," McGraw-Hill Book Company, Inc., New York, 1952.*)

trolyte will be proportional to the square root of the ionic strength. One therefore plots the left side of Eq. (122) against $\sqrt{\mu}$ as shown for the complicated but experimentally convenient salt $[Co(NH_3)_4C_2O_4][Co(NH_3)_2(NO_2)_2\text{-}C_2O_4]$ in Fig. 17-4. The data for solutions with singly charged ions support the Debye-Hückel predictions of a linear relation, and the straight line of Fig. 17-4 has been drawn with the predicted slope of 0.5091. The solutions containing more highly charged ions agree rather less well with the Debye-Hückel prediction.

For this particular set of data one sees that the linear relation is rather rough and that support for the Debye-Hückel theory is given but is not very convincing here. It is just such difficulties that the theory frequently encounters, particularly in solutions other than those of extremely low ionic strength.

An extrapolation can be made in Fig. 17-4, with or without the Debye-Hückel theory, and one obtains for the left side of Eq. (122), at zero ionic strength, the value -3.377. Again the limit of zero ionic strength corresponds to the complete absence of ionic interactions and therefore to $\gamma_\pm = 1$ and $\log \gamma_\pm = 0$. At this limit Eq. (122) gives therefore

$$\tfrac{1}{2} \log K_{th} = -3.377$$

or $$K_{th} = 1.76 \times 10^{-7} \tag{123}$$

With this value one is again able to turn the previous relation around to give an expression for the activity coefficient of the slightly soluble salt at any concentration as

$$\log \gamma_\pm = -3.377 - \log s \tag{124}$$

The solubility data used to construct Fig. 17-4 can therefore be made to give $\gamma_\pm$ for the dissolved salt in all the solutions studied.

Salts other than those of the one-to-one type can be handled in a similar manner. For the solubility equilibrium

$$A_2B \rightleftharpoons 2A^+ + B^=$$ (125)

the solubility product is

$$K_{th} = (a_{A^+})^2(a_{B^-}) = \gamma_+^2\gamma_-[A^+]^2[B^=]$$
$$= \gamma_\pm^3[A^+]^2[B^=]$$ (126)

If the solubility is s moles/liter, the concentration of A^+ will be $2s$ and of B will be s. In terms of the solubility one has

$$K_{th} = \gamma_\pm^3(2s)^2(s) = \gamma_\pm^3 4s^3$$ (127)

Taking logarithms and rearranging now gives

$$\log s = \tfrac{1}{3} (\log K_{th} - \log 4) - \log \gamma_\pm$$ (128)

Data on the solubility of a salt of the type A_2B as a function of the ionic strength of the solution can now be used, in the same manner as for the salt AB, to give the value of K_{th} and values for $\gamma_\pm$.

Data obtained from such solubility measurements are shown in Fig. 17-5. Some scattering of the points does occur, but there is generally agreement with the straight lines of the Debye-Hückel limiting law.

The Debye-Hückel theory gives therefore a molecular interpretation of the behavior of ions that satisfactorily accounts for their thermodynamic behavior in solutions of ionic strength less than about 0.01. The limiting Debye-Hückel law has, moreover, almost the neatness of a law for ideal systems. It characterizes the solution, for aqueous solutions at 25°C, simply by the dielectric constant of water and the ionic strength of the solution and characterizes the ion only by the absolute value of its charge. In dilute enough solutions, a molecular interpretation needs, apparently, to take into account no other solute or solvent property.

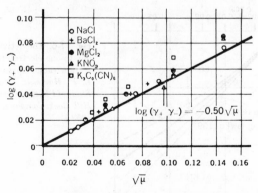

Fig. 17-5. The activity-coefficient–ionic-strength relation from the solubility of the salt $[Co(NH_3)_4C_2O_4][Co(NH_3)_2(NO_2)(C_2O_4)]$ in aqueous solution at 15°C with various added electrolytes. [*J. N. Brönsted and V. K. La Mer, J. Am. Chem. Soc.*, **46**: 550 (1924).]

The situation is much more complicated in solutions with higher ionic strength.

17-15. Activity Coefficients in More Concentrated Solutions. Data for the activity coefficients of a number of strong electrolytes are shown in Table 17-5. If attention is given to concentrations that have ionic strengths of less than about 0.1, a similar pattern of activity-coefficient behavior for different electrolytes is noticed. Figure 17-6 shows some of these data, and such curves can be fitted by an equation of the type

$$\frac{\log \gamma_\pm}{-Z_+Z_-} = \frac{-0.5091 \sqrt{\mu}}{1 + \sqrt{\mu}} + b\mu \tag{129}$$

where b is an empirical constant. More simply, all the available data are approximately fitted by the expression

$$\frac{\log \gamma_\pm}{-Z_+Z_-} = \frac{-0.5091 \sqrt{\mu}}{1 + \sqrt{\mu}} \tag{130}$$

as shown in Fig. 17-6. Even in the ionic-strength range of less than 0.1, however, it is apparent that the ionic charge is not a sufficient description of an ion to account for its activity coefficient.

At concentrations above those dealt with in Fig. 17-6, nonideality of the solutions, as expressed by the activity coefficients, becomes very striking, as the plots of the data of Table 17-5 in Fig. 17-7 show. Even electrolytes of the same charge type have very different activity-coefficient curves. No satisfactory theoretical or even semiempirical explanation of these curves is available.

The phenomenon of an ion atmosphere and the resultant stabilization on which the Debye-Hückel theory is based still undoubtedly operates. This effect is, however, much enhanced, even to the extent that ion pairs and ion

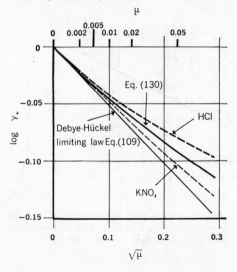

Fig. 17-6. The activity coefficients of one-to-one electrolytes in the concentration range up to 0.01 M. (*From L. P. Hammett, "Introduction to the Study of Physical Chemistry," McGraw-Hill Book Company, Inc., New York, 1952.*)

Table 17-5. Mean-activity Coefficients $\gamma_\pm$ for Electrolytes in Water at 25°C

Molality	Debye-Hückel theory for $AB \rightarrow A^+ + B^-$	HCl	NaCl	NaOH	Debye-Hückel theory for $A_2B \rightarrow 2A^+ + B^-$ or $AB_2 \rightarrow A^{++} + 2B^-$	H₂SO₄	CaCl₂	Debye-Hückel theory for $AB \rightarrow A^{++} + B^-$	ZnSO₄	CaSO₄
0.001	0.965	0.965	0.966	......	0.880	......	0.888	0.744	0.734	0.762
0.005	0.920	0.930	0.928	......	0.750	0.643	0.789	0.515	0.477	......
0.01	0.890	0.906	0.903	0.899	0.667	0.545	0.732	......	0.387	0.404
0.05	0.770	0.833	0.821	0.805	......	0.341	0.584	......	0.202	0.216
0.10	......	0.798	0.778	0.759	......	0.266	0.524	......	0.148	0.150
0.50	......	0.769	0.680	0.681	......	0.155	0.510	......	0.063	0.067
1.00	......	0.811	0.656	0.667	......	0.131	0.725	......	0.044	
2.00	......	1.011	0.670	0.685	......	0.125	1.554	......	0.035	
4.00	......	1.74	0.791	......	......	0.172		......		

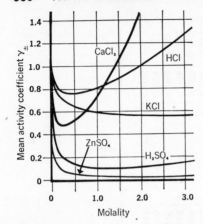

Fig. 17-7. The mean-activity coefficient of some electrolytes in the concentration range up to 3 M. (*Adapted from L. P. Hammett, "Introduction to the Study of Physical Chemistry," McGraw-Hill Book Company, Inc., New York, 1952.*)

triplets or other species should be recognized. Such electrostatic associations will necessarily lower the free energies of the ions and produce a value of $\gamma_\pm$ of considerably less than unity.

A qualitative explanation of the activity coefficients that increase with concentration and even become greater than unity can be given in terms of the solvation of the ions. As the ions tie up solvent molecules, the effective concentration, i.e., the moles solute per mole free solvent, becomes greater than the concentration calculated as moles solute per mole solvent. The solute in the apparently more concentrated solution has a higher free energy than would be expected, and this shows up as an increased activity coefficient.

A quantitative explanation for data such as those of Fig. 17-7 is, however, as yet nonexistent. In solution chemistry one of the principal goals of research is that of clearly recognizing the factors that are involved and fitting the data such as are shown in Fig. 17-7 into a quantitative theory.

17-16. The Use of Constant Ionic Strength. The activity coefficients for ions in solutions of higher ionic strengths can depart very appreciably from unity. The study of any equilibrium involving ions under these conditions cannot therefore be made simply in terms of concentrations—as one always seems to do in practice problems dealing with ionic equilibria. The activities of the ions should be used, but it is frequently difficult to obtain the activity coefficients that are necessary for the calculation of activities from concentrations.

A frequently encountered approach that attempts to avoid this difficulty arranges, by the addition of a relatively large amount of nonreacting electrolyte, to keep the ionic strength at a high but essentially constant value. Although this procedure makes all the activity coefficients very different from unity, it is intended to keep the activity coefficients of any participating ion constant regardless of the variation in the amount of the other reacting ions. The activity coefficients of the ions in the equilibrium

$$Fe^{3+} + I^- \rightleftharpoons Fe^{++} + \tfrac{1}{2}I_2 \tag{131}$$

would, for example, be expected to be very sensitive to changes in the ionic strength of the system. That this equilibrium is set up would not be apparent if one attempted to use the concentrations in an equilibrium-constant expression. As the data of Table 17-6 indicate, however, in the presence of 0.1 M HCl the activity coefficients apparently are not changed as the amounts of Fe^{3+}, I^-, and Fe^{++} are varied and a quite constant concentration-equilibrium

Table 17-6. Equilibrium Constant at 25°C for the Reaction $Fe^{3+} + I^- \rightarrow Fe^{++} + \frac{1}{2}I_2$*
(Values for K are based on concentrations of the reagents, and a constant ionic strength is maintained by 1.65 M KCl and 0.1 M HCl)

[Fe^{3+}]	[I^-]	[Fe^{++}]	[I_2]	K
0.001223	0.00114	0.001257	0.0053	21
0.002644	0.00224	0.003536	0.00129	21.4
0.00483	0.00358	0.007535	0.00238	21.3
0.00900	0.00549	0.01574	0.00415	20.5
0.00436	0.00161	0.000804	0.00032	20.5
0.001104	0.00526	0.003856	0.00104	21.4
0.00043	0.01713	0.005752	0.00076	21.6
0.00192	0.01117	0.01045	0.00185	21.0

* From J. N. Brønsted and K. Pedersen, *Z. physik. Chem.*, **103**: 307 (1923).

constant results.   It must be recognized that this constant may be very different from the thermodynamic-equilibrium constant.   The experiment really shows only that an equilibrium is established according to the reaction of Eq. (131).

17-17. The Effect of Electrostatic Interactions on Reaction Rates.   The introduction of the concept of activities and the development of methods for relating activities to concentrations allows the methods of thermodynamics to be applied to solutions of ionic species where the electrostatic interactions are often very considerable.   It is true, however, that not only are the equilibrium conditions of a system affected by these interactions but so also are the rates of chemical reactions proceeding in such systems.   Although thermodynamic quantities cannot be carried over with thermodynamic rigor to the treatment of rate effects, some of the ideas previously introduced are valuable in the discussion of reaction rates in ionic systems.

It is particularly profitable, as was shown by Brønsted and Bjerrum, to follow through the transition-state theory with the recognition that activities rather than concentrations should be used in the equilibrium-constant expression for the formation of the activated complex.

The general bimolecular reaction, allowing for charges on the reagents and on the activated complex, can be written as

$$A^{Z_A} + B^{Z_B} \rightleftharpoons (AB)^{Z_A+Z_B} \rightarrow \text{products} \tag{132}$$

where Z_A and Z_B are the charges of the reagents A and B.   The equilibrium constant for the formation of the activated complex must now be written as follows:

$$K^{\ddagger} = \frac{a^{\ddagger}}{a_A a_B} = \frac{c^{\ddagger}}{c_A c_B} \frac{\gamma^{\ddagger}}{\gamma_A \gamma_B} \tag{133}$$

As in the treatment in Sec. 11-15, the transition-state theory attributes the rate of a reaction to the product of the concentration of the activated complex and a frequency factor.   Thus the rate

$$-\frac{dc_A}{dt} = k_2 c_A c_B \tag{134}$$

is interpreted as

$$k_2 c_A c_B = \nu c^{\ddagger} = \frac{kT}{h} c^{\ddagger} \qquad (135)$$

Substitution of the expression of Eq. (133) for the activated complex concentration gives

$$k_2 = \frac{kT}{h} K^{\ddagger} \frac{\gamma_A \gamma_B}{\gamma^{\ddagger}} \qquad (136)$$

This treatment leads, therefore, to the appearance of the activity coefficients of the reagents and of the activated complex in the rate constant.

At high ionic concentrations it must be anticipated that the rate constant will behave in some not easily predicted manner if the activated complex carries a charge and has therefore some indeterminate activity coefficient.

In more dilute solutions reliance can be placed on the Debye-Hückel limiting law,

$$\log \gamma_+ = -0.5091 Z_+^2$$
$$\log \gamma_- = -0.5091 Z_-^2 \qquad (137)$$

These expressions for the activity coefficients can be inserted into the logarithm of Eq. (136) to give

$$\log k_2 = \log\left(\frac{kT}{h} K^{\ddagger}\right) - 0.5091 \sqrt{\mu} \, [Z_A^2 + Z_B^2 - (Z_A + Z_B)^2]$$
$$= \log\left(\frac{kT}{h} K^{\ddagger}\right) + 0.5091 \sqrt{\mu} \, Z_A Z_B \qquad (138)$$

This result predicts that the rate constant for a reaction depends not only on the $(kT/h)K^{\ddagger}$ term that appears for noncharged systems but also on the ionic strength of the solution and the charges of the reagents.

The dependence for a given reaction is determined by the product of the charges of the reagents, and the prediction is made that the rate will increase with increasing ionic strength if both reagents have charges of the same sign and will decrease with increasing ionic strength if the reagents are oppositely charged.

It should again be pointed out, however, that in solutions of higher ionic strength no simple dependence of the rate constant on the ionic strength can be expected. Again one frequently resorts to studies on solutions with a large excess of a nonparticipating electrolyte present to preserve a constant ionic strength. While this approach is often successful in providings data of some value, the occurrence of specific interactions must again be anticipated.

Problems

1. At not too high pressures the PV behavior of gases conforms to the equation $PV = RT + BP$. For 1 mole of oxygen at 25°C and for pressures up to about 1 atm the expression becomes $PV = R(298) - 0.0211P$ liter atm.

   (a) Calculate the fugacity of oxygen at 0.1, 0.5, and 1 atm.

   (b) At what pressure does the fugacity have the value 1 atm?

(c) What is the activity at the pressure of part b?

(d) What are the activities and the activity coefficients at 0.1, 0.5, and 1 atm pressure?

Ans. γ (at 1 atm) = 0.99914.

2. Verify, by graphical integrations of Fig. 1-9, some points on the curves of Fig. 17-1.

3. Explain, in terms of the source of nonideal behavior introduced by van der Waals, what might cause an activity coefficient of a nonideal gas to be greater than unity and what might cause it to be less than unity.

4. The critical data for H_2, N_2, and NH_3 are given in Table 1-3. Estimate, with the aid of Fig. 17-1, the activity coefficients of these gases at 1,000 atm and (a) 250°C and (b) 500°C.

5. At 800°K the following values are reported (Tables of Thermal Properties of Gases, *Natl. Bur. Standards* (*U.S.*) *Circ.* 564) for the density of steam:

Pressure (atm)............	1	10	20	40	80
Density (g/cc)............	0.00027464	0.0027648	0.0055709	0.011312	0.023344

Pressure (atm)........	120	160	200	240	280	300
Density (g/cc).........	0.036184	0.049937	0.064724	0.08070	0.09803	0.1073

What are the fugacity, the activity, and the activity coefficient of steam at 800°K and 300 atm? Compare this value with those obtained from the critical data and Fig. 17-1.

Ans. γ = 0.799.

6. The equilibrium constant for the reaction $H_2 + CO_2 \rightarrow H_2O + CO$ at 986°C is 1.60 at rather low pressures, where all the gases behave essentially ideally.

Estimate the value that the equilibrium constant, expressed in pressures, would have at a total gas pressure of 500 atm.

7. Calculate the mole fraction, the activity, and the activity coefficient for water for solutions at 100°C containing:

(a) 11.8 g NaCl and 100 g water, for which the vapor pressure is 708 mm Hg

(b) 35.4 g NaCl and 100 g water, for which the vapor pressure is 584 mm Hg

Ans. (b) γ = 0.851.

8. Benzene and toluene form a solution which, as shown by the vapor-pressure data of Fig. 14-17, behaves essentially ideally. What are the activity and activity coefficient of benzene, treated as the solvent, in solutions with benzene mole fractions of 1.0, 0.8, 0.5, and 0.10 at 20°C?

9. The vapor pressure of the system acetone-chloroform as a function of mole fraction is shown in Fig. 14-19.

Treating acetone as the solvent, estimate from Fig. 14-19 its activity and activity coefficient in solutions that have 1.0, 0.8, 0.5, and 0.20 mole fraction.

Treat chloroform as solvent, and estimate from Fig. 14-19 its activity and activity coefficient in solutions that have 1.0, 0.8, 0.5, and 0.20 mole fraction.

10. A dilute solution of sucrose in water at 25°C has a vapor pressure of water such that the activity of water is 0.984. What pressure must be applied to the solution to raise the activity of water to unity?

Ans. 22 atm.

11. If the mean-activity coefficient of the ions formed from the dissociation of Na_3PO_4 is 0.887 in a certain solution, what is the activity coefficient ($\gamma_+^3 \gamma_-$) of the salt?

Ans. Na_3PO_4 = 0.62.

12. If the activity coefficient for $CaCl_2$ in a 0.1 M solution is 0.515, what is the mean-activity coefficient for the ions?

13. For 1 M solutions at 25°C the activities $(\gamma_+\gamma_-)$ of the electrolytes NaCl, $NaNO_3$, HNO_3, and HCl are 0.657, 0.548, 0.724, and 0.809, respectively. Show that these data are such that the activities of electrolytes could not be broken down to contributions from the separate ions, as was done, for example, for conductivities at infinite dilution.

14. Calculate the ionic strengths of solutions that contain:

(a) 0.3 M $CaCl_2$

(b) 0.3 M Na_3PO_4

(c) 0.1 M Na_2SO_4 plus 0.2 M NaCl

(d) 0.0078 M acetic acid, which is 4.8 per cent dissociated, and 0.5 M dioxane

$Ans.$ (a) 0.9; (c) 0.5.

15. Calculate, according to the limiting law of the Debye-Hückel theory, the activity coefficient of Ba^{++} and of Cl^- and the mean activity coefficient of $BaCl_2$ in a 0.005 M aqueous solution at 25°C.

$Ans.$ $\gamma_+ = 0.563$, $\gamma_- = 0.866$, $\gamma_\pm = 0.750$.

16. Calculate, according to the limiting form of the Debye-Hückel theory, the activity coefficients of each of the ions Na^+, $SO_4^=$, OH^-, and H^+ in a solution that contains both 0.003 M Na_2SO_4 and 0.001 M NaOH.

17. Calculate the activity coefficients for the H^+ and the acetate ion in a solution which is 0.0078 M in acetic acid. The degree of dissociation at this concentration is 4.8 per cent.

18. From the conductance data of Table 16-2 and the limiting law of the Debye-Hückel theory deduce the mean-activity coefficient of the ions of NH_4OH in the concentration range for which data are given.

$Ans.$ At 0.01, $\gamma_\pm = 0.976$.

18

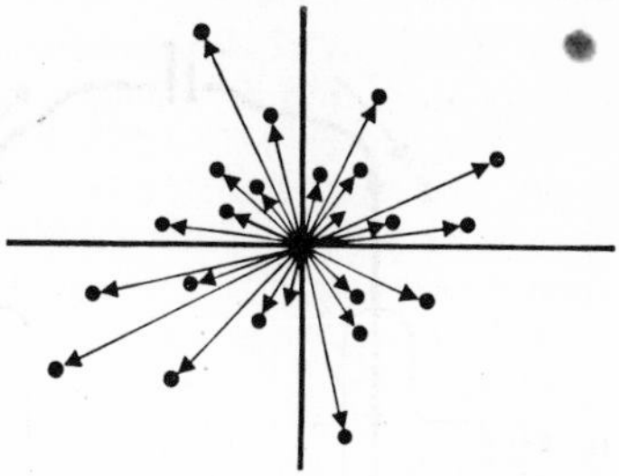

The Electromotive Force
of Chemical Cells

In previous treatments of the thermodynamics of chemical reactions quantitative use could not be made of the fact that the free-energy change for a reaction is equal to the negative of the useful work which can theoretically be obtained from the reaction. It was necessary to develop a number of more devious ways for determining free-energy changes from measurable thermal quantities.

In the present chapter arrangements are considered whereby chemical reactions can be studied at equilibrium and the work done during the equilibrium reaction can be determined. The procedure leads to a direct measurement of the free energy of the reaction and, as we shall see, frequently to a very accurate value for this free energy. The arrangement consists in allowing the reaction to proceed in an electrochemical, or galvanic, cell and determining the work electrically.

As in other thermodynamic studies we shall not be concerned necessarily with theories of the molecular and ionic behaviors of the systems being studied. It will be found, however, that the thermodynamic data obtained here provide valuable data with which theories of the nature of ionic solutions can be compared.

18-1. The Electrochemical Process. Electrochemical processes can be introduced by a consideration of the example illustrated in Fig. 18-1. Two platinum electrodes dip into a solution of hydrochloric acid. The electrode on the left is in contact with H_2 gas, while that on the right is in contact with Cl_2 gas. Platinum is indicated for the electrodes since it is an inert material and will take no chemical part in the reaction.

In Chap. 13 we saw that metals contain a reservoir of electrons. At the left electrode there are therefore the possible reagents H_2, H, and e^-, and these

585

Fig. 18-1. The electrolysis of an aqueous solution of HCl to form H_2 and Cl_2 by application of a sufficiently high voltage.

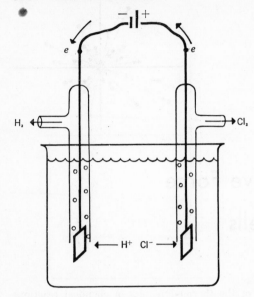

could be involved in the reaction

$$\tfrac{1}{2}H_2 \rightleftharpoons H^+ + e^- \tag{1}$$

At the right electrode, similarly, there is the possibility of a reaction

$$\tfrac{1}{2}Cl_2 + e^- \rightleftharpoons Cl^- \tag{2}$$

The decomposition of HCl solution to form H_2 and Cl_2, that is, the electrolysis of HCl, can, in fact, be effected by the application of a sufficient voltage to the electrodes of a cell such as that of Fig. 18-1. When this is done, the over-all reaction

$$HCl \rightarrow \tfrac{1}{2}H_2 + \tfrac{1}{2}Cl_2 \tag{3}$$

is observed to occur and, therefore, both the possible electrode reactions [Eqs. (1) and (2)] are forced to the left by the applied voltage. Such an electrolysis decomposition is often performed with a large, unbalanced applied voltage, and the reaction does not then proceed under equilibrium or reversible conditions.

There will, however, be some voltage that will be just sufficient to cause the reaction to proceed, the pressures of H_2 and Cl_2 and the concentration of HCl having some particular values. Under such conditions the reaction proceeds at, or very nearly at, equilibrium. If a slightly lower voltage is applied and the same concentration of HCl and pressures of H_2 and Cl_2 are maintained, the reaction will proceed in the opposite direction; that is, H_2 and Cl_2 will be used up and converted to HCl. Electrons will then be driven around the circuit in the opposite direction, as shown in Fig. 18-2, to that in an electrolysis experiment. We see from this discussion that there will be some applied voltage which will keep the reaction at equilibrium. For an applied voltage infinitesimally higher or lower than this equilibrium voltage, the reaction will proceed in one direction or the other.

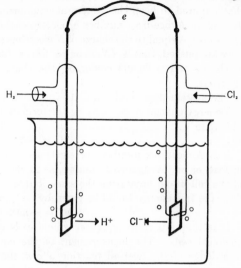

It is clear that the electrode reactions written above proceed because the electrons produced at one electrode can travel through the external circuit and be used up at the other electrode. Although the two electrode reactions have been written separately, only the *over-all reaction*, which is the sum of the two electrode reactions, is, in fact, observed. In the present example the electrode reactions have been written so that the electrons appear as reactants in one reaction and as products in the other. The over-all, or net, reaction is obtained by adding these electrode reactions. This addition must be such that the electrons appearing as products in one reaction are used up as reactants in the other. With this in mind one can add electrode reactions to give a balanced over-all reaction.

It is the over-all reaction which is studied at equilibrium by balancing the chemical tendency for the reaction to occur with an opposing voltage. Under such balanced conditions the process is reversible; i.e., it can be shifted one way or the other by an infinitesimal change in the applied voltage or by a similar change in the concentrations of the involved reagents. The net work that is done when such a balanced reaction proceeds at constant pressure is, as was pointed out in Chap. 7, equal to the negative of the free-energy change for the reaction. A large number of reactions of electrolytes in solution can be performed in an electrochemical cell, and if the free-energy changes in such reactions are to be determined, it is necessary to show that the net useful work can be measured.

How much work is performed in the reaction which forms 1 mole of HCl at essentially equilibrium conditions? In this reaction an Avogadro's number of electrons flow around the external circuit from left to right while the system is kept near equilibrium by an opposing voltage ε that is infinitesimally less than that required to keep the system at equilibrium. The system does work by driving an Avogadro's number of electrons through this voltage. This electrical work is equal to the charge of N electrons times the voltage through which they are pushed, that is, $(Ne)\varepsilon$ or $\mathfrak{F}\varepsilon$, where the symbol $\mathfrak{F}$ represents 1 faraday of charge and is 96,493 coulombs, the charge of an Avogadro's number of electrons.

The system does work, and its free energy therefore decreases. For the free-energy change accompanying the formation of 1 mole of HCl we therefore can write

$$\Delta G = -\mathfrak{F}\varepsilon \tag{4}$$

If n Avogadro's numbers of electrons had been involved in the reaction instead of one Avogadro's number, as in the example, the voltage, or emf, ε of the cell would have been the same, but since $n\mathfrak{F}$ coulombs of charge would flow, the free energy would be given by

$$\Delta G = -n\mathfrak{F}\varepsilon \tag{5}$$

It is this important equation which leads us to study the emf of electrochemical cells. The measurement of the equilibrium emf together with a knowledge of the over-all reaction allows the direct calculation of an often precise value for the free-energy change of the reaction.

18-2. Potentiometric Measurement of EMF. It is necessary that the voltage produced by an electrochemical cell be measured at equilibrium conditions if the measurement is to be of use in calculating a free-energy change. A voltmeter is therefore not a suitable instrument for measuring voltages since it must draw current from the cell to make the measurement. A potentiometer is a device that measures the voltage of a cell by opposing it with an applied voltage and therefore gives the desired equilibrium emf. The principle on which a potentiometer operates is now briefly described.

Figure 18-3 shows a schematic representation of a simple potentiometer. A working battery B is attached to a slide-wire type of resistance in such a way as to drive electrons through the circuit as indicated. The electrochemical

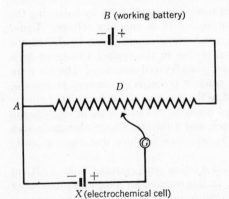

B (working battery)

D

A

G

X (electrochemical cell)

Fig. 18-3. The potentiometric method for measuring the voltage produced by an electrochemical cell operating at a state of balance.

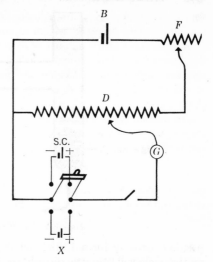

Fig. 18-4. A direct-reading potentiometer.

cell whose emf is being measured is attached, along with a galvanometer and a variable contact, on the slide wire to drive electrons, as also indicated.   The current flowing in the upper circuit produces a voltage applied to the lower circuit in accordance with the IR drop across the section AD of the slide wire. One now adjusts the position of the contact D until this voltage just balances that of the test cell, as indicated by a zero deflection of the galvanometer. The voltage drop across AD, measured perhaps by the resistance and the current flowing in the upper circuit, is then equal to that of the cell when no current flows through the cell.   This is the desired equilibrium emf since the cell is in a state of balance.

The more generally used *direct-reading* potentiometer, illustrated in Fig. 18-4, can also be mentioned.   Use is now made of a *standard cell* which has a known and constant voltage.   The most frequently used standard cell, which is illustrated in Fig. 18-5 and which will be understandable from later sections of this chapter, is a Weston cell that has a voltage of 1.0183 volts.

The slide wire is arranged with a convenient scale, maybe 0 to 2, and the contact D is set at 1.0183 on this slide.   The switch is now thrown to the standard cell, and the current is varied in the upper circuit by adjusting the resistance F until the galvanometer shows that balance has been obtained. By this procedure the circuit is arranged so that slide-wire readings correspond directly to emfs of the cell to be measured.

One now leaves the position of the contact at F fixed.   The current flowing through the upper circuit remains constant, and since $\varepsilon = IR$ across the slide wire, any position D on the slide wire will correspond to a given resistance AD and to a voltage that is proportional to this.   The scale of 0 to 2 on the slide wire corresponds therefore to a voltage as well as a resistance scale.   Furthermore, this scale has been made to read actual voltages by fixing the 1.0183

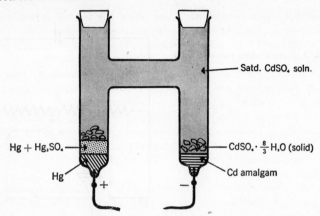

Fig. 18-5. The Weston standard cell.

position correctly for a 1.0183-volt cell. It follows that all other positions on this scale will also give directly the voltage of the section of the slide wire connected to the lower circuit and therefore the voltage of the electrochemical cell in the lower circuit.

The emf of the unknown cell X is determined by throwing the switch to that cell and moving the position D until balance is reached. The slide-wire reading gives directly the desired emf.

In practice, of course, one does not make use of simple slide wires as indicated in the figure. The principle of operation is, however, exactly the same.

We are now in a position to determine the equilibrium emf of an electrochemical cell, but before proceeding to a study of such cells it is necessary that we consider the types of electrodes that are used to form these cells.

18-3. Types of Electrodes. The example of Figs. 18-1 and 18-2, which was used to introduce the subject of galvanic cells, showed that the process occurring in the cell could be treated in terms of the processes at the two electrodes. Although one can study only cells which consist of two electrodes, it is convenient to describe the types of electrochemical arrangements that are used in terms of the separate electrodes. A variety of reactions can be made to occur electrochemically, and a variety of electrodes are used. A description is here given of only a few of the more important types.

The reactions that occur at these electrodes will also be given. Since the over-all reaction of the cell can always be treated in terms of the two electrode reactions, an understanding of the chemistry of electrode reactions results in an understanding of electrochemical reactions.

The physical arrangement of the electrodes that constitute a cell consists either of electrodes which dip directly into the solution, as in the H_2, Cl_2 example, or of electrodes that are in separate compartments connected through a *salt bridge* that allows ions to move through the solution. The basis for the use of a salt bridge will be dealt with later. For the present it is enough to recognize that this arrangement is used when the two electrodes require different solutions. Each electrode is then in its own solution protected by a tube of a saturated KCl, gelatin solution. Figure 18-6 shows an electrode so assembled.

The different types of electrodes, and the electrode reactions, that are most frequently encountered can now be introduced. In later sections it will be shown how these are assembled into electrochemical cells.

The Gas Electrode. The H_2 and Cl_2 electrodes of the previous example are such electrodes. The arrangement has already been shown in Fig. 18-1. Most frequently the cell is open to the atmosphere, and the gas around the electrode is therefore at atmospheric pressure. The electrode material can, in principle, be any inert metal.

One finds, however, that, for the electrode to be *reversible*, considerable care in the choice and the treatment of the inert metal is necessary. One desires an electrode to be such that, when the external voltage is changed by a very small amount from the equilibrium value, the reaction will proceed one way or the other. For inert electrodes, like gold or polished platinum, one finds this not to be the case, a considerable driving force being required to alter the direction of the reaction. One finds, on the other hand, that platinum with a coat of fine platinum powder, i.e., platinum black, behaves suitably.

Apparently only some inert electrodes provide a sufficiently easy path for reactions, such as

$$\tfrac{1}{2}H_2 \rightleftharpoons H^+ + e^- \tag{6}$$

For the electrode to be reversible it is necessary that ions such as H^+ be able

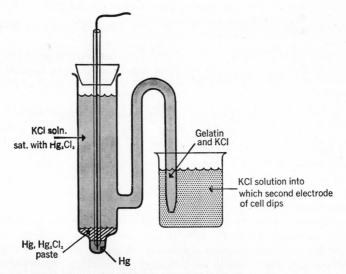

KCl soln.
sat. with Hg_2Cl_2

Gelatin
and KCl

KCl solution into
which second electrode
of cell dips

Hg, Hg_2Cl_2
paste

Hg

Fig. 18-6. The calomel electrode.

to pick up electrons from the metal or molecules such as H_2 be able to give up electrons to the metal, with a minimum of driving force in either direction. On surfaces such as platinum black there are formed, apparently, hydrogen atoms that are immediately available for the release of an electron and the formation of H^+ ions or for the combination into H_2 molecules. In any case such a surface provides a suitable means for an equilibrium electrode process. The exact mechanism of the electrode reaction is, in general, not easily depicted.

A shorthand notation for electrodes that will be found to be convenient describes the H_2 electrode as

$$Pt|H_2(P \text{ atm})|HCl(c \text{ moles/liter})$$

The vertical lines separate the different phases of the electrode. The pressure of the gas and the concentration and composition of the solution can be included as indicated.

Oxidation-Reduction Electrodes. Although all electrodes involve oxidation-reduction reactions in the sense that electrons are being gained or lost at the electrode, this name is generally used for electrodes consisting of an inert metal dipping into a solution containing two different oxidation states of a species. An example consists of a platinum wire dipping into a solution containing ferrous and ferric ions. Such a cell is abbreviated as

$$Pt|Fe^{++}(c_1), Fe^{3+}(c_2)$$

The comma is used to separate the two chemical species which are in the same solution. These electrodes are similar to the gas electrodes except that the two species involved in the electrode reaction are ions. The electrode reaction in the example is

$$Fe^{++} \rightleftharpoons Fe^{3+} + e^- \tag{7}$$

and there is the possibility of the electrode either donating or accepting electrons.

One finds far less difficulty in obtaining a reversible electrode of this type. Apparently the ions can readily accept or donate electrons to the metal surface. In fact, a suitable electrode consists of an ordinary piece of platinum wire for the inert metal.

Oxidation-reduction electrodes can also be made with organic molecules that can exist in two different oxidation states. The most generally used material of this type is the system of hydroquinone and quinone, which can form the oxidation-reduction system

$$\text{(hydroquinone)} \rightleftharpoons \text{(quinone)} + 2H^+ + 2e^- \tag{8}$$

The presence of a platinum electrode in a solution containing these two species again clearly provides an electrode that can donate or accept electrons. One usually represents hydroquinone by QH_2 and quinone by Q, and the cell is then abbreviated as

$$Pt|QH_2, Q, H^+$$

The occurrence of H^+ as a reagent makes it necessary also to state its concentration in the system. This electrode is generally known as the *quinhydrone* electrode from the name of the crystalline compound $QH_2 \cdot Q$, in which form the material is added to the solution.

Metal–Metal-ion Electrodes. The simplest of the electrodes in which the electrode material plays a chemical role is one in which a metal electrode dips into a solution containing ions of the metal. An example is that of a metallic silver electrode in a silver nitrate solution. The electrode is represented as

$$Ag|Ag^+(c)$$

and the electrode reaction is

$$Ag \rightleftharpoons Ag^+ + e^- \tag{9}$$

Such an electrode can be set up with any metal that is of intermediate activity. Very active metals react directly with the water itself.

Amalgam Electrodes. A variation of the previous electrode is one in which the metal is in the form of an amalgam, i.e., is dissolved in mercury, rather than in the pure form. Electrical contact is made by a platinum wire dipping into the amalgam pool. The reaction is the same as in the metal–metal-ion electrode, the mercury playing no chemical role.

The particular value of amalgam electrodes is that one can use active metals such as sodium in such electrodes. An attempt to use pure sodium for an electrode would, of course, result only in the direct reaction of the sodium with water. A sodium-amalgam electrode is represented as

$$Na(\text{in mercury at } c_1)|Na^+(c_2)$$

where the concentration of the sodium metal in the mercury as well as that of the sodium ion in the solution must be given. In addition to allowing the study of active metals the amalgam electrode is of interest in illustrating some of the thermodynamic relations which will be obtained for electrochemical cells.

Metal–Insoluble-salt Electrodes. A more elaborate, but usually satisfactory and frequently used electrode consists of a metal in contact with an insoluble salt of the metal, which in turn is in contact with a solution containing the anion of the salt. An example is represented as

$$Ag|AgCl|Cl^-(c)$$

The electrode process at such an electrode is

$$\begin{array}{c} Ag \rightleftharpoons Ag^+ + e^- \\ \underline{Ag^+ + Cl^- \rightleftharpoons AgCl(s)} \\ Ag + Cl^- \rightleftharpoons AgCl(s) + e^- \end{array} \tag{10}$$

The over-all reaction shows how electrons can be released by the formation of AgCl from metallic silver and chloride ions or picked up by the reverse reaction. The electrode reaction involves only the concentration of Cl^- as a variable. This can be contrasted with the Ag|Ag$^+$ electrode, which has the Ag$^+$ concentration as a variable.

The most frequently used electrode of this type is the *calomel electrode*. This consists of metallic mercury in contact with calomel, Hg_2Cl_2, which is in contact with a chloride solution. Figure 18-5 shows the usual arrangement of this electrode. The electrode reaction is

$$\begin{array}{c} Hg \rightleftharpoons Hg^+ + e^- \\ \underline{Hg^+ + Cl^- \rightleftharpoons \frac{1}{2}Hg_2Cl_2} \\ Hg + Cl^- \rightleftharpoons \frac{1}{2}Hg_2Cl_2 + e^- \end{array} \qquad (11)$$

The calomel electrode is quite easily prepared and is frequently used in practice. One generally uses a chloride solution of 0.1, 1.0 M, or saturated KCl. The "saturated calomel electrode" is the most common, and for this electrode the calomel, Hg_2Cl_2, is ground up with solid KCl and the solution is a saturated KCl solution. For this electrode the concentration of the chloride is therefore fixed at a given temperature, and one has an electrode whose emf is completely determined. This is, as we shall see, sometimes convenient.

18-4. Electrochemical Cells and Sign Conventions. The electrodes of the previous section can be combined in pairs to form electrochemical cells. The emf of such cells can be measured, and the free-energy change for the over-all reaction can be determined. The galvanic cell formed from two electrodes that operate in the same solution is most susceptible to exact theoretical interpretation and experimental study. The cell shown in Fig. 18-7 consisting of a Pt|H$_2$|H$^+$ and an Ag|AgCl|Cl$^-$ electrode is an example of such a cell. A hydrochloric acid solution is suitable for both electrodes.

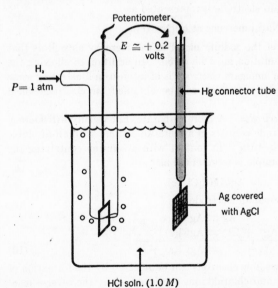

Fig. 18-7. Electrode arrangement corresponding to the cell Pt|H$_2$(1 atm)|HCl(1.0 M)|AgCl|Ag.

It would impose too great a limitation if such cells were the only ones which could be studied.   As mentioned previously, use can be made of cells consisting of electrodes operating in different solutions.   These are usually joined by a KCl salt bridge.   While quantitative difficulties are introduced by this procedure, the qualitative aspects of electrochemical cells treated in this section are completely applicable.

Two electrodes which are in a solution through which ions can move and which are joined by an external circuit constitute a galvanic cell.   Each electrode is able to gain or lose electrons.   For a given concentration of all the variable reagents, however, one electrode will generally have a greater tendency to drive electrons into the external circuit than the other electrode.   It is very convenient, *after having written down the cell as consisting of a particular electrode on the left and another on the right,* to describe the direction in which the electrons tend to flow by stating that the emf of the cell is positive or negative.   It should be clear that we are at liberty to attach either sign to a tendency of electrons to flow in either direction.   The procedure that is adopted here is that used by most American physical chemists.

An arrangement of the electrodes is decided upon, such as is represented by

$$Pt|H_2(1 \text{ atm})|HCl(1.0\ M)|AgCl|Ag$$

or as is depicted in Fig. 18-7.

The sign convention is that *an emf will be called positive if there is a tendency for electrons to be driven through the external circuit from left to right.* In the present example measurements show that the cell tends to drive electrons around the circuit, as indicated in Fig. 18-7, from left to right with an emf of about 0.2 volt.   We say that the cell has an emf of $+0.2$ volt.   Had we written down the cell in the reverse direction, we would have found that electrons were driven from right to left and the cell would then be said to have an emf of -0.2 volt.

Since the free energy of the cell reaction as well as the emf of the cell is of interest, we must also agree on how we are going to write this reaction.   Once it is decided which electrode is to be written on the left and which on the right, one proceeds to write the electrode reactions such that *electrons are given up to the external circuit by the left electrode and accepted from the external circuit by the right electrode.*   In the present example this gives

At left electrode	$\frac{1}{2}H_2 \rightleftharpoons H^+ + e^-$
At right electrode	$AgCl + e^- \rightleftharpoons Ag + Cl^-$
Over-all reaction	$\frac{1}{2}H_2 + AgCl \rightleftharpoons Ag + H^+ + Cl^-$ (12)

A positive emf for the cell implies an electron flow such that the reactions so written tend to proceed spontaneously in the direction in which they are written.   This corresponds to a decrease in the free energy as the reaction proceeds, and the relation between the free energy of the over-all reaction and the emf of the cell is therefore

$$\Delta G = -n\mathcal{F}\mathcal{E}$$

According to these sign conventions one has a spontaneous reaction, with the accompanying free-energy decrease, in the direction in which the reaction is written when the emf of the cell is positive. If the cell shows no driving force, the reaction has no spontaneous tendency to proceed and both ΔG and $\mathcal{E}$ are zero. The reaction tends to proceed spontaneously in the direction opposite to that written when the emf of the cell is negative.

The convenience introduced by strictly following these rules will become apparent as more electrochemical cells are considered.

18-5. Standard EMFs and Electrode Potentials. A method for the presentation of the data that are obtained from measurements of the equilibrium emf of electrochemical cells must now be developed. One expects, and a thermodynamic proof of this will be given in the next section, that varying the concentration of any reagents that are involved in the electrode process will affect the emf of the cell. In view of this, the emfs of cells with some agreed-upon reference, or standard, concentrations are reported. In keeping with the standard states introduced in the previous chapter, these standard-state conditions are chosen to consist of gases at unit activity, implying for most gases approximately 1 atm pressure, and solutes also at unit activity. For solutes, which for electrochemical cells are frequently ions, the activities, as we saw in the previous chapter, can be quite appreciably different from molar concentrations. The way in which activity coefficients can be determined from emf measurements will shortly be presented. For the present it is sufficient to recognize that a standard state is chosen and that it is desired to tabulate emfs of cells which have their variable reagents at unit activity.

It is impractical, however, to list the emfs of all possible combinations of electrodes, and it would be much more convenient to have some means of tabulating the relative electron-donating powers of the individual electrodes.

It is never possible to measure the emf of a single electrode. It is just this fact which allows a value for the electrode potential of some one electrode to be arbitrarily assigned. This reference electrode potential can then be used as a basis for the determination of the electrode potentials of all other electrodes. Quite arbitrarily, the standard electrode potential of the $\text{Pt}|\text{H}_2(a = 1$ atm$)|\text{H}^+(a = 1)$ electrode is taken as zero. The emf of a cell containing this electrode can now be measured, and the electrode potential of the other electrode can be determined.

It should be recognized that the standard electrode potential of an electrode represents the tendency of the electrode to deliver electrons to the external circuit relative to the tendency of the $\text{Pt}|\text{H}_2|\text{H}^+$ electrode to do so. A table of standard electrode potentials can now be built up. Measurement, for example, of the emf of the cell

$$\text{Pt}|\text{H}_2(1 \text{ atm})|\text{HCl}(a = 1)|\text{Cl}_2(1 \text{ atm})|\text{Pt}$$

gives the value $+1.358$ volts. This represents the difference in the tendency of the two electrodes to push electrons into the external circuit, the positive sign indicating that the tendency of the left electrode is greater. If standard potentials are denoted by a superscript $°$, we have

$$\mathcal{E}° = \mathcal{E}°_{\text{H}_2} - \mathcal{E}°_{\text{Cl}_2} = +1.358 \tag{13}$$

and with
$$\mathcal{E}^\circ_{H_2} = 0$$
$$\mathcal{E}^\circ_{Cl_2} = -1.358 \text{ volts} \tag{14}$$

The results for this cell show that, since the measured emf is positive, the hydrogen electrode gives up electrons and that these electrons are accepted by the chlorine electrode. The greater tendency of the hydrogen electrode to give off electrons is indicated by the more positive electrode potential, that is, 0 as against -1.358, that it has compared with the chlorine electrode.

In a similar manner one can arrange other electrodes along with the hydrogen electrode and use the cell emfs to determine the electrode potential of other electrodes.

One can, of course, also proceed by using any electrode that has been compared with the hydrogen electrode. The emf of the cell

$$Pt|Cl_2(1 \text{ atm})|HCl(a = 1)|AgCl(s)|Ag$$

is found to be -1.136 volts. From this datum one obtains

and
$$\mathcal{E}^\circ = \mathcal{E}^\circ_{Cl_2} - \mathcal{E}^\circ_{Ag, AgCl} = -1.136 \tag{15}$$
$$\mathcal{E}^\circ_{Ag, AgCl} = \mathcal{E}^\circ_{Cl_2} + 1.136$$
$$= -1.358 + 1.136 = -0.222 \text{ volt} \tag{16}$$

By means such as these, convenient pairs of electrodes can be selected and electrode potentials determined. Table 18-1, page 599, shows the results that are obtained for the more frequently encountered electrodes. These standard electrode potentials are called *oxidation* potentials because the listed numbers give the relative tendency for the electrode reaction to proceed with the loss of electrons, i.e., for oxidation to occur. The electrodes at the top of the table have a high tendency to give up electrons; i.e., the written reactions tend to proceed spontaneously. Those low down in the table have little tendency to proceed as written. It should be apparent that the plus and minus signs arise only because we arbitrarily assign a zero value to the H_2 electrode. One might have given this reference electrode some other value such as $+10$ volts, in which case the values in the table would all have been shifted upward by $+10$ volts.

The use of this table in calculating a cell emf can be illustrated by the example of the cell

$$Pt|Tl^+(a = 1), Tl^{3+}(a = 1)||Cl^-(a = 1)|Hg_2Cl_2(s)|Hg$$

where the double vertical line indicates a salt bridge separating the two solutions.

The electrode reactions and standard electrode emfs can be combined to give

Left electrode	$\frac{1}{2}Tl^+ \rightleftharpoons \frac{1}{2}Tl^{3+} + e^-$	$\mathcal{E}^\circ = -1.211$
Right electrode	$\frac{1}{2}Hg_2Cl_2 + e^- \rightleftharpoons Hg + Cl^-$	$-\mathcal{E}^\circ = +0.268$
Over-all reaction	$\frac{1}{2}Tl^+ + \frac{1}{2}Hg_2Cl_2 \rightleftharpoons \frac{1}{2}Tl^{3+} + Hg + Cl^-$	$\mathcal{E}^\circ = -0.943 \text{ volt}$

$$\tag{17}$$

Furthermore, for the over-all reaction

$$\Delta G^\circ = -n\mathcal{F}\mathcal{E}^\circ = -(1)(96,500)(-0.943)/4.18$$
$$= +21,800 \text{ cal} \tag{18}$$

The calculation tells us that the current will tend to flow from right to left through the external circuit of such a cell and that the reaction will tend to proceed spontaneously in the opposite direction to that written.

Two features of this calculation should be pointed out. In the first place, the reaction at the right electrode has been turned around so that it is shown as a reduction reaction. The sign of the value of the electrode potential that is found in Table 18-1 must therefore be changed. The right-electrode equation is then a reduction reaction, and the emf of $+0.268$ is the reduction potential of the electrode. One can then add the two electrode equations and their emfs to get the over-all results. If one prefers, on the other hand, one may write both equations as oxidation processes, as they are found in Table 18-1, and then subtract them to get the net effect of the cell.

The second point to be mentioned is that one can write the reactions, such as in the example, with one or two electrons exhibited. If two electrons are shown, this corresponds to two equivalents of reactants and the free-energy change will be twice as much as for one equivalent. The emf, of course, will not be altered by a change in the amount of material involved. We might write therefore

Left electrode	$Tl^+ \rightleftharpoons Tl^{3+} + 2e^-$	$\mathcal{E}° = -1.211$
Right electrode	$Hg_2Cl_2 + 2e^- \rightleftharpoons 2Hg + 2Cl^-$	$-\mathcal{E}° = +0.268$
Over-all reaction	$Tl^+ + Hg_2Cl_2 \rightleftharpoons Tl^{3+} + 2Hg + 2Cl^-$	$\mathcal{E}° = -0.943 \text{ volt}$

$$\text{(19)}$$

For the over-all reaction as written we calculate

$$\Delta G° = -n\mathcal{F}\mathcal{E}° = -\frac{(2)(96,500)(-0.943)}{4.18} = +43,600 \text{ cal} \qquad (20)$$

In a similar manner, one can determine the emf of any cell and the free-energy change for the over-all reaction for which the electrode potentials are listed in Table 18-1.

These results, however, apply only to standard-state conditions. To make any real use of these data, we must have some means for determining the emfs and free-energy changes when the reagents have concentrations other than those of the standard state.

18-6. The Concentration and Activity Dependence of the EMF. The dependence of the emf of a cell on the concentration, or more directly on the activity, of the variable reagents can be calculated from our knowledge of the relation between the free energy and the activity.

Consider an electrochemical cell for which the over-all chemical reaction is

$$aA + bB \rightleftharpoons cC + dD \qquad (21)$$

Further suppose that A, B, C, and D are reagents whose concentration can be varied; i.e., they are gases, or ions, or molecules in solution. If, in addition, there are solids involved in the reaction, they will contribute only a constant term to the results, as we shall see.

For species A the free energy of 1 mole can be written as

$$G_A = G_A° + RT \ln a_A \qquad (22)$$

Table 18-1. Standard Oxidation Potentials at 25°C

Electrode	Electrode reaction	$\varepsilon°$
Li|Li$^+$	Li $\rightleftharpoons$ Li$^+$ + e	3.025
K|K$^+$	K $\rightleftharpoons$ K$^+$ + e	2.922
Ca|Ca^{++}	Ca $\rightleftharpoons$ Ca^{++} + 2e	2.87
Na|Na$^+$	Na $\rightleftharpoons$ Na$^+$ + e	2.713
Mg|Mg^{++}	Mg $\rightleftharpoons$ Mg^{++} + 2e	2.40
Zn|Zn^{++}	Zn $\rightleftharpoons$ Zn^{++} + 2e	0.758
Fe|Fe^{++}	Fe $\rightleftharpoons$ Fe^{++} + 2e	0.44
Pt|Cr^{++}, Cr^{3+}	Cr^{++} $\rightleftharpoons$ Cr^{3+} + e	0.40
Cd|Cd^{++}	Cd $\rightleftharpoons$ Cd^{++} + 2e	0.398
Pb|PbSO$_4$|SO$^-$	Pb + SO$_4^-$ $\rightleftharpoons$ PbSO$_4$ + 2e	0.355
Sn|Sn^{++}	Sn $\rightleftharpoons$ Sn^{++} + 2e	0.14
Pb|Pb^{++}	Pb $\rightleftharpoons$ Pb^{++} + 2e	0.12
Pt|H$_2$|H$^+$	H$_2$ $\rightleftharpoons$ 2H$^+$ + 2e	Zero
Pt|Ti^{3+}, Ti^{4+}	Ti^{3+} $\rightleftharpoons$ Ti^{4+} + e	0.0
Ag|AgBr|Br$^-$	Ag + Br$^-$ $\rightleftharpoons$ AgBr + e	−0.073
Cu|CuCl|Cl$^-$	Cu + Cl$^-$ $\rightleftharpoons$ CuCl + e	−0.129
Ag|AgCl|Cl$^-$	Ag + Cl$^-$ $\rightleftharpoons$ AgCl + e	−0.2225
Hg|Hg$_2$Cl$_2$|Cl$^-$	2Hg + 2Cl$^-$ $\rightleftharpoons$ Hg$_2$Cl$_2$ + 2e	−0.2675
Cu|Cu^{++}	Cu $\rightleftharpoons$ Cu^{++} + 2e	−0.344
Pt|Fe(CN)$_6^{4-}$, Fe(CN)$_6^{3-}$	Fe(CN)$_6^{4-}$ $\rightleftharpoons$ Fe(CN)$_6^{3-}$ + e	−0.48
Pt|I$_2$|I$^-$	3I$^-$ $\rightleftharpoons$ I$_3^-$ + 2e	−0.54
Pt|MnO$_4^-$, MnO$_4^-$	MnO$_4^-$ $\rightleftharpoons$ MnO$_4^-$ + e	−0.66
Pt|O$_2$H$_2$O$_2$, H$^+$	H$_2$O$_2$ $\rightleftharpoons$ O$_2$ + 2H$^+$ + 2e	−0.68
Pt|H$_2$Q, Q|H	H$_2$Q $\rightleftharpoons$ Q + 2H$^+$ + 2e	−0.6996
Pt|Fe^{++}, Fe^{3+}	Fe^{++} $\rightleftharpoons$ Fe^{3+} + e	−0.771
Hg|Hg$_2^{++}$	2Hg $\rightleftharpoons$ Hg$_2^{++}$ + 2e	−0.799
Ag|Ag$^+$	Ag $\rightleftharpoons$ Ag$^+$ + e	−0.800
Pt|Hg$_2^{++}$, Hg^{++}	Hg$_2^{++}$ $\rightleftharpoons$ 2Hg$^+$ + 2e	−0.901
Au|AuCl$_4^-$, Cl$^-$	Au + 4Cl$^-$ $\rightleftharpoons$ AuCl$_4^-$ + 3e	−1.00
Pt|Br$_2$|Br$^-$	2Br$^-$ $\rightleftharpoons$ Br$_2$ + 2e	−1.066
Pt|MnO$_2$|Mn^{++}, H$^+$	Mn^{++} + 2H$_2$O $\rightleftharpoons$ MnO$_2$ + 4H$^+$ + 2e	−1.33
Pt|Cl$_2$|Cl$^-$	2Cl$^-$ $\rightleftharpoons$ Cl$_2$ + 2e	−1.359
Pt|Ce^{3+}, Ce^{4+}	Ce^{3+} $\rightleftharpoons$ Ce^{4+} + e	−1.61
Pt|PbSO$_4$|PbO$_2$|H$_2$SO$_4$	PbSO$_4$ + 2H$_2$O $\rightleftharpoons$ PbO$_2$ + SO$_4^-$ + 4H$^+$ + 2e	−1.68
Pg|Co^{++}, Co^{3+}	Co^{++} $\rightleftharpoons$ Co^{3+} + e	−1.82

and for a moles of reagent A the free energy is

$$aG = aG_A° + aRT \ln a_A$$
$$= aG_A° + RT \ln (a_A)^a \qquad (23)$$

From expressions like these for all four reagents, the free-energy change for the over-all cell reaction can be deduced, as was done in Chap. 7, and it gives

$$\Delta G = \Delta G° + RT \ln \frac{(a_C)^c (a_D)^d}{(a_A)^a (a_B)^b} \qquad (24)$$

where $\Delta G°$ is the difference in free energy of the products and the reactants when all reagents are in their standard states. Furthermore, according to the discussion of Sec. 18-1,

$$\Delta G = -n\mathfrak{F}\varepsilon \qquad \text{and} \qquad \Delta G° = -n\mathfrak{F}\varepsilon°$$

which gives

$$\varepsilon = \varepsilon° - \frac{RT}{n\mathfrak{F}} \ln \frac{(a_C)^c(a_D)^d}{(a_A)^a(a_B)^b} \tag{25}$$

This important equation shows how the emf of a cell can be calculated from the standard electrode potentials of Table 18-1 and the activity coefficients of the reagents. It is clear that, when the activities of all the reagents are unity, the logarithmic term drops out and $\varepsilon = \varepsilon°$, that is, the emf for the standard states.

At 25°C, the temperature of the standard electrode potentials and that at which most electrochemical results are reported, the factor before the logarithm term can be explicitly worked out and gives

$$\varepsilon = \varepsilon° - \frac{0.05915}{n} \log \frac{(a_C)^c(a_D)^d}{(a_A)^a(a_B)^b} \tag{26}$$

Included in the numerical factor is the term for the conversion to logarithms to the base 10.

It should be recognized that the activity term has the familiar form of the equilibrium-constant expression. It is not, however, the equilibrium constant since the activities of the reagents have the values that are determined by the solutions used to make up the cell, and these are not generally the equilibrium values.

As in the development of the equilibrium-constant expression, the concentrations of solid or otherwise fixed concentration reagents are not explicitly included. The contribution to the free energy and the emf of the cell of such reagents is implicitly included in the $\Delta G°$ and $\varepsilon°$ terms.

The use of Eq. (26) is illustrated by the calculation of the emf of the cell

$$\text{Ag}|\text{AgCl}(s)|\text{Cl}^-(a = 0.05),\ \text{Fe}^{3+}(a = 0.1),\ \text{Fe}^{++}(a = 0.02)|\text{Pt}$$

The over-all reaction and the standard emfs are calculated from the reactions and the data of Table 18-1 as

Left electrode	$\text{Ag} + \text{Cl}^- \rightleftharpoons \text{AgCl} + e^-$	$\varepsilon° = -0.2225$
Right electrode	$\text{Fe}^{3+} + e^- \rightleftharpoons \text{Fe}^{++}$	$-\varepsilon° = +0.771$
Over-all reaction	$\text{Ag} + \text{Fe}^{3+} + \text{Cl}^- \rightleftharpoons \text{Fe}^{++} + \text{AgCl}$	$\varepsilon° = +0.549$ volt

$$\tag{27}$$

Equation (26) now gives

$$\begin{aligned}
\varepsilon &= \varepsilon° - \frac{0.05915}{n} \log \frac{a_{\text{Fe}^{++}}}{(a_{\text{Fe}^{3+}})(a_{\text{Cl}^-})} \\
&= +0.549 - \frac{0.05915}{1} \log \frac{0.02}{(0.1)(0.05)} \\
&= +0.549 - 0.036 = +0.513 \text{ volt}
\end{aligned} \tag{28}$$

An alternative way of performing the calculation is to obtain the electrode emfs for the activities of the reagents and then combine these electrode emfs. Thus, the left-electrode reaction is

$$\text{Ag} + \text{Cl}^- \rightleftharpoons \text{AgCl} + e^- \tag{29}$$

and the left-electrode potential is

$$\mathcal{E}_{\text{left}} = \mathcal{E}_{\text{left}}^{\circ} - \frac{0.05915}{n} \log \frac{1}{a_{\text{Cl}^-}}$$

$$= -0.2225 - 0.05915 \log \frac{1}{0.05}$$

$$= -0.2225 - 0.0771 = -0.2996 \text{ volt} \tag{30}$$

For the right electrode, written as an oxidation reaction this time,

$$\text{Fe}^{++} \rightleftharpoons \text{Fe}^{3+} + e^- \tag{31}$$

and

$$\mathcal{E}_{\text{right}} = \mathcal{E}_{\text{right}}^{\circ} - \frac{0.05915}{n} \log \frac{a_{\text{Fe}^{3+}}}{a_{\text{Fe}^{++}}}$$

$$= -0.771 - \frac{0.05915}{1} \log \frac{0.1}{0.02}$$

$$= -0.771 - 0.041 = -0.812 \text{ volt} \tag{32}$$

Finally, the cell emf is obtained as

$$\mathcal{E} = \mathcal{E}_{\text{left}}^{\circ} - \mathcal{E}_{\text{right}}^{\circ} = -0.2996 + 0.812$$

$$= +0.512 \text{ volt} \tag{33}$$

as before.

Either procedure can be used with equal success. One perhaps needs to be cautioned again that the two electrode reactions must be written with the same number of electrons before they can be combined. While the standard emfs are not changed by the amounts involved, the concentration-dependent term is.

18-7. Activity Coefficients from EMF Measurements. Real use of the equations of the previous section can be made only if the activities of the electrolytes in the cell solution can be evaluated. Some methods for doing this have been mentioned in the previous chapter, but it is a fact that emf measurements themselves generally provide the most useful and accurate method. Again it is convenient to determine the relation between activities and concentrations by means of the activity coefficients.

A satisfactory method for determining the standard emfs must also be given. They have been defined as being the emf of the cell when all variable concentration reagents have unit activity. The definition is not satisfactory unless a valid method is given for determining when the activities are unity so that the standard emfs can be obtained.

An example will show how standard emfs and activity coefficients can be obtained electrochemically. Consider the cell

$$\text{Ag}|\text{AgCl}(s)|\text{HCl}(c)|\text{H}_2(1 \text{ atm})|\text{Pt}$$

At a pressure of 1 atm, hydrogen will behave ideally, and its activity will be very nearly equal to its pressure.

The over-all reaction is determined by summing the electrode reactions, thus

$$\text{Ag} + \text{Cl}^- \rightleftharpoons \text{AgCl}(s) + e^-$$
$$\underline{\text{H}^+ + e^- \rightleftharpoons \tfrac{1}{2}\text{H}_2}$$
$$\text{Ag} + \text{H}^+ + \text{Cl}^- \rightleftharpoons \text{AgCl}(s) + \tfrac{1}{2}\text{H}_2 \tag{34}$$

The emf of the cell at 25°C can be interpreted, according to Eq. (25), as

$$\mathcal{E} = \mathcal{E}° - \frac{0.05915}{1} \log \frac{(P_{H_2})^{\frac{1}{2}}}{(a_{H^+})(a_{Cl^-})} \tag{35}$$

At a hydrogen pressure of 1 atm this becomes

$$\mathcal{E} = \mathcal{E}° + 0.05915 \log (a_{H^+})(a_{Cl^-}) \tag{36}$$

In terms of concentrations and activity coefficients the expression can be written as

$$\begin{aligned} \mathcal{E} &= \mathcal{E}° + 0.05915 \log (\gamma_+\gamma_-)[H^+][Cl^-] \\ &= \mathcal{E}° + 0.05915 \log \gamma_+\gamma_- + 0.05915 \log [H^+][Cl^-] \end{aligned} \tag{37}$$

The square brackets imply, as is customary, the "active mass" of the reagent, and for solutes the active mass is taken as the molar concentration. The directly measurable quantities are now rearranged to the left side of the equation to give

$$\mathcal{E} - 0.05915 \log [H^+][Cl^-] = \mathcal{E}° + 0.05915 \log \gamma_+\gamma_- \tag{38}$$

Furthermore, for solutions containing appreciable HCl, the concentrations of H^+ and Cl^- are equal and correspond to c, the hydrochloric acid concentration. Thus

$$\mathcal{E} - 0.05915 \log c^2 = \mathcal{E}° + 0.05915 \log \gamma_{\pm}^2 \tag{39}$$

and finally

$$\mathcal{E} - 0.11830 \log c = \mathcal{E}° + 0.11830 \log \gamma_{\pm} \tag{40}$$

The right side of the equation is made up of a constant term and the logarithmic term, which, for solutions in the Debye-Hückel limiting-law region, can be expected to be proportional to $c^{\frac{1}{2}}$. The left side of the equation is therefore plotted against $c^{\frac{1}{2}}$ as is shown in Fig. 18-8.

At $c = 0$ the activity coefficient must go to unity, and the logarithmic term on the right side of the equation will vanish. The extrapolation of the data of Fig. 18-8 to $c^{\frac{1}{2}} = 0$ gives therefore a value of $\mathcal{E}°$. In this way one finds

$$\mathcal{E}° = -0.2225 \text{ volt} \tag{41}$$

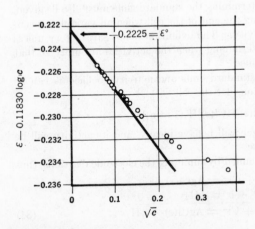

Fig. 18-8. Determination of $\mathcal{E}°$ and $\gamma_{\pm}(HCl)$ for the cell. Ag|AgCl(s)| HCl(c)|H₂(1 atm)|Pt from the measured values of $\mathcal{E}$ at various concentrations of HCl. (The straight-line extrapolation is drawn with the slope predicted by the Debye-Hückel limiting law.) (*Partly from L. P. Hammett, "Introduction to the Study of Physical Chemistry," McGraw-Hill Book Company, Inc., New York, 1952.*)

It is seen by looking at the original cell, or the cell reactions, that

$$\mathcal{E}° = \mathcal{E}°_{Ag/AgCl} - \mathcal{E}°_{H_2} \tag{42}$$

Since $\mathcal{E}°_{H_2}$ is by definition equal to zero, the desired result

$$\mathcal{E}°_{Ag/AgCl} = -0.2225 \text{ volt} \tag{43}$$

as listed in Table 18-1, is obtained. In a similar way the standard electrode potentials of other electrodes are obtained.

Now it can be shown how activity coefficients of HCl can also be determined from the data of Fig. 18-8. Reference to Eq. (40) shows that once a value for $\mathcal{E}°$ is obtained, the measured value of the left side of the equation allows the calculation of the only remaining unknown, the log $\gamma_{\pm}$ term. One obtains therefore, as shown in Table 18-2, the mean-activity coefficients of HCl at any concentration for which emf data are available.

In a similar way, the activity coefficient of other electrolytes involved in an electrochemical reaction can be determined. As before, no way is found for the determination of the individual activity coefficients and, therefore, again mean-activity coefficients are all that need be considered.

18-8. Equilibrium Constants and Solubility Products from EMF Data. The data of Table 18-1 constitute a wealth of information on the free energies of inorganic reactions. Although reported as emfs, these data are readily converted to free energies by the expression $\Delta G° = -n\mathcal{F}\mathcal{E}°$. Such free-energy data are of use in the determination of equilibrium properties and, in particular, of the equilibrium constant for the over-all cell reaction.

Consider, for example, the possibility of reducing ferric iron to ferrous iron by the use of metallic zinc as a reducing agent. The reaction in which one would be interested might be performed in the cell

$$Zn|Zn^{++}| \,|Fe^{3+}, Fe^{++}|Pt$$

and the reaction would be

$$\frac{1}{2}Zn \rightleftharpoons \frac{1}{2}Zn^{++} + e^- \qquad \mathcal{E}° = +0.7620$$

$$\underline{Fe^{3+} + e^- \rightleftharpoons Fe^{++} \qquad -\mathcal{E}° = +0.771}$$

$$Fe^{3+} + \frac{1}{2}Zn \rightleftharpoons Fe^{++} + \frac{1}{2}Zn^{++} \qquad \mathcal{E}° = +1.533 \text{ volts} \tag{44}$$

The cell emf is written as

$$\mathcal{E} = +1.533 - \frac{0.05915}{1} \log \frac{a_{Fe^{++}}(a_{Zn^{++}})^{\frac{1}{2}}}{a_{Fe^{3+}}} \tag{45}$$

Table 18-2. Mean-activity Coefficients for HCl from the EMF of the Cell
$$Ag|AgCl(s)|HCl(c)|H_2(1 \text{ atm})|Pt$$

c_{HCl} (moles/liter)	$-\mathcal{E}$ (volts)	$\gamma_{\pm}$
0.003215	0.52053	0.942
0.005619	0.49257	0.926
0.009138	0.46860	0.909
0.013407	0.44974	0.895
0.02563	0.41824	0.866
0.1238	0.34199	0.788

At equilibrium the cell would be able to perform no useful work, and its emf must then be zero. A similar argument based on free energy gives the same result since $\Delta G = -n\mathcal{F}\mathcal{E}$ and, as was seen in Chap. 7, $\Delta G = 0$ at equilibrium. For equilibrium activities of the variable reagents of Eq. (45) one has, therefore,

$$\mathcal{E} = 0 \tag{46}$$

and

$$1.533 = \frac{0.05915}{1} \log \left[\frac{a_{Fe^{++}}(a_{Zn^{++}})^{\frac{1}{2}}}{a_{Fe^{3+}}} \right]_{equil} \tag{47}$$

The activity expression is now the familiar equilibrium constant, expressed correctly in activities. Thus

$$\left[\frac{a_{Fe^{++}}(a_{Zn^{++}})^{\frac{1}{2}}}{a_{Fe^{3+}}} \right]_{equil} = K = 8 \times 10^{25} \tag{48}$$

The result shows that, for any reasonable value of the activity or concentration of Zn^{++}, essentially all the iron will be reduced to the ferrous state by zinc.

For some cells the over-all reaction corresponds to the solution of an insoluble salt. In such cases the equilibrium constant that can be determined is a solubility product. This can be illustrated by the cell

$$Ag|Ag^+, Br^-\|AgBr(s)|Ag$$

The electrode reactions and the emfs are

$$\begin{array}{ll} Ag \rightleftharpoons Ag^+ + e^- & \mathcal{E}° = -0.7995 \\ \underline{AgBr(s) + e^- \rightleftharpoons Ag + Br^-} & \underline{-\mathcal{E}° = +0.0711} \\ AgBr(s) \rightleftharpoons Ag^+ + Br^- & \mathcal{E}° = -0.7284 \end{array} \tag{49}$$

The cell emf is written as

$$\mathcal{E} = -0.7284 - \frac{0.05915}{1} \log \, (a_{Ag^+})(a_{Br^-}) \tag{50}$$

The solubility of silver bromide is very small, and the activity coefficients will be sufficiently close to unity to allow, if no other ions are present in appreciable amounts, the activities to be replaced by concentrations. Again at equilibrium the emf of the cell will be zero and

$$0.7284 = -0.05915 \log \, \{[Ag^+][Br^-]\}_{equil} \tag{51}$$

or

$$\{[Ag^+][Br^-]\}_{equil} = K_{sol} = 4.8 \times 10^{-13} \tag{52}$$

The examples of this section are intended to show that the data of Table 18-1 can be used to determine the equilibrium constant for any reaction which is the over-all reaction for a cell made from electrodes included in Table 18-1.

18-9. Electrode-concentration Cells. A particularly simple electrochemical reaction is one that performs the dilution of either the electrode material itself, as treated here, or of the electrolyte, as studied in the next section. For the electrode material to be involved in such a process, it must have a variable concentration. Gaseous electrodes and amalgam electrodes fall into this classification.

A cell can be constructed from amalgams with two different concentrations of the same metal. The cell

$$Pb\text{-}Hg(a_1)|PbSO_4(soln)|Hg\text{-}Pb(a_2)$$

allows the electrode reactions

$$Pb(a_1) \rightleftharpoons Pb^{++} + 2e^-$$
$$\underline{Pb^{++} + 2e^- \rightleftharpoons Pb(a_2)}$$
$$Pb(a_1) \rightleftharpoons Pb(a_2) \tag{53}$$

to be written.   No chemical change occurs, and the reaction consists of the transfer of lead from an amalgam of one concentration to that of another concentration.   The emf of such a cell, which necessarily has $\varepsilon° = 0$, is

$$\varepsilon = -\frac{0.05915}{2} \log \frac{a_2}{a_1} \tag{54}$$

The lead will tend to go spontaneously from the high-activity amalgam to that of low activity.   For example, if a_1 is greater than a_2, ε is positive and the reaction proceeds in the direction indicated.

One finds that solutions of metals in mercury constitute fairly ideal solutions and that the emfs are almost correctly calculated by using concentrations instead of activities.   Table 18-3 shows some data which illustrate this.

The electrode-concentration cells consisting of gas electrodes can be illustrated by the cell

$$Pt|H_2(P_1)|HCl|H_2(P_2)|Pt$$

At all ordinary pressures hydrogen behaves very nearly ideally, and the emf corresponding to the over-all cell reaction

$$H_2(P_1) \rightleftharpoons H_2(P_2) \tag{55}$$

can be written as

$$\varepsilon = -\frac{0.05915}{2} \log \frac{P_2}{P_1} \tag{56}$$

For satisfactorily reversible platinum electrodes one finds experimental results in agreement with this expression.

18-10. Electrolyte-concentration Cells.   A second type of cell whose emf is derived only from the free-energy change of a dilution reaction is that in which the electrolyte of the cell is involved in the dilution.   If one attempts to construct such a cell by having two solutions of different concentrations in physical contact with each other, complications arise because of the nonequilibrium processes that occur at the liquid-liquid junction.   For the present only the

Table 18-3. EMFs of Cadmium-amalgam Electrode-concentration Cells

Grams Cd/100 g Hg		Emf (volts)	
Left electrode	Right electrode	Observed	Calculated $= \dfrac{0.05915}{2} \log \dfrac{10}{1}$
1.000	0.1000	0.02966	0.02957
0.1000	0.01000	0.02960	0.02957
0.01000	0.001000	0.02956	0.02957
0.001000	0.0001000	0.02950	0.02957

simpler *concentration cells without liquid junction* are considered. Such cells can be illustrated with two cells of the type

$$Pt|H_2|HCl(c)|AgCl(s)|Ag$$

each of which has a reaction

$$\tfrac{1}{2}H_2 + AgCl \rightleftharpoons Ag + H^+(c) + Cl^-(c) \tag{57}$$

Consider two such cells electrically connected through their silver electrodes in the opposed manner,

$$Pt|H_2HCl(c_1)|AgCl|Ag\text{---}Ag|AgCl|HCl(c_2)|H_2|Pt$$

The over-all reaction is now the sum of the two simple cell reactions. If the pressure of hydrogen gas is the same for both terminal electrodes, the electrode reactions can be combined to give

Left cell	$\tfrac{1}{2}H_2 + AgCl \rightleftharpoons Ag + H^+(c_1) + Cl^-(c_1)$
Right cell	$Ag + H^+(c_2) + Cl^-(c_2) \rightleftharpoons \tfrac{1}{2}H_2 + AgCl$
Over-all reaction	$H^+(c_2) + Cl^-(c_2) \rightleftharpoons H^+(c_1) + H^+(c_1)$ (58)

The over-all reaction involves therefore no chemical change and consists only of the transfer of HCl from a concentration c_2 to a concentration c_1. The emf of the complete cell is expressed as

$$\begin{aligned}
\varepsilon &= -\frac{0.05915}{1} \log \frac{(a_{H^+})_1(a_{Cl^-})_1}{(a_{H^+})_2(a_{Cl^-})_2} \\
&= -0.05915 \log \frac{[a_\pm]_1^2}{[a_\pm]_2^2} \\
&= -0.11830 \log \frac{(a_\pm)_1}{(a_\pm)_2} \tag{59}
\end{aligned}$$

Again one can see that the spontaneous process takes HCl from a higher activity, or concentration, to a lower activity, or concentration. If, for example, c_2 is greater than c_1 and therefore $(a_\pm)_2$ is greater than $(a_\pm)_1$, the emf will be positive and the reaction will proceed in the direction in which it is written.

One can clearly use such concentration cells to determine the activity of an electrolyte at one concentration compared with the activity of an electrolyte at another concentration.

The principal purpose in presenting these concentration cells here is, however, to provide a contrast to the situation that arises when concentration cells with liquid junctions are dealt with.

18-11. Electrolyte-concentration Cells with Liquid Junction. The treatment of emfs has so far ignored the problem that arises if one seeks to couple two electrodes which operate in different solutions. If, for instance, one studies the cell consisting of a $Zn|Zn^{++}$ electrode and a $Cu|Cu^{++}$ electrode, one must separate the two solutions, probably $ZnSO_4$ and $CuSO_4$, so that they cannot mix with each other. If the solutions do mix, copper will plate out directly onto the zinc electrode and no emf will be obtained. We are forced therefore to form a liquid junction between the solutions, and, as we shall see, this gives rise to a *junction potential*. Since the direct contact between solutions of different concentration is not a balanced state as required for reversible processes, the system is not directly susceptible to thermodynamic analysis. The source of the junction potential will, however, be seen if the cell reaction of a concentration cell is treated in detail.

The dilution of HCl was studied in the previous section but can also be accomplished in a cell with a liquid junction as illustrated in Fig. 18-9. Assume that two HCl solutions of different concentration can be brought together and prevented from mixing. The flowing of two streams of solution together sometimes accomplishes this. One then can set up the cell

$$\text{Pt}|\text{H}_2|\text{HCl}(c_1)|\text{HCl}(c_2)|\text{H}_2|\text{Pt}$$

The emf of the cell can be related to the over-all reaction that occurs when 1 faraday of current flows. The reactions as herein occur at electrodes and those that occur at the liquid junction can be written separately. The electrode reactions are

At left electrode $\qquad\qquad \frac{1}{2}\text{H}_2 \rightarrow \text{H}^+(c_1) + e^-$

At right electrode $\qquad\quad \text{H}^+(c_2) + e^- \rightarrow \frac{1}{2}\text{H}_2$

Over-all electrode reaction $\overline{\qquad\quad \text{H}^+(c_2) \rightarrow \text{H}^+(c_1) \qquad}$ (60)

The junction reaction is understood by reference to Fig. 18-9. As the current flows according to our convention, 1 faraday of positive current must pass through the cell and therefore across the junction. The fraction of current carried by the ions is expressed in terms of their transference numbers,

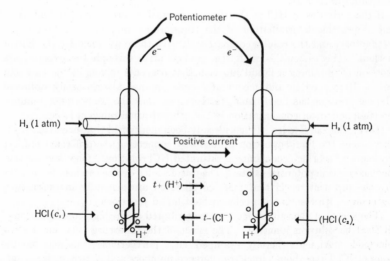

$$\tfrac{1}{2}\text{H}_2 \rightleftharpoons \text{H}^+(c_1) + e^- \qquad\qquad\qquad \text{H}^+(c_2) + e^- \rightleftharpoons \tfrac{1}{2}\text{H}_2$$

Fig. 18-9. An electrochemical cell with a liquid junction.

and t_+ equivalents of H^+ move to the right while t_- equivalents of Cl^- move to the left. The junction reactions are therefore

$$t_+H^+(c_1) \rightarrow t_+H^+(c_2)$$

or $$(1 - t_-)H^+(c_1) \rightarrow (1 - t_-)H^+(c_2)$$

and $$t_-Cl^-(c_2) \rightarrow t_-Cl^-(c_1) \tag{61}$$

The electrode reaction and the junction reactions are now combined to give the over-all cell reaction. Thus

Electrode reaction $\qquad\qquad H^+(c_2) \rightarrow H^+(c_1)$

Junction reactions $\qquad H^+(c_1) - t_-H^+(c_1) \rightarrow H^+(c_2) - t_-H^+(c_2)$

$$\qquad\qquad\qquad\qquad t_-Cl^-(c_2) \rightarrow t_-Cl^-(c_1)$$

Over-all cell reaction $\quad t_-[H^+(c_2) + Cl^-(c_2)] \rightarrow t_-[H^+(c_1) + Cl^-(c_1)] \tag{62}$

The emf of this cell, which has $\mathcal{E}° = 0$, can now be written as

$$\mathcal{E} = -\frac{0.05915}{1} \log \frac{[(a_{H^+})_2(a_{Cl^-})_2]^{t_-}}{[(a_{H^+})_1(a_{Cl^-})_1]^{t_-}}$$

$$= -0.05915t_- \log \frac{[a_\pm]_2^2}{[a_\pm]_1^2}$$

$$= -0.11830t_- \log \frac{(a_\pm)_2}{(a_\pm)_1} \tag{63}$$

The emf of this cell, unlike that without a liquid junction, depends on the transference numbers. Such cells are frequently described as *concentration cells with transference.*

If the activities of HCl at the two concentrations are known, the measured emf allows the determination of the transference number. The method is satisfactory, and the results compare well with those obtained by the Hittorf method. The difficulties with the method arise through the experimental problem of obtaining a liquid junction that prevents mixing of the two solutions. Reproducible and meaningful emfs are not always easily obtained. The assumption has been made, furthermore, that the transference numbers are independent of concentration in the concentration range c_1 to c_2.

18-12. The Salt Bridge. It has already been mentioned that one attempts to circumvent the liquid-junction problem by connecting the different solutions by means of a bridge containing a saturated KCl solution. One then assumes that no junction potential exists. The use of such a device can best be justified by the empirical result that emfs so obtained are generally in satisfactory agreement with results from cells without liquid junctions.

The success of the salt bridge can be attributed to the high concentration of KCl at the solution junction. The effect of the difference between the two electrode solutions is thereby swamped out. Furthermore, the fact that the ions of KCl have about equal transference numbers and diffusibilities is said to be important. The mechanism of the salt bridge is, however, difficult to analyze, and only with a detailed understanding of its operation (it is not a thermodynamic device) can the role of these quantities be understood. The salt bridge is often used as a convenient device for constructing an electrode, as in the assembly of Fig. 18-6. Such an electrode can dip into the solution of another electrode to form an electrochemical cell. When the two electrode solutions could have been mixed and have not been mixed only because of cell-construction convenience, the cell is susceptible to thermodynamic treatment and thermodynamic functions enter into the cell emf expression; i.e., the activity of an electrolyte will occur, but an individual ion activity will not. The cell

$$Hg|Hg_2Cl_2(s), KCl(1\ N)||HCl|H_2(1\ atm)|Pt$$

might be constructed, for example, and the cell reaction

$$Hg_2Cl_2 + H_2 \rightleftharpoons 2Hg + 2Cl^- + 2H^+ \tag{64}$$

would be written. The cell emf expression is then

$$\mathcal{E} = \mathcal{E}^\circ - \frac{(2)(0.05915)}{2} \log a_{Cl^-} a_{H^+} \tag{65}$$

A typical thermodynamic-activity expression, $a_{Cl^-} a_{H^+}$ or $a_\pm^2$, occurs.

The nonthermodynamic nature of the salt bridge is illustrated when the electrode solutions must be separated for an emf to be produced. The cell

$$Pt|H_2(1\ atm)|HCl(c = 0.01)||HCl(c = 0.1)|H_2(1\ atm)|Pt$$

can be constructed and an emf obtained. The electrode reactions are

Left electrode $\qquad \frac{1}{2}H_2 \rightleftharpoons H^+(0.01) + e^-$

Right electrode $\quad H^+(0.1) + e^- \rightleftharpoons \frac{1}{2}H_2$ $\qquad\qquad$ (66)

The net reaction, on the assumption that no junction reaction need be considered, is

$$H^+(0.10) \rightleftharpoons H^+(0.01) \tag{67}$$

Since the $\mathcal{E}^\circ$ value is zero, the cell emf can be written as

$$\mathcal{E} = -0.05915 \log \frac{a_{0.01H^+}}{a_{0.10H^+}} \tag{68}$$

This apparent approach to the activities of individual ions of an electrolyte is, however, upset by the assumptions made concerning the effectiveness of the salt bridge.

Although a cell making use of a salt bridge is not one that can be analyzed by strict thermodynamic arguments, in a practical way the salt bridge is effective and allows cells to be studied that consist of electrodes that require different solutions.

The example of the reduction of ferric to ferrous ion by metallic zinc can illustrate this further. The salt-bridge arrangement of Sec. 18-8,

$$Zn|Zn^{++}||Fe^{3+}, Fe^{++}|Pt$$

gives, with the assumption that the salt bridge eliminates any junction potential, the result

$$\left[\frac{(a_{Fe^{++}})(a_{Zn^{++}})^{\frac{1}{2}}}{a_{Fe^{3+}}} \right]_{equil} = 8 \times 10^{25} \tag{69}$$

Such a result is of real analytical interest in that it allows the calculation of the amount of Fe^{3+} ion remaining in that oxidation state when a reduction with zinc is performed. The expression of Eq. (69) is, however, never of consequence in any strict thermodynamic study.

The type of thermodynamic question that might be asked about this system deals with the thermodynamic equilibrium constant for, for example, the reaction

$$Zn + 2FeCl_3(aq) \rightleftharpoons ZnCl_2(aq) + 2FeCl_2(aq)$$

The equilibrium-constant expression can be written as

$$K_{th} = \frac{(a_{ZnCl_2})(a_{FeCl_2})^2}{(a_{FeCl_3})^2} \tag{70}$$

Although the activity of an electrolyte in solution can be obtained by thermodynamic methods, as was the activity of HCl in Sec. 18-7, no thermodynamic way exists to evaluate individual ion activities. It follows that no rigorous thermodynamic treatment will allow the activities of the chloride ions to be canceled out from Eq. (70) to give a value for the expression of Eq. (69).

Thus, with the use of a salt bridge, results of considerable interest but of no exact thermodynamic value can be obtained.

18-13. The Glass Electrode. Before proceeding to an important application of emf measurements, brief mention should be made of a component of the most frequently encountered electrochemical instrument. This component is an electrode called the *glass electrode*. Figure 18-10 indicates the typical construction of a glass electrode, which, however, is commercially available in a variety of sizes and shapes. The *electrode*, not the cell, usually consists of the arrangement

$$Ag|AgCl(s)|HCl(c = 1)|glass$$

The value of the electrode stems from the fact that, when it is placed in a solution of given acidity and the cell is completed by use of another electrode, the emf of the cell appears to depend primarily on the difference in the concentration or activity of the hydrogen ions on either side of the glass.

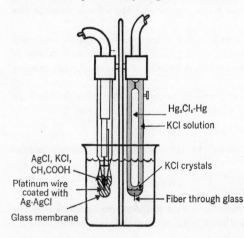

Hg₂Cl₂·Hg
KCl solution

AgCl, KCl, CH₃COOH
Platinum wire coated with Ag·AgCl
Glass membrane

KCl crystals
Fiber through glass

Fig. 18-10. The glass electrode and calomel electrode of a pH meter. (*From F. Daniels, J. H. Mathews, J. W. Williams, and staff, "Experimental Physical Chemistry," 4th ed., McGraw-Hill Book Company, Inc., New York, 1949.*)

The glass membrane of the glass electrode separates two different solutions, as does the KCl salt bridge. The emf of a cell involving the glass electrode can be expected therefore to be similarly lacking in rigorous thermodynamic interpretation. Unlike the salt bridge, which provides for electrical conduction across the liquid junction, the glass membrane apparently leads to a cell whose emf is primarily responsive to hydrogen ions. The detailed mechanism by which this membrane, and therefore the glass electrode, operates is difficult to analyze. Such analysis, furthermore, does not depend on thermodynamic considerations and does not interpret the mechanism in terms of thermodynamic quantities.

Much of the importance of the glass electrode stems from its lack of response to various oxidizing and reducing agents and to a large variety of ionic species. Difficulties do occur, however, if the glass electrode is used in solutions of high sodium-ion concentration or in solution sufficiently alkaline to attack the glass membrane.

18-14. pH Definition and Measurement.   In many areas of chemistry it is very convenient to correlate the properties of the system with something related to the hydrogen-ion concentration. Thus, in a titration of an acid with a base one might try to follow the process and determine the end point by any of a number of physical measurements. Properties that are closely dependent on the hydrogen-ion concentration would be most satisfactory. In a like manner it appears that some reactions, as was discussed in Chap. 11, are *acid-catalyzed;* i.e., it appears to be possible to correlate the reaction rate with the concentration of the hydrogen ion.

Such applications are not strictly thermodynamic, and in these applications it is not clearly specified whether it is the hydrogen-ion concentration that is needed or whether it is some effective hydrogen-ion concentration. There seems, therefore, little necessity to try to use the thermodynamically suggested activities or activity coefficients. The fact that the activity of a single ion would be encountered emphasizes the impropriety of inserting this thermodynamic concept.

A convenient form for the expression of hydrogen-ion concentrations was suggested in 1909 by Sorensen. He introduced the term pH, and his original definition gave

$$pH = - \log [H^+] \tag{71}$$

Hydrogen-ion concentrations, as was shown in Sec. 16-6, can be deduced for dilute solutions of acids from conductance measurements, and with such data the pH, according to Eq. (71), can be obtained.

Most applications, however, require a measure of something like the hydrogen-ion concentration in solutions that may be concentrated and that may contain a number of other ionic species. Conductance measurements are therefore unsatisfactory, and one is led to consider some electrochemical cell whose emf might give a suitable hydrogen-ion index.

One might consider, for example, the cell

$$Pt|H_2(1 \text{ atm}) \text{ soln}| \ |Hg_2Cl_2(\text{satd})|Hg_2Cl_2(s)|Hg$$

in which a hydrogen electrode operates in the solution of interest and the cell is completed by a calomel electrode connected through a salt bridge. The electrode reactions are

Left electrode $\qquad \frac{1}{2}H_2 \rightleftharpoons H^+ + e^-$

Right electrode $\quad \frac{1}{2}Hg_2Cl_2(s) + e^- \rightleftharpoons Hg + Cl^-(satd)$

$$\frac{1}{2}H_2 + \frac{1}{2}Hg_2Cl_2 \rightleftharpoons H^+ + Cl^-(satd) + Hg \qquad (72)$$

If the salt bridge is assumed to be effective and the chloride concentration and activity are fixed and included in a constant emf term, one can write

$$\mathcal{E} = \text{const} - \frac{0.05915}{1} \log a_{H^+} \qquad (73)$$

The measured emf, after the cell has been standardized by measurements on, for example, a 1 M HCl solution, gives an indication of the hydrogen-ion concentration or activity, the latter being, as pointed out, not well defined. Such a cell does, however, give the information that would be needed, for example, to follow an acid-base titration or to correlate the rate of an acid-catalyzed reaction with the acidity of the solution. The practical difficulties and inconvenience of the hydrogen electrode makes, however, the hydrogen-calomel cell unsuitable.

By far the most frequently used electrochemical device is the *pH meter*, which makes use of the combination of a glass electrode and a calomel electrode. The emf of such an assembly is found to depend on the acidity of a solution in much the same way as the hydrogen-calomel electrode. Thus one can formally write for the pH meter the equation

$$\mathcal{E} = (\mathcal{E})^\circ - 0.05915 \log a_{H^+}$$

or $\qquad\qquad\qquad -\log a_{H^+} = \dfrac{\mathcal{E} - \mathcal{E}^\circ}{0.05915} \qquad (74)$

A value of $\mathcal{E}^\circ$ in Eq. (74) is not a standard oxidation potential, but it is a constant which can be evaluated from a measurement on a solution of known hydrogen-ion concentration. The measured $\mathcal{E}$ of a pH meter can then be inserted to give a numerical value for the right side of the equation when some test solution is used. The scale of the pH meter can be arranged to give directly the right side of Eq. (74) rather than the value of $\mathcal{E}$. Equation (74) suggests that this number will be a suitable hydrogen-ion index. It is convenient therefore to drop the original Sorensen pH definition and instead to define pH as

$$pH = \frac{\mathcal{E} - \mathcal{E}_0}{0.05915} \qquad (75)$$

where $\mathcal{E}$ is the emf of the pH meter assembly. Other, similar pH definitions are also possible. A suitable choice of $\mathcal{E}_0$ allows this pH scale to coincide quite well with that of Eq. (71) based on conductance results.

It is important to recognize that the operational definition of Eq. (75) leads to a hydrogen-ion index that has many important applications. The pH so defined, however, is only loosely related to thermodynamic quantities.   A complete and detailed understanding of the glass electrode, or of a salt bridge, would lead to a molecular-type interpretation of pH, and this interpretation would not necessarily involve thermodynamic activities or activity coefficients.

One of the important uses of the measurement of pH is the determination of a *potential-titration curve*.   Figure 18-11 illustrates the results that are obtained in typical acid-base titrations.

18-15. The Temperature Dependence of EMF.   The direct relation given by Eq. (5), between the free-energy change for a reaction and the emf of a cell in which this reaction occurs, implies, according to the treatment of Sec. 7-6, that a measurement of the temperature dependence of the emf will lead to a value for the entropy and the heat of the reaction.   The relation

$$\left[\frac{\partial(\Delta G)}{\partial T}\right]_P = -\Delta S \tag{76}$$

becomes, with the substitution of

$$\Delta G = -n\mathfrak{F}\mathcal{E}$$

the entropy-determining relation

$$-n\mathfrak{F}\left(\frac{\partial\mathcal{E}}{\partial T}\right)_P = -\Delta S$$

or

$$\Delta S = n\mathfrak{F}\left(\frac{\partial\mathcal{E}}{\partial T}\right)_P \tag{77}$$

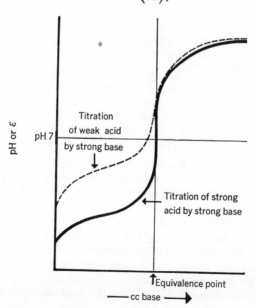

Fig. 18-11. The shape of potentiometric-titration curves.

By this expression the entropy of the reaction can be determined from the temperature coefficient of the cell emf.

This entropy value can furthermore be inserted into the expression, for a given temperature,

$$\Delta H = \Delta G + T \,\Delta S \tag{78}$$

to give a value for the enthalpy change for the reaction.

Thus ΔG, ΔH, and ΔS can be evaluated for the cell reaction from measurements of the emf and the temperature coefficient of the emf. This procedure is often a more convenient way of obtaining these thermodynamic properties than direct calorimetric measurements. Electromotive-force studies provide therefore an appreciable amount of thermodynamic information for systems involving ions in aqueous solution.

For example, the cell

$$\text{Pt}|\text{H}_2|\text{HCl(soln)}|\text{AgCl}|\text{Ag}$$

has a standard emf, i.e., with variable reagents at unit activity, of 0.2224 volt at 25°C and a temperature coefficient of −0.000645 volt/°C.

The cell reaction is

$$\begin{array}{c} \frac{1}{2}\text{H}_2 \rightleftharpoons \text{H}^+ + e^- \\ \underline{\text{AgCl} + e^- \rightleftharpoons \text{Ag} + \text{Cl}^-} \\ \hline \text{AgCl} + \frac{1}{2}\text{H}_2 \rightleftharpoons \text{Ag} + \text{H}^+(a = 1) + \text{Cl}^-(a = 1) \end{array} \tag{79}$$

and for this reaction one obtains the thermodynamic results

$$\begin{aligned} \Delta G^\circ &= -n\mathfrak{F}\mathcal{E}^\circ \\ &= -(1)(96{,}493)(0.2224) \\ &= -21{,}450 \text{ joules} = -5140 \text{ cal} \end{aligned} \tag{80}$$

$$\begin{aligned} \Delta S^\circ &= n\mathfrak{F}\left(\frac{\partial \mathcal{E}^\circ}{\partial T}\right)_P \\ &= (1)(96{,}493)(-0.000645) \\ &= -62.2 \text{ joules/deg} = -14.9 \text{ cal/deg} \end{aligned} \tag{81}$$

and

$$\begin{aligned} \Delta H^\circ &= \Delta G^\circ + T \,\Delta S^\circ \\ &= -5{,}140 + (298)(-14.9) \\ &= -5{,}140 - 4{,}440 = -9580 \text{ cal} \end{aligned} \tag{82}$$

18-16. Thermodynamic Properties of Ions in Aqueous Solution. In a manner similar to that illustrated by the example of the previous section one can calculate from standard emf data the values of ΔG, ΔS, and ΔH for electrochemical reactions. As in previous treatments of these reaction quantities, it is of value and convenient to be able to tabulate data for individual species rather than for reactions. Again certain standard, or reference, values must be chosen. Standard states have already been agreed upon for all the nonionic species that occur, and it has been agreed that the standard free energy of the elements be taken as zero for these standard states.

For the previous example, for instance, the reagents are in their reference, or standard, states, and one can write

$$\Delta G^\circ = G^\circ_{Ag} + G^\circ_{H^+(a=1)} + G^\circ_{Cl^-(a=1)} - G^\circ_{AgCl} - \tfrac{1}{2}G^\circ_{H_2}$$

or $-5,140 = 0 + G^\circ_{H^+(a=1)} + G^\circ_{Cl^-(a=1)} - (-26,220) - 0$

and $G^\circ_{H^+(a=1)} + G^\circ_{Cl^-(a=1)} = -31,360$ cal   (83)

Analyses of all electrochemical cells will lead to similar results in that the free-energy terms of the ions of an electrolyte will appear. In order to tabulate individual ionic free energies, it is necessary arbitrarily to assign a standard ionic free energy. The accepted assignment is

$$G^\circ_{H^+(a=1)} = 0 \tag{84}$$

and with this reference value the ionic free energies of other ions can be tabulated. Thus, Eq. (83) gives

$$G^\circ_{Cl^-(a=1)} = -31,360 \text{ cal} \tag{85}$$

The entropies can be similarly treated. For the reaction of Eq. (79), for example,

$$\Delta S^\circ = S^\circ_{Ag} + S^\circ_{H^+(a=1)} + S^\circ_{Cl^-(a=1)} - S^\circ_{AgCl} - \tfrac{1}{2}S^\circ_{H_2} \tag{86}$$

Since absolute values of entropies can be determined, one uses these values, as listed in Table 6-3, to obtain

$$-14.9 = 10.2 + S^\circ_{H^+(a=1)} + S^\circ_{Cl^-(a=1)} - 23.0 - 15.6$$

or $S^\circ_{H^+(a=1)} + S^\circ_{Cl^-(a=1)} = 13.5$ (87)

Again one cannot deduce individual ion entropies from this absolute value for the total entropy of dissociated HCl. It is again customary to set

$$S^\circ_{H^+(a=1)} = 0 \tag{88}$$

so that ionic entropies can be tabulated. Such entropies should be recognized as standard ionic entropies and not absolute entropies. One finds, for example, that the standard ionic entropies can have negative values, a result that, of course, could not occur if absolute entropies were listed.

Finally ionic enthalpies can be deduced. Thus in the example

$$\Delta H^\circ = H^\circ_{Ag} + H^\circ_{H^+(a=1)} + H^\circ_{Cl^-(a=1)} - H^\circ_{AgCl} - \tfrac{1}{2}H^\circ_{H_2}$$

or $-9,580 = 0 + H^\circ_{H^+(a=1)} + H^\circ_{Cl^-(a=1)} - (-30,360) - 0$

and $H^\circ_{H^+(a=1)} + H^\circ_{Cl^-(a=1)} = -39,940$ cal   (89)

Again with the use of $H^+(a = 1)$ as a reference and the enthalpy of this ion taken as zero one can obtain standard ionic enthalpies such as

$$H^\circ_{Cl^-(a=1)} = -39,940 \text{ cal} \tag{90}$$

With such treatments one can obtain thermodynamic data for electrolytes at unit activity that can be tabulated for the ions of the electrolyte, as is done in Table 18-4.

The wealth of thermodynamic data in Table 18-4 cannot easily be given molecular interpretations. It might be expected, for example, that all monatomic ions should have the same entropy since this entropy might be interpreted in terms of the degrees of freedom of a single particle. Such a view leads, however, to the realization that the entropy of an ion, and likewise its free energy and enthalpy, is primarily determined by the behavior that the ion

Table 18-4. Standard Thermodynamic Properties of Ions in Aqueous Solutions at 25°C*

	H°_{298} (kcal/mole)	S°_{298} (cal/deg mole)	G°_{298} (kcal/mole)
H+	0	0	0
Li+	− 66.55	+ 3.4	− 70.22
Na+	− 57.28	+14.4	− 62.59
K+	− 60.04	+24.5	− 67.47
NH₄+	− 31.74	+27.0	− 19.00
Ag+	+ 25.31	+17.7	+ 18.43
Ca++	−129.77	−13.2	−132.2
Ba++	−128.67	+ 3	−134.0
Ce³+	−173.7	−44	−170.5
La³+	−176.2	−44	−172.9
OH−	− 54.96	− 2.52	− 37.60
F−	− 78.66	− 2.3	− 66.08
Cl−	− 40.02	+13.2	− 31.35
Br−	− 28.90	+19.3	− 24.57
I−	− 13.37	+26.1	− 12.35
CN−	+ 36.1	+28.2	+ 39.6
NO₃−	− 49.37	+35.0	− 26.43
SO₄⁼	−216.9	+ 4.1	−177.3
HSO₄−	−211.7	+30.3	−179.9

* As given by W. M. Latimer, "Oxidation Potentials,"
Prentice-Hall Inc., Englewood Cliffs, N.J., 1952.

imposes on the surrounding water molecules. One sees, for example, that the small or highly charged ions, which would be expected to have a large amount of solvation, generally do have low entropies. The rigidity imposed on the solvating molecules can be held responsible for these low values. Unfortunately our present knowledge of the details of condensed systems is inadequate for us to do much more than recognize such qualitative features.

Problems

1. An electrolysis of HCl solution produces 94 cc of H_2 and 94 cc of Cl_2, measured at 25°C and 740 mm pressure.

(*a*) How many faradays of charge were passed through the cell?

(*b*) How many coulombs?

(*c*) If the electrolysis was performed over a period of 10 min, what was the average current?

Ans. (*a*) 0.00748; (*c*) 1.20 amp.

2. Write the cell reactions for the following cells, and use Table 18-1 to determine the emfs of the cells under standard conditions:

(*a*) Cd|Cd++||KCl|Hg₂Cl₂|Hg

(*b*) Pt|Tl+, Tl³+||Cu++|Cu

(*c*) Pb|PbSO₄(*s*)|SO₄⁼||Cu++|Cu

(*d*) Pt|H₂|HCl, Q, QH₂|Pt

Ans. (*a*) 0.665 volt.

3. Deduce, by writing electrochemical cells and calculating their emfs, the standard free-energy changes for the reactions:

(a) $\frac{1}{2}Br_2 + Ag \rightleftharpoons AgBr(s)$

(b) $H_2 + Cu^{++} \rightleftharpoons 2H^+ + Cu$

(c) $\frac{1}{2}Cl_2 + Br^- \rightleftharpoons Cl^- + \frac{1}{2}Br_2$

(d) $Ca^{++} + 2Na \rightleftharpoons Ca + 2Na^+$

(e) $Hg_2Cl_2 \rightleftharpoons 2Hg + Cl_2$

$Ans.$ (a) 0.993 volt, -22.9 kcal.

4. Calculate the emf of the cell and $\Delta G°$ for the cell reaction of

$$Pt|Cl_2(1 \text{ atm})|ZnCl_2(a = 1)Zn$$

using the electrode potentials of Table 18-1 and:

(a) Combining one electrode reaction written as an oxidation process and the other as a reduction process

(b) Combining both electrode reactions written as oxidation processes

5. In what direction would the concentrations of the variable reagents in each of the reactions of Prob. 4 be changed to attain cells with zero emf?

6. The emf of the cell $Pt|H_2(1 \text{ atm})|HBr(c)|AgBr(s)|Ag$ has the following values at 25°C according to the measurements of Keston [$J. Am. Chem. Soc.$, 57: 1671 (1935)]:

c (moles/liter)	0.0003198	0.0004042	0.0008444	0.001355	0.001850	0.002396	0.003719
ε (volts)	0.48469	0.47381	0.43636	0.41243	0.39667	0.38383	0.36173

By a suitable graphical method deduce:

(a) $\varepsilon°$ for the cell

(b) The activity coefficients for HBr at each of the reported concentrations

7. The emf of the cell in which the reaction $H_2 + Hg_2Cl_2 \rightarrow 2Hg + 2HCl$ occurs has been studied by Lewis and Randall [$J. Am. Chem. Soc.$, 36: 1969 (1944)] as a function of pressure at 25°C. The pressure was obtained by allowing the hydrogen gas to escape against a hydrostatic head measured in centimeters of water. Their results are:

P (cm water in excess of 1 atm)	0	37	63	84
ε (volts)	0.40088	0.40137	0.40163	0.40190

Compare the pressure dependence of these results with the thermodynamic predictions.

8. The cell $Zn|ZnCl_2(c)|AgCl(s)|Ag$ has been studied by Lewis and Lacey [$J. Am. Chem. Soc.$, 36: 804 (1914)] at 25°C; they report:

c (moles/liter)	0.000772	0.001253	0.001453	0.003112	0.006022	0.01021
ε (volts)	1.2475	1.2289	1.2219	1.1953	1.1742	1.1558

(a) Using a Debye-Hückel limiting-law extrapolation, deduce, as well as possible from these data, the value of $\varepsilon°$ and the activity coefficients of $ZnCl_2$ at each concentration.

(b) Compare the value deduced for $\varepsilon°$ from these data with that obtained from the data of Table 18-1.

9. From the data of Table 18-1, calculate the solubility product of $PbSO_4$ at 25°C.

$Ans.$ 1.12×10^{-8}.

10. Calculate $\Delta G°$ and the equilibrium constant for the reaction $H_2 + O_2 \rightleftharpoons H_2O_2$ at 25°C. At what total pressure would ΔG be equal to zero?

19

Adsorption and Heterogeneous Catalysis

It has been mentioned in the discussion of the liquid state that molecules on the surface of a liquid have a different environment and therefore a different free energy from the molecules in the bulk of the material. In most chemical systems the fraction of the molecules on a surface and the free-energy difference between the surface and the bulk material are relatively small. Now systems are considered in which the surface effects are dominant. Mention will be made of a liquid film spread out in another liquid, but attention will be devoted principally to systems in which the molecules of a gas are concentrated on the surface of a solid. The molecules are said to be *adsorbed* on the solid surface, and this process is distinguished from the penetration of one component throughout the body of a second, called *absorption*. The chapter will be begun with a direct study of the adsorption process and the adsorbed layer.

Such studies are now almost always directed toward an understanding of the chemical reactions that occur at the surface. The surface, it will be shown, enters into reactions as a catalyst. It is interesting that this type of catalysis, called *heterogeneous catalysis*, is understandable only on the basis of some of the information deduced in absorption studies, while, on the other hand, conclusions that are drawn from the chemical reactions on a surface help to answer some of the problems unsolved by direct adsorption studies.

The goal of modern physical-chemical studies of surface phenomena is the understanding of these phenomena by means of a molecular model. However, systems which have a very thin, often monomolecular, layer of gas adsorbed on a complex solid adsorbent resist most of the methods that have already been studied to elucidate the molecular world. The current theories of surface reactions are still very tentative and loosely supported. Furthermore, little can be said about the nature and behavior of surface molecules.

618

Some of the background information and treatments on which the ideas that exist are based will, however, be introduced.

It should be pointed out immediately that heterogeneous catalysis is a procedure of great importance in industrial chemistry. This fact and the challenge of the many unexplained phenomena make the study of the absorbed state one of the most exciting areas of modern physical-chemical research.

ADSORPTION

Although the distinction between *adsorption* and *absorption* is not always clear-cut and the noncommittal word *sorption* is sometimes used, the processes that will be considered here will be essentially surface effects and the word adsorption will be used.

The most important and interesting type of adsorption is certainly that in which gases are adsorbed on a solid. Before treating this subject, however, the much simpler and more easily treated process of the adsorption, or spreading, of a film of one liquid on the surface of another will be dealt with briefly.

19-1. Liquid Films on Liquids. The most interesting and easily studied liquid films are formed by allowing a small quantity of a *surface-active* material, for example, a long-chain organic acid like stearic acid,

$$CH_3(CH_2)_{16}COOH$$

to spread out on the surface of water. Such molecules are suitable because the acid group shows an attraction for water (short-chain acids are, in fact, soluble in water) that makes the material spread out over the water surface while the long hydrocarbon end prevents the material from dissolving. It can now be shown that such films can be made to form a *monomolecular layer* on the water surface.

Modern studies of such films are made on an apparatus, called a *surface*

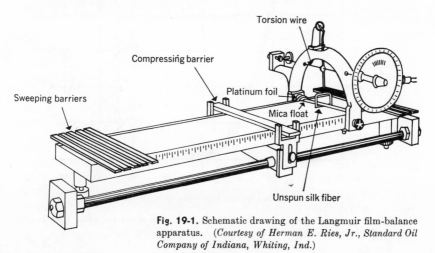

Fig. 19-1. Schematic drawing of the Langmuir film-balance apparatus. (*Courtesy of Herman E. Ries, Jr., Standard Oil Company of Indiana, Whiting, Ind.*)

balance, developed by Langmuir in 1917. The apparatus is shown in Fig. 19-1. The trough is filled with water, and a measured amount of the surface-active material is added. The movable barrier is pushed forward, and measurements of the force exerted on the fixed barrier are read off the delicate tension device. It is customary to plot the results as the force in dynes per centimeter on the fixed barrier versus the surface area per molecule of the surface-active agent, i.e., the surface area covered by the surface-active agent divided by the number of molecules in the sample. Typical results for stearic acid are shown in Fig. 19-2.

The initial slow increase in film force with decreasing surface area indicates that the surface is not completely covered by the surface-active film. The beginning of the steep part of the curve is taken to correspond to the completion of the film; further decrease in area must compress the film itself, and a large

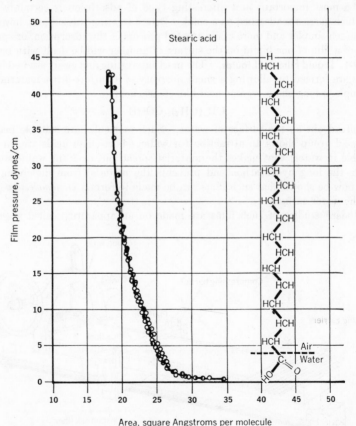

Fig. 19-2. Pressure-area isotherm and molecular orientation of stearic acid. (*Courtesy of Herman E. Ries, Jr., Standard Oil Company of Indiana, Whiting, Ind.*)

increase in force is necessary.   Finally the film buckles and folds, and the area can be decreased without any further increase in force.

A calculation can now be made which supports the idea that the onset of the steep part of the curve corresponds to a monomolecular film.   For stearic acid this film has, according to Fig. 19-2, an area of 20.5 sq A per molecule.   This value can now be shown to be about that expected for the cross-section area occupied by a stearic acid molecule.

The film is assumed to consist of molecules arranged approximately as depicted in Fig. 19-3.   The volume occupied by Avogadro's number of molecules of stearic acid can be taken to be approximately that of 1 mole of liquid stearic acid, i.e.,

$$\text{Vol of } N \text{ molecules} = \frac{M}{\rho} = \frac{284}{0.85} = 330 \text{ cc}$$

and
$$\text{Vol of 1 molecule} = \frac{1}{N}\frac{M}{\rho} = 550 \text{ A}^3$$

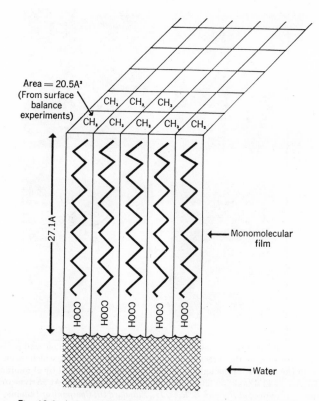

Fig. 19-3. A monomolecular surface film of stearic acid on water.

The length of the zigzag chain of carbon atoms can be estimated, as Fig. 19-3 shows, as

$$\text{Length of stearic acid} = (17)(1.25) = 21 \text{ A}$$

From these estimates one deduces the cross-section area as

$$\text{Cross-section area} = \frac{550}{21} = 26 \text{ sq A}$$

This result is in sufficient agreement with the value of 20.5 sq A from the film-balance experiment to suggest the existence of a monomolecular layer at the beginning of the steep portion of the force-area curve, such as that of Fig. 19-2.

The nature of these surface layers is nicely shown by microphotographs, as indicated in Fig. 19-4. These surfaces have been *shadow-cast* by coating them with a very thin layer of chromium from a beam directed at an angle to the surface. If the angle of the shadow-casting beam is known, the length of any shadow can be used to deduce the height of any projection. In this

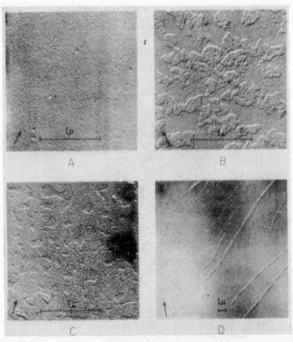

Fig. 19-4. Electron micrographs of monolayer films of *n*-hexatriacontanoic acid [CH₃(CH₂)₃₄- COOH]. The arrows give the direction of chromium shadow-casting which was done at an angle of 15° to the surface. The light areas are shadows not covered by chromium. (One micron is 10^4 A.) (*A*) Blank, no film. (*B*) At 15 dynes/cm. (*C*) At 25 dynes/cm. (*D*) After collapse. (*Courtesy of Herman E. Ries, Jr., Standard Oil Company of Indiana, Whiting, Ind.*)

way the results for the collapsed layer of Fig. 19-4 can be interpreted in terms of double "sandwich" layers of the fatty acid lying on top of the mono-molecular surface film.

Some features of these liquid films will be encountered in the study of the adsorption of gases on solids. The concept of a monomolecular layer will be of great importance, but the transition to multiple layers will, for gases on solids, be less easily detected. Likewise, the surface area of the adsorbent will be talked about but will seldom be as definite a concept as in liquid-film systems. Part of this difficulty stems from the nonhomogeneity that must be anticipated for solid adsorbents. Finally, the nature of the attraction of the surface layer for the adsorbent will be studied and will be found to be rather more complicated than the essentially physical, or van der Waals', attractions that act on the surface film on a liquid. It is, of course, all these added complexities which make the study of the nature and reactions of gases adsorbed on solids of special interest.

An extension of studies of liquid-surface films could be made to liquid-liquid interfaces. The molecules of stearic acid, for example, would be expected to concentrate at an oil-water interface just as they do at an air-water interface. All such systems are clearly important in studies of lubrication and in the wetting action of water containing soaps or detergents.

19-2. Classifications of Adsorptions of Gases on Solids. It is very convenient in the study of adsorption to recognize that most adsorptions can be placed in one of two categories. These categories are suggested by the possibilities of having essentially physical forces holding the gas molecules to the solid or of having chemical bonds serve the function. The categories of *physical adsorption* and chemical adsorption, or, more commonly, *chemisorption*, thus arise. The observed characteristics of any adsorption process usually allow it to be placed in one or the other category. Table 19-1 outlines the experimental features that allow a process to be so categorized. The different behaviors of the two types of adsorption should be recognized as having the

Table 19-1. Characteristics of Physical Adsorption and Chemisorption

Physical adsorption	*Chemisorption*
Heat of adsorption less than about 10 kcal/mole	Heat of adsorption greater than about 20 kcal/mole
Adsorption is appreciable only at temperatures below the boiling point of the adsorbate	Adsorption can occur at high temperatures
The incremental increase in the amount adsorbed increases with each incremental increase in pressure of the adsorbate	The incremental increase in the amount adsorbed decreases with each incremental increase in the pressure of the adsorbate
The amount of adsorption on a surface is more a function of the adsorbate than the adsorbent	The amount of adsorption is characteristic of both adsorbate and adsorbent
No appreciable activation energy is involved in the adsorption process	An activation energy may be involved in the adsorption process
Multilayer adsorption occurs	Adsorption leads to, at most, a monolayer

features of a physical process, such as condensation, or those of a chemical reaction. It should be pointed out that whether or not more than a monolayer is being formed is not directly observable but, as we shall see, can often be deduced from experimental data.

Most interest in adsorption, and in the closely related field of heterogeneous catalysis, is in chemisorption. Two of the items mentioned in Table 19-1 will therefore be dealt with in more detail and with particular emphasis on chemisorption.

19-3. Heat of Adsorption. In all adsorptions, heat is given out, and ΔH for the process

$$\text{Gas} \rightarrow \text{adsorbed layer} \tag{1}$$

is negative. Heats of adsorptions are, however, generally listed without sign. The necessity for a negative ΔH, in contrast to chemical reactions in general, arises from the fact that the entropy of the ordered, constrained adsorbed layer is always less than that of the gas; i.e., for the reaction of Eq. (1), ΔS is invariably negative. It follows that, for the process of Eq. (1) to be spontaneous and have a negative value for ΔG, the value for ΔH must be negative and greater than $T \Delta S$.

For physical adsorption the heats involved are of the order of heats of vaporization, i.e., generally less than 10 kcal/mole, and, in keeping with the idea that physical adsorption may be leading to the formation of multilayers, these heats are more dependent on the nature of the gas than they are on that of the solid adsorbent.

Adsorptions that are classed as chemisorptions, on the other hand, have heats of adsorption that compare with those of ordinary chemical reactions; in other words, they have heats of anywhere up to about 150 kcal/mole.

The approximate values mentioned for physical and chemical adsorptions are not intended to imply a constancy for these heats as a function of the amount of gas adsorbed. Some of the variations in differential heats of adsorption in the chemisorption region are shown in Fig. 19-5. The frequently observed curve over the region of adsorption from low coverages to multilayer formation has a high initial heat that falls off at large amounts of adsorption. This behavior is taken as indicative of an initial chemisorption, to form something like a monolayer, followed by the formation of multiple layers that are bound by physical forces.

Even within a range attributed to chemisorption, however, the heat of adsorption is usually found to be a function of the amount adsorbed. A number of molecular explanations have been offered for this variation. Active sites can be assumed to exist on the adsorbent, and as these are occupied by the first additions of gas, the binding of later additions must occur on less active sites and the strength of binding falls off. Alternatively, the binding of some gas to the solid can occur with the giving up of electrons to the solid by the adsorbed molecules or with the withdrawing of electrons from the solid, and, as such processes continue, the solid becomes more and more reluctant to

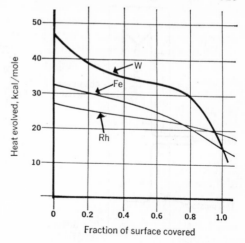

Fig. 19-5. The heat of adsorption for H_2 on clean metal surfaces. [*From O. Beeck, Discussions Faraday Soc.*, p. 118 (1950).]

gain or lose more electrons. Such an explanation is particularly appropriate to semiconducting and conducting adsorbents. The final important factor that has been suggested is that the mutual repulsion of the adsorbed molecules, especially if they acquire a net charge when they are adsorbed, operates to oppose the addition of further molecules.

19-4. The Adsorption Isotherm. The most frequently encountered adsorption experiment is the measurement of the relation between the amount of gas adsorbed by a given amount of adsorbent and the pressure of the gas. Such measurements are usually made at a constant temperature, and the results are generally presented graphically as an *adsorption isotherm*. Experimentally one measures either the volume of gas taken up by a given amount of adsorbent or the change in weight of the adsorbent when it is exposed to a gas at a given pressure. The apparatus that can be used are shown in Fig. 19-6.

A great variety of adsorption-isotherm shapes are found. Chemisorption is usually accompanied by an initial steeply rising curve that gradually flattens off. The initial rise is taken as corresponding to the strong tendency of the surface to bind the gas molecules, and the leveling off can be attributed to the saturation of these forces, perhaps by one or more of the three mechanisms mentioned in Sec. 19-3. Physical adsorption, on the other hand, is accompanied by an adsorption isotherm that tends to have an increasingly positive slope with increasing gas pressure. Each incremental increase in gas pressure produces a larger increase in the amount of gas adsorbed—up to the limit of a pressure equal to the vapor pressure of the material being adsorbed, at which pressure the adsorption isotherm ascends vertically as condensation occurs.

Some adsorption isotherms, as Fig. 19-7 suggests, can be interpreted as a

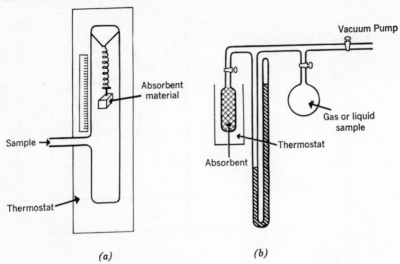

Fig. 19-6. Adsorption isotherm apparatus. (*a*) Gravimetric. (*b*) Volumetric.

combination of these chemisorption and physical-adsorption curves. As we shall see, however, no simple, or even complex, explanation can be expected for the detailed shapes of all adsorption isotherms.

19-5. The Langmuir Adsorption Isotherm. A model for the adsorption process, and particularly for the chemisorption process, was presented by Langmuir in 1916 and led him to a simple, but important, theoretical derivation of an adsorption isotherm. The chemisorption process is pictured as leading ultimately to a unimolecular film over the surface of the adsorbent, and the derived adsorption isotherm results from an investigation of the equilibrium that is set up between the gas phase and the partially formed monolayer. When the gas is at a pressure P, the fraction of the surface that is covered is represented by θ. The equilibrium state can be interpreted in terms of the dynamic equilibrium that results from an equal rate of evaporation of the adsorbed material and rate of condensation of the gas-phase molecules.

The Langmuir theory suggests that the rate of evaporation can be taken to be proportional to the fraction of the surface covered and can be written therefore as $k_1\theta$, where k_1 is some proportionality constant. This simple proportionality is an assumption that ignores the complications that often make the heat of adsorption dependent on the extent of coverage and that may well be expected to spoil the simple assumption of an evaporation rate proportional to $k_1\theta$. The rate of condensation, furthermore, is taken to be proportional both to the gas pressure P, which according to the kinetic-molecular theory of Chap. 2 determines the number of molecular collisions per unit area per unit time, and to the fraction of the surface not already covered by

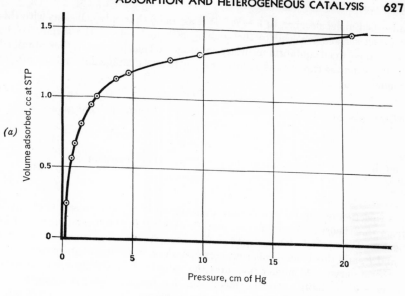

(a)

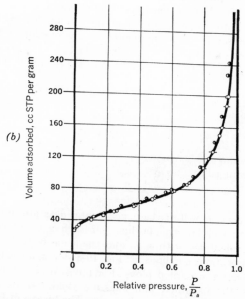

(b)

Fig. 19-7. (a) The adsorption isotherm for H_2 on Cu powder at 25°C. [*From A. F. H. Ward, Proc. Roy. Soc. (London)*, **A133**: 506 (1931).] (b) The adsorption of N_2 up to the vapor pressure of N_2, on silica. (*From P. Emmett, "Catalysis," vol. I, Reinhold Publishing Corporation, New York*, 1954.)

adsorbed molecules, i.e., to $1 - \theta$. It is assumed that only collisions with this exposed surface can lead to the sticking of a molecule to the surface. The relation between equilibrium surface coverage and gas pressure is then obtained by equating the expressions deduced for the rate of evaporation and the rate of condensation, i.e.,

$$k_1\theta = k_2P(1 - \theta) \tag{2}$$

where k_2 is another proportionality constant. Rearrangement gives

$$\theta = \frac{k_2P}{k_1 + k_2P} \tag{3}$$

and introduction of $a = k_1/k_2$ allows this result to be written as

$$\theta = \frac{P}{a + P} \tag{4}$$

Inspection of Eq. (4) shows that a chemisorption-type isotherm is obtained from this theory. At small values of P, where P in the denominator can be neglected compared with a, Eq. (4) reduces to a simple proportionality between θ and P, and this behavior is that corresponding to the initial steep rise of the isotherm curve. At higher pressures the value of P in the denominator contributes appreciably, and the increasing denominator leads to values of θ that do not increase proportionally to the increase in P. For sufficiently large values of P, θ approaches the constant value of unity.

Experimental isotherm data consist of the amount of gas adsorbed by a given weight of adsorbent as a function of the gas pressure. For adsorption, up to a monolayer, the amount of gas y adsorbed at some pressure P and the amount of gas y_m needed to form a monolayer are related to θ according to

$$\frac{y}{y_m} = \theta \tag{5}$$

and Eq. (4) becomes

$$y = \frac{y_mP}{a + P} \tag{6}$$

Experimental results can be compared with the Langmuir theory most easily if Eq. (6) is rearranged to

$$\frac{P}{y} = \frac{a}{y_m} + \frac{P}{y_m} \tag{7}$$

A plot of P/y versus P will, if the experimental data are in accord with the Langmuir theory, yield a straight line. If such a curve is obtained, the intercept can be identified with a/y_m and the slope with $1/y_m$. For many chemisorptions one finds, as Fig. 19-8 shows, a good linear relationship on the Langmuir suggested plot. For physical adsorption isotherms or S-shaped curves, the Langmuir plot does not yield a straight line, and the theory is clearly not applicable to such cases. The success of Eq. (7) in fitting experimental chemisorption-type curves must not, of course, be taken as necessarily confirming the model and assumptions that have been used in the derivation.

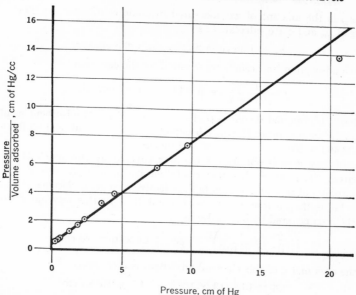

Fig. 19-8. The Langmuir plot for the adsorption of H_2 on Cu powder at 25°C shown in Fig. 19-7.

Other theories have been developed to explain the more complete adsorption process that leads to multilayer formation. The most important of these treatments is due to Brunauer, Emmett, and Teller. Their theory, like that of Langmuir, leads to an isotherm expression, usually abbreviated as the BET isotherm. Although this expression receives considerable attention as a basis for surface-area determinations, which will next be dealt with, it will not be necessary for us to investigate here the BET theory.

19-6. Determination of Surface Areas. It is important, if one is to obtain a definite picture of the happenings on a surface, to have some way of estimating the surface area. Since many of the solids that are used in adsorption studies are highly irregular and porous, like charcoal, the area cannot be measured directly and an adsorption method, generally using the BET isotherm, is ordinarily employed. Although the Langmuir isotherm can represent only the chemisorption process, it can be used to show that a surface area can be deduced from adsorption studies.

The specific example of the adsorbent used for the experiments that led to one of the isotherms of Fig. 19-7 can be considered. The Langmuir plot of these data in Fig. 19-8 gives

$$\text{Slope} = \frac{1}{y_m} = 0.735(\text{cc at STP})^{-1} \tag{8}$$

$$\text{Intercept} = \frac{a}{y_m} = 0.4 \text{ cm Hg/cc at STP} \tag{9}$$

where y is the amount of gas measured in cubic centimeters at STP. The values of y_m and a are calculated as

$$y_m = 1.36 \text{ cc at STP} \qquad a = 0.5 \text{ cm Hg} \tag{10}$$

and the adsorption isotherm is represented by the equation

$$y = \frac{1.36P}{0.5 + P} \text{ cc at STP} \qquad \text{for } P(\text{cm Hg}) \tag{11}$$

The result is obtained therefore that the surface of 1 g of adsorbent would be covered by an amount of H_2 which occupies a volume of 1.36 cc at STP, i.e., by $1.36/22,400 \times 6.0 \times 10^{23} = 3.6 \times 10^{19}$ molecules.

The surface area is obtained if the area covered by this much H_2 can be estimated. The easiest, if rather crude, method is to make use of the bulk volume of liquid H_2 and to calculate the effective area per molecule as $(V_{\text{liq}}/N)^{\frac{2}{3}}$, where V_{liq} is the volume of 1 mole of liquid H_2. In this way one estimates that the area covered by one molecule is

$$\left(\frac{2}{0.070} \frac{1}{6 \times 10^{23}}\right)^{\frac{2}{3}} \qquad \text{or} \qquad 13 \times 10^{-16} \text{ sq cm}$$

and the area of 1 g of this charcoal adsorbent is therefore

$$(3.6 \times 10^{19})(13 \times 10^{-16}) = 4.7 \times 10^4 \text{ sq cm} \tag{12}$$

In practice one relies on the BET isotherm and makes use of physical-adsorption data rather than the chemisorption data used in this Langmuir example. The calculation procedures are, however, equivalent.

Surface areas estimated from such adsorption studies can often be accepted as generally reliable but approximate. Table 19-2 shows the type of variation in area estimated from different isotherms, and Table 19-3 shows some typical surface areas of adsorbents.

There may, of course, be a number of subtleties connected with the surface that may lead to puzzling area values. The presence of fine pores or capillaries may, for example, be such as to allow one gas to penetrate, while another gas with larger molecules finds the pores inaccessible. In this connection it is of interest to note the "molecular-sieve" materials that consist of dehydrated zeolites. They appear to have pores that are of sufficiently uniform size so

Table 19-2. Estimates of Surface Area of Clean Nickel Films from the Physical Adsorption of Different Gases*

Gas	Area/molecule (sq A)	Vol adsorbed to give monolayer (on 1 g nickel film)	Surface area of 1 g nickel film (sq cm)
Kr	14.6	6.15×10^{19}† molecules	9.0×10^4
Kr	14.6	5.85×10^{19}†	8.6×10^4
CH_4	15.7	5.40×10^{19}	8.5×10^4
$n—C_4H_{10}$	24.5	3.48×10^{19}	8.5×10^4

*From O. Beeck and A. W. Ritchie, *Discussions Faraday Soc.*, **8**: 159 (1950).
† On different films.

Table 19-3. Volumes of Adsorbed Nitrogen to Form a Monolayer and the Surface Areas of a Number of Catalysts*

(Area covered by an adsorbed nitrogen molecules taken as 16.2 sq A)

Material	Monolayer volume (cc at STP/g)	Surface area (sq cm/g)
Fused Cu catalyst.................	0.09	0.39×10^4
Fe, K_2O catalyst 930...............	0.14	0.61×10^4
Fe, Al_2O_3, K_2O catalyst 931..........	0.81	3.5×10^4
Fe, Al_2O_3 catalyst 954..............	2.86	12.4×10^4
Cr_2O_3 gel........................	53.3	230×10^4
Silica gel.........................	116.2	500×10^4

* From Paul H. Emmett, "Catalysis I," Reinhold Publishing Corporation, New York, 1955.

that an adsorbent can be obtained that can, for example, accept n-paraffin molecules but not branched-chain molecules.

The use of chemisorption data for surface determinations, it should be pointed out, would introduce the very questionable assumption that the "active" surface area is the same both for the gas with which the area is determined and for any other gas that might be studied. In practice it is much more satisfactory to use the BET-isotherm expression to deduce the surface area since the BET isotherm includes adsorption to form multilayers.

19-7. Adsorption from Solution.   A very important, but little understood, process is the adsorption of a solute of a solution onto a solid adsorbent. This procedure is used, for example, in the decolorizing of solutions using, ordinarily, activated charcoal. The separation technique of chromatography also makes use of the relative adsorption tendencies of the solutes of a solution.

This process of adsorption from solution is even more difficult to treat theoretically than is the corresponding gas-on-solid process. It appears, however, that only a monomolecular layer is formed, any further addition being strongly opposed by the solvating power of the solvent.

A fairly satisfactory empirical isotherm, which can be applied to adsorptions of gases with considerable success but which has been used principally for adsorption from solution, has been suggested by Freundlich. If y is the weight of solute adsorbed per gram of adsorbent and c is the concentration of the solute in the solution, this empirical relation is

$$y = kc^{1/n} \tag{13}$$

where k and n are empirical constants. The equation is conveniently used in the logarithmic form

$$\log y = \log k + \frac{1}{n} \log c \tag{14}$$

When applied to gases, y is the amount of gas adsorbed and c is replaced by the pressure of the gas. Experimental results conform to the Freundlich expression if a plot of $\log y$ against $\log c$ yields a straight line. The constants can

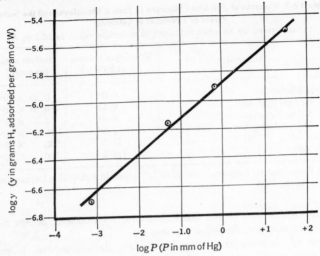

Fig. 19-9. A Freundlich plot of the isotherm data for H_2 adsorbed on tungsten at 400°C. [*From the more extensive data of W. G. Frankenberg, J. Am. Chem. Soc.,* **66**: 1827 (1944).]

then be determined from the slope and intercept. Figure 19-9 shows data treated in terms of the Freundlich expression.

19-8. The Nature of the Adsorbed State. Physical adsorption consists in the binding of molecules to the surface of the adsorbent by essentially van der Waals' forces, and the molecules of the adsorbed layers can be expected to be altered only to about the extent that gas molecules are when they are condensed to the liquid state.

Chemisorption, on the other hand, must be expected to produce major changes in the electronic distribution and the bonding in the adsorbed molecules. Much of the current interest in adsorption, and in heterogeneous catalysis, is centered around the description of the molecules that are bound to a solid in chemisorption. Some of the ideas that have been put forward and some of the experiments that have proved to be helpful can now be mentioned.

The use of the word *chemisorption* implies that bonding of the gas molecules to the solid occurs by ordinary chemical bonds, i.e., that the bonds can be described in terms of ionic and covalent character. Such an assumption is profitable for many systems, but one must be prepared, for example, for the sea of electrons of a metal to play a role in the bonding of surface groups that has no direct counterpart in simple chemical systems. It appears from surface dipole moments, however, that the adsorption of Na vapor on tungsten leads to a surface layer of Na^+ ions and a bonding to the tungsten that is comparable with ordinary ionic bonds. Likewise, the infrared spectrum of carbon monoxide adsorbed on platinum indicates the essential invariance of the bonding in the CO bond and suggests a bonding picture such as

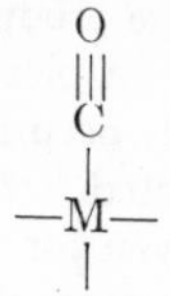

The electron movement in adsorptions such as these can be studied by measuring the magnetic properties of highly dispersed metal particles as a function of the adsorbed gas. The studies of coordination compounds by magnetic measurements was seen, in Sec. 10-16, to reveal the number of unpaired electrons in the metal atom. In a similar way the magnetic properties of a metallic particle depend on the net number of unpaired electrons. If the adsorbed molecules feed electrons into the partially filled d orbitals, or d band, of the metal, the magnetic susceptibility will decrease, and vice versa. From such measurements Selwood has deduced the following electron shifts for adsorbed species on nickel:[*]

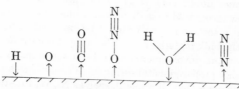

Such results emphasize that adsorption is at least as complex a phenomenon as chemical-bond formation and that all the variations in electron distribution that we are accustomed to in homogeneous chemical systems will also appear in the bonding of surface molecules to the adsorbent.

Adsorption of saturated hydrocarbons, and hydrogen, presents another problem in that these molecules have no sites for additional chemical bonds. Primarily from exchange studies, such as the passing of a mixture of D_2 and a hydrocarbon over an adsorbent, one deduces that some dissociative mechanism operates. For C_2H_6, for example, one might write the adsorbed state as

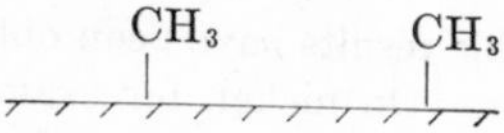

$$CH_3 \qquad CH_3$$

or as

$$CH_3$$
$$\backslash$$
$$CH_2 \qquad H$$

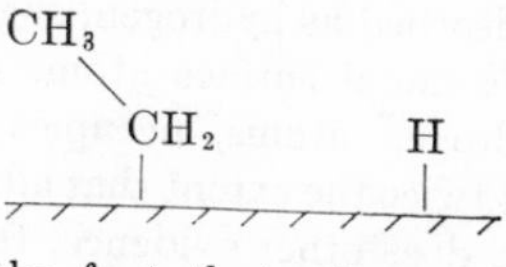

The first is suggested by the fact that ethane can be "cracked" to form methane, while the second is suggested by the deuterium exchange occurring in an adsorbed mixture of ethane and D_2.

Of particular interest in this connection are results such as those which

[*] P. W. Selwood, "Magnetochemistry," Interscience Publishers, Inc., New York, 1956.

show that cyclopentane in an excess of D_2 tends to form, at low temperatures on a suitable adsorbent, the exchange product $C_5H_5D_5$ rather than a more or a less deuterium-containing product. A picture for the adsorbed molecule lying on the catalyst with exchange readily occurring only on one side of the approximately planar carbon ring is suggested.

No general principles can be given for the nature of the adsorption bond of any gas on any adsorbent. It appears that a great variety of features must be considered. Not only must the surface of the catalyst be considered but also the electron reservoir or sink that the solid presents. It is becoming clear that chemisorption encompasses a great variety of chemical reactions and that these reactions cannot be understood in terms of one or a few simple processes. At present, however, many suggestions as to the reactions of surface molecules are being made and much information will be forthcoming on the nature of chemisorbed species.

19-9. Importance of the Preparation of the Surface. Much of the early work directed toward an understanding of the adsorbed state in chemisorption has recently come under doubt because of uncertainties as to the nature of the surface. It is now recognized that there is an almost infinite variety of surface reactions and that a surface reaction cannot be expected to be correlated with the properties of the bulk material unless the state of the surface is well defined.

The most important developments have been those made in the study of adsorption on freshly prepared metal surfaces. Primarily as a result of Beeck's work it has been shown that, if a metal, such as Ni, W, Pt, etc., is evaporated from an electrically heated filament in an evacuated system, a film several thousand atoms thick can be deposited on the surface of a Pyrex adsorption cell. The film, moreover, is of such a large surface area that it is not appreciably coated by adsorption of the residual gas in the reaction cell. With this technique it has been possible to obtain adsorption isotherms and heats of adsorption that are apparently characteristic of the pure metal. It has been shown, furthermore, that most attempts to clean a surface by prolonged evacuation have been futile and therefore that the subsequent adsorption studies have been made on surfaces that already are partially covered with a layer of oxygen or nitrogen.

A number of very valuable results have been obtained from studies on these well-defined metal surfaces. On nickel, for example, twice as much carbon monoxide appears to be adsorbed as hydrogen, suggesting that carbon monoxide is attached to a single metal surface atom, whereas hydrogen, possibly dissociated into two hydrogen atoms, occupies two sites. Adsorption of oxygen proceeds to at least twice the extent that adsorption of carbon monoxide does, and this suggests, as does other evidence, that oxygen diffuses into the metal lattice and forms what are essentially metal oxides.

Of special interest is the observation that the adsorption of small amounts of ethylene leads to the evolution of ethane and the formation on the catalyst surface of a $(CH)_n$ polymeric material. Apparently the ethylene adsorption occurs with appreciable bond dissociation.

Finally it should be mentioned that the use of clean metal surfaces has led to some correlation between the adsorption process and the nature of the adsorbent metal. Some correlation has been found, for example, between the available d orbitals of the metal atoms and the heat of adsorption of hydrogen, and this correlation suggests an adsorption mechanism in which the hydrogen molecules dissociate into atoms and the atoms form bonds with the metal atoms on the surface.

The work with clean metal surfaces has emphasized the complexities that undoubtedly occur when metal powders, chemically deposited metal films, oxides of metals, and nonmetals are used as adsorbents. It is, however, these more complicated surfaces that exhibit the many remarkable and industrially important catalytic effects. The study of surface phenomena cannot, therefore, be restricted to clean metal surfaces.

HETEROGENEOUS CATALYSIS

Many chemical processes occur in the presence of certain surfaces that do not proceed at all, or do so very slowly, in the absence of such surfaces. Such reactions are said to be exhibiting *heterogeneous catalysis*. The effect of the surface is often so profound that it may be difficult to keep in mind that its effect is that of hastening the approach to an equilibrium state. A catalyst may, and generally will, provide very different accelerations for the approach of different reactions to their equilibrium state. Full use of this important influence in chemical reactions requires a detailed understanding of the reactions that are occurring on the surface of the catalyst.

The most dramatic surface catalytic effects must be attributed to reactions of chemisorbed species. Physical adsorption is effective in raising the local concentration of the reagents and in supplying a reservoir of thermal energy to these reagents. These factors are, however, probably of minor importance in heterogeneous catalysis. Chemisorption, on the other hand, may result in a rather drastic disruption of the bonding in an adsorbed molecule. It is easily seen that such molecules, or molecular fragments, may enter into reactions in a manner quite different from that in which the unperturbed gas-phase molecules do. In kinetic terms, the molecules on the surface are such that they may react through a state of much lower activation energy than can the normal molecules.

It follows that heterogeneous catalysis can be understood in detail only when the nature of the adsorbed species is so understood. At present, only some features of heterogeneous catalysis can be given a molecular description. It is true, however, that one of the most fruitful approaches to an understanding of the adsorbed state is through studies of the reactions that the molecules of this state undergo.

19-10. Some Experimental Methods and Results. Heterogeneous catalysis is usually studied by passing the gaseous reagent, or reagents, through a tube having a section containing the catalyst. The catalyst can then be held at any desired temperature by an external oven, and the reaction will proceed catalytically at that temperature. On leaving the catalyst chamber the reaction mixture will usually be effectively frozen by the absence of the catalyst, and the products that are collected may be analyzed by any convenient method.

Many different catalysts are used, and since the exact treatment and mode of preparation are of great importance, many variations in catalytic activity are observed. It is now recognized that the attainment of a "clean" surface for which catalytic activity may be correlated with the properties of the catalytic material itself is no simple matter. The method discussed in the previous section, for example, depends on the evaporation of a metal in a high vacuum to form a fresh metallic surface. Some of the more frequently studied and used catalysts are listed in Table 19-4. The important class of *supported catalysts* included there consists of a catalytically active material laid down on some porous support.

One of the areas in which heterogeneous catalysis finds widespread industrial application is that of petroleum refining. Reactions are desired that convert low-octane hydrocarbons and low- and high-vapor-pressure hydrocarbons to high-octane gasoline, and catalytic reactions are necessary to make such reactions feasible. Table 19-4 summarizes some of the processes that are in use in petroleum refining and in other industrial processes.

Even this brief table shows the variety of reactions that can be stimulated by suitable catalysts. The desire for suitable catalysts for such processes has contributed to the considerable effort that has been directed toward an understanding of the catalytic process.

19-11. Kinetics of Heterogeneous Decompositions. The study of the kinetics of single-phase reactions led, in Chap. 11, to a considerable understanding of the details of reaction mechanisms. A similar study of heterogeneously catalyzed reactions leads only to the more explicit recognition that the catalytic effect is a surface reaction. The study of some relatively simple decompositions that are heterogeneously catalyzed will illustrate this.

The kinetics of decomposition can often be accounted for on the assumption that the rate is proportional to the amount of the reagent on the surface. In line with this assumption it is convenient to treat three situations that are

Table 19-4. Some Representative Catalysts and Catalytic Reactions

Catalyst	*Process*
Silica alumina gel....................	Cracking of heavy petroleum fractions
Chromic oxide gel, chromia-on-alumina, nickel-aluminum oxide..............	Hydrogenation, dehydrogenation of hydrocarbons
Phosphoric acid on kieselguhr.........	Polymerization of alkenes
Co, ThO_2, MgO on kieselguhr (Fischer-Tropsh catalyst)..................	Synthesis of hydrocarbons from H_2 and CO
Iron.............................	Synthesis of ammonia
Copper...........................	Dehydrogenation of alcohols to aldehydes
Platinum.........................	Isomerization of hydrocarbons
$Al(C_2H_5)_3$; $TiCl_4$....................	Polymerization of olefins

distinguished by the relation between the pressure of the gas and the amount that is adsorbed on the surface. An even greater variety exists, however, in the dependence of rate of reaction on reagent pressure, but all the complexities cannot be considered here.

First, for low surface coverages the amount of gas adsorbed is, according to the Langmuir isotherm, approximately proportional to the gas pressure. The rate of decomposition, if decomposition is indeed a surface reaction, would be expected, if no other complication occurs, to be proportional to the gas pressure. The rate with which the gas is decomposed, dn/dt moles/sec, would be given by

$$- \frac{dn}{dt} = kP \tag{15}$$

where k is a proportionality constant. For a constant-volume system dn can be replaced by $(V/RT)\, dP$ so that the rate law would be

$$- \frac{dP}{dt} = \frac{RT}{V} kP$$

or

$$\ln \frac{P_0}{P} = \frac{RTk}{V} t \tag{16}$$

where the initial gas pressure is P_0 at time $t = 0$.

The decomposition of phosphine on glass,

$$PH_3 \rightarrow P + \tfrac{3}{2} H_2 \tag{17}$$

as shown by the data of Fig. 19-10, conforms to this rate law and therefore presumably proceeds by the decomposition of adsorbed molecules. That the surface is involved is readily shown by increasing the surface area, by the addition of glass wool, for example, and observing the higher rate constant.

The second decomposition-rate-expression type that will be mentioned here is anticipated for moderate adsorption for which the amount adsorbed can be expected, according to the Langmuir isotherm, to be proportional to the expression $P/(1 + aP)$. The decomposition might then follow the rate expression

$$- \frac{dP}{dt} = \frac{RTk}{V} \frac{P}{1 + aP} \tag{18}$$

Fig. 19-10. The decomposition of phosphine on a glass surface as a function of time at 446°C. The partial pressure of phosphine at time t is P and at zero time is P_0. [*From D. M. Kooij, Z. physik. Chem.*, **12: 155** (1893).]

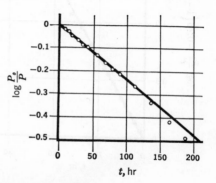

where k is a constant. Separation of variables gives

$$-\frac{dP}{P} - adP = \frac{RTk}{V}dt \tag{19}$$

and integration between the limits P_0 at time $t = 0$ and P at time t gives

$$\log\frac{P_0}{P} + \frac{a}{2.303}(P_0 - P) = \frac{RTk}{2.303V}t \tag{20}$$

The experimental results for the decomposition of stibine on an antimony surface

$$SbH_3 \rightarrow Sb + \tfrac{3}{2}H_2 \tag{21}$$

fit this rate law. It is necessary to show that, for some value of a, a plot of the left side of Eq. (20) against t yields a straight line, and, as Fig. 19-11 shows, such a plot can be obtained.

Finally, for a strongly adsorbed gas the surface coverage is essentially complete, and the amount of adsorbed material is essentially independent of the pressure. The rate of decomposition would then be expected to be independent of P, and the rate law would be written as

$$-\frac{dP}{dt} = k \tag{22}$$

and

$$P = -kt + \text{const} \tag{23}$$

The data for the decomposition of ammonia on a tungsten surface are shown plotted in Fig. 19-12 so as to illustrate their conformity to this relation.

Even decompositions of the type used in these examples do not, however, necessarily follow such simply explained rate laws. One or more of the

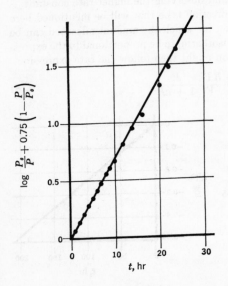

Fig. 19-11. The decomposition of stibine on an antimony surface as a function of time. The pressure of stibine is P at time t and P_0 at time zero. [*From A. Stock and M. Bodenstein, Ber.*, **40**: 570 (1907).]

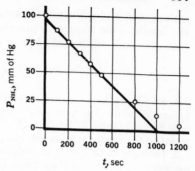

Fig. 19-12. The decomposition of ammonia on a tungsten surface at 856°C. [*From C. N. Hinshelwood and R. E. Burk, J. Chem. Soc.,* **127**: 1105 (1925).]

decomposition products may be adsorbed on the catalyst. In such cases the products inhibit the reaction by competing with the reagent for the catalyst surface. An example of this situation is provided by the decomposition of ammonia on a platinum filament. The Langmuir-isotherm derivation leads, with two adsorbed species, to the coverage expressions for the simultaneous adsorption of NH_3 and H_2,

$$\theta_{NH_3} = \frac{b_{NH_3}P_{NH_3}}{1 + b_{NH_3}P_{NH_3} + b_{H_2}P_{H_2}} \quad \text{and} \quad \theta_{H_2} = \frac{b_{H_2}P_{H_2}}{1 + b_{NH_3}P_{NH_3} + b_{H_2}P_{H_2}} \quad (24)$$

Adsorption studies of the separate reagents show that hydrogen is adsorbed to a much greater extent than is ammonia and therefore that $b_{NH_3}P_{NH_3} \ll b_{H_2}P_{H_2}$. For appreciable hydrogen pressures, furthermore, $b_{H_2}P_{H_2}$ will be greater than unity, and the fraction of the surface covered by ammonia becomes

$$\theta_{NH_3} = \frac{b_{NH_3}P_{NH_3}}{b_{H_2}P_{H_2}} \quad (25)$$

If the rate of the decomposition is dependent on the amount of ammonia on the surface, the constant-volume rate expression

$$-\frac{dP_{NH_3}}{dt} = k\frac{P_{NH_3}}{P_{H_2}} \quad (26)$$

is expected. Such a rate law does, in fact, fit the observed decomposition data of ammonia on a platinum surface.

This type of inhibition is an illustration of the important *catalyst-poison* behavior. The adsorption of a product, or a foreign substance, can compete for the catalyst surface and thereby inhibit the reaction. The effect of a small amount of such adsorption can be very great and leads to the recognition either that some catalysts have only a few active sites at which reactions can occur or that a small amount of adsorbent can alter the electron content of the catalyst to spoil its activity.

This brief discussion of the kinetics of heterogeneously catalyzed reactions should indicate that such studies can bear out the fact that such reactions are surface reactions. It becomes difficult, however, to study the nature of the surface reaction by kinetic measurements. For a reaction of any complexity the details of the adsorption processes and the details of the surface reaction cannot be deduced from the kinetic data alone.

Problems

1. Sketch the force versus total-surface-area curve that would be expected in a Langmuir surface-film experiment when a 0.1-cc sample of a solution containing 0.1 mole/liter of palmitic acid, $CH_3(C_{14}H_{28})COOH$, in the volatile solvent, ethyl alcohol, is placed on the surface of water and compressed on a Langmuir film balance.

2. Estimate, to the extent that you can from Fig. 19-4, the thickness of the almost completed layer of $CH_3(CH_2)_{34}COOH$ indicated in parts B and C. Similar estimates on the strips in part D show them to be two molecules thick.

3. Suggest a mechanism of surface-film collapse that leads to the formation of strips that are two molecules thick lying on top of the monomolecular layer.

4. The data of Langmuir [*J. Am. Chem. Soc.*, **40**: 1361 (1918)] for the adsorption of nitrogen on mica at 90°K give:

P (atm)	2.8	3.4	4.0	4.9	6.0	7.3	9.4	12.8	17.1	23.5	33.5
Amt. adsorbed (cu mm at 20°C and 760 mm)	12.0	13.4	15.1	17.0	19.0	21.6	23.9	25.5	28.2	30.8	33.0

Show that these data fit a Langmuir-isotherm expression, and evaluate the constants in the expression.

Estimate the area covered by a single nitrogen molecule from the fact that the density of liquid nitrogen is 0.81 g/cc.

Estimate the surface area of the mica sample in the Langmuir experiment.

$$Ans. \ y_m = 1.62 \times 10^{-6} \ moles.$$

5. Acetic acid is adsorbed from solution by activated charcoal. The following data have been reported for the amounts y of acetic acid adsorbed as a function of the concentration c of the equilibrium solution:

c (moles/liter)	0.018	0.031	0.062	0.126	0.268	0.471	0.882
y (moles)	0.47	0.62	0.80	1.11	1.55	2.04	2.48

Show that these data fit a Freundlich isotherm, and determine the constants in the Freundlich-isotherm expression.

6. Show that at low surface coverages the Langmuir isotherm corresponds to the Freundlich expression with $n = 1$. Show also that at high surface coverages the Langmuir equation corresponds to the Freundlich expression with n equal to infinity.

7. Obtain Eqs. (24) for the fraction of surface covered by each of two adsorbents if the adsorptions follow Langmuir's adsorption isotherm.

20

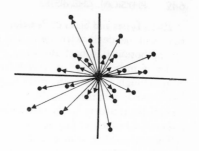

Macromolecules

Many approaches, both theoretical and experimental, to the study of the behavior of chemical systems have already been developed and applied. In these studies a distinction has generally been made between a molecular treatment and a macroscopic one. An important and very interesting class of systems occurs which is, in a way, intermediate between these extremes. These systems often consist of, or contain, molecules that are so large that they can be treated either as large molecules or as small macroscopic particles. Most particles that are of current interest and are in this size range, about 100 to 10,000 A, are found to be single molecules, and the term *macromolecule* is convenient.

A number of different physical-chemical approaches are required to reveal the nature of these systems. Some of these special techniques have already been mentioned but find their greatest current application in the study of macromolecule systems. Still other techniques must be introduced for these special systems. The deduction of the details of these large and often very complex molecules is one of the present exciting challenges presented to the physical chemist. Many of the systems, as will be seen, have great biological importance. Some of this area of study is often included in biochemistry, but even the more compounded term *molecular biochemistry* seems appropriate. It is desirable, in the short study of macromolecules that can be presented here, to discuss both synthetic and naturally occurring macromolecules side by side. Although the areas of plastics and biological materials may seem little related, it will be found that the physical-chemical study of the basic chemical units of these areas has very much in common. It is convenient to distinguish, for these studies, between macromolecules in the solid state and in solution. After a more general introduction to the types of systems that occur or can be produced with particles in this size range, these two principal sections, i.e., solutions and the solid state, will be treated so that information on the structure, shape, and behavior of macromolecules can be obtained.

641

20-1. Types and Sizes of Particles. The existence of particles in the size range that will be dealt with here was suggested by the early observation made by the botanist Robert Brown of the random motion of pollen grains as seen under a microscope. It was later recognized that these particles, though large enough to be seen, were small enough to reveal the effects of random molecular bombardment, the so-called *Brownian motion.* By the end of the nineteenth century, study of small-particle systems, called *colloids*, became an important branch of physical chemistry.

The unique behavior of colloids is now recognized to be exhibited by particles in the size range of about 100 to 10,000 A. One of the most commonly recognized features of such systems is that they scatter light as, for example, is observed when a beam of sunlight passes through dusty air or through thin skimmed milk. Furthermore the particles of a colloidal system do not settle out and, as the chemist has invariably experienced with some silver chloride precipitates, tend to pass through ordinary filter paper. Colloidal systems frequently occur and, as Table 20-1 shows, can be of many different phase types.

A closer look at the chemical world shows, however, that there are particles in this size range that are of great interest and importance but are not listed in Table 20-1. These stem from the existence of single molecules that are sufficiently large so that individual molecules have colloidal dimensions. In view of present interest, these macromolecule systems can be classed as synthetic polymers and as the naturally occurring macromolecules. Most interest in the natural materials is now centered on *proteins* and *nucleic acids*, but natural macromolecules also include the *polysaccharides* and the *polyisoprenes*, the latter being the molecules of natural rubber. These categories of macromolecules are outlined in Table 20-2.

In addition to the many types of highly dispersed systems listed in Table 20-1 and the macromolecules, which will be our principal subject of study in this chapter, listed in Table 20-2, mention should also be made of the colloidal-sized groups known as *micelles.* The turbidity exhibited by soap or detergent solutions is the best-known indication of micelle formation. Since the molecules of soap or detergent are very small compared with colloidal dimensions,

Table 20-1. Some Common Types of Colloids Classified as to Phase Type

Name	Type	Examples
Aerosol............	Solid particles in gas	Smoke
Aerosol............	Liquid particles in gas	Fog
Sol...............	Solid particles in liquid	S, Au, AgCl in H_2O
Emulsion..........	Liquid particles in liquid	Mayonnaise, milk
Foam.............	Gas bubbles in liquid	Whipped cream
Gels..............	Liquid in solid matrix	Jellies

Table 20-2. Classes of Macromolecules

Classes	Examples
Synthetic macromolecules..........	Addition polymers, polyethylene Condensation polymers, nylon
Natural macromolecules:	
Proteins.....................	Fibrous: keratin, silk fibroin Globular hemoglobin
Nucleic acids..................	Deoxyribonucleic acid (DNA)
Polysaccharides...............	Cellulose
Polyisoprene..................	Natural rubber

the particles causing the turbidity are groups, or *micelles*, of these molecules. Their formation is very analogous to that of monomolecular films studied in the previous chapter. Most soaps and detergents have a long hydrocarbon "tail" and a polar "head." In the soaps the head is the sodium or potassium salt of the carboxylic acid, that is, $RCOO^-K^+$, while in the detergents the head is the salt of a sulfonic acid, i.e., of the type $R-SO_3^-Na^+$. A micelle can be expected to form in a manner depicted in Fig. 20-1. It will be seen later that the charged layer around the surface of the particles is important for the stability of the individual micelles.

All our studies will now be directed toward an understanding of macro-molecule systems. It will be clear that many of the methods that are dealt with are applicable to all systems with colloidal-sized particles. No specific treatment of the important system of sols, i.e., solids dispersed in liquids, will be given. Such colloids are now studied largely in connection with their role in the precipitation process and therefore are more suitably treated in a study of analytical chemistry.

20-2. Synthetic Polymers. A few of the more important synthetic linear polymers are listed in Table 20-3. These *linear polymers* are character-ized by covalently bound skeletons that extend throughout the length of the molecule. Probably the nicest example is provided by the synthetic polymer,

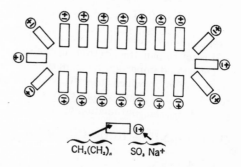

Fig. 20-1. The structure of a micelle. An actual micelle must, however, con-sist of hundreds of soap or detergent molecules.

$CH_3(CH_2)_n$ $SO_3 Na^+$

Table 20-3. Some Synthetic Linear Polymers

	Chemical unit	Molecular weight
Polyethylene.............	$[-CH_2-]_n$	5,000–40,000
Polystyrene.............	$\begin{bmatrix} & C_6H_5 \\ & \mid \\ -CH-CH_2- \end{bmatrix}_n$	60,000–1,500,000
Nylon................	$\begin{bmatrix} H & H & O & & O \\ \mid & \mid & \parallel & & \parallel \\ -N(CH_2)_6N-C-(CH_2)_4-C- \end{bmatrix}_n$	10,000–30,000

polyethylene,

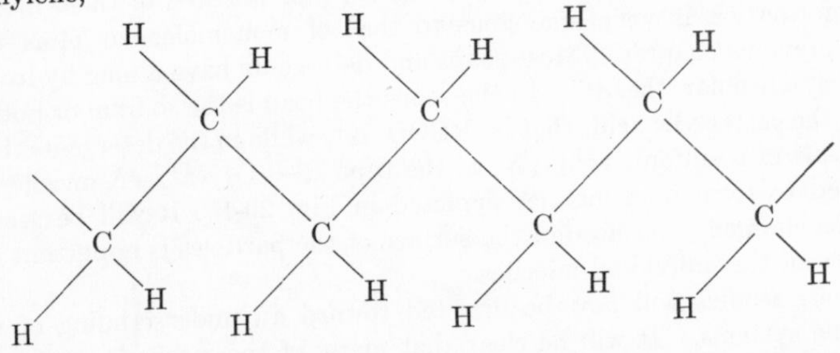

Synthetic polymers are made from the corresponding monomers by one of two general types of reactions. One reaction type is that of *addition polymerization*. The mechanism of this type of polymerization reaction consists in the adding on of monomer units to the growing polymer chain by a free-radical, carbonium-ion (cationic-polymerization), or carbanion (anionic-polymerization) mechanism. The formation of polyethylene from ethylene proceeds, in the high-pressure process, by a free radical addition which is probably initiated by oxygen molecules. Once started, the polymerization proceeds by the process

$$CH_3-(CH_2)_n-\dot{C}H_2 + CH_2{=}CH_2 \rightarrow CH_3-(CH_2)_{n+2}-\dot{C}H_2$$

$$CH_3-(CH_2)_{n+2}-\dot{C}H_2 + CH_2{=}CH_2 \rightarrow \text{etc.}$$

Termination occurs when two radical centers in the system come together and react to pair the electrons of the free radicals.

The second important reaction type for the formation of a polymer is that of *condensation*, in which, usually, water is split out as the monomer units join together. The synthesis of nylon from hexamethylenediamine and adipic acid proceeds by the continuation of the raction

$$H_2N(CH_2)_6NH_2 + HOOC(CH_2)_4COOH \rightarrow$$

$$H_2N(CH_2)_6N\overset{\overset{\displaystyle O}{\parallel}}{-}C-(CH_2)_4COOH + H_2O$$

The polymers listed in Table 20-3 consist predominantly of linear molecules with minor amounts of branching and cross linking.   It should be mentioned, however, that *cross-linked* polymers do exist, or can be formed, and that these constitute a very important type of material.   Cross-linked polymers have, at least to some extent, a three-dimensional array of covalent bonds.   Common examples are vulcanized rubber and rigid plastics like Bakelite.   The vulcanization of rubber can be illustrated by the addition of sulfur monochloride, S_2Cl_2, to rubber.   The synthetic-rubber molecule chains

$$\cdots CH{=}\underset{\underset{CH_3}{|}}{C}{-}CH_2{-}CH_2{-}CH{=}\underset{\underset{CH_3}{|}}{C}{-}CH_2{-}CH_2\cdots$$

are joined together by sulfur cross links in the manner

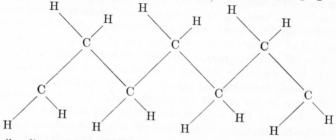

etc.

Such cross linking produces a characteristic infusible, insoluble material. It is the latter that prevents the very illuminating solution studies from being made on such polymers.

Synthesis of a polymer, such as polyethylene, proceeds principally by the free-radical addition that has been indicated.   In fact, one finds that a certain number of side chains are usually produced to give a less perfect linear polymer than that ordinarily shown diagrammatically.

A polyethylene chain may adopt, and does so to some extent in solid polyethylene, the energetically favored, but statistically unlikely, zigzag shape

If a similar diagram is attempted for a polymer like polypropylene, one recognizes a number of different possibilities.   Polypropylene, as ordinarily prepared, has the methyl groups on every second carbon atom attached at random on either side of the chain and is known as an *atactic* polymer.

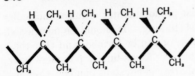

By very carefully selecting the polymerization catalyst it is possible to produce a *stereospecific* form, known as an *isotactic* polymer, with the structure shown in Fig. 20-2. The regular arrangement of the side-chain groups produces considerable changes in the way in which the molecules can pack together and therefore markedly affects the physical properties of the resulting polymeric material.

Finally, mention should be made of inorganic polymers. The single crystal particles of a finely dispersed ionic or metallic material could be taken as an example. More suitable, however, are the polymers such as occur in the silicones, the metaphosphate glasses, and sulfur. The silicones are synthetic linear polymers of the type

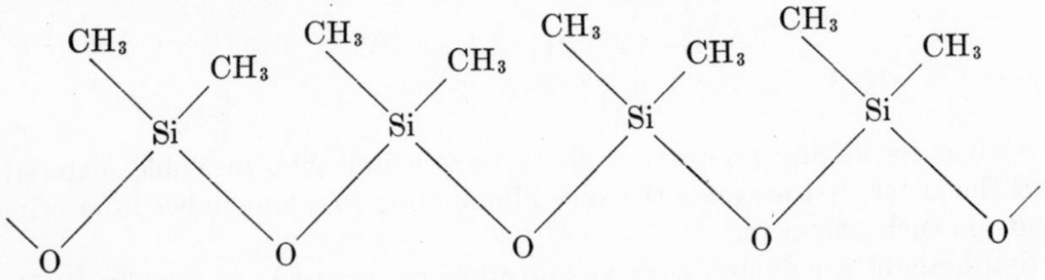

where rotation about the Si—O bonds must be expected to be relatively free. The silicones form liquids and soft plastics or rubbers.

20-3. Proteins. The world of living things is made up of a great variety of chemical substances, many of which fall into the category of macromolecules. In the animal world many of these macromolecules are proteins. These basic units of life have an amazing complexity that until recently seemed to be such as to remain forever beyond man's understanding. Much of our present understanding of the nature and biological role of proteins has come about through chemical and biological studies that cannot be dealt with here. In recent years, however, many physical-chemical attacks have been made on the problem of protein structure and behavior. These studies have contributed in great measure to our present remarkable understanding of proteins. It will be clear, however, that much remains to be done and that the physical-chemical techniques that are now practiced will be refined and new ones will be developed to provide answers to the many questions that still exist.

Very many different proteins can be isolated from the whole variety of living matter. All these proteins can be broken down by hydrolysis to yield organic molecules, all of which are amino acids. These amino acids, furthermore, all have the structure

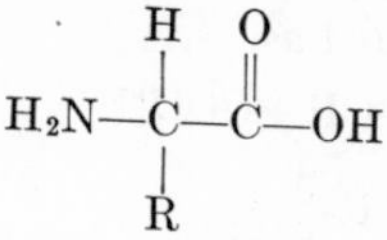

$$H_2N-\underset{\underset{R}{|}}{\overset{\overset{H}{|}}{C}}-\overset{\overset{O}{\|}}{C}-OH$$

i.e., they are α-amino acids, the name signifying that the NH_2 group is attached to the carbon atom adjacent to the acid function. These α-amino acids are distinguished by different R groups. The amino acids that are constituents of proteins are listed in Table 20-4.

Amino acids such as these can be visualized as being linked together through something like a condensation reaction to form *polypeptides*. The attachment of one amino acid to another is through a *peptide bond* that is similar to

Table 20-4. The Amino Acids Obtained from Protein Hydrolysis*

		Neutral amino acids	
Glycine	$CH_2(NH_2)CO_2H$		
Alanine	$CH_3CH(NH_2)CO_2H$	Serine	$HOCH_2CH(NH_2)CO_2H$
Valine	$(CH_3)_2CHCH(NH_2)CO_2H$	Threonine	$CH_3CH(OH)CH(NH_2)CO_2H$
Leucine	$(CH_3)_2CHCH_2CH(NH_2)CO_2H$	Methionine	$CH_3SCH_2CH_2CH(NH_2)CO_2H$
Isoleucine	$CH_3CH_2CH(CH_3)CH(NH_2)CO_2H$	Cysteine	$HSCH_2CH(NH_2)CO_2H$
Phenylalanine	$C_6H_5CH_2CH(NH_2)CO_2H$	Cystine	$\overset{\underset{|}{}}{S}CH_2CH(NH_2)CO_2H$
			$\overset{\underset{|}{}}{S}CH_2CH(NH_2)CO_2H$

Tyrosine   HO—⟨ ⟩—$CH_2CH(NH_2)CO_2H$ Proline

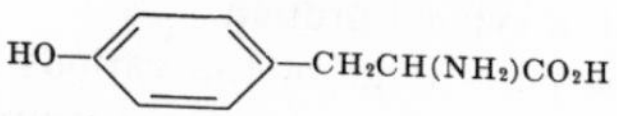

Diiodotyrosine   HO—⟨ ⟩—$CH_2CH(NH_2)CO_2H$ Hydroxyproline   HO

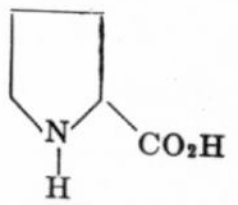

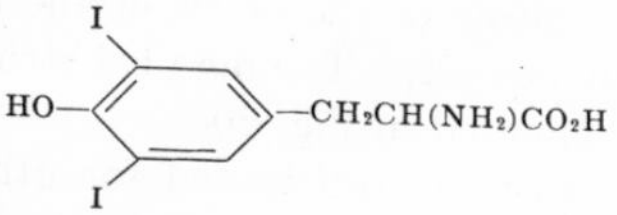

Thyroxine   HO—⟨ ⟩—O—⟨ ⟩—$CH_2CH(NH_2)CO_2H$

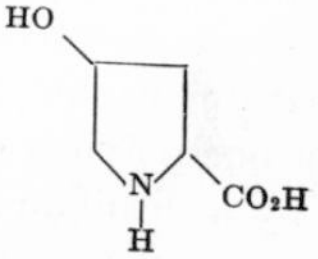

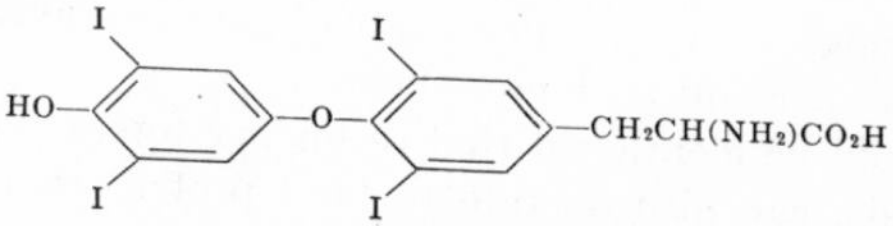

Tryptophan $CH_2CH(NH_2)CO_2H$

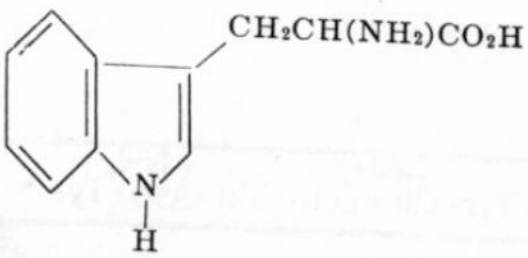

Acidic amino acids

Aspartic acid $HO_2CCH_2CH(NH_2)CO_2H$

Glutamic acid $HO_2CCH_2CH_2CH(NH_2)CO_2H$

Basic amino acids

Lysine $H_2N(CH_2)_4CH(NH_2)CO_2H$

Arginine $H_2N\overset{\underset{\|}{NH}}{C}NH(CH_2)_3CH(NH_2)CO_2H$ Histidine

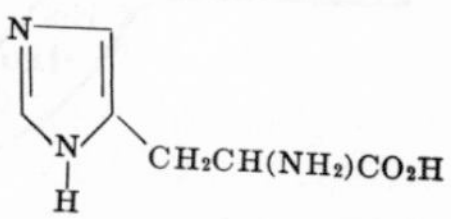

Ornithine $H_2N(CH_2)_3CH(NH_2)CO_2H$

*From D. J. Cram and G. S. Hammond, "Organic Chemistry," McGraw-Hill Book Company, Inc., New York, 1959.

that previously illustrated in the formation of nylon. The condensation of two amino acids can be depicted as

$$H_2N\text{—CH—COOH} + H_2N\text{—CH—COOH} \rightarrow$$
$$\underset{R_1}{|} \qquad\qquad \underset{R_2}{|}$$

$$H_2N\text{—CH—}\overset{\overset{O}{\|}}{C}\text{—NH—CH—COOH} + H_2O$$
$$\underset{R_1}{|} \qquad\qquad\qquad \underset{R_2}{|}$$

By repetition of such a reaction amino acids can be built up into macromolecules.

True proteins, however, cannot be so easily synthesized. They consist of similar polymers of amino acids, but in a protein there is a definite sequence of a number of different amino acids. If chemically and structurally the exact order of the amino acids seems rather trivial, this is not the case biologically. It is the sequence of amino acids that is an important characteristic of the protein. The sequence, moreover, continues throughout the protein molecule, which, depending on the protein, will have a molecular weight of the order of ten to hundreds of thousands. There are, therefore, hundreds of amino acids linked in a particular manner in a typical protein.

The chemical constitution, i.e., the percentage of the various amino acids present, has been worked out for many proteins. In recent years, moreover, the remarkable feat of a complete analysis of the order of the amino acids of a protein has been accomplished by Sanger. The detailed structure of the relatively simple protein, insulin, is indicated in Fig. 20-3.

A feature of this protein, which must be anticipated for others, is that it is not one polymeric sequence but rather two essentially linear chains cross-linked by a disulfide bridge. Any detailed study of the size and shape of such molecules must take into account such cross links.

In this regard it should be mentioned that secondary forces, which are not covalent chemical bonds, can also operate to bind protein chains together. Such forces are usually hydrogen bonds or electrostatic-charge interactions.

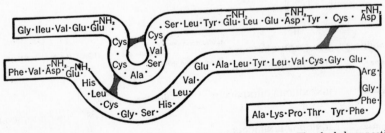

Fig. 20-3. The arrangement of amino acids in the protein insulin. The shaded connecting links are disulfide bonds. Abbreviations correspond to the amino acids in Table 20-4. (*Courtesy of Prof. Irving M. Klotz, Northwestern University.*)

Hydrogen bonds are important because the protein chain contains a sequence of groups that can engage in hydrogen bonding. Principal of these groups are the NH and C=O groups, which, if suitably positioned relative to each other, can form the hydrogen bond

$$\diagdown \!\!\! N\!-\!H\cdots O\!=\!C \diagdown$$

Electrostatic interactions occur because of the presence of acidic and basic centers in some of the amino acids of proteins. In this connection it is important to note that an individual amino acid can be titrated by either acid or base and that the charged species

$$H_3N^+\!-\!\underset{\underset{R}{|}}{CH}\!-\!COOH \qquad \text{in acid}$$

and
$$H_2N\!-\!\underset{\underset{R}{|}}{CH}\!-\!COO^- \qquad \text{in base}$$

are formed. Furthermore, it appears that the molecule in approximately neutral aqueous solution adopts the zwitterion form

$$H_3N^+\!-\!\underset{\underset{R}{|}}{CH}\!-\!COO^-$$

rather than the noncharged configuration

$$H_2N\!-\!\underset{\underset{R}{|}}{CH}\!-\!COOH$$

In the proteins, although most of these amine and carboxylic acid groups are used up in peptide-bond formation, there are free basic and acidic centers which can act in a similar way to give the molecule a net positive or negative charge. Such charges produce secondary forces that have a considerable effect, not only on the electrical properties of proteins, but also on the geometric configuration. Like charges can, for example, repel each other to cause the molecule to open up, while opposite charges can act to pull the molecule together.

Secondary forces are effective in determining, in solution, the shape that the polymer molecule adopts, i.e., whether it tends to ball up or be extended, and in the solid state both the shape of the protein molecule and the way in which neighboring protein chains are packed together.

In structural studies it is customary to distinguish between *fibrous* and *globular* proteins. The fibrous proteins tend to occur as long chains and are found in structural tissue such as wool, hair, nail, and muscle. The globular proteins, on the other hand, tend to be more or less spherical and, unlike the fibrous proteins, are often water-soluble. Such substances as enzymes, hemoglobin, and egg white fall into this category.

Many features of both types of proteins will be revealed by the physical-chemical studies that will be dealt with in later sections of this chapter.

20-4. Nucleic Acids. The great variety of form that proteins can assume leads one to the question as to how the information for the synthesis of all the protein molecules can be contained in each cell of a living organism. Genetic studies lead to the conclusion that each living cell carries in it sets of information, or codes, for the building up of all the proteins associated with the life of the cell. It appears, furthermore, that the chromosomes, which originate in the nucleus of the cell, are the units in which this vast quantity of information is stored. When a cell divides to form two new cells, the chromosomes (of which man has 48 in each body cell) go through a remarkable series of maneuvers and ultimately split into two parts. One part goes into each of the new cells and continues to function as the information center for protein and other syntheses. The chromosomes contain subdivisions called *genes*, and these control various biochemical syntheses.

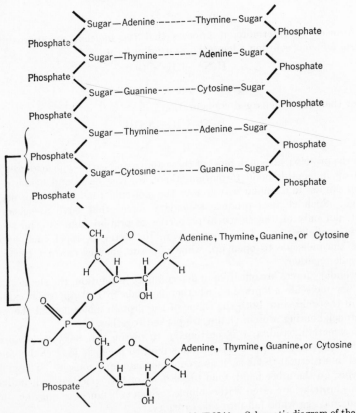

Fig. 20-4a. The structure of deoxyribonucleic acid (DNA). Schematic diagram of the DNA chain structure.

The chromosomes are rich in macromolecule species which, since chromosomes occur in the cell nucleus, are called *nucleic acids*. It is these macromolecules which are now recognized as performing the prime function of the genes. Elucidation of the structure and function of nucleic acids, in so far as known at present, will be seen to be at least as great an accomplishment as the corresponding progress that has been made in protein studies.

Nucleic acids occur in at least two main types: deoxyribonucleic acid (DNA) and ribonucleic acid (RNA). In this brief treatment attention will be restricted to DNA, which, as Fig. 20-4a indicates, consists of a backbone of alternate sugar residues and phosphate groups. The macromolecule nature of the molecule is best brought out by the more schematic representation of the chain, also shown in Fig. 20-4a. Attached to each sugar group of the chain is one of four nitrogen-containing groups. Although we shall not become involved with the detailed behavior of these groups, their geometry is important and they are shown in Fig. 20-4b.

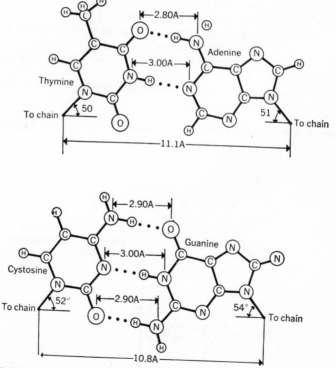

Fig. 20-4b. The structure of deoxyribonucleic acid (DNA). Detail of the hydrogen bonding and geometry of the base pairs of DNA.

It anticipates some of our later structural studies to mention further that DNA consists of two macromolecule chains that are associated by secondary forces as indicated in Fig. 20-4. When it is pointed out that there are about 10^{10} side-group positions in a DNA molecule and that the four different groups are attached in some order that apparently represents a code, there is the possibility for storing a vast amount of information. Furthermore, the presence of two macromolecule chains anticipates the cell-division process, in which the information unit is divided and new units appear in the two new cells. The biological consequences of a detailed molecular structure for the nucleic acids are fascinating. We shall see that the structural aspects, on which our physical-chemical studies will focus, are equally remarkable.

20-5. The Polysaccharides. The third important type of natural polymers is the polysaccharide molecule. Simple sugar units can be depicted as condensing with the elimination of water to form disaccharides, such as sucrose, and polysaccharides, such as starch and cellulose.

Figure 20-5 shows the structure of glucose and the repeating unit in cellulose. Cellulose is the chief constituent of wood and cotton. It is perhaps not strictly correct to include such molecules in a study which claims to deal with particles in the range of colloidal sizes. The cellulose molecules can presumably be of macroscopic length, and the average molecular weight of such natural products is not easily determined since any process that breaks the material apart to free the individual molecules may at the same time cleave the molecular chain.

20-6. The Polyisoprenes. Natural rubber is a polymeric material which is composed of linear polymers of the isoprene, $CH_2{=}\overset{\overset{\displaystyle CH_3}{|}}{C}{-}CH{=}CH_2$, molecule.

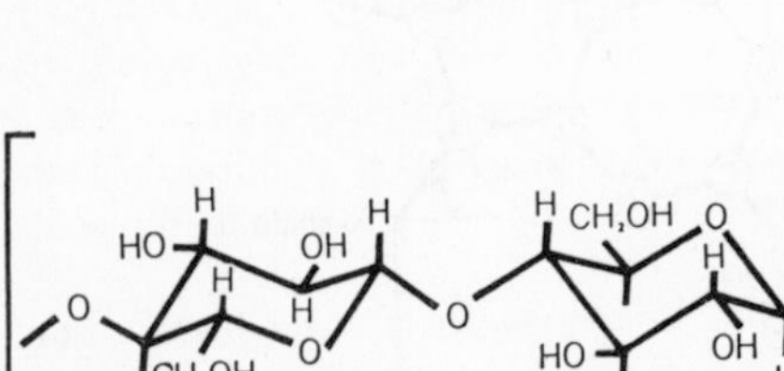

Glucose

Fig. 20-5. The structure of glucose and cellulose.

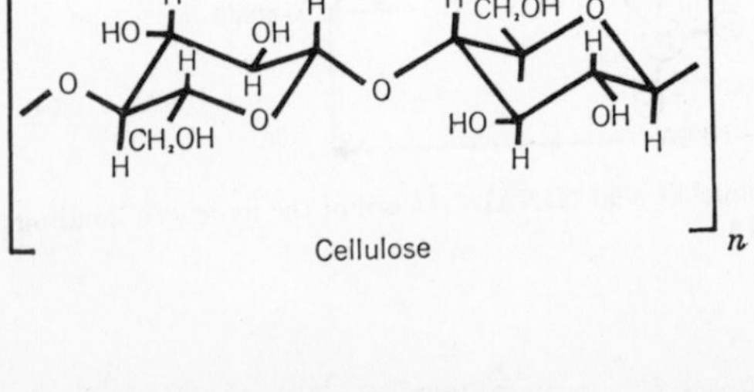

Cellulose

This monomer can in fact be polymerized catalytically to give a synthetic rubber. In naturally occurring rubber the linear polymers have nearly all the remaining double bonds connected in the polymer chain to give a cis configuration, and the polymer can be drawn as

A transpolyisoprene also occurs and is known as *gutta-percha*. The molecule can be represented as

Unlike rubber it is a tough, hard substance.

MACROMOLECULES IN SOLUTION

Much of our information on the size and general shape of macromolecules has been deduced from various properties of solutions containing these molecules. In this section some of the methods used to understand the behavior of solutions of macromolecules will be investigated, and in the process of such studies a number of properties of the macromolecules themselves will be discovered. It is first necessary, however, to discuss the meaning of molecular weight when applied to a polymeric material.

20-7. Molecular Weights of Polymers. Polymerization reactions, both synthetic and natural, can lead to high-molecular-weight compounds. The reaction chain is, however, broken by some termination process that usually occurs in a random manner with respect to the size to which the polymer has already grown. It follows that polymers have a *range of molecular weights* and that any data for the size or weight of the molecules of a polymer must represent some sort of average value. It will be seen that attempts to deduce molecular weights of polymers lead to *number-average* and *weight-average* molecular weights.

The number average, denoted by M_n, is defined as the weight of sample divided by the total number of moles n in the sample, i.e.,

$$M_n = \frac{\text{weight}}{n} \tag{1}$$

Any measurement that leads to the number of particles, or molecules, that are present in a given weight of sample will allow the calculation of a number-average molecular weight. If the sample can be considered as made up of fractions consisting of n_1 moles of molecular weight M_1, n_2 moles of molecular weight M_2, and so forth, then

$$M_n = \frac{n_1 M_1 + n_2 M_2 + \cdots}{n_1 + n_2 + \cdots}$$

$$= \frac{\sum_i n_i M_i}{\sum_i n_i} \tag{2}$$

In other experiments each particle makes a contribution to the measured result according to its molecular weight. The average molecular weight deduced from such measurements is therefore more dependent on the number of heavier molecules than it is in experiments dependent simply on the total number of particles. The appropriate average for such determinations is the *weight average*, defined as

$$M_w = \frac{\sum_i n_i M_i^2}{\sum_i n_i M_i} \tag{3}$$

For an appreciable distribution of molecular sizes in a polymer sample, these two molecular weights M_n and M_w will be appreciably different.

20-8. Osmotic-pressure Determinations of Molecular Weights. A measurement of any of the colligative properties of a solution of macromolecules leads, essentially, to a counting of the solute molecules in a given amount of solvent, as was discussed in Chap. 15. There it was pointed out that for the solutions of low molality, such as are always obtained with macromolecules, the only colligative property that is conveniently measured is the osmotic pressure. Such measurements are one of the most important means of molecular-weight determinations. It should be evident from the nature of colligative properties, i.e., they depend only on the number and not on the nature of the solute molecule, that a number average molecular weight is obtained.

The high concentration, in terms of weight of solute per weight of solvent, even for low molalities, means that solute interactions will occur and nonideal behavior will result. It is almost always necessary therefore to extrapolate the measurements to infinite dilution, as was done in Chap. 15. Sensitive osmotic-pressure instruments now allow measurements to be made on very dilute solutions, and molecular weights even up to 500,000 can be obtained.

20-9. Diffusion. A number of hydrodynamic experiments lead to information about the size and shape of macromolecules in solution. The first of these that will be considered is the diffusion of the macromolecules of a solution across a carefully made, well-defined liquid boundary into pure solvent. Experimentally one finds that the rate of diffusion is proportional to the concentration difference across the boundary, or, more conveniently, to the concentration gradient dc/dx, where c is the macromolecule concentration in grams per cubic centimeter of solution. The rate of diffusion is found, furthermore, to be proportional to the cross-section area A. If the diffusion rate is written as dw/dt, the number of grams of macromolecules transferred across the boundary per second, one has Fick's law of diffusion,

$$\frac{dw}{dt} = -DA\,\frac{dc}{dx} \tag{4}$$

The proportionality constant D is called the *diffusion coefficient*, and the negative sign is introduced so that D will have a positive value. The diffusion coefficient can be recognized as the amount of solute that diffuses across a 1-sq cm area in 1 sec under the influence of a concentration gradient of $1\ \mathrm{g/(cc)(cm)}$. The diffusion coefficient is characteristic therefore, for a given solvent at a given temperature, of the diffusing tendency of the solute. Some measurements of diffusion coefficients for macromolecules are listed in Table 20-5.

It is necessary now to see whether or not these experimental diffusion coefficients can be related to any properties of the system and particularly of the macromolecule. To do this, a molecular view of the diffusion process is taken.

Consider diffusion across a distance interval dx over which the concentration changes from c to $c - dc$. The force that drives the molecules to the more dilute region can be obtained from the difference in free energy of solution of concentration c and of concentration $c - dc$. If the corresponding mole fractions of solute are x_B and $x_B - dx_B$ and Henry's law is assumed, the discussion of Sec. 14-14 leads to the free-energy difference per molecule of

$$G_{c-dc} - G_c = \frac{RT}{N} \ln \frac{x_B - dx_B}{x_B} \tag{5}$$

where N is Avogadro's number. For dilute solutions the concentration in grams per cubic centimeter is proportional to mole fraction, and Eq. (2) can be

Table 20-5. Diffusion and Sedimentation Coefficients and Derived Molecular Weights for Some Proteins

(Values are for aqueous solutions at 20°C)

Protein	Sp vol v (cc/g)	Sedimentation coeff. s (sec)	Diffusion coeff. D (sq cm/sec)	Mol wt from Eq. (24)
Insulin	0.75	3.5×10^{-13}	8.2×10^{-7}	41,000
Hemoglobin	0.75	4.4×10^{-13}	6.3×10^{-7}	67,000
Catalase	0.73	11.3×10^{-13}	4.1×10^{-7}	250,000
Urease	0.73	18.6×10^{-13}	3.5×10^{-7}	470,000
Tobacco mosaic virus	0.73	185×10^{-13}	0.53×10^{-7}	31,000,000

rewritten as
$$G_{c-dc} - G_c = \frac{RT}{N} \ln \frac{c - dc}{c} \tag{6}$$

or
$$dG = \frac{RT}{N} \ln \left(1 - \frac{dc}{c} \right)$$
$$\cong -\frac{RT}{N} \frac{dc}{c} \tag{7}$$

where the relation $\ln (1 - y) = -y$ for small y has been used.

This free-energy difference corresponds to the work that is done in the transfer of one macromolecule across the distance dx and can therefore be written as a force times the distance dx. Thus

$$\text{Driving force} = \frac{dG}{dx} = -\frac{RT}{N} \frac{1}{c} \frac{dc}{dx} \tag{8}$$

A frictional force sets in to balance this diffusion force when some constant velocity is reached. The frictional force exerted by a viscous fluid, of viscosity η, has been derived for a macroscopic sphere of radius r by Stokes as

$$\text{Frictional force} = 6\pi r \eta v$$
$$= 6\pi r \eta \frac{dx}{dt} \tag{9}$$

It appears to be suitable to apply this expression to the motion of reasonably spherical macromolecules. The diffusion velocity increases therefore until the force of Eq. (8) just balances that of Eq. (9). Then

$$6\pi r \eta \frac{dx}{dt} = -\frac{RT}{N} \frac{1}{c} \frac{dc}{dx}$$

or
$$\frac{c \, dx}{dt} = -\frac{RT}{6\pi r N \eta} \frac{dc}{dx} \tag{10}$$

Comparison with the empirical Fick's-law expression can be made when it is recognized that $c \, dx$ can be identified with dw since these terms are the weight of solute diffusing across the boundary in time dt. (All the molecules, which have an average diffusion velocity that carries them a distance dx in time dt, will cross the boundary in time dt if they start within a distance dx of the boundary. The mass of these molecules is the volume, dx times the unit cross-section area, times the concentration c in grams per cubic centimeter. Thus $dw = c \, dx$.) Equation (10) becomes

$$\frac{dw}{dt} = -\frac{RT}{6\pi r N \eta} \frac{dc}{dx} \tag{11}$$

Comparison of this molecularly derived diffusion-rate expression with Eq. (4) allows the interpretation of the observed diffusion constant D as

$$D = \frac{RT}{6\pi r N \eta} \tag{12}$$

Measurements of D and η could therefore lead to a value of the radius r for the macromolecule. Such a procedure is a little unsatisfactory in that the molecules will not necessarily obey Stokes' law for spherical particles, and, furthermore, the macromolecules will generally be solvated and in moving through the solution will, to some extent, carry along this solvation layer. The molecular interpretation of D, as given by Eq. (12), is important, however, in determining the effective value of the group of terms $6\pi r N \eta$ for a given solute and solvent.

20-10. Sedimentation and the Ultracentrifuge. In the previous section the tendency of a solute to diffuse across a concentration gradient was treated. Macromolecules in solution can be made to alter their distribution in space by subjecting them to other forces. In the simplest experiment a solution is allowed to stand so that the force of gravity acts. A greater and more easily observed effect can be produced, however, by means of an ultracentrifuge in which a sample of the macromolecule solution rotates at a very high speed, in the neighborhood of 10,000 to 80,000 revolutions/min. The ultracentrifuge, some features of which are shown in Fig. 20-6, is a very important tool for macromolecule research.

The behavior of solutions of macromolecules on ultracentrifugation will now be investigated. Two essentially different types of experiments can be performed. One either can centrifuge the sample until an equilibrium distribution is obtained, or, alternatively, one can observe the rate of movement of the macromolecules during the centrifugation.

The first method, called *sedimentation equilibrium*, allows the process to proceed until an equilibrium distribution of the solute throughout the cell is obtained. Thermodynamics has introduced free energy as a convenient quantity for the study of equilibrium, and it can be used here to deal with the equilibrium concentration gradient that develops. In particular, the centrifugal and diffusional contributions to the free energies G_{r_1} and G_{r_2} at the radial positions r_1 and r_2 are calculated. At equilibrium the values of G_{r_1} and G_{r_2} must be equal.

The centrifugal force on a particle of mass m at a distance r from the center of rotation experiences a force, as was shown in Chap. 3, given by

$$f_{\text{centrifugal}} = m'r\omega^2 \tag{13}$$

where ω is the angular velocity in radians per second and m' is the effective mass of the particle. The free-energy difference between the particle at r_1

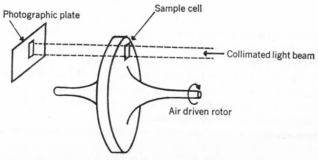

Fig. 20-6. Rotor and cell for oil-turbine ultracentrifuge. [*T. Svedberg, Endeavour*, **6**: 89 (1947).]

and at r_2 is obtained by finding the work required to move the particle from r_1 to r_2. The centrifugal free-energy difference, which is more negative at larger values of r, is thus

$$\Delta G_{\text{centrifugal}} = -\int_{r_1}^{r_2} (m'r\omega^2)\, dr$$

$$= -\frac{m'\omega^2}{2}(r_2^2 - r_1^2) \tag{14}$$

This factor tends to concentrate all the particles at large values of r, where the free energy is low.

In solution, however, this centrifugal effect operates only because the macromolecules may be more dense than the solvent, and the quantity m' in Eq. (14) must be interpreted as an effective mass. The relation between the effective and actual masses can be determined from the difference in weight of 1 g of solute and the weight of solvent that occupies the same volume. If the volume of 1 g of solute is v, the weight of a volume v of solvent is $v\rho$, where ρ is the solvent density. The buoyancy-correction term, the difference in weight of a volume v, is $1 - v\rho$, and the corrected centrifugal free-energy contribution is

$$\Delta G_{\text{centrifugal}} = -\frac{m(1 - v\rho)\omega^2(r_2^2 - r_1^2)}{2} \tag{15}$$

Balance is brought about by the diffusion tendency, which, according to Eq. (3), is, for one molecule,

$$\Delta G_{\text{diffusion}} = \frac{RT}{N} \ln \frac{c_2}{c_1} \tag{16}$$

where c_2 and c_1 are concentrations, which can be in grams per cubic centimeter, at r_2 and r_1.

At equilibrium the decrease in ΔG given by Eq. (15) just balances the increase given by Eq. (16), and for the process of moving solute from r_1 to r_2 one has

$$\Delta G_{\text{centrifugal}} + \Delta G_{\text{diffusion}} = 0$$

which gives, on rearrangement,

$$M = Nm = \frac{RT \ln (c_2/c_1)}{(1 - v\rho)(\omega^2/2)(r_1^2 - r_2^2)} \tag{17}$$

Thus, if measurements of the relative concentrations are made at two positions after equilibrium has been obtained, one can use Eq. (17) to calculate a value for the weight of the individual particles or for the weight of an Avogadro's number of particles, i.e., the molecular weight.

The second ultracentrifuge method starts with a well-defined boundary, or layer of solution near the center of rotation, and follows the movement of this layer toward the outside of the cell as a function of time. Such a method is termed a *sedimentation-velocity* experiment.

The force tending to move the macromolecules to the outside of the cell is given by

$$f_{\text{centrifugal}} = m(1 - v\rho)r\omega^2 \tag{18}$$

This force is balanced for some constant-drift velocity dr/dt by a frictional force that is given by Stokes' law as

$$f_{friction} = 6\pi\eta r \frac{dr}{dt} \qquad (19)$$

Equating these forces to find the constant-drift velocity, one obtains

$$m(1 - v\rho)r\omega^2 = 6\pi\eta r \frac{dr}{dt} \qquad (20)$$

A characteristic of a given macromolecule in a given solution is its *sedimentation coefficient s*, defined as the velocity dr/dt with which the macromolecules move per unit centrifugal field $r\omega^2$. It is therefore often values of

$$s = \frac{dr/dt}{r\omega^2} \qquad (21)$$

that are tabulated to express the results of a sedimentation velocity experiment. In cgs units the value of s for many macromolecules comes out to be of the order of 10^{-13} cm/sec per unit centrifugal field. A convenient unit having this value has therefore been introduced and is called a *svedberg* in honor of T. Svedberg, who did much of the early work with the ultracentrifuge. According to Eq. (20)

$$s = \frac{dr/dt}{r\omega^2} = \frac{m(1 - v\rho)}{6\pi\eta r} \qquad (22)$$

Rearrangement and multiplication by Avogadro's number gives

$$M = Nm = \frac{6\pi\eta r N s}{1 - v\rho} \qquad (23)$$

Now the troublesome and poorly defined terms involving η and r can be replaced by their effective values, such as appear in the measurable quantity D of Eq. (12), to give the desired result

$$M = \frac{RTs}{D(1 - v\rho)} \qquad (24)$$

Thus measurements of the sedimentation and diffusion coefficients and of the densities of the solvent and solute allow the deduction of the molecular weight of the macromolecules. The necessary data for such calculations for a few macromolecular materials are given in Table 20-5, page 655.

A particular advantage of the sedimentation-velocity technique is that a macromolecule solution containing two or more types of macromolecules is separated according to the molecular weights of the components. Figure 20-7 shows the sedimentation diagrams that are obtained at various times for such a system.

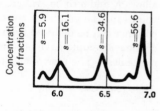

Fig. 20-7. Separation of Limulus Hemocyanin into fractions with different sedimentation constants, given in svedbergs. Centrifugal force is 120,000 times gravity and time after reaching full speed is 35 min. [*From T. Svedberg and J. B. Nichols, Proc. Roy. Soc. (London)*, **B127**: 1 (1939).]

20-11. Viscosity. Another hydrodynamic property of solutions of marco-molecules which is dependent on the molecular weight is the viscosity of a solution of the macromolecule material. Unlike the previous methods for obtaining molecular weights, however, measurements of viscosity do not yield absolute values. But the measurements are easily made and find wide use in the determination of the molecular weight of a given sample or batch of polymer. Use must be made of calibration measurements of viscosities of solutions containing polymer fractions whose molecular weights have been determined by other methods.

The viscosity, or more properly the coefficient of viscosity, has been treated for gases and liquids in Chaps. 2 and 12 and has been seen to measure the resistance to flow of a solution. The addition of polymer molecules to a solvent invariably increases the viscosity over that of the pure solvent. In relating this increased viscosity to the properties of the solute a number of functions of the measured viscosity coefficients η_0 of the pure solvent and η of the solution are used. These are shown in Table 20-6.

Most directly related to the nature of the individual solute molecules is the intrinsic viscosity, which has the effect of macromolecule intermolecular interaction removed by the extrapolation to infinite dilution. It represents the fractional change in the viscosity of a solution per unit concentration of polymer, or macromolecule, at infinite dilution.

Determinations of the intrinsic viscosity for different molecular-weight fractions of the same polymer lead to the expression, which is best looked on as being empirical,

$$[\eta] = KM^a \tag{25}$$

where K and a are empirical constants which depend on the solvent, the polymer, and the temperature. The study of known molecular-weight fractions allows K and a to be evaluated, as is illustrated in the plot of Fig. 20-8. With values for the empirical constants, the molecular weight of any batch of the polymer can be deduced from the easily performed measurements of viscosity.

Some attempts have been made to relate the values of a to the shape of the molecules. The more elongated a molecule is, the more effective are the high-

Table 20-6. Some Viscosity Terms Derived from the Measured Solvent and Solution Viscosities, η_0 and η, Respectively

(c is often, but not always, used as g/100 cc)

Name	Definition
Relative viscosity	$\dfrac{\eta}{\eta_0}$
Specific viscosity	$\dfrac{\eta - \eta_0}{\eta_0}$
Reduced specific viscosity	$\dfrac{1}{c}\dfrac{\eta - \eta_0}{\eta_0}$
Intrinsic viscosity	$[\eta] = \lim\limits_{c \to 0}\left(\dfrac{1}{c}\dfrac{\eta - \eta_0}{\eta_0}\right)$
	$= \lim\limits_{c \to 0}\left[\dfrac{1}{c}\left(\dfrac{\eta}{\eta_0} - 1\right)\right]$

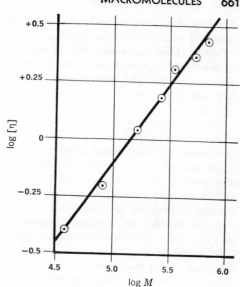

Fig. 20-8. Relation of $[\eta]$ to M for polyisobutylene fractions in cyclohexane at 30°C. [*From W. R. Krigbaum and P. J. Flory, J. Am. Chem. Soc.,* **75**: 1775 (1953).]

molecular-weight fractions in reducing the viscosity of the solution, and the values of a are expected to rise from typical average values of 0.6 or 0.7 to 1 or 2. As Table 20-7 shows, many polymer solutions do, however, have values of a that are near 0.6 and 0.7.

The effect of the shape of a polymer molecule is more noticeable in experiments in which the viscosity of the same polymer is studied in different solvents. In a "good" solvent it is expected that the polymer chains will be solvated and will open up, while in a "poor" solvent they will tend to remain coiled up. The expectation of a high intrinsic viscosity for polymers in good solvents compared with poor solvents is borne out by the result for polystyrene of 1.20 to 1.30 in good aromatic solvents and 0.65 to 0.75 in poor aliphatic solvents.

Again some deductions as to the shape of polymer molecules are possible.

Table 20-7. Constants for Eq. (25) for Various Polymer-Solvent Systems*

Polymer	Solvent	t°C	Mol-wt range	K	a
Polystyrene..........	Benzene	25	32,000–1,300,000	1.03×10^{-4}	0.74
Polystyrene..........	Methyl ethyl ketone	25	2,500–1,700,000	3.9×10^{-4}	0.58
Polyisobutylene......	Cyclohexane	30	6,000–3,150,000	2.6×10^{-4}	0.70
Polyisobutylene......	Benzene	24	1,000–3,150,000	8.3×10^{-4}	0.50
Natural rubber.......	Toluene	25	40,000–1,500,000	5.0×10^{-4}	0.67

* From P. J. Flory, "Principles of Polymer Chemistry," Cornell University Press, Ithaca, New York, 1953.

The important use of viscosity measurements is, however, in the rapid determination of relative molecular weights.

*20-12. Light Scattering. One of the most distinctive features of a colloidal or macromolecule solution is the scattered light, or Tyndall effect, that is observed when a light beam is passed through such a solution. This scattered light can be used in two different ways to help elucidate the nature of colloidal solutions.

The first application is made in the *ultramicroscope*, which is shown schematically in Fig. 20-9. Here the sample is observed through a microscope at right angles to the direction of the entering light beam. Each colloid particle, larger than about 10 A diameter in very favorable cases, will produce an observable point of scattered light. The individual particles can then be counted, and if the microscope focuses on a definite, known volume of solution, the number of particles per unit volume can be determined. Such data, along with the measurable weight of macromolecule material per unit volume, lead to a value of the average mass of the individual particles.

It should be emphasized that none of the details of the particles can be observed. They merely act as scattering centers, and one observes points of light. Furthermore, unless the refractive index of the colloid particle is very different from that of the solvent, the scattered light is too weak to be seen. The similarity of the refractive index of most macromolecules to the medium in which they are dispersed means that little scattered light will be given off. The method is therefore mostly applicable to inorganic colloids.

The second application of the scattering of light depends on the measurement and interpretation of the amount of light scattered in various directions as a beam of light passes through a solution of macromolecules. In some experiments the total amount of the scattered light is deduced from the decrease in intensity of the incident beam as it passes through the sample. Just as for Beer's law for the absorption of light (Sec. 11-17), one has the relation

$$I = I_0 e^{-\tau l} \tag{26}$$

where τ is the measure of the decrease in incident-beam intensity per unit length of a given solution and is known as the *turbidity*. In some experiments, on the other hand, the intensity of light scattered in various directions is

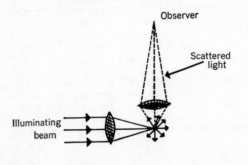

Observer

Scattered light

Illuminating beam

Fig. 20-9. The detection of particles in the ultramicroscope.

measured directly, rather than inferred, from the decrease in intensity of the incident beam.

That the scattered light is related to the particle size and shape can now be shown. We first consider the effect of particles that are small compared with the wavelength of the radiation. Incident plane-polarized radiation imposes, as Fig. 20-10 illustrates, an electric field

$$\mathcal{E} = \mathcal{E}_0 \sin 2\pi\nu t \tag{27}$$

at the particle. If the particle has a polarizability α, there will be an induced-dipole moment given by

$$\mu_{\text{induced}} = \alpha\mathcal{E}$$
$$= \alpha\mathcal{E}_0 \sin 2\pi\nu t \tag{28}$$

It is this oscillating-dipole moment that emits secondary radiation and causes the particle to be a scattering center.

It has been mentioned in connection with the difficulties of early atomic theories that in classical electromagnetic theory an accelerated charge must emit electromagnetic radiation. This result can be applied to show what secondary radiation will be emitted by the oscillating induced dipole.

The oscillating-dipole moment of Eq. (28) can be formally written as a charge of value $\alpha\mathcal{E}_0$ oscillating with a unit amplitude relative to an equal and opposite charge. Thus we can write

$$\mu_{\text{induced}} = (\alpha\mathcal{E}_0)x \tag{29}$$
with
$$x = \sin 2\pi\nu t \tag{30}$$

In this way a picture is obtained of an induced charge $\alpha\mathcal{E}_0$ in the irradiated particle vibrating with simple harmonic motion. This motion, furthermore, involves an acceleration d^2x/dt^2 which is calculated from Eq. (30) as

$$\frac{d^2x}{dt^2} = 4\pi^2\nu^2 \sin 2\pi\nu t \tag{31}$$

It is necessary now to quote, without derivation, the very important classical electromagnetic result that the acceleration of a charge q results in the emission of electromagnetic radiation which produces at a distance r and angle ϕ, as in Fig. 20-11, from the oscillating charge, an electric field e given by the expression

$$e = -\frac{q}{c^2}\left(\frac{d^2x}{dt^2}\right)\frac{\cos \phi}{r} \tag{32}$$

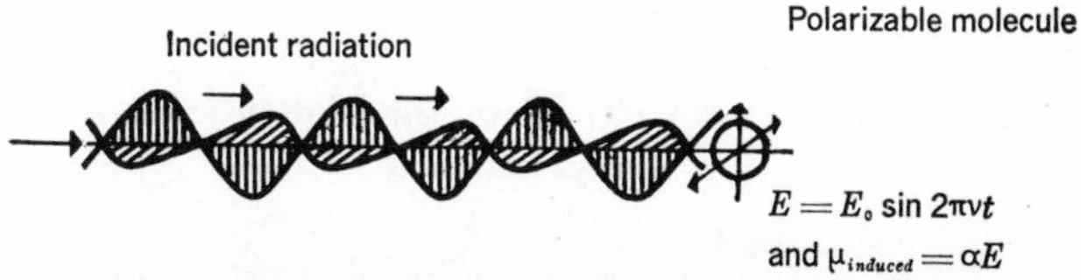

Fig 20-10. The induced-dipole moments produced by the two components of incident radiation.

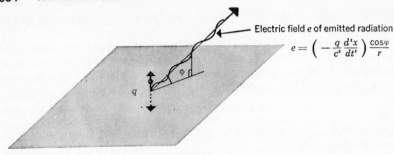

$$e = \left(-\frac{q}{c^2}\frac{d^2x}{dt^2} \right)\frac{\cos\varphi}{r}$$

Electric field e of emitted radiation

Oscillating charge q

Fig. 20-11. The angular dependence of the radiation emitted from an oscillating charge.

With this result one calculates that the radiation field of the dipole induced in the particle by one component of the incident radiation is

$$e = -\frac{(\alpha \mathcal{E}_0)(4\pi^2\nu^2\sin 2\pi\nu t)\cos\phi}{c^2r} \tag{33}$$

The propagation of this radiation through space with a velocity c can be represented by including a sinusoidal space dependence to give

$$e = -\frac{4\pi^2\nu^2\mathcal{E}_0\sin 2\pi\nu(t - x/c)\cos\phi}{c^2r} \tag{34}$$

It is, however, not the electric field of the radiation but rather the energy content that is of interest. As mentioned in Sec. 10-5, the energy is directly related to the square of the field amplitude, and with this relation the intensity, or energy, of the secondary beam is calculated as

$$i = \frac{16\pi^4\nu^4}{c^4r^2}\alpha^2\mathcal{E}_0^2\sin^2 2\pi\nu\left(t - \frac{x}{c}\right)\cos^2\phi \tag{35}$$

What is of importance for comparison with experimental results is the intensity of scattered radiation, at various angles, compared with the intensity of the incident radiation. This incident plane-polarized radiation can be depicted as entering the sample according to the relation

$$I_0 = \mathcal{E}_0^2\sin^2 2\pi\nu\left(t - \frac{x}{c}\right) \tag{36}$$

and this expression can be inserted into Eq. (35) to give

$$\frac{i}{I_0} = \frac{16\pi^4\nu^4}{c^4r^2}\alpha^2\cos^2\phi \tag{37}$$

Introduction of the radiation wavelength by the relation $\nu = c/\lambda$ gives

$$\frac{i}{I_0} = \frac{16\pi^4}{r^2}\frac{\alpha^2\cos^2\phi}{\lambda^4} \tag{38}$$

When ordinary, nonpolarized radiation is used for the incident beam, the induced-dipole moment in the sample can be considered to have two mutually perpendicular components. The scattered beam consists then of two perpendicular components like that of Eq. (38). This net scattered beam is then related to the angle θ of Fig. 20-12 by the equation

$$\frac{i}{I_0} = \frac{8\pi^4\alpha^2}{\lambda^4 r^2} (1 + \cos^2 \theta) \tag{39}$$

This angular dependence is best verified by checking that it gives the correct summation of the two plane-polarized components in various special directions.

The intensity predicted by Eq. (39) for the scattered beam from small particles is illustrated in Fig. 20-12.

It should be noticed that the forward and backward scattering are equal. Furthermore, the fourth-power dependence of the scattering on the wavelength shown by Eq. (39) should be noticed. It is, for example, to this enhanced scattering of short-wavelength radiation that the blue color of the sky is attributed. The short-wavelength blue end of the visible spectrum is scattered more than the long-wavelength red end, and the "background" color of the sky is therefore blue.

The interpretation of the scattering of radiation that has culminated in Eq. (39) can be brought to a comparison with the experimental quantity, the

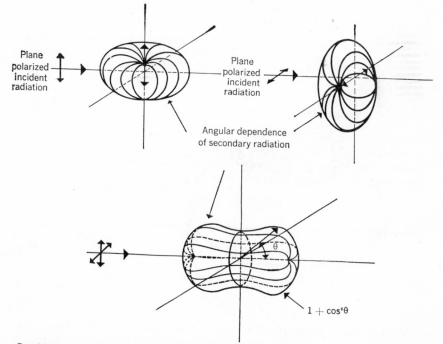

Fig. 20-12. The angular dependence of secondary, or scattered, radiation from a particle that is small compared with the wavelength of the radiation.

turbidity. For many samples the amount of scattering is small, and the turbidity expression

$$\frac{I}{I_0} = e^{-\tau l} \tag{40}$$

or

$$\tau l = -\ln \frac{I}{I_0}$$

can be written, for unit-cell length, as

$$\tau = -\ln \left(\frac{I}{I_0} - \frac{I_0}{I_0} + 1 \right)$$
$$= -\ln \left(\frac{I - I_0}{I_0} + 1 \right)$$
$$\cong \frac{I_0 - I}{I_0} \tag{41}$$

The term $I_0 - I$ is the intensity removed from the incident beam and is therefore the integral over all angles of the scattered radiation of Eq. (39). The measure of turbidity can therefore be evaluated, according to the differential surface element of Fig. 20-13, as

$$\tau = \int_0^\pi \frac{i}{I_0} 2\pi r^2 \sin \theta \, d\theta \tag{42}$$

Substitution of the expression for scattered intensity i of Eq. (39) and integration gives

$$\tau = \frac{8\pi}{3} \left(\frac{2\pi}{\lambda} \right)^4 \alpha^2 \tag{43}$$

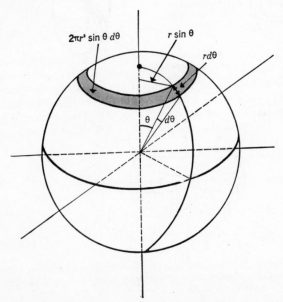

Fig. 20-13. The surface element for the integration of the scattered radiation.

For a concentration of c g/cc and a molecular weight M there will be $(c/M)N$ molecules per cubic centimeter, and the turbidity of such a material will be

$$\tau = \frac{8\pi}{3}\left(\frac{2\pi}{\lambda}\right)^4 \alpha^2 \frac{cN}{M} \tag{44}$$

To obtain a calculation of molecular weight from a measured turbidity, it is necessary to have a value of the molecular polarizability. In Sec. 10-10 the approximate expression of Eq. (99) can be reduced for $n_R \cong 1$, as is the case for gases, to the relation between α and the refractive index n_R of

$$2\pi\left(\frac{c}{M}N\right)\alpha = n_R - 1 \tag{45}$$

With this result the turbidity of a gaseous system, in which the particles are small compared with the wavelength, can be written as

$$\tau = \frac{32\pi^3 M(n_R - 1)^2}{3\lambda^4 cN} \tag{46}$$

With this expression the measurable turbidity can be related to the molecular weight of the gas-phase particles, the mass of material per unit volume, and the refractive index of the gaseous system. This expression has, in fact, been turned around so that a value for Avogadro's number has been obtained from the scattering produced by gas samples.

For the systems of interest here, i.e., macromolecules in a liquid medium, it is necessary to introduce the fact that the scattering depends on the *difference* between the refractive index of the particles and that of the medium. If n_R is the refractive index of the solution and n_R° that of the pure solvent, the appropriate relation comparable with Eq. (46) turns out to be

$$\tau = \frac{32\pi^3 M n_R^\circ}{3\lambda^4 cN}(n_R - n_R^\circ)^2 \tag{47}$$

Now measurements of τ and n_R for a solution of a given value of c and n_R° allow the calculation of the molecular weight M. In practice turbidities are measured as a function of concentration, and an extrapolation to infinite dilution is made. It should be mentioned that, since the polarizability increases with increasing molecular size, the amount scattered by an individual molecule is proportional to its size. The molecular weight that is obtained is therefore a weight-average molecular weight.

In practice this expression is usually written as

$$\tau = \frac{32\pi^3 n_R^\circ}{3\lambda^4 N}\left(\frac{n_R - n_R^\circ}{c}\right)^2 \frac{c}{M}$$

or

$$\tau = H\frac{c}{M} \tag{48}$$

where

$$H = \frac{32\pi^3 n_R^{\circ'}}{3\lambda^4 N}\left(\frac{n_R - n_R^\circ}{c}\right)^2 \tag{49}$$

In dilute solutions, moreover, the term for the change of refractive index with concentration can be written as a differential, and H then is

$$H = \frac{32\pi^3 n_R^\circ}{3\lambda^4 N}\left(\frac{dn_R}{dc}\right)^2 \tag{50}$$

From measurements of refractive index for the wavelength of light used in the scattering experiments H can be evaluated, and the turbidity can be measured. Equation (50) can then be used to calculate a molecular weight. In practice an extrapolation to infinite dilution is necessary, and, for particles of appreciable size compared with the wavelength of light, so also is recognition of the angular dependence of the scattered light.

A little must now be said about the scattering that results when the molecules are not small with respect to the wavelength of the light. Visible light has wavelengths between about 4,000 and 8,000 A, and these lengths are just about the dimensions expected for many macromolecules. As for electron scattering from different atoms of a molecule in an electron-diffraction experiment the scattering from different parts of the molecule will now interfere with one another. The effect is, in fact, very similar to that studied in detail for electron diffraction. The macromolecule is best thought of as some geometric shape presenting a continuum of scattering centers rather than a few discrete centers. A detailed calculation for the amount of light scattered as a function of angle, for a given wavelength and assumed molecular size and shape, can be performed by integrating the Wierl equation of Sec. 10-5 over all parts of the molecule. The type of light-scattering angular dependence that can result for molecules with dimensions like that of the wavelength of the scattered light is indicated in Fig. 20-14. The details of the pattern are dependent on the shape of the molecule as well as on its over-all size. Measurements of light scattering now give promise of being one of the most powerful methods for studying the geometry of macromolecules in solution.

In lieu of a detailed analysis of the molecular shape that would lead to the

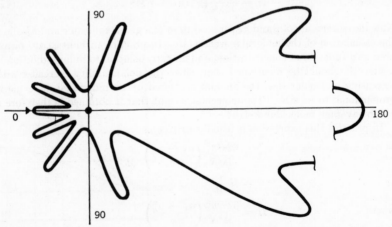

Fig. 20-14. The scattering of visible light from a spherical particle of radius 5,000 A. [*From V. K. La Mer and M. Kerker, Light Scattered by Particles, Scientific American,* **188**: 69 (1953).]

observed angular dependence of the scattered radiation, it is often sufficient to measure the intensity of the scattered beam at two angles, usually 45 and 135°, to the incident beam. The ratio of these intensities reflects the over-all shape of the macromolecule in solution. Calculations have been made, using essentially the Wierl equation for some simple shapes, and these are shown in Fig. 20-15. From observations of the scattered intensity at the angles of 45 and 135°, such curves can be consulted and lead to some information of the usually unapproachable quantity, the shape of a molecule in solution.

20-13. Electrokinetic Effects. The behavior of colloidal particles dispersed in an aqueous medium is greatly affected by the fact that the particles often carry an electrical charge. The presence of acidic and basic groups in proteins, for example, means that there will generally be positive or negative charges on the protein molecule. The number and sign of these charges will depend on whether the solution is acidic or basic. Charges are also carried by inorganic colloidal particles, such as AgCl, where the charge can be attributed to a preferential adsorption of Ag^+ or Cl^- ions on the surface of the particles. The nature of the net charge on the particles is clearly important in questions of the tendency of the colloidal particles to come together, or *flocculate*, since this process must overcome the electrostatic repulsion between particles.

The electrical nature of colloidal particles can best be studied in experiments which make the colloid particles and the surrounding medium move relative to one another. Such experiments are said to treat *electrokinetic phenomena*.

The charge distribution around a charged colloid particle might be expected to be that indicated in Fig. 20-16. A protein molecule has been used for illustration, but although the charged groups of the protein molecule can be more definitely attributed to the reaction of chemical groups such as —COOH and —NH₂, the charge distribution is expected to be similar in inorganic colloids. The effective charge of a particle in electrokinetic experiments is the *fixed charge*, which is made up of the actual charge of the particle and any ionic charges that are held sufficiently close to the particle so that they will remain with the particle as it moves through the solution. The total charge

Fig. **20-15.** The ratio of the intensity of the scattered light at 45° to that at 135°. The wavelength of the light is λ, and L is the diameter for spheres, the rms distance between ends for coils, and the length for rods.

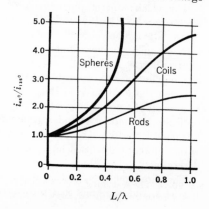

L/λ

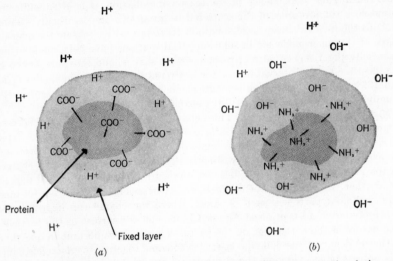

Fig. 20-16. The fixed charges associated with a protein molecule in (a) basic solution and (b) acidic solution (schematic).

of the system of colloid particles and solution is necessarily electrically neutral, and opposite charges to that of the fixed charge will tend to surround the colloid particle and will form a diffuse layer which will move with the solution rather than the particle. The situation is shown schematically in Fig. 20-16. Electrokinetic phenomena can all be given a qualitative explanation in terms of the concept of the charge fixed to each particle and the surrounding charge which moves with the liquid medium. Attempts at quantitative interpretations introduce the *zeta*, or *electrokinetic*, *potential* which expresses the potential drop between the fixed charges and the body of the solution.

The electrokinetic phenomena of most practical importance is that of *electrophoresis*. In the study of proteins, for example, one forms a boundary between a buffer solution containing a protein sample and the pure buffer solution in a manner similar to that used in studying diffusion. With an electrophoresis instrument one applies a potential difference between electrodes dipping in the two solutions and observes the movement of the boundary between the solutions and thus determines the motion of the macromolecules as a result of a potential gradient. The movement of the boundary is observed optically, the refractive-index gradient at the boundary causing the light to be refracted from its path. In this way the extent to which the macromolecules with different mobilities have migrated from the original boundary can be determined.

The direction of migration is, of course, dependent on the charge of the particles, and one finds that proteins move to the anode for sufficiently basic solutions, to the cathode for sufficiently acidic solutions, and show no electrophoretic effect at the isoelectric point.

Different proteins may show different *mobilities*. Electrophoresis is therefore a valuable tool for separating biological fractions into pure components. In this respect, it supplements the ultracentrifuge, which separates according to molecular weight. Electrophoresis experiments can show that, even if a sample is homogeneous with respect to molecular weight, it may contain different components having different electrical properties. Figure 20-17 shows the separation that can be obtained in a complicated natural-product preparation.

The mobilities found for colloidal particles, and particularly for proteins, depend, of course, on the pH of the solution. In general, the mobilities, i.e., the velocity acquired by the particles for a potential gradient of 1 volt/cm, are around 20×10^{-5} cm/sec for 1 volt/cm and are seen, therefore, to be only a little less than the mobilities found for simple ions, as listed in Table 16-6.

The results of electrophoresis studies allow macromolecules to be characterized by a *mobility* defined as the velocity of migration per unit applied electric-field strength. For proteins this mobility is very dependent on the pH of the solution, being zero at the isoelectric point and having mobilities of opposite sign on either side of the isoelectric point.

Two interesting electrokinetic effects result from the possibility of fixing the position of the charged macromolecules. Thus a membrane or layer of fibrous macromolecules can be introduced into a buffer solution. Again the macromolecules adopt some fixed charge. Unlike any of the systems dealt with in our study of electrochemistry, we now have the movable liquid carrying a *net* charge, the balancing charges being in the fixed macromolecules. The situation is shown diagrammatically in Fig. 20-18. If now an electric potential is applied, the movable ions and their surrounding solvent move to the oppositely charged electrode, where the ions are discharged. The effect of this movement is to carry the solvent, and the movable ions, through the membrane. This process is known as *electroosmosis* and has some practical applications as an adjunct to ordinary osmosis. One should recognize that both electrophoresis and electroosmosis involve the relative flow of the charged

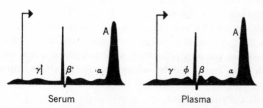

Serum   Plasma

Fig. 20-17. The electrophoretic patterns obtained with (*left*) normal human serum and (*right*) plasma are shown. The main components are identified as A for albumin, ϕ for fibrinogen, and α, β, and γ for the different globulins. Fibrinogen is lacking in serum.

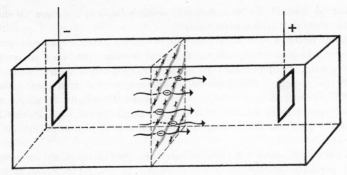

Fig. 20-18. Electroosmosis through a porous membrane holding a fixed positive charge.

macromolecules and the oppositely charged surrounding liquid and are therefore essentially the same phenomenon.

With a similar arrangement as that used for electroosmosis one can reverse the procedure and produce a potential as a result of forcing the buffer solution to flow through the macromolecule matrix. The potential difference that is developed is known as a *streaming potential*.

The quantitative treatment of all these electrokinetic phenomena depends on the charge fixed to the particle and the movable charges surrounding the particle. Since this charge distribution produces the zeta potential, the phenomena can be analyzed either directly in terms of the charges or, as is more generally done, in terms of the zeta potential.

Before leaving the subject of the charges of colloidal particles it should be mentioned again that it is these charges which account for much of the stability of colloids. For highly solvated macromolecules in water, i.e., *hydrophilic colloids*, the solvating layers of water help to prevent the individual particles from agglomerating. For nonsolvated particles in water, i.e., hydrophobic colloids, however, such solvation is unimportant, and only the electrical effect operates. The particles of AgCl, for example, carry a net fixed negative charge, due to a preferential adsorption of Cl⁻ ions surrounded by a diffuse, balancing, positively charged region rich in Ag⁺ ions. Because of the electrostatic repulsion between their negative charges, the colloidal particles cannot easily come together. Agglomeration, or flocculation, can be made to occur, however, by adding an electrolyte, particularly one with positive ions of high charge. These added positive charges will surround the colloid, or as might be said, will decrease its zeta potential, and will allow them to approach one another. With inorganic colloids, where solvation is less important than in protein systems, the action of charges in stabilizing or precipitating the colloidal particles is very important.

20-14. The Donnan Membrane Equilibrium and Dialysis. One final electrical phenomenon encountered with macromolecules should now be mentioned. This phenomenon, known as the *Donnan equilibrium*, is not, however, an electrokinetic effect. We shall see, for example, that it does not depend on the zeta potential. The Donnan equilibrium shows up when a colloidal solution in which the particles are charged, most commonly an aqueous protein solution, is separated by a semipermeable membrane from the pure water or from the solution without the colloid. The complications that arise as a result of the charged protein molecules can be seen by reference to Fig. 20-19. It is supposed that the particles P, which can be thought of as protein molecules, carry some negative charge and that an appropriate number of sodium ions balance this charge. Suppose that an osmosis cell is set up, or that dialysis is performed with this solution and a solution of sodium chloride, as in Fig. 20-19. The macromolecules $P^{(-)}$ cannot pass through the membrane. The Cl^- ions, on the other hand, can, and they will tend to diffuse from the high concentration on the right to the low concentration on the left. To preserve electrical neutrality, an equal number of Na^+ ions will pass from right to left across the membrane. An osmotic-pressure measurement would therefore be complicated by the additional number of particles in the macromolecule side of the membrane.

Suppose that the dialysis or osmosis of the solution containing $P^{(-)}$ and Na^+ is performed against water. Here the Na^+ ions will tend to diffuse to the low concentration region on the right. Electrical neutrality can now be maintained only by additional dissociation of water to form H^+ ions on the left and OH^- ions on the right. Unless a buffer is used, the pH of the solutions will therefore change during the experiment.

The quantitative nature of these effects can be set down for a system of two equal volumes separated by a semipermeable membrane. If c_1 and c_2 are the initial concentrations and x is the concentration change due to the diffusion of NaCl, the situation is described as:

Initially
$$Na^+ \quad P^{(-)} \quad \Big|\Big| \quad Na \quad Cl^-$$
$$c_1 \qquad c_1 \qquad\qquad c_2 \qquad c_2$$

At equilibrium
$$Na^+ \quad P^{(-)} \quad Cl^- \quad \Big|\Big| \quad Na^+ \qquad Cl^-$$
$$c_1 + x \quad c_1 \quad x \qquad\quad c_2 - x \quad c_2 - x$$

The concentrations are written such that both compartments remain elec-

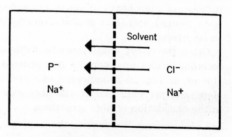

Fig. 20-19. The passage of solvent and ions through a semipermeable membrane in an osmosis experiment using a solution of macromolecules and electrolyte.

trically neutral. The transfer of Na^+ ions and Cl^- ions, subject to this neutrality condition, will proceed until the free energy of NaCl in both compartments is equal. More conveniently, this equilibrium stipulation can be expressed as equal activities of NaCl in the two compartments. Thus, in the left compartment

$$(a_{NaCl})_l = (a_{Na^+})_l (a_{Cl^-})_l = (\gamma_\pm)_l^2 [Na^+]_l [Cl^-]_l \tag{51}$$

while in the right compartment

$$(a_{NaCl})_r = (a_{Na^+})_r (a_{Cl^-})_r = (\gamma_\pm)_r^2 [Na^+]_r [Cl^-]_r \tag{52}$$

If the mean-activity coefficients in the two compartments can be taken as equal, usually as a result of equal ionic strengths, the Donnan equilibrium relation is obtained as

$$[Na_l^+][Cl_l^-] = [Na_r^+][Cl_r^-]$$

or
$$(c_1 + x)(x) = (c_2 - x)(c_2 - x) \tag{53}$$

Rearrangement gives the concentration of the NaCl that is transferred to the colloid compartment as

$$x = \frac{c_2^2}{c_1 + 2c_2} \tag{54}$$

This expression, or a more general one for multivalent ions, is important in any experiment with charged particles in solution that are in any way fixed, or moved, in relation to the other ions in the solution.

MACROMOLECULES IN THE SOLID STATE

As our previous study of the solid state has shown, the existence of an ordered crystalline sample allows, through X-ray diffraction, a rather direct means for the determination of molecular structure. In spite of the complexity of the protein molecules and the frequent lack of simple single crystals of polymers, this technique has been applied and has met with considerable success in unraveling the structures of these macromolecules in the solid state.

An X-ray-diffraction study of a single crystal of macromolecules can proceed, in principle, in the same manner as that illustrated by the simple example of Chap. 13. In practice, however, the unit cell is usually so large that it is not possible to deduce the position of each of its many atoms. It is often possible, nevertheless, to determine repeated periods that give important clues as to the arrangement and structure of the macromolecule. Likewise, the presence of a few heavy atoms in a macromolecule allows these reference points to be located, and these permit a description of the remainder of the molecule to be attempted.

Often the X-ray study must be made on a fiberlike material in which the macromolecules are more or less ordered along the fiber axis. From such studies, as Fig. 20-20 indicates, one can often deduce any repeated distances along and perpendicular to the fiber axis. Such results can be of great aid in the elucidation of fiber structures.

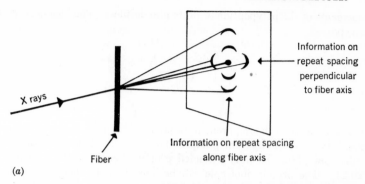

Information on
repeat spacing
perpendicular
to fiber axis

X rays

Fiber

Information on repeat spacing
along fiber axis

(a)

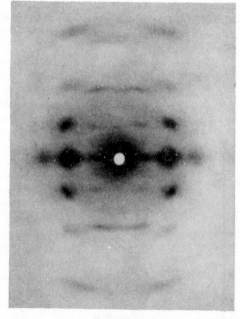

Fig. 20-20. X-ray patterns of fibers. (a) Schematic diagram of X-ray-fiber pattern. (b) The X-ray diffraction pattern of silk fibroin showing the pattern characteristic of the extended or β-keratin structure. (*From W. T. Astbury, "Fundamentals of Fibre Structure," Oxford University Press, New York, 1933.*)

(b)

These tools and some of the structural properties of proteins, nucleic acids, and solid polymers will now be dealt with.

20-15. The Structure of Proteins. A number of proteins and their simpler analogues, the polymers of amino acids known as *polypeptides*, exist or can be prepared in fiber or crystalline form. The technique of X-ray diffraction can therefore be applied.

It is possible to carry over the standard bond lengths and bond angles from simpler molecules and to use these values to construct the geometry of the basic elements of the polypeptide or protein molecules. The idea of resonance of the type

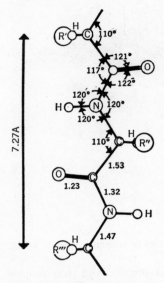

suggests, according to the requirement of planarity of a double-bond structure, the planarity of such six-atom groups. Distances carried over from simple molecules now allow the fully extended protein skeleton to be drawn, as in Fig. 20-21. The protein molecule can be looked upon, therefore, as far as structural arrangements are concerned, as a succession of planar groups as shown in Fig. 20-21, where we have attempted to show that the α-carbon atom, although involved in two planar units, does not fix any necessary relationship between these planes.

The principal questions of polypeptide and protein structure can now be reduced to the following: (1) What are the possible arrangements of these planar groups relative to each other in the chains? (2) How is one chain arranged relative to its neighbors?

Recognition of the importance of hydrogen bonding in protein structures, and of the carry-over of the dimensions of Fig. 20-21, limits, to a very great extent, the structures that need to be considered. For some proteins a detailed crystal or fiber structure can, in fact, be drawn from the recognition of these two features and the relatively meager X-ray-diffraction data. The hydrogen-bonding requirement is that each N—H bond and each C=O group, of the same protein chain or a neighboring chain, be arranged so that a good hydrogen bond can be formed. The geometry required appears, from simpler crystal studies, to be

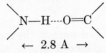

$\leftarrow$ 2.8 A $\rightarrow$

Fig. 20-21. Dimensions of the fully extended polypeptide chain as derived from recent crystal-structure data. [*From R. B. Corey and J. Donohue, J. Am. Chem. Soc.*, **72**: 2899 (1950).]

Many structural studies have been made on fibrous proteins. Keratin, which is the protein of wool, hair, and horns, will serve as a specific example of this class of proteins. Fibers of this protein are remarkably elastic; they can be stretched to twice their normal length, and when the tension is released, they return to their original length. It is found that the normal and extended fibers show different X-ray-diffraction patterns. It is convenient to distinguish the normal unstretched keratin and its X-ray pattern by the prefix α and the stretched keratin and its X-ray pattern by the prefix β.

A typical X-ray-diffraction pattern of β keratin is shown in Fig. 20-20. From such photographs, and the $n\lambda = 2d \sin \theta$ relation discussed in Sec. 13-6, it has been deduced that there are repeated distances of 3.33 A along the fiber axis and of 9.7 and 4.65 A perpendicular to the fiber axis and perpendicular to each other. The value of 3.33 A, being about half the repeat distance 7.27 A, suggests, in comparison with Fig. 20-21, an amino acid–residue length. An approximate accounting for the three unit distances can, in fact, be achieved in terms of sheets of fully extended molecular chains.

The discrepancy between the repeat distance of 7.27 A predicted on the basis of this structure and the observed repeat distance of 3.33 A was removed by the suggestion of Pauling and Corey that instead of the planar extended structure a *pleated-sheet* structure shown in Fig. 20-22 was formed. In this way not

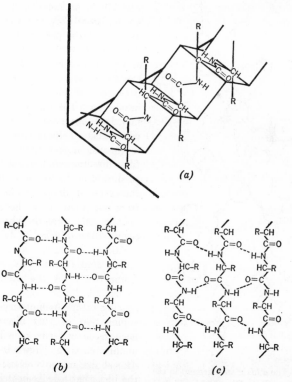

(a)

(b)   *(c)*

Fig. 20-22. The pleated sheet protein structures. (a) The protein chain configuration. (b) Chains arranged in an antiparallel manner. (c) Chains arranged in a parallel manner.

only could the X-ray distances be accounted for but also good hydrogen bonding could be maintained between the N—H and C=O bonds of adjacent chains.

The structure of α-keratin must reflect the fact that the fiber is only about half as long as for β-keratin. Some folding or coiling of the protein chains must exist. A structure which accounts for the decrease in fiber length, preserves good hydrogen bonding and the basic distances, and is in accord with X-ray-diffraction results was deduced by Pauling and Corey. Helical structures were considered, and that which is appropriate to α-keratin is distinguished from other possible helical structures by its designation as an *α helix*. The structure is shown in Fig. 20-23, and one should be able to see in these drawings the planar six-atom groups previously mentioned. This structure fits all the requirements and predicts a repeated distance along the fiber axis, say, from N to N, of between 1.47 and 1.53 A. Layer lines indicating a spacing of 1.5 A have, in fact, been observed in some proteins in which this α helix is expected.

Another repeat distance along the fiber direction that might be expected to show up is the pitch of the helix, i.e., the vertical distance along the axis from one point on the helix to a point on the helix directly above the first point. The α helix has 3.6 amino acid residues per turn, and since each amino acid corresponds to a vertical distance of 1.5 A, the pitch is expected to be $3.6 \times 1.5 = 5.4$ A. In fact, a spacing of 5.1 A is observed. A neat explanation of this discrepancy has been given in terms of a helix with a nonlinear axis as shown in Fig. 20-24. This shape, moreover, leads nicely into the idea that α-helix protein molecules can form bundles or cables as illustrated

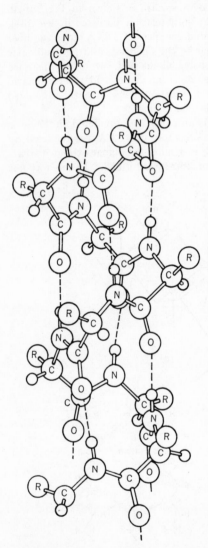

Fig. 20-23. The atomic arrangement in the α helix. [*From R. B. Corey and L. Pauling, Rend. ist. lombardo sci.*, **89:** 10 (1955).]

Fig. 20-24. The α helix given a slight coil so that a seven- or three-strand cable can be formed. [*From L. Pauling and R. B. Corey, Nature*, **171**: 59 (1953).]

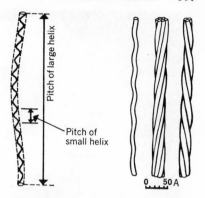

in Fig. 20-24.   These ideas allow one to see how the detailed structure of large protein groups, of a size that is almost large enough to be seen with an electron microscope, can be deduced.

Studies of fibrous proteins lead, as the above discussion indicates, to the idea of the pleated sheet and the α helix.   Many detailed problems of fibrous protein structure remain: the effect of bulky side groups, the role of disulfide cross links, and so forth.   Much progress has been made, and, in particular, the idea of a helical macromolecule chain has been very fruitful.

The second important type of protein is the globular protein.   The gross properties of these molecules suggest a spherical or balled-up shape rather than the essentially linear one adopted by fibrous proteins.   The tendency at present, however, is to think of the globular protein as consisting of an α helix which is wound in some way into a more or less spherical shape.   In spite of the nicely crystalline form that is sometimes adopted by these proteins, the lack of a specific direction of the molecular chain makes the X-ray analysis of their structure very difficult.   They become, as it were, huge molecules in a crystal lattice that X-ray-diffraction studies must tackle in a rather direct manner.

Some progress is being made.   This progress has followed from the assumption of an α-helix arrangement and the X-ray-diffraction study of proteins containing a few heavy atoms.   These heavy atoms act as strong scattering centers, and the X-ray analysis can treat the spacing between planes containing these relatively few atoms and can, to begin with, ignore the complexity introduced by all the other atoms of the molecule.

A globular protein that has been analyzed in considerable detail is myoglobin.   Although the positions of the individual atoms have not been identified, the convolutions of the α-helix chain can be followed.   A photograph of a model of the proposed structure is shown in Fig. 20-25.

This section should indicate that the physical-chemical approach to structure problems is making exciting advances even in studies of molecules as complex as proteins.

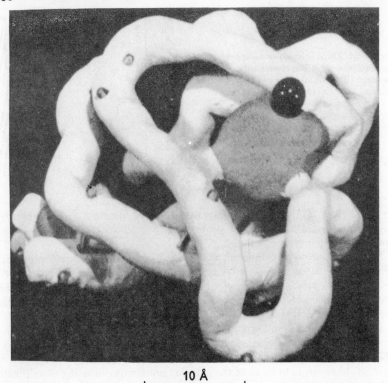

10 Å

Fig. 20-25. The configuration of myoglobin. The dark gray disk is the heme group; the little black ball attached to it is an artificially introduced group required for the X-ray analysis of the macromolecule. The white parts show the polypeptide configuration at a resolution of about 6 A. (*From M. F. Perutz, Endeavor, p. 196, 1958.*)

20-16. The Structure of Nucleic Acids.   A number of the general ideas which have been successful in protein-structure studies appear also be be applicable to studies of nucleic acids.   The chemical units of the nucleic acid deoxyribonucleic acid (DNA) have been pointed out in Sec. 20-4.   It remains to suggest a geometric arrangement for the two molecular chains of Fig. 20-4.

In 1953 Watson and Crick, primarily on the basis of X-ray-diffraction studies, proposed that the two molecular chains formed a double helix and that the basic groups of Fig. 20-4 formed hydrogen bonds in a manner which holds the two spirals in position.   The proposed structure is shown in Fig. 20-26.   It consists of a double helix about 20 A in diameter and has two residues for every 3.4 A along the helix.   A DNA molecule with a molecular weight of 10 million would have the remarkable length of 50,000 A, that is, 0.005 mm.   Although the double helix would seem to be a rather stiff structure, it appears reasonable

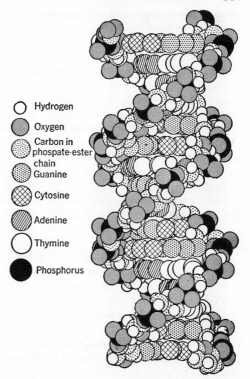

Fig. 20-26. Double helix model of the structure of DNA proposed by Watson and Crick. [*From L. D. Hamilton, CA, A Bulletin of Cancer Progress,* **5**: 159 (1955).]

○ Hydrogen

◉ Oxygen

◉ Carbon in phospate-ester chain

◉ Guanine

⊗ Cytosine

◐ Adenine

○ Thymine

● Phosphorus

that it adopts a coiled or folded shape. The hydrogen-bonding requirements can be satisfied between the chains by the stipulation that a thymine side group lines up opposite an adenine group and a guanine group opposite a cytosine group. In this way, as Fig. 20-26 shows, the central core of the two-strand helix can maintain a diameter of about 11 A, and a number of good hydrogen bonds can be formed.

In terms of the double-helix structure of Watson and Crick, the division of a DNA molecule into two daughter molecules, such as occurs in cell division, is pictured as an uncoiling of the double helix. It is in this regard, in addition to its immediate structural interest, that the structural ideas on nucleic acids are of immense interest to biochemists and biologists as well as to physical chemists.

20-17. Crystallinity of High Polymers. The characteristic of most synthetic polymeric materials like polyethylene that sets their X-ray or solid-state study apart from typical studies is the tendency of the polymeric material to be only partly crystalline. Thus, one must deal with the *degree of crystallinity* as well as with the structure of the crystalline and amorphous regions. The principal tool for this study remains that of X-ray diffraction.

Differently prepared, or differently treated, samples of polymeric materials show different degrees of crystallinity. A particularly marked difference is shown by isotactic and atactic polymers. The X-ray-diffraction patterns of such types of polypropylene are shown in Fig. 20-27. The isotactic material gives a pattern that corresponds to those mentioned in Chap. 13 in connection with X-ray-powder patterns. The isotactic polymer consists therefore of randomly oriented, small crystalline regions. The diffuseness of the pattern from the atactic material indicates that in this form of the polymer there is little crystallinity and the material is essentially amorphous.

The broadening of the diffraction lines that is observed in patterns from partly crystalline polymeric material can be used to estimate the size of the crystalline regions. The broadening results from interference effects that lead to only incomplete constructive and destructive interference. In this way crystallite sizes in the range of tens to hundreds of angstoms have been deduced.

From such measurements, and others, one is led to a diagram for a typical polymeric material, as shown in Fig. 20-28. The amount and size of the crystallites are expected to vary with the particular polymer and with its physical treatment.

Other physical properties can also be used to deduce the degree of crystallinity. The heat of fusion of a polymeric material, for instance, can be compared with that expected for a completely crystalline material. A similar use can be made of the density of the polymer as compared with that expected for crystalline material and for that of completely amorphous material as found in a liquid hydrocarbon.

These ideas on the molecular nature of these synthetic polymer materials are the basis on which the physical properties of the materials are to be understood. The elasticity, for example, can be interpreted in terms of a realignment of the molecular chains in the amorphous regions and of the crystallites, and the X-ray pattern of the stretched material shows, in fact, a similarity to fiber patterns, indicating an ordering of the directions of the molecular chains.

Alterations in the structure of the polymer, such as cross linking produced by irradiation of the material with high-energy radiation, produce molecular changes that lead to marked changes in the physical properties, of which the rigidity imposed by cross linking is probably the most important. The detailed attempts that are being made to understand the physical properties in terms of the molecular configurations cannot, however, be treated here.

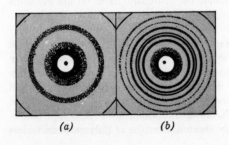

Fig. 20-27. The X-ray diagram of (a) atactic polypropylene, which has only a small amount of crystallinity, and (b) highly crystalline isotactic polypropylene.

(a)   (b)

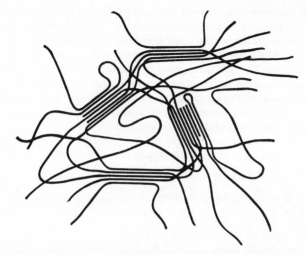

Fig. 20-28. The arrangement of molecular chains in a partly crystalline linear polymeric material.

20-18. Electron Microscopy. The most straightforward way to investigate the structure of macromolecules would be to make use of a microscope of sufficient resolving power. No progress in this direction can be hoped for by using visible radiation, as does an ordinary microscope, because the wavelength of light, about 6,000 A, is longer than the details of the particles which one hopes to observe. All that one sees is that the molecule acts as a scattering center, a principle used in the ultramicroscope. The suggestion that electrons have a wave nature leads not only to their use in electron-diffraction experiments treated in Secs. 10-4 to 10-6 but also to their use in place of ordinary electromagnetic radiation in a microscope. According to Eq. (10-42) the wavelength of the electron beam can be made less than 1 A with fairly readily available voltages of around 10,000 volts. It follows, therefore, that such radiation is in principle capable of resolving details of structure almost down to the range at which diffraction methods are effective.

Early developments following the suggestion of the wave nature of electrons showed that a beam of electrons could be focused by electric and magnetic fields. It then became possible to construct a microscope using an electron beam rather than electromagnetic radiation as used in an optical microscope. In view of the previous discussion of electron diffraction, it is apparent that the system must be evacuated so that the electron beam is not diffracted by molecules of air in the system. This requirement and the high energy of the electron beam impose some frequently troublesome restrictions on the nature of the samples that can be studied.

The electron beam passes through the sample, supported on a thin film or screen, and the differences in scattering power of the different parts of the sample lead to a photograph of the transmitted beam that indicates the structure of the sample, in so far as the structure is related to variations in electron scattering power. Under the most favorable conditions magnifications of 30,000 are possible, giving resolution of structural details down to about 10 A. In most cases, details with dimensions of 100 or 1,000 A are all that can be satisfactorily recognized. The method, however, is still being developed, and in many macromolecule systems the electron microscope can reveal structural details that are not far removed from structures that can be understood from the molecular results of diffraction experiments.

Problems

1. The molecular weights of a synthetic polymer are distributed according to the expression $\frac{1}{N}\frac{dN}{dM} = 0.61 \times 10^{-4}e^{-\left(\frac{M-10,000}{10,000}\right)^2}$, where N is the number of molecules with molecular weight M.

Plot the molecular-weight-distribution curve.

Determine graphically the number and weight-average molecular weights.

Ans. M (number av) = 11,000, M (weight av) = 14,500.

2. From the diffusion coefficients of Table 20-5, estimate the radii of the listed macromolecules, using Eq. (12). The viscosity of water at 25°C is 0.894 centipoise.

Compare the molecular weights that would be obtained by this method with those listed in Table 20-5.

Ans. For insulin, $M = 84,000$.

3. A silver chloride–aqueous colloidal solution was examined in an ultramicroscope. In a field of view 0.05 mm diameter and 0.05 mm depth an average of 8.4 particles were counted.

If the solution had been prepared by the dilution of a solution containing 0.0032 g of AgCl per cubic centimeter by a factor of 1 to 10,000, what was the average weight of the AgCl particles? Is this a number or weight average?

4. The molecular weight of egg albumin is about 40,000. What is the freezing-point depression, and what are the vapor-pressure lowering and the osmotic pressure at 25°C of an aqueous solution containing 10 g/liter?

Index